__Author Index (Volumes I-II)

AUTHOR
PRICE GUIDES

AUTHOR
PRICE GUIDES

Volume Two

REVISED

Compiled
by

Allen *and* Patricia Ahearn

With the assistance
of

Carl Hahn

Q&B

Dickerson, Maryland

ISBN: 1-883060-09-5

Q&B

Quill & Brush
1137 Sugarloaf Mountain Road
Dickerson, Maryland 20842

For
Our Grandchildren
(the collectors, dealers, librarians,
writers and publishers
of the future)

John
Justin
Jacqueline
Noelle
Kelley
Ariana
Frank
Matthew
Thomas
Michael
Stephanie
and
Bridgette

CONTENTS

ACKNOWLEDGMENTS

We wish to thank the dealers whose catalogs we have used not only in compiling these guides initially, but in improving them over the years. We want to specifically thank those dealers, collectors, librarians and publishers who took the time to provide additional detailed information to us - Alan Andres, Allan Asselstine, David Axelrod, George Banister, Audrey Bell, Bill Berger, Seth Berner, Christiana Blake, Kay Bourne, Chris Bready, Matt Bruccoli, Jackson Bryer, Robert Crass, Randy Himmel, Robert Hittel, William Holland, Robert Kent, John Knott, Frederick R. Longan, David MacLean, Phil McComish, Charles Michaud, Hans Petzoldt, Len Rzepczynski, Andre Rombs, Daren Salter, Clair Schulz, Jim Trepanier, Robert Van Norman, David Van Vactor, Jim Visbeck and Floyd Watkins.

A special thanks to all those cited in the preambles to the individual guides.

Without the help of all of these people, the guides would not be possible.

INTRODUCTION

We started the *Author Price Guides* (APGs) in 1985. The market has changed drastically since that time. Prices for highly collected books have soared. We had always thought that fine copies of first editions were undervalued in the 60's, 70's and early 80's. Now we see prices that astound us, but do not seem to be unrealistic for truly fine copies. We believe the guides have helped expand the interest in first edition collecting and hope all who use them find them useful.

The *Author Price Guides* are intended to provide sufficient information to identify the first edition (first printing) of particular books (in hand) and provide estimates for these books as of the date of this book.

The *Author Price Guides* are prepared based on available information in bibliographies, dealer catalogs, auction records and our personal experience buying and selling first editions through our store, the Quill & Brush.

The series was started because there are few price guides covering all of an individual author's books; and the basic information necessary to identify first editions is not always available, even when "complete" bibliographies have been published.

In order to arrive at the price estimates, we have used auction records and all catalogs received over the last five years, as well as our own experience of over 30 years in the market. We realize that it is possible that some of the estimates may be unrealistically low or high but we believe that the vast majority of the estimates are in the ball park, plus or minus 20%. Some of the prices may seem high in relation to a particular bookseller's personal experience, however, the estimated prices are for copies without defects, and unfortunately most copies do have some defects. Booksellers usually rationalize these defects as minimal, but collectors find any defect is a good excuse not to buy. This is the reason we have provided estimates with and without dustwrappers. The point is that a copy in a well worn and chipped dustwrapper may **not** be worth much more than the APG estimate for a very good to fine copy without dustwrapper. Conversely, a very fine to mint copy of a book may be worth considerably more than the APG estimate.

The price estimates included in the APG's reflect current estimates and not projections. As such the APG's price estimates are not intended to place an upper limit on what a collector or librarian should pay for a fine copy, the estimates are, after all, just a guide based on an informed opinion. We have published a price guide to the identification and price of first books (1975, 1978, 1982, 1985 1989 and 1995 {latter two published by Putnams}). An analysis of the prices in the last edition indicates only about one percent of the titles decreased in price over a ten year period while some increased 30 times in value. This is not a sales pitch for investing in first editions, (or perhaps it is if you are willing to wait ten years), but is only mentioned to make the point that historically the prices of first editions have risen and we do not believe it would be reasonable to expect the APG price estimates to hold steady when dealers find the demand for certain titles indicate higher prices. It should also be understood that in most cases these dealers have paid higher prices in order to purchase the books for resale.

Many, probably most books were preceded by proofs or advance copies in paperwraps and are only listed if we can identify something about them in detail. Therefore, we include uncorrected proofs or advance reading copies in the guides only when we can indicate the color of the cover.

"A" items are the primary works of an author and we include all books, pamphlets and broadsides. In addition, we might occasionally include books edited by the authors and books that include introductions or forewords by the author. We do not include anthologies which include the author's work or magazine appearances.

The number of copies in the first printing will be included if known. We are attempting to collect this information but must admit it is not easy. Our experience thus far indicates that the most effective way to obtain the quantities is to find someone who works for the publishing house and is willing to take the time to locate the records (if they still exist) or have them located. We have had some success with Delacorte, Knopf, Little Brown, Houghton Mifflin, New Directions, Norton, Putnams, Simon & Schuster, and Viking. Even these publishers have changed personnel and we find when we go back we are not successful in getting information; thus we would appreciate any assistance with publishers that you could provide. Our goal, over time, is to obtain the quantities, ascertain that publishers' records do not exist, or that the information will not be released by the publisher. We have recorded data from *Publishers Weekly* and put (PW) after the quantities derived from this source. We believe the users should be aware these quantities may be overstated in some cases. The differences in the initial quantity announced in *Publishers Weekly* and the actual production quantity, if reduced, reflects the fact that the advance orders from booksellers did not support the larger print run. We are keeping records of our sources for the quantities and would be happy to furnish this information to bibliographers who have legitimate need.

We regularly update the APG's and believe this will afford an opportunity not only to update price estimates but also increase the accuracy of the information contained in each APG.

We hope the guides prove useful and that their content and accuracy will improve over succeeding years.

INSTRUCTIONS FOR USE

NUMBER - The individual numbered entries are entered chronologically based on the information available to the compilers at the time of preparation. Within each individual numbered entry the various printings are also listed chronologically with the following arbitrary sequence given to books that were published *simultaneously*:

signed lettered copy
signed numbered copy

hardbound trade edition
trade edition in paperwraps

We try to ascertain the precedence of U.S. or U.K. editions but, if we have no publication information, we assume the country of origin of the author would be the first.

TITLE - The first entry after the number is the title of the book in capital letters. The titles of the individual books are shown as they appear on the title pages (some abbreviations were used in the titles).

PUBLISHER - The second entry is the name of the publisher as it appears on the title page. If the publisher's name does not appear on the title page, the publisher's entry is enclosed in parenthesis, e.g. (Viking).

PLACE OF PUBLICATION - The third entry is the city of publication as it appears on the title page. If the city does not actually appear on the title page this entry is included in parenthesis, e.g. (NY). If more than one place is listed on the title page only the primary location, usually New York or London will be shown.

DATE - The fourth entry is the year the book was published. If the date of publication is not actually printed on the title page, the year will appear in this entry in parenthesis, e.g. (1971). Dates in parenthesis will be the date the book was copyrighted unless other information is available. If the date of publication or copyright date do not appear in the book "no-date" or the abbreviation "n-d" will appear and the date will be in parenthesis if known.

EDITION - The fifth entry is a code number which provides information on how to identify the first printing (first edition) of the particular book:

[ ] The open bracket after a title means the bibliography does not include enough information to identify the first edition; and we have not actually seen a copy. It will be noted that in many cases where there is an open bracket, the place or date may be in parenthesis on the title page. In these cases, we obtained this information from other

dealer catalogs, as most dealers are conscientious in putting the place and date in parenthesis if they do not appear on the title page. Specific information to fill in these blanks would, of course, be welcomed.

[0] The book contains *no* statement of printing or edition. Usually only the copyright information and publisher, and perhaps the printer.

[1] The copyright page actually states the edition -"First Printing," "First Edition," "First Impression," "Published 19--," "First Published in 19--," and *does not* indicate any later printing. The important thing is that it actually indicates it is a first and/or includes the date and **does not state** any later printing information.

[2] This entry is for limited editions. In addition to any of the other methods of indicating the edition, these books contain a separate page (although, occasionally it might be on the copyright page), which furnishes any or all of the following detailed information - publisher, printer, date of publication, type of paper used, number of copies, the number of the particular book and the author's signature. These separate pages are bound either in the front of the book preceding the text or immediately following the last page of text. The inclusion of this page in the book is the most important factor in identifying these particular editions.

[3] The copyright page may or may not state "First Edition." "First Printing," etc. (as in [1] above) but more importantly it has a series of numbers or letters containing either a "1" or an "A"; i.e., "1 2 3 4 5...," "1 3 5 7 9 11 10 8 6 4 2," or "A B C D E F.." etc. All books (with the exceptions noted in [4] below) containing a series of numbers or letters without the "1" or "A," are later printings, **even if the book states "First Edition."**

[4] This designation is for either Random House; and Harcourt up until 1984. Both state "First Edition" on the copyright page. Random House includes a series of numbers starting with "2" and Harcourt a series of letters starting with "B." Both publishers remove the statement

"First Edition" on the second printing of the book. Harcourt we believe in 1984 (based on Alice Walker's books) changed to using "A B C D ..." on their first editions. We assume they take both the "A" and the statement "First Edition" off on the second printing.

[5] This designates methods used by the following publishers. The user will be able to tell which of the following is applicable for a particular book by checking under the publisher of the book in the second entry of the guide (publisher).

APPLETON - Used the numerical identification "(1)" at the foot of the last text page of the book. This was changed to a "(2)" on the second printing, "(3)" on the third printing, etc.

GEORGE H. DORAN - Placed a design "GHD" on the copyright page of the first printing and removed it on later printings.

FARRAR & RINEHART - Placed "FR" on the copyright page of the first printing and removed it on later printings.

FARRAR & STRAUS - Placed the letters "FS" on the copyright page of the first printing and removed it on later printings.

RINEHART & CO. - Placed an "R" in a circle on the copyright page of the first printing and removed it on later printings.

CHARLES SCRIBNER'S SONS - Placed the letter "A" on the copyright page of the first printing and removed it on later printings, starting in 1930. In the 1950's Scribner started using a letter and a series of numbers starting with an "A" on the First Printings [e.g. A-6.65(v)] and changing to a "B" on the Second Printings [e.g. B-8.66(v)]. This code, [5], applies to any book Scribner published using either the "A" alone or in a series.

PAPERWRAPS (wraps) - The inclusion of "wraps" indicates this edition of the book was not hardbound, but issued in paperwraps. Alternatively, if "wraps" does not appear, the book is hardbound and has a dustwrapper unless otherwise stated.

NUMBER OF COPIES - This entry indicates the total number of copies (cc) in the particular edition, if known. It also indicates if the book is a numbered (no) or lettered (ltr) copy and if it was signed (sgd) by the author. If the number includes (PW) it means the source was *Publishers Weekly*, which means the number is usually a maximum as there are many instances where lower first printings were actually ordered based on advance sales.

ISSUE POINTS | OTHER DETAILS - If there is more than one issue of a particular first edition, the points necessary to identify the issue are furnished. This entry may also include a comment or other information.

PAGE NUMBERS - If page and line numbers are necessary to identify issues they are shown as follows - page 87 line 13 = "p.87:13."

REFERENCE - Each APG will list the bibliographical source or sources for that guide. If a particular APG has more than one reference, it can be assumed the primary source, reference (a) has been used for those books covered and Ref.b thereafter. In other words, if Ref.a was published in 1975, it was used for books up to 1975 unless otherwise stated; and if Ref.b was published in 1990, it would have been used from 1975 to 1990 unless otherwise stated. If certain editions or issue points were obtained from specific dealer catalogs, the names of the firm and catalog date will be shown.

PRICES - The prices after each entry are the compiler's estimates of the retail prices current as of the date of the price guide. The *first* number is the estimated price for the book without its dustwrapper or without the original box or slipcase. The *second* number is the estimated price of the book in its original dustwrapper and/or box/slipcase on books published in 1920 or later. If only one price is shown, the particular book was issued in paperwraps, or was published before 1920.

The prices shown are estimates based on the compiler's knowledge of the current market and should be considered as such. The first edition marketplace is a volatile one, based on supply and demand. The prices for certain books have risen greatly over the last few years, while the majority of books have shown only modest price rises, usually keeping pace with inflation but not doubling or tripling in price annually as (relatively) few books have done. The compilers make no pretensions that these guides are perfectly accurate. In the final analysis each user will have to make their own judgment in evaluating the book-in-hand. The guide, hopefully, will prove useful in arriving at an informed judgment.

No value has been assigned (NVA) to a title if the quantity was so small that a copy is truly rare; if we have not seen a copy or a recorded price and are not sure if it is common or scarce; or if we know a title has been sold at what appears to us to be a relatively high price, and we do not feel comfortable with that price as an accurate estimate.

ABBREVIATIONS:

cc	copies
ltd	limited
no	numbered
NVA	No Value Assigned
PW	*Publishers Weekly*
sgd	signed
( )	indicates that information contained therein is not on the title page of the book; or miscellaneous information
+	used at the end of a title which includes the words "And Other Stories (Poems/Essays)"
...	indicates that the complete title or other information has been abbreviated

Note: We have abbreviated the places of publication using standard abbreviations, i.e. NY=New York

EXAMPLE:

013a: DANTE Faber & Faber L (1929) [1] 2,000 cc. Gray dustwrapper printed in blue and black. Earliest state of dustwrapper has no review excerpts on front flap and back cover $50/250

Translation:

013a: {the author's 13th book in the price guide} DANTE {title} Faber & Faber {publisher} L {London} (1929) {date not on title page} [1] {states "First printing"/"First published..." etc.} 2,000 cc {number of copies} Gray dustwrapper printed in blue... {issue points} $50/250 {$50 without a dw | $250 with dw}

CONDITION:

1975 to 1995: These are really "modern" first editions. Ninety-nine percent of these books are fiction or poetry. Because they have been published so recently, the prices listed herein would be for very fine copies in **DUSTWRAPPERS** (unless in wraps or a limited edition in slipcase) with *NO DEFECTS* (including such minor things as price-clipped dustwrappers, former owners' names written in, bookplates, remainder marks on bottom page edges, closed tears or tape repairs in the dustwrappers--even though there may be no actual loss of paper on the dustwrappers).

1945 to 1974: These books are a little older, but still copies must be in **ORIGINAL DUSTWRAPPERS** (unless in wraps or a limited edition in slipcase) with no major defects. These books do not have to look as new as the foregoing (1970-90). Also, the price-clipped dustwrapper and closed tears would be more acceptable, but the book has to be fine with the dustwrapper showing only minor wear, fading, or soiling.

1920 to 1944: The book must be very good to fine with only minimal (if any) soiling, **IN A DUSTWRAPPER** (unless in wraps or a limited edition in slipcase) that is clean with only minimal soiling or fading and only a few small chips (1/8 inch or less) and closed tears.

1890 to 1919: The book must be clean and bright with no loss or tears on the edges. The estimated prices are for copies without dustwrappers. It should be noted that books published in multiple volumes (usually three volumes, but also two and four volume editions), are rare and prices here are for very good copies in matching condition. Fine to very fine copies would probably bring much more.

JOHN BARTH

John Barth was born in Cambridge, Maryland in May, 1930. He was educated at the Juilliard School of Music (New York) and Johns Hopkins University (Baltimore) where he is currently a Professor of English and Creative Writing. His first book, *The Floating Opera*, was set (loosely) in Cambridge, Maryland, which is the setting for many of his books. He received the National Book Award for Fiction in 1973 for *Chimera*.

REFERENCES:

(a) Weixlmann, Joseph. JOHN BARTH: *A Bibliography*. New York/London: Garland Publishing, Inc., 1976.

(b) Bruccoli, Matthew J., and Clark, E. E. Frazer Jr. (editors). FIRST PRINTINGS OF AMERICAN AUTHORS. Vol. 2. Detroit, Michigan: Gale Research Co. (1978).

(c) Inventory or dealer catalogs.

001a: THE FLOATING OPERA Appleton, New York (1956). [5] 1,682 cc (ref. a&b) $100/500

001b: THE FLOATING OPERA (REVISED) Doubleday, Garden City, 1967. [0] 4,500 cc. "This ... Edition ... Revised By Author" $20/100

001c: THE FLOATING OPERA (REVISED) Secker & Warburg, London (1968). [] Uncorrected proof in orange and white wraps (Waiting For Godot 6/88) $125.

001d: THE FLOATING OPERA (REVISED) Secker & Warburg, London (1968). [1] 4,000 cc. States "This edition first published..." (ref.c) $15/75

002a: THE END OF THE ROAD Doubleday, Garden City, 1958. [1] 3,500 cc. Also noted, a copy in binding entirely devoid of text. Publisher's omission, trial binding? (The Fine Books Company 4/96) $125/450

002b: THE END OF THE ROAD Secker & Warburg, London, 1962. [0] 3,000 cc $30/150

002c: THE END OF THE ROAD (REVISED) Doubleday, Garden City, 1967. [1] 4,500 cc. "Revised Edition" stated $15/75

003a: THE SOT WEED FACTOR Doubleday, Garden City, 1960. [1] 3,000 cc. Dustwrapper design by Edward Gorey $125/600

003b: THE SOT WEED FACTOR Secker & Warburg, London (1961). [0] 6,100 cc $30/150

003c: THE SOT WEED FACTOR (REVISED) Doubleday, Garden City, 1967. [1] 8,000 cc. "Revised Edition" stated. Bill Berger reports "$7.50" with "N22" on last page; $7.95" with "J45" and $10" with "H42." Assume these would be three different printings $15/75

003d: THE SOT WEED FACTOR Franklin Press, Franklin Center, 1980. [2] Sgd, "limited" edition in full leather. First illustrated $100.

004a: GILES GOAT BOY or THE REVISED NEW SYLLABUS Doubleday, Garden City (1966). [2] 250 sgd/ltd cc. Issued without dustwrapper. In a mottled brown slipcase with a lilac-brown label (ref.a) $200/250

004b: GILES GOAT BOY Doubleday, Garden City, 1966. [0] 15,000 cc. First edition has "H18" on last page of text (ref. a&c) $25/125

004c: GILES GOAT BOY Secker & Warburg, London (1967). [0] 8,500 cc $15/75

005a: LOST IN THE FUNHOUSE Doubleday Garden City (1968). [2] 250 sgd no. cc. Issued without dustwrapper in slipcase $150/200

005b: LOST IN THE FUNHOUSE Doubleday, Garden City, 1968. [1] 25,000 cc $15/60

005c: LOST IN THE FUNHOUSE Secker & Warburg, London (1969). [0] 1,800 cc $25/125

006a: A CONVERSATION WITH JOHN BARTH (Union College, Schenectady 1972.) [0] Wraps. Edited by Frank Gado $75.

007a: CHIMERA Random House, New York (1972). [] Uncorrected proof in narrow green wraps $125.

007b: CHIMERA Random House, New York (1972). [2] 300 sgd no. cc. Issued in clear acetate dustwrapper and slate-blue slipcase $100/150

007c: CHIMERA Random House, New York (1972). [1] 24,982 cc. Winner of the National Book Award for 1973 $10/50

007d: CHIMERA Andre Deutsch (London, 1974). [0] 2,500 cc $10/50

008a: NATIONAL BOOK AWARD IN FICTION, 1973 ... FOR CHIMERA ACCEPTANCE REMARKS Alice Tully Hall, Lincoln Center, 1973. [0] One Xeroxed page, 27 lines of text. Not for sale. Published April 11, 1973. Number of copies unknown $100.

009a: TODD ANDREWS TO THE AUTHOR Lord John Press, Northridge, 1979. [2] 50 sgd no. cc. Leather bound, issued without dustwrapper (ref.c) $150.

009b: TODD ANDREWS TO THE AUTHOR Lord John Press, Northridge, 1979. [2] 300 sgd no. cc. Issued without dustwrapper (ref.c) $75.

010a: LETTERS Putnam, New York (1979). [0] Uncorrected proof in red-orange wraps. Also noted in plain blue dustwrapper and oversize proof dustwrapper (Ken Lopez 2/92) $75/150

010b: LETTERS Putnam, New York (1979). [2] 500 sgd no. cc. Issued in slipcase issued without dustwrapper (ref.c). Also noted with "or" in place of number and complimentary slip laid-in $75/100

010c: LETTERS Putnam, New York (1979). [0] Noted in dustwrappers lettered in gold (or copper) and silver (priority unknown) $7/40

010d: LETTERS Secker & Warburg, London, 1980. [1] American sheets with cancel title page, spine imprint still Putnam (Robert Temple #42) $7/40

011a: TWO MEDITATIONS Walker Art Center / Toothpaste Press, Minn. (no date). [2] 85 sgd no. cc. Broadside $125.

012a: THE LITERATURE OF EXHAUSTION AND THE LITERATURE OF REPLENISHMENT Lord John Press, Northridge, 1982. [2] 100 sgd no. cc. Deluxe edition $125.

012b: THE LITERATURE OF EXHAUSTION AND THE LITERATURE OF REPLENISHMENT Lord John Press, Northridge, 1982. [2] 300 sgd no. cc $75.

013a: SABBATICAL Putnam, New York (1982). [0] Uncorrected Proof in orange wraps (H. E. Turlington #28) $75.

013b: SABBATICAL Putnam, New York (1982). [2] 750 sgd no. cc. Issued in slipcase without dustwrapper (ref.c) $50/90

013c: SABBATICAL Putnam, New York, (1982). [0] 31,000 cc $7/35

013d: SABBATICAL Secker & Warburg, London (1982). [ ] 2,500 cc $8/40

014a: DON'T COUNT ON IT: *A Note on the Number of the 1001 Nights* Lord John Press, Northridge, 1984. [2] 50 sgd no. cc. Deluxe edition (ref.c) $125.

014b: DON'T COUNT ON IT: *A Note on the Number of the 1001 Nights* Lord John Press, Northridge, 1984. [2] 150 sgd no cc (ref.c) $75.

015a: THE FRIDAY BOOK: *Essays & Other Non-Fiction* Putnam, New York (1984). [0] Uncorrected Proof in green wraps (ref.c) $75.

015b: THE FRIDAY BOOK: *Essays & Other Non-Fiction* Putnam, New York (1984). [0] $8/40

016a: THE TIDEWATER TALES Putnam, New York (1987). [] Uncorrected proof in yellow wraps $75.

016b: THE TIDEWATER TALES Putnam, New York (1987). [3] 18,500 cc. (Published 6/22/87 @ $24.95) $8/40

016c: THE TIDEWATER TALES Methuen, London (1988). [] $8/40

017a: THE LAST VOYAGE OF SOMEBODY THE SAILOR Little Brown, Boston, 1991. [] Advance Review Copy in pictorial wraps $60.

017b: THE LAST VOYAGE OF SOMEBODY THE SAILOR Little Brown, Boston, 1991. [3] Also states "First Edition." (Published 2/91 @ $22.95) $7/35

017c: THE LAST VOYAGE OF SOMEBODY THE SAILOR Hodder & Stoughton, London (1991). [] (Chloe's Books 1/95) $8/40

018a: ONCE UPON A TIME: *A Floating Opera* Little, Brown, Boston, 1994. [] Uncorrected Proof in blue wraps $75.

018b: ONCE UPON A TIME: *A Floating Opera* Little, Brown, Boston, 1994. [] (Published 5/94 @ $23.95) $5/30

019a: FURTHER FRIDAYS Little, Brown, Boston, 1995. [] Proof in 8½ x 11 inch format, printed on rectos only (In Our Time 8/95) $60.

019b: FURTHER FRIDAYS Little, Brown, Boston, 1995. [] Uncorrected Proof in beige wraps (Waverley Books 4/95) $75.

019c: FURTHER FRIDAYS Little, Brown, Boston / New York / Toronto / London (1995). [3] $5/25

020a: ON WITH THE STORY Little, Brown, Boston (1996). [] Uncorrected proof in wraps (Ken Lopez 12/96) $75.

020b: ON WITH THE STORY Little, Brown, Boston (1996). [] Advance copy, unbound signatures laid into trial dustwrapper with blank flaps (In Our Time 7/96) $75/150

020c: ON WITH THE STORY Little, Brown, Boston (1996). [] Advance reading copy in glossy pictorial wraps (Ken Lopez 12/96) $50.

020d: ON WITH THE STORY Little, Brown, Boston/ New York / Toronto/ London (1996) [3] Also states "First Edition" $5/25

THOMAS BERGER

Berger was born in Cincinnati, Ohio in 1924. He was educated at the University of Cincinnati and Columbia University (New York). Berger served in the Army during W.W.II (1943-46). He has been employed as a professor and visiting lecturer at various universities over the years.

REFERENCES:

(a) Lepper, Gary M. A BIBLIOGRAPHICAL REFERENCE TO SEVENTY-FIVE MODERN AMERICAN AUTHORS. Berkeley: Serendipity Books, 1976.

(b) Bruccoli, Matthew J., and Clark, E. E. Frazer Jr., (editors). FIRST PRINTINGS OF AMERICAN AUTHORS. Vol. 2. Detroit: Gale Research (1978).

(c) Inventory.

001a: CRAZY IN BERLIN Scribners, New York (1958). [5] (Ref.a states first issue lacks rear flyleaf, but never seen) $60/300

002a: REINHART IN LOVE Scribners, New York (1962). [5] $30/150

002b: REINHART IN LOVE Eyre and Spottiswoode, London (1963). [1] Includes sentence (second from top of p.109) missing from U. S. edition, for what that is worth (per Robert Loren Link) $15/75

003a: LITTLE BIG MAN Dial Press, New York, 1964. [0] First issue dustwrapper without notice that book was Dial Prize winner $50/300

003b: LITTLE BIG MAN Dial Press, New York, 1964. [0] Second issue dustwrapper with notice that book was Dial Prize Winner $50/200

003c: LITTLE BIG MAN Eyre and Spottiswoode, London, 1965. [] Uncorrected proof in plain pink wrappers (Nicholas and Helen Burrows 2/96 $200.

003d: LITTLE BIG MAN Eyre and Spottiswoode, London (1965). [1] $25/125

004a: KILLING TIME Dial Press, New York, 1964. [] Uncorrected Proof in tan wraps (Books, Inc. 6/95) $175.

004b: KILLING TIME Dial Press, New York, 1964. [1] $15/60

004c: KILLING TIME Eyre and Spottiswoode, London (1968). [1] (Ref. c) $10/50

005a: VITAL PARTS Baron, New York, 1970. [0] $10/50

005b: VITAL PARTS Eyre and Spottiswoode, London, 1971. [] (Ref. b) $10/50

006a: REGIMENT OF WOMEN Simon & Schuster, New York (1973). [1] $12/60

006b: REGIMENT OF WOMEN Eyre, Methuen, London (1974). [1] (Ref. c) $10/40

007a: SNEAKY PEOPLE Simon & Schuster, New York (1975). [3] $8/40

007b: SNEAKY PEOPLE Magnum Books (London, 1980). [1] Wraps $25.

008a: WHO IS TEDDY VILLANOVA? Delacorte (New York, 1977). [1] $8/40

008b: WHO IS TEDDY VILLANOVA? Eyre Methuen, London (1977). [] (Ref.c) $8/40

009a: ARTHUR REX *A Legendary Novel* Delacorte (New York, 1978). [] Uncorrected proof in mustard colored wraps $100.

009b: ARTHUR REX *A Lengendary Novel* Delacorte (New York, 1978) [1] $12/60

009c: ARTHUR REX *A Legendary Novel* Magnum Books (London, 1980?). [] Wraps $30.

010a: NEIGHBORS Delacorte, New York, 1980. [1] $8/40

010b: NEIGHBORS Magnum Books (London, 1981). [1] "Magnum edition published 1981." Wraps $25.

011a: REINHART'S WOMEN Delacorte, New York (1981). [1] $6/30

011b: REINHART'S WOMEN Methuen, London, 1982 [] Using U. S. plates (Robert Loren Link 8/91) $10/40

012a: THE FEUD Delacorte (New York, 1983). [] Uncorrected proof in blue wraps $75.

012b: THE FEUD Delacorte (New York, 1983) [1] $6/30

012c: THE FEUD Methuen, London, 1984. [] $10/40

013a: GRANTED WISHES Lord John Press, Northridge, 1984. [2] 26 sgd ltr cc. Issued without dustwrapper or slipcase (in print) $200.

013b: GRANTED WISHES Lord John Press, Northridge, 1984. [2] 250 sgd no. cc. Issued without dustwrapper or slipcase (in print) $75.

014a: NOWHERE Delacorte (New York, 1985). [] Uncorrected proof in blue wraps (Bev Chaney 6/91) $60.

014b: NOWHERE Delacorte (New York, 1985). [1] $6/30

014c: NOWHERE Methuen, London (1986). [] $6/30

015a: BEING INVISIBLE Little Brown, Boston (1987). [1] (Published April 15, 1987 @ $16.95) $6/30

015b: BEING INVISIBLE Methuen, London, 1988. [] $7/35

016a: THE HOUSEGUEST Little Brown, Boston (1988). [] Uncorrected proof in gold wraps (Waiting For Godot 10/90) $60.

016b: THE HOUSEGUEST Little Brown, Boston (1988). [1] (Published April 1988 @ $16.95) $7/35

016c: THE HOUSEGUEST Weidenfeld & Nicolson, London (1989). [] $7/35

017a: CHANGING THE PAST Little Brown, Boston, 1989. [] (Published September 1989 @ $18.95) $5/25

017b: CHANGING THE PAST Weidenfeld & Nicolson, London, 1990. [] (Ian McKelvie 11/92) $6/30

018a: ORRIE'S STORY Little Brown, Boston (1990). [] (Published October 1990 @ $18.95) $5/25

019a: MEETING EVIL Little, Brown, Boston (1992). [] (Duga's Books 9/95) $5/25

020a: ROBERT CREWS Morrow, New York, 1994. [] Uncorrected proof in white wraps (Waverley Books 2/94) $40.

020b: ROBERT CREWS Morrow, New York, 1994. [] $5/25

021a: SUSPECTS Morrow, New York (1996). [3] Uncorrected bound galleys. In pictorial wraps. Also states "First Edition" $40.

021b: SUSPECTS Morrow, New York (1996). [3]
Also states "First Edition". (Published @ $23.00.) $5/25

JOHN CHEEVER
1912-1984

John Cheever was born in Quincy, Massachusetts in 1912. He served in the Army during World War II and thereafter devoted himself primarily to writing short stories while occasionally teaching at various colleges. He was a consistently successful short story writer and was awarded a Pulitzer Prize for his collected stories in 1979.

REFERENCES:

(a) Lepper, Gary M. A BIBLIOGRAPHICAL INTRODUCTION TO SEVENTY-FIVE MODERN AMERICAN AUTHORS. Berkeley: Serendipity Books, 1976.

(b) Private Collection.

(c) Chaney, Bev Jr., and Burton, William (compilers). JOHN CHEEVER: *A Bibliographical Checklist*. In the *American Book Collector*, August 1986.

(d) Eppard, Philip B. (editor). FIRST PRINTINGS OF AMERICAN AUTHORS. Vol. 5. Detroit: Gale Research (1987).

001a: THE WAY SOME PEOPLE LIVE Random House, New York (1943). [1] $300/1,250

002a: THE ENORMOUS RADIO Funk & Wagnalls, New York, 1953. [1] "I" on copyright page. In dustwrapper priced $3.50 with "Funk & Wagnalls New York 10" on rear panel. (Also see 027a) $60/300

002b: THE ENORMOUS RADIO Gollancz, London, 1953. [0] (Ref.b) $30/150

003a: STORIES Straus & Cudahy, New York (1956). [1] (Note: Jean Stafford, Daniel Fuchs and William Maxwell also contributed) $20/100

003b: A BOOK OF STORIES Gollancz, London, 1957. [] (Ref.d.) Also noted without publisher's imprint at base of spine (Ian McKelvie 1994) $20/100

004a: THE WAPSHOT CHRONICLE Harper & Bros., New York (1957). [1] National Book Award Winner for 1958. (Published March 25, 1957 @ $3.50) $35/175

004b: THE WAPSHOT CHRONICLE Gollancz, London, 1957. [0] (Ref.b.) (Also noted with Book Society wrap-around band) $25/125

004c: THE WAPSHOT CHRONICLE Time-Life, New York (1965). [1] Wraps. Has "x" on last page ("xx" indicates second printing, etc). New introduction by author $30.

004d: THE WAPSHOT CHRONICLE Time Reading Program, Alexandria (1982). [0] Simulated cloth without dustwrapper same introduction as 004c $25.

004e: THE WAPSHOT CHRONICLE Franklin Library, Franklin Center, 1978. [2] Signed. Full leather with "Limited Edition" on title page. New note by Cheever (Ref.b). $125.

005a: THE HOUSEBREAKER OF SHADY HILL Harper & Bros., New York (1958). [1] $35/175

005b: THE HOUSEBREAKER OF SHADY HILL Gollancz, London, 1958. [0] (Ref.b) $25/125

006a: SOME PEOPLE, PLACES & THINGS THAT WILL NOT APPEAR IN MY NEXT NOVEL Harper & Bros., New York (1961). [1] $30/150

006b: SOME PEOPLE, PLACES & THINGS THAT WILL NOT APPEAR IN MY NEXT NOVEL Gollancz, London, 1961. [0] (Ref.c) $20/100

007a: THE WAPSHOT SCANDAL Harper & Row, New York (1964). [1] Uncorrected proof in tall wraps (ref.b) $300.

007b: THE WAPSHOT SCANDAL Harper & Row, New York (1964). [1] $15/75

007c: THE WAPSHOT SCANDAL Gollancz, London, 1964. [0] Uncorrected proof in wraps (ref.b) $200.

007d: THE WAPSHOT SCANDAL Gollancz, London, 1964. [0] (Ref.b) $15/75

008a: THE BRIGADIER AND THE GOLF WIDOW Harper & Row, New York (1964). [1] Uncorrected proof in wraps (ref.b) $200.

008b: THE BRIGADIER AND THE GOLF WIDOW Harper & Row, New York (1964). [2] (Quantity unknown.) Signed by author on tipped in sheet (before title page) $150/200

008c: THE BRIGADIER AND THE GOLF WIDOW Harper & Row, New York (1964). [1] First issue dustwrapper with author's picture on back panel $15/75

008d: THE BRIGADIER AND THE GOLF WIDOW Harper & Row, New York (1964). [1] Second issue dustwrapper with "From the Early Reviews of ..." this book on back panel. Both have "01064" bottom of front flap $15/50

008e: THE BRIGADIER AND THE GOLF WIDOW Gollancz, London, 1965. [0] (Ref.c) $15/75

009a: MIMI BOYER Bodley Gallery, New York, 1964. [0] Exhibition brochure (folded sheet) with text by Cheever $250.

010a: SHADY HILL STORIES Eihosa Ltd., Tokyo (1965). [] Flex cover in dustwrapper (Glenn Horowitz #8) $175.

011a: THE SWIMMER Stein & Day, New York (1967). [0] By Eleanor Perry. Filmscript based on the story by Cheever (ref.b) $15/75

011b: THE SWIMMER Hoko-Shobo (Tokyo, 1967). [] Wraps. Compiled with notes by Yoichiro Kobori (Waiting For Godot L-1) $100.

012a: THE ANGEL OF THE BRIDGE Hoko-Shobo (Tokyo 1967) [] Wraps. Compiled with notes by Yoichiro Kobori (Waiting For Godot L-1). (See also item 029a) $100.

013a: HOMAGE TO SHAKESPEARE Country Squires Books, Stevenson, Conn. (1968) [] Uncorrected proof in plain blue wraps $300.

013b: HOMAGE TO SHAKESPEARE Country Squires Books, Stevenson, Conn. (1968). [2] 150 sgd no. cc. In dustwrapper $200/275

014a: (ELIZABETH AMES) [No pubisher, place or date.] [] Proof in wraps without title or imprint (Bromer Books 10/92) $2,000.

014b: ELIZABETH AMES (The Corp of the Yaddo, Saratoga Springs, 1968) [0] Wraps. 2-page tribute to founder of Yaddo. May have been as few as 12 copies $1,500.

015a: BULLET PARK Knopf, New York, 1969. [1] Uncorrected proof in wraps $150.

015b: BULLET PARK Knopf, New York, 1969. [1] $8/40

015c: BULLET PARK Jonathan Cape, London, 1969. [] Uncorrected proof in salmon-pink wraps (Nicholas Pounder 6/96) $100

015d: BULLET PARK Jonathan Cape, London (1969). [1] (Ref.b) $10/50

016a: THE WORLD OF APPLES Knopf, New York, 1973. [1] Uncorrected proof in wraps $125.

016b: THE WORLD OF APPLES Knopf, New York, 1973. [1] Noted in both white and black cloth (Waiting For Godot #11) $8/40

016c: THE WORLD OF APPLES Jonathan Cape, London (1974). [1] (Ref.b) $8/40

017a: FALCONER Knopf, New York, 1977. [1] Uncorrected proof in salmon colored wraps (Waiting For Godot #8). Also noted as dated "1976" (Joseph The Provider #32) $200.

017b: FALCONER Knopf, New York, 1977. [1] (Ref.b) $10/50

017c: FALCONER Jonathan Cape, London (1977). [1] Uncorrected proof in wraps (ref.b) $125.

017d: FALCONER Jonathan Cape, London, (1977). [1] (Ref.b) $10/50

018a: THE STORIES OF JOHN CHEEVER Knopf, New York, 1978. [1] Uncorrected proofs in pale green printed wraps. Winner of the Pulitzer Prize for 1979 and National Book Critics Circle Award for 1978 $300.

018b: THE STORIES OF JOHN CHEEVER Knopf, New York, 1978. [1] $25/125

018c: THE STORIES OF JOHN CHEEVER Jonathan Cape, London (1979). [1] (Ref.b) $15/75

018d: THE STORIES OF JOHN CHEEVER Franklin Library, Franklin Center, 1980. [2] Signed (limitation not specified). Pulitzer prize series. Illustrated by Mitchell Hooks. Full leather (ref.b) $150.

019a: THE DAY THE PIG FELL IN THE WELL Lord John Press, Northridge, 1978. [2] 26 Sgd/ltr cc. Issued without dustwrapper or slipcase. (Also at least one author's copy in different binding $375.

019b: THE DAY THE PIG FELL IN THE WELL Lord John Press, Northridge, 1978 [2] 275 sgd no. cc. Issued without dustwrapper or slipcase (ref.b) $175.

020a: WAPSHOT CHRONICLE, WAPSHOT SCANDAL Harper & Row, New York (1979). [1] First combined edition (ref.d) $7/35

021a: OSSINING TOWN 22 KILOMETER ROAD RACE Ossining, New York, 1979. [0] Wraps. Large pamphlet, includes an introduction "The Ossining Marathon" by Cheever (ref.b) $125.

022a: THE LEAVES, THE LIONFISH AND THE BEAR Sylvester & Orphanos, Los Angeles, 1980. [2] 4 cc with printed name of recipient. Text is revised from previous magazine appearance (ref.c) $450.

022b: THE LEAVES, THE LIONFISH AND THE BEAR Sylvester & Orphanos, Los Angeles, 1980. [2] 26 sgd ltr cc (ref.b) $400.

022c: THE LEAVES, THE LIONFISH AND THE BEAR Sylvester & Orphanos, Los Angeles, 1980. [2] 300 sgd no. cc (ref.b) $125.

022d: THE LEAVES, THE LIONFISH AND THE BEAR Sylvester & Orphanos, Los Angeles, 1980. [2] Out-of-series (copies given as presentation) (ref.b). Number unknown $150.

023a: OH, WHAT A PARADISE IT SEEMS Knopf, New York, 1982. [1] Uncorrected proof in cream colored wraps (also noted as white, as well as light tan, but assume the same) $75.

023b: OH, WHAT A PARADISE IT SEEMS Knopf, New York, 1982. [1] (Published February 10, 1982 @ $10.) $7/35

023c: OH, WHAT A PARADISE IT SEEMS Jonathan Cape, London (1982). [1] Uncorrected proof. In red printed wraps and oversize proof dustwrapper (Ian McKelvie 4/91). Also noted in printed burnt-almond colored wraps (Bev Chaney, Jr. 3/97) $60/125

023d: OH, WHAT A PARADISE IT SEEMS Jonathan Cape, London (1982). [1] (Ref.b) $6/30

024a: THE NATIONAL PASTIME Sylvester & Orphanos, Los Angeles (1982). [2] 4 sgd no. cc with printed name of recipient $500.

024b: THE NATIONAL PASTIME Sylvester & Orphanos, Los Angeles (1982). [2] 26 sgd ltr cc $450.

024c: THE NATIONAL PASTIME Sylvester & Orphanos, Los Angeles (1982). [2] 300 sgd no. cc. Issued without dustwrapper or slipcase (ref.b) $200.

025a: CHRISTMAS IS A SAD SEASON FOR THE POOR Tales for Travellers (San Francisco, 1982). [0] Wraps. No. 4 in Selected Short Stories Series. First separate appearance (ref.b). (The series was issued in a "map" folded format) $35.

026a: THE COUNTRY HUSBAND San Suya, Tokyo (1983). [0] Wraps. Edited and notes by Haruma Okado $75.

027a: THE ENORMOUS RADIO Creative Education, Mankato, 1983. [] Pictorial boards. Issued without dustwrapper. First separate appearance $40.

028a: ATLANTIC CROSSING Ex Ophidia (Tuscaloosa, 1986) [2] 90 (99?) no. cc. Issued in full leather in drop-tray box (ref.c) $475.

029a: THE ANGEL OF THE BRIDGE Redpath, Minn., 1987. [0] Wraps. 5,000 cc in envelope $30.

030a: EXPELLED Sylvester & Orphanos (Los Angeles), 1988. [2] 9 cc with printed name of the recipient. Signed by Malcolm Cowley (foreword), John Updike (afterword), Warren Chappell (illus.), and Cheever. Miniature book issued without dustwrapper. In slipcase $450/500

030b: EXPELLED Sylvester & Orphanos (Los Angeles), 1988. [2] 26 sgd ltr cc Issued without dustwrapper. In slipcase? $400/450

030c: EXPELLED Sylvester & Orphanos (Los Angeles), 1988. [2] 150 sgd no. cc. Miniature book issued without dustwrapper. In slipcase $275/325

031a: CONVERSATIONS WITH JOHN CHEEVER University Press of Mississippi, Jackson (1988) [] $25/50

031b: CONVERSATIONS WITH JOHN CHEEVER University Press of Mississippi, Jackson (1988). [] Wraps $30.

032a: THE UNCOLLECTED STORIES OF JOHN CHEEVER 1930-1981 Academy, Chicago, 1988. [] Uncorrected proof. In wraps $2,000.

032b: THE UNCOLLECTED STORIES OF JOHN CHEEVER 1930-1981 Academy, Chicago (1988). [] 22 page advance excerpt. In wraps. Copies seen with and without sticker "This sampler is not authorized by the family of John Cheever" $40.

033a: THE LETTERS OF JOHN CHEEVER Simon & Schuster, New York (1988). [3] Uncorrected proof. In yellow wraps. Edited by Benjamin Cheever $60.

033b: THE LETTERS OF JOHN CHEEVER Simon & Schuster, New York (1988). [3] (Published 11/88 @ $19.95) $10/35

033c: THE LETTERS OF JOHN CHEEVER Jonathan Cape, London, 1989. [] $10/40

034a: THE JOURNALS OF JOHN CHEEVER Knopf, New York, 1991. [] Uncorrected proof. In white or buff wraps $60.

034b: THE JOURNALS OF JOHN CHEEVER Knopf, New York, 1991. [1] (Published 10/91 @ $25.) Edited by Robert Gottlieb $6/30

034c: THE JOURNALS OF JOHN CHEEVER Jonathan Cape, London, 1991. [] Edited by Robert Gottlieb $8/40

035a: GLAD TIDINGS *A Friendship in Letters The Correspondence of John Cheever and John D. Weaver 1945-1982* Harper Collins, New York (1993). [] Uncorrected proof. In white wraps $50.

035b: GLAD TIDINGS *A Friendship in Letters The Correspondence of John Cheever and John D. Weaver 1945-1982* Harper Collins, New York, 1993. [] $5/25

036a: THIRTEEN UNCOLLECTED STORIES OF JOHN CHEEVER Academy, Chicago, 1994. [] 30,000 cc. (Published 3/94 @ $20.) $5/25

Winston S. Churchill.

SIR WINSTON S. CHURCHILL
(1874-1965)

For the English speaking world, at least, Winston Churchill dominated the first half of this century. He was the one man who served in important government positions during both the World Wars. As Prime Minister he was noted for his eloquence and memorable phrases. He was an international statesman, parliamentarian, prime minister, orator, war correspondent, historian, artist and Noble Prize Winner; but he was always proud of the fact that he earned his living as a writer. Before the turn of the century he was paid 5 pounds a column by the Daily Telegraph for his dispatches from the North West frontier and by the time he was 26 years old, while still serving as a cavalry officer, he had written five books. His collected works run to 38 volumes. An amazing output for a man so involved in day to day history.

Notes on pricing and identification:

The estimated prices are for very good to fine copies without dustwrapper before 1920 (both with and without dustwrapper from 1920 foreword). The Woods bibliography seems to state the fact that a particular book or pamphlet actually contains the wording "First Edition," therefore we have assumed that none of the numerous pamphlets actually state "First Edition." Further, we assume all of the pamphlets are in self-wraps unless "card-covers" or "paperwraps" are mentioned. By this we mean that the speech or statement begins on the first page and there is no other cover. We found very few data points for pricing these pamphlets and extrapolated from what little we found, which means that the estimated prices may be way out of line in some cases.

On the sets we priced the *First World War* individually and as a set, but on the others (*Marborough*, *WWII*, *English Speaking People*) we only priced the sets.

We are aware that we are far from Churchill experts, but still hope this guide will prove useful; and that errors and omissions will be pointed out so that the first revision will be even more accurate.

REFERENCES:

(a) Woods, Frederick. A BIBLIOGRAPHY OF THE WORKS OF SIR WINSTON CHURCHILL. Second Revised Edition. (Surrey): St. Paul's Bibliographies (1979).

(b) Inventory, dealer catalogs, etc.

We would like to thank Jeff Klaess for laying out the bibliographical data from Woods, which was not as easy as it would seem. We also appreciate the clarification provided by Richard M. Langsworth (International Churchill Society) and Marvin Nicely.

001a: THE STORY OF THE MALAKAND FIELD FORCE. Longmans, Green, London, 1898. [0] 2,000 cc (a&b). Published March 14. Apple-green cloth, black endpapers, frontis portrait sewn in, and folding map tipped on to stub of frontis. 32 pages of ads at back on thinner paper, separately numbered. Author's name appears on spine as Winston L. Spencer Churchill. First issue, with advertisements dated 12/97 and lacking the errata slip (Nigel Williams 8/95) $6,000.

001b: THE STORY OF THE MALAKAND FIELD FORCE Longmans, Green, London, 1898. [0] Second state. As above but with errata slip tipped-in immediately preceding first folding map $5,000.

001c: THE STORY OF THE MALAKAND FIELD FORCE Longmans, Green, London, 1898. [0] 2,000 cc. Colonial Library. "This edition intended for circulation ...India and the British Colonies." The front cover and spine have "1897" but actually distributed after 001a $2,500.

Note: No American edition. An unspecified number of copies were shipped to the U.S. to be sold by Longmans Green, NY, 1898

001d: THE STORY OF THE MALAKAND FIELD FORCE Longmans, Green, London, 1901. [] Second edition with substantial revisions and a new preface $1,500.

002a: THE RIVER WAR Longmans, Green, London, 1899. [0] 2,000 cc. 2 vols. Published November 6. Illustrated by Angus McNeill

Vol. 1: folding maps facing pages 146, 234, 308, 338, 402, 406, 420, 424, 430, 432 and 462.

Vol. 2: folding maps facing pages 80, 98, 128, 144, 154, 156, 160, 172 and 224

The set: $6,000.

002b: THE RIVER WAR Longmans, Green, New York, 1899. [0] 2 vols. Published December 9 $5,000.

002c: THE RIVER WAR Longmans, Green, London, 1902. [] 1,000 cc (c&d). One volume. Published October 15. "New and Revised Edition" on title page. Folding maps facing pages 238, 256, 272, 284, 298 and 302. Text reduced and one chapter added. 40 page catalog at back on thinner paper and separately numbered (some copies issued without catalog) $1,250.

002d: THE RIVER WAR Longmans Green, New York, 1902. [] Copies of 002c were exported to New York for American publication on December 1 $1,000.

002e: THE RIVER WAR Thomas Nelson, London (1915). [0] (First cheap edition.) Published in August. Blue cloth, top page edges gilt $250.

002f: THE RIVER WAR Eyre & Spottiswoode, London, 1933. [1] 3,000 cc. "First Cheap Edition 1933." New introduction. Brown cloth $150/350

002g: THE RIVER WAR Scribners, New York, 1933. [] (Glenn Horowitz #16.) Not in ref.a $100/300

003a: SAVROLA Longmans, Green, New York, 1900. [0] 4,000 cc. Published February 3 (although copyright copies were received in November 1899). Dark blue cloth. 24 unnumbered pages of advertisements $1,250.

Note: type-set in Boston. Two sets of Electroplates taken, one set sent to London, title page and copyright page to be re-set in London, U.S. copyright notice removed, but not re-set, resulting in 2 states of first U.K. edition

003b: SAVROLA Longmans, Green, London, 1900. [0] 1,500 cc (b&c). Published February 13. Blue-green cloth, black endpapers. This issue has verso of title page blank (no copyright notice). Number of copies without copyright information unknown. Ref.a regards this as being simultaneous with 3c, but it would seem to us that it would more logically precede $1,500.

003c: SAVROLA Longmans, Green, London, 1900. [0] Blue-green cloth, black endpapers (issue with U.K. copyright notice on verso of title page) $1,000.

003d: SAVROLA Longmans, Green, London, 1900. [0] 1,500 cc. Colonial edition. Issued simultaneously with 003c $1,000.

003e: SAVROLA George Newnes, Ltd., Strand, W.C. (1908). [0] First illustrated edition. Red and blue printed wraps. Published in May $450.

003f: SAVROLA Random House, New York (1956). [1] "First printing/copyright 1956..." New short foreword by Churchill. Navy blue cloth and scarlet cloth (ref.b) $30/150

004a: LONDON TO LADYSMITH Longmans, Green, London, 1900. [0] 10,000 cc. Published May 15. Fawn pictorial cloth, black endpapers. Folding maps facing title, and pages 366, 448; 32 pages of ads on thinner paper, separately numbered $1,000.

004b: LONDON TO LADYSMITH Longmans, Green, London, 1900. [0] 500 cc. Published May 18. We have had a copy exactly the same as 004a but with "New Impression" added to title page, which we assume is this second printing $400.

004c: LONDON TO LADYSMITH Longmans, Green, New York, 1900. [0] 3,000 cc. Published June 16 $750.

004d: LONDON TO LADYSMITH Copp, Clark, Toronto (1900). [] Smooth light brown cloth. Believe to be printed in the U.S. (Steven Temple 7/88) $450.

005a: IAN HAMILTON'S MARCH Longmans, Green, London, 1900. [0] 5,000 cc. Published October 12. Dark red cloth, black endpapers. Folding map tipped-in preceding 4 pages ads, then 32 page catalog on thinner paper, separately numbered $1,250.

005b: IAN HAMILTON'S MARCH Longmans, Green, New York, 1900. [0] 1,533 cc. Published December 1 $750.

006a: MR. WINSTON CHURCHILL ON THE EDUCATION BILL No publisher or place, 1902. [0] 8 page off-print reprinted from the *Lancashire Daily Post* of November 11. (This is Woods first entry under 6) $1,500.

006b: MR. BRODRICK'S ARMY Arthur L. Humphreys, London, 1903. [0] 44 page, 8 3/8" x 5 1/2" pamphlet (Woods believes this to be the true first of 006c but, that it was not released. Identical text) $NVA

006c: MR. BRODRICK'S ARMY Arthur L. Humphreys, London, 1903. [0] Published in April. Publisher address as 187 Piccadilly, W. 8 13/16" x 6 3/8" pamphlet in dark red matte card cover, "Price One Shilling." (Richard Langworth in his article in

Antiquarian Bookman, Jan. 16, 1989, mentions that a copy sold at auction for 10,000 pounds) $NVA

006d: MR. BRODRICK'S ARMY (Churchilliana Co., Sacramento, 1977.) [] (Ref.b) $60.

007a: FREE TRADE LEAGUE. *North-west Manchester Division Branch* Free Trade League, Manchester, 1904. [0] Pamphlet of speech given June 15. 20 pages plus covers $1,250.

008a: MR. WINSTON CHURCHILL ON THE ALIENS BILL Liberal Publications Department, London, 1904. [0] 2 pages. Reprinted from *The Liberal Magazine*, December 1904 $750.

009a: WHY I AM A FREE TRADER W. T. Stead, London, 1905. [0] Wraps. 24 pages plus cover $1,250.

010a: LORD RANDOLPH CHURCHILL Macmillan, London, 1906. [0] 2 vols. 8,000 cc. Plum cloth. Published January 2 $750.

010b: LORD RANDOLPH CHURCHILL Macmillan, New York, 1906. [1] On verso of title page: "Published January 1906." 2 vols. Published February 10 $500.

010c: LORD RANDOLPH CHURCHILL Macmillan, London, 1907. [1] 1 vol. 3,000 cc. Plum cloth. Published in May. "Second Edition...1907." (Ref.a has price of 7/6 while Any Amount of Books catalogued a copy in 1986 with price of 10s) $250.

010d: LORD RANDOLPH CHURCHILL Odhams Press, London (1952). [0] Published February 5. Contains new introduction and Appendix V appears for first time. Red cloth $30/150

011a: FOR FREE TRADE Arthur L. Humphreys, London, 1906. [0] Dark red matte card cover. Published in April $1250.

011b: FOR FREE TRADE Churchilliana Co., Sacramento, 1977. [] $60.

012a: LIBERALISM AND SOCIALISM Scottish Liberal Association, Glasgow / Edinburgh, 1906. [0] Wraps. 15(16) pages $1,000.

013a: TO THE ELECTORS OF NORTH-WEST MANCHESTER North-West Manchester Liberal Association, 1906. [0] Wraps. 4 pages $850.

014a: NATIONAL DEMONSTRATIONS IN FAVOUR OF LAND AND HOUSING REFORM Liberal Publications Department, London, 1907. [0] Wraps. 20 pages $1,000.

015a: SPEECHES British Cotton Growing Association, Manchester, 1907. [0] 20 pages $1,000.

016a: FREE TRADE IN ITS BEARING ON INTERNATIONAL RELATIONS International Free Trade Congress, London, 1908. [0] 10 pages, plus cover $1,000.

017a: FOR LIBERALISM AND FREE TRADE John Leng, Dundee, 1908. [0] 32 pages $1,000.

018a: MY AFRICAN JOURNEY Hodder and Stoughton, London, 1908. [0] 12,500 cc. Red pictorial cloth. Published in December. A later issue was issued without the illustration or lettering on front cover. Also "second binding in maroon cloth" (Bowie & Co. 8/92 but not in ref.a) $850.

018b: MY AFRICAN JOURNEY Hodder & Stoughton, New York, 1908. [] Few copies issued to protect copyright. Binding similar to the later issue with plain vs. pictorial cover (Pepper & Stern 4/91) $2,000.

018c: MY AFRICAN JOURNEY Doran?, New York (1909). [0] Published on April 17. The only copy we've seen had a Doran tipped-in title page, blank on back, in later issue Hodder & Stoughton binding. Ref.a was incorrect in stating that Doubleday, Doran was the publisher as that firm didn't exist until the late 1920's. This issue is so scarce it would seem that it was not really "published" here $1,500.

019a: LIBERALISM AND SOCIALISM Liberal Publications Dept., London, 1908. [0] 4 pages $850.

020a: BUDGET ISSUES Liberal Publications Dept., London, 1909. [0] 16 pages $850.

021a: THE MENACE OF LAND MONOPOLY Free Trade and Land Values League, Melbourne, 1909. [0] 4 pages $850.

021b: THE MENACE OF LAND MONOPOLY Henry George Foundation, Melbourne, 1941. [0] 16 pages plus cover $500.

021c: ON HUMAN RIGHTS Henry George Foundation, Melbourne, 1942. [0] New title $400.

022a: LIBERALISM AND THE SOCIAL PROBLEM Hodder and Stoughton, London, 1909. [0] 5,000 cc. In plum buckram. Published in November $1,000.

022b: LIBERALISM AND THE SOCIAL PROBLEM Hodder and Stoughton, New York, 1909. [] Few copies to protect copyright with tipped-in title page. Plum buckram lettered in gilt on spine (Pepper & Stern 4/91) $2,000.

022c: LIBERALISM AND THE SOCIAL PROBLEM Doubleday, Doran, New York, 1910. [] Published in February $750.

023a: TO THE ELECTORS OF DUNDEE John Leng, Dundee, 1909. [0] (Dated December 28, 1909 from the Board of Trade. Woods thinks may have been published in 1910) $750.

024a: THE PEOPLE'S RIGHTS Hodder and Stoughton, London (1910). [0] Published January 14. Cherry red cloth, flecked with pink. Index at rear $1,250.

024b: THE PEOPLE'S RIGHTS Hodder and Stoughton, London (1910). [0] Wraps. Issued simultaneously. First state with Index $1,000.

024c: THE PEOPLE'S RIGHTS Hodder and Stoughton, London (1910). [0] Second issue with Index deleted and a second Appendix added $750.

024d: THE PEOPLE'S RIGHTS Taplinger, New York (1971). [1] "First published in U.S. in 1971" $15/75

025a: PRISON AND PRISONERS A Speech in the House of Commons 20th July, 1910. Cassell and Company, Ltd., London, 1910. [0] Gray wraps, printed in blue. Published August 6 $850.

026a: MR. CHURCHILL ON THE PEERS Liberal Publications Dept., London, 1910. [0] 1(2) pages (from a letter to his constituents, November 14, 1910) $500.

027a: CHURCHILL SAID ... United Scotland Movement, Glasgow, 1911. [0] 2 pages $400.

028a: CHURCHILL SAID Scottish National Congress, Glasgow, 1911. [0] 2 pages (Note: both 027 and 028 quote from same speech but are entirely separate publications) $400.

029a: AN ADDRESS TO YOUNG LIBERALS National League of Young Liberals, London, 1912. [0] 12 pages (Young Liberals Pamphlet No. 7) $750.

030a: IRISH HOME RULE Liberal Publications Dept., London, 1912. [0] 16 pages $850.

031a: MR. CHURCHILL'S MESSAGE TO ULSTER Home Rule Council, London, 1912. [0] 12 pages. Same speech as 030a $600.

032a: THE LIBERAL GOVERNMENT AND NAVAL POLICY Liberal Publications Dept., London, 1912. [0] 24 pages $750.

033a: ON NAVAL ARMAMENTS American Assoc. For International Conciliation, New York, 1913. [0] 13(14) pages (an offprint from *The Times*) $600.

034a: THE TORIES AND THE ARMY Liberal Publications Dept., London, 1914. [0] 8 pages $500.

035a: NAVY ESTIMATES IN THE GREAT WAR Liberal Publications Dept., London, 1915. [0] 20 pages $500.

036a: THE FIGHTING LINE Macmillan, London, 1916. [0] 32 pages $500.

037a: THE MUNITIONS MIRACLE National War Aims Committee, London, 1918. [0] 16 pages $500.

038a: THE RHINE ARMY Ministry of Information (H.M.S.O.), London, 1919. [0] 8 pages $450.

039a: REASON AND REALITY Harrison and Sons L 1920 [0] 32 pages $450.

040a: THE POSITION ABROAD AND AT HOME No publisher, London, 1920. [0] 12 pages $400.

041a: ADDRESS H.M.S.O., London, 1920. [0] 6 pages in wraps $400.

042a: DUNDEE PARLIAMENTARY ELECTION John Leng, Dundee, 1922. [0] 4 pages $400.

043a: INVITATION TO A POLITICAL MEETING Liberal Association, Dundee, 1922. [0] 8 pages $400.

044a: THE WORLD CRISIS - 1911-1914 Thornton Butterworth Ltd., London (1923). [1] 7,380 cc. Volume I. Published April 10. Folding maps pages 304, 320, 376, 432 and 472. Errata slip tipped-in between p.(vi)-1 $100/300

044b: THE WORLD CRISIS - 1915 Scribners, New York, 1923. [1] Volume I. "Published April 1923" (ref.b). This is the only U.S. edition mentioned in ref.a $75/200

044c: THE WORLD CRISIS - 1915 Thornton Butterworth Ltd., London (1923). [1] 7,500 cc. Volume II. Published October 30. Folding maps pages 144, 240, 328, two facing p.516 $100/300

044d: THE WORLD CRISIS - 1915 Scribners, New York, 1923. [1] Volume II. "Published April 1923" (ref.b) $75/200

044e: THE WORLD CRISIS - 1916-1918 Thornton Butterworth Ltd., London (1927). [1] Volume III (in 2 vols.). Part 1: folding maps pages 82, 164, 206, two folding statistical tables with errata slip tipped-in, facing p.52 and Part 2: Folding maps pages 330, 368, 372, 374, 530 and 534. 7,523 cc of the pair published March 3 $150/400

044f: THE WORLD CRISIS - 1916-1918 Scribners, New York, 1927. [0] Volume I (vol. III) (ref.b) $75/200

044g: THE WORLD CRISIS - 1916-1918 Scribners, New York, 1927. [0] Volume II (vol. IV) (ref.b) $75/200

044h: THE WORLD CRISIS - THE AFTERMATH Thornton Butterworth Ltd., London (1929). [1] 7,500 cc. Volume IV. Published March 7. Folding maps pages 102, 230 276 and 438. Errata slip tipped-in between pages 10-11 $75/250

044i: THE WORLD CRISIS - THE AFTERMATH Scribners, New York, 1929. [0] Volume V (ref.b) $50/150

044j: THE WORLD CRISIS - THE EASTERN FRONT Thornton Butterworth Ltd., London (1931). [1] 5,150 cc. Volume V. Published November 2. Folding maps pages 98, 142, 156, 250, 256, 308, 324, 338, 346, 368 and one following the Index $75/200

044k: THE UNKNOWN WAR - THE EASTERN FRONT Scribners, New York, 1931. [5] Volume VI (ref.b) $50/150

The five London volumes (in six) $750/2,000
The five American volumes (in six) $600/1,500

044l: THE WORLD CRISIS 1911-1918 Thornton Butterworth Ltd., London (1931). [0] 5,000 cc. Published February 26. One volume edition, abridged and revised with an additional chapter on "The Battle of the Marne" added $150/400

044m: THE WORLD CRISIS 1911-1918 Scribners, New York, 1931. [] Abridged and revised edition as above $100/300

044n: THE WORLD CRISIS Thornton Butterworth Ltd., London (1933). [] 1,354 cc. The Sandhurst edition. Adds folding facsimile of a letter (facing p.426) $500.

044o: THE WORLD CRISIS 1911-1918 Oldham Press, London, 1938. First 2 vol. set: a revision of the original publication with a new foreword by the author for this edition. Blue binding; issued without dustwrapper. (Books Etc. 11/92) $100.

045a: THE ALTERNATIVE TO SOCIALISM Harrison and Sons, London, 1924. [0] 16 pages $400.

046a: SHALL WE COMMIT SUICIDE? (Eilert Printing Co., New York [back cover]), 1924. [0] 11(12) pages. "Reprinted from Nash's *Pall Mall Magazine* of September 24, 1924." $400.

047a: ADDRESS Privately printed, London, 1925. [0] 4 pages in wraps $400.

048a: CO-OPS AND INCOME TAX Conservative Party, London, 1927. [0] 3(4) pages $400.

049a: RINGING THE ALARM Anti-Socialist and Anti-Communist Union, London, 1929. [0] 12 pages $400.

050a: THE NAVY LEAGUE The Navy League, London, 1930. [0] 8 pages in wraps $400.

051a: PARLIAMENTARY GOVERNMENT AND THE ECONOMIC PROBLEM Clarendon Press, Oxford, 1930. [0] Bound in gray tinted laid paper, printed in green. 20 pages. Published July 11 $400.

052a: MY EARLY LIFE Thornton Butterworth Ltd., London (1930). [1] 5,750 cc (052a & b). Published October 20. Boxed list of 11 of Churchill's works on verso of half-title $300/1,250

052b: MY EARLY LIFE Thornton Butterworth Ltd., London (1930). [1] Second issue adds 12th title *The World Crisis* $200/1,000

052c: A ROVING COMMISSION Scribners, New York, 1930. [5] New title Published October 31. Red cloth, covers and spine printed in gilt $125/500

052d: A ROVING COMMISSION Scribners, New York, 1939. [0] Introduction by Dorothy Thompson. Folding map facing p.352. Dark blue cloth, covers and spine printed in silver $75/200

053a: INDIA Thornton Butterworth Ltd., London (1931). [1] Orange cloth. Published on May 27 $300/850

053b: INDIA Thornton Butterworth Ltd., London (1931). [1] Orange wraps with price of 1/ -net. (Second printing in green wraps. No other difference) $500.

054a: THOUGHTS AND ADVENTURES Thornton Butterworth Ltd., London (1932). [1] 4,000 cc. Published November 10. Sandy-brown cloth $250/850

054b: AMID THESE STORMS Scribners, New York, 1932. [0] No copy noted with Scribner "A" even though this was their normal designation on first editions after 1930 $150/500

055a: MARLBOROUGH *His Life and Times* George G. Harrap, London, 1933. [] Volume I. Advance Proof in blue-gray printed wraps. Bound without plates and index. Although the first volume of *Marlborough* was extensively revised, in manuscript, galleys, and for the second edition, there are apparently no variations between these bound page proofs and the published text (Maggs Brothers Ltd. 3/95) $600.

055b: MARLBOROUGH *His Life and Times* George G. Harrap. 4 volumes.

Vol. I: London (1933). [2] 155 signed no cc (5 copies not for sale). Full orange morocco. In slipcase with paper labels with number of the set. Folding map between pages (16)-17. Also noted in black morocco (David Mayou 5/92)

Vol. II: London (1934). [2] 155 cc (5 copies not for sale). Binding as Vol. I but label of slipcase not numbered. 3 folding maps, sewn in between pages 606-607, errata slip tipped-in facing p.434

Vol. III: London (1936). [2] 155 cc (5 copies not for sale). Binding as Vol. I but label of slipcase not numbered

Vol. IV: London (1938). [2] 155 cc (5 copies not for sale). Binding as Vol. I but label of slipcase not numbered

The set $9,000.

Note: Swann auctioned a set in 1994 described as in original cloth.

055c: MARLBOROUGH *His Life and Times* George G. Harrap. 4 volumes. Trade edition:

Vol. I: London (1933). [0] Plum buckram over beveled boards. Folding map between pages 558-559, errata slip tipped-in between pages (16)-17

Vol. II: London (1934). [0] Binding as in Vol. I. 3 folding maps sewn in between pages 606-607, errata slip tipped-in facing p.434. Total of 15,000 cc in two impressions

Vol. III: London (1936). [0] Binding as in Vol. I. 3 folding maps tipped-in between pages 556-557, errata slip tipped-in facing p.(18). 10,000 cc published Oct. 23

Vol. IV: London (1938). [0] Binding as in Vol. I, but the color is much darker than preceding volumes. 10,000 cc published September 2

The set $450/1,250

055d: MARLBOROUGH *His Life and Times* Scribners. 6 volumes:

Vol. I and Vol. II (published as a set). New York, 1933. [5] Deep green cloth. Fore-edge lightly trimmed

Vol. III and Vol. IV (published as a set). New York, 1935. Binding as Vol. I. Folding maps (Vol. III) facing pages 98, 106 and 268; and (Vol. IV) pages 40, 78, 106, 112 and three facing p.(256). The pair in a plain slipcase

Vol. V. New York, 1937. Binding as Vol. I. Errata slip tipped-in between pages (18)-19

Vol. VI. New York, 1938. Binding as Vol. I. Folding maps facing p.166 and two facing p.656

The 6 volume set $250/750

055e: MARLBOROUGH *His Life and Times* George G. Harrap, London (1947). [1] New two-volume edition. Part I: folding maps facing pages 190, 484, 556, 564, 806 and 868; 3 folding maps facing p.900, folding facsimiles of letters, etc. facing pages 240, 382, 700, 838 and 855. Part II: folding maps facing pages 118, 380, (488) and 622; 3 folding maps facing pages 1040, folding facsimile of letter facing p.393 $150/400

056a: CHARLES IXth DUKE OF MARLBOROUGH Burns, Oates & Washbourne, London (1934). [] Wraps. Tributes by Churchill and C.C. Martindale $100.

057a: THE GREAT WAR (George Newnes, London, 1933-34.) First illustrated in 26 parts in illustrated wraps (Buddenbrooks 9/89) $650.

058a: INDIA *The Great Betrayal* The India Defence League, London, 1935. [0] 8 pages in wraps $350.

059a: A MESSAGE New Common Wealth Society, London (1935). [0] 4 pages (in the form of a postcard with a reply card attached) $250.

060a: THE TRUTH ABOUT HITLER Trustees for Freedom, London, 1936. [0] 11(12) pages in yellow card wraps $450.

061a: SPEECH The New Commonwealth, London, 1936. [0] 12 pages in cream matte card wraps. Speech given at a luncheon of the New Commonwealth $350.

062a: GREAT CONTEMPORARIES Thornton Butterworth Ltd., London, 1937.[] Advance Issue in printed orange wraps (Adam Blakeney 2/93) $650.

062b: GREAT CONTEMPORARIES Thornton Butterworth Ltd., London (1937). [1] 5,000 cc. Published October 4. Dark blue buckram, top edge stained blue $150/500

062c: GREAT CONTEMPORARIES Putnam, New York, 1937. [0] $75/250

062d: GREAT CONTEMPORARIES Thornton Butterworth Ltd., London (1938). [1] "Revised Edition 1938." 5,000 cc. Includes 4 additional articles $100/350

062e: GREAT CONTEMPORARIES Macmillan, London. 1942. [] (1943 in ref. a). Two articles about Trotsky and Roosevelt omitted for political reasons (ref. a) and on Savinkov (added 1938) (Steven Temple 10/94) $75/250

063a: HOMAGE TO KIPLING Rudyard Kipling Memorial Fund, London, 1937. [0] 12 pages $350.

064a: COMMUNISM American Coalition, Washington, D.C. (1938). [] Broadside with an excerpt from *Great Contemporaries* (Glenn Horowitz #14) $300.

065a: ARMS AND THE COVENANT George G. Harrap, London (1938). [0] 3,381 cc (a & b). Dark blue cloth, top edge stained blue. Published June 24 at 18s. First issue dustwrapper red on yellow $200/850

065b: ARMS AND THE COVENANT George G. Harrap, London (1938). [0] Second issue dustwrapper in blue $200/650

065c: ARMS AND COVENANT George G. Harrap, London (1940). [0] 1,382 cc of first issue sheets were used in a "cheap" edition $100/400

065d: WHILE ENGLAND SLEPT Putnams, New York, 1938. [0] New title for U.S. edition. Blue cloth, top edge stained red. 5,000 cc published September 30 $50/250

066a: STEP BY STEP Thornton Butterworth Ltd., London (1939). [1] 7,500 cc. Green cloth. Published June 27 $200/750

066b: STEP BY STEP Putnam, New York, 1939. [0] 5,000 cc. Published August 25 $100/350

067a: U-BOAT WARFARE Ministry of Information, London, 1939. [0] 4 pages $300.

068a: THE WAR AT SEA Ministry of Information, London, 1939. [0] 4 pages $300.

069a: THE GLORIOUS BATTLE OF THE RIVER PLATE Ministry of Information, London, 1939. [0] 4 pages $300.

070a: ALLIES NOW IN THEIR STRIDE Ministry of Information, London, 1940. [0] 7(8) pages $300.

071a: THE STATE OF THE WAR Ministry of Information, London, 1940. [0] 4 pages $300.

072a: NAVY ESTIMATES Ministry of Information, London, 1940. [0] 7(8) pages $300.

073a: A STERNER WAR Ministry of Information, London, 1940. [0] 4 pages $300.

074a: THE WAR AT SEA Ministry of Information, London, 1940. [0] 8 pages $300.

075a: CONQUER WE SHALL Ministry of Information, London, 1940. [0] 4 pages $400.

076a: ADDRESS British Library of Information, London, 1940. [0] Speech delivered in House of Commons on June 4, 1940. 10(12) pages $300.

076b: ADDRESS British Library of Information, New York, 1940. [0] Priority unknown. Assume same number of pages as 076a $300.

076c: WINSTON SPENCER CHURCHILL SPEECH OF JUNE 4th, 1940 No publisher, Los Angeles, 1964. [] Bound in maroon morroco $300.

076d: A SPEECH Northern Educational Press, Leeds, 1972. [0] 10(12) pages in card wraps $300.

077a: SPEECH British Library of Information, New York, 1940. [0] Speech given by the Prime Minister in House of Commons on June 18, 1940. 8 pages $250.

078a: MESSAGE (M.O.I. or Ministry of Home Security?), London, 1940. [0] 1(2) pages in the form of a letter from No. 10 Downing Street. Signed in facsimile (to Senior Officers of the Fighting and Civil Services) $250.

079a: SPEECH British Library of Information, New York, 1940. [0] 3 (4) pages. Speech broadcast July 14, 1940 $250.

080a: SPEECH British Library of Information, New York, 1940. [] 6 pages Speech delivered in House of Commons July 4, 1940 $250.

081a: A SPEECH Ministry of Information, (London) 1940. [0] Uncorrected proof. In pale gray wraps printed in red. 16 pages. (Blackwell's Rare Books 2/97) $400

081b: A SPEECH Ministry of Information, (London), 1940. [0] 16 pages, light blue matte card wraps, printed in maroon. Speech given in the House of Commons on August 20, 1940. "Never in the field of human conflict was so much owed by so many to so few." Last page has "The Baynard Press." Also noted in light tan wraps printed in maroon $600.

081c: BRITAIN'S STRENGTH British Library of Information, New York, 1940. [0] 8 pages. Speech in the House of Commons on August 20, 1940 "Never in the field of human conflict was so much owed by so many to so few" $600.

082a: SPEECH TO THE PEOPLE OF FRANCE British Library of Information, New York, 1940. [0] 3(4) pages. Broadcast October 21, 1940 $150.

083a: WAR PROBLEMS FACING BRITAIN British Library of Information, New York, 1940. [0] 8 pages. Speech in House of Commons on November 5, 1940 $175.

084a: SPEECH TO THE ITALIAN PEOPLE British Library of Information, New York, 1940. [0] 7(8) pages. Broadcast December 23, 1940 $150.

085a: DO NOT DESPAIR Ministry of Information?, London, 1940. [0] 1(2) pages in the form of a postcard $100.

086a: ADDRESSES DELIVERED IN THE YEAR 1940 TO THE PEOPLE OF GREAT BRITAIN (Grabhorn Press), San Francisco, 1940. [2] 250 cc. Folio (ref.b) $450.

087a: BROADCAST ADDRESS TO THE PEOPLE OF GREAT BRITAIN (Grabhorn Press), San Francisco, 1941. [2] 250 cc (ref.b) $600.

088a: BLENHEIM George G. Harrap, London (1941). [1] Red and black wraps. Published in February for the British Publishers Guild $175.

089a: SPEECH British Library of Information, London, 1941. [0] 3(4) pages in wraps. Speech by the Prime Minister to the Pilgrims $175.

090a: INTO BATTLE Cassell, London (1941). [1] Light blue cloth (Woods notes there were perhaps 30,000 published but production records destroyed).

First state lacks leaf 128 a/b with the speech "War With Germany" delivered September 3, 1939. First volume of *War Speeches* $150/350

090b: INTO BATTLE Cassell, London (1941). [1] Contains leaf tipped-in in correct chronological order $50/250

090c: BLOOD, SWEAT, AND TEARS McClelland & Steward, Toronto (1941). [0] 448 pages. Does not have the speech "War With Germany" which was tipped into the 2nd issue of the U.K. edition and also does not include January 1941 speech in the U.S. edition. Printed in Canada. We assume that this preceded the U.S. edition as it seems to be printed from the first state of the English edition (Steven Temple 5/92) $50/200

090d: BLOOD, SWEAT, AND TEARS McClelland & Steward, Toronto (1941). [0] Presumed second issue with 525 pages with 3 speeches "The War Situation," "The Italian People" and "Give Us The Tools" added after p.488 (pages 505-520 tipped-in). (Steven Temple 5/92) $40/200

090e: BLOOD, SWEAT, AND TEARS Putnams, New York (1941). [0] 50,000 cc. Published April 14. Adds speech (of January 9, 1941) not in UK edition. Blue cloth, top edge stained red. (There was a Book-of-the-Month Club edition of this title. It does not have a price on the dustwrapper flap. It is in red cloth with top edge blue) $50/200

091a: SPEECH British Library of Information, New York, 1941. [0] Broadcast February 9. 10(12) pages $175.

091b: SPEECH (Universal Life, Winnipeg, Canada, 1941.) [0] Small pamphlet (about 3 1/2" x 6"). "Put Your Confidence in Us." Also contains Canadian Prime Minister King's "There is only one way to meet total war ..." broadcast February 2. May precede 087a (ref.b) $175.

092a: SPEECH British Library of Information, New York, 1941. [0] Speech given to the Pilgrim Society on March 18. 3(4) pages in wraps $175.

093a: BEATING THE INVADER Ministry of Information in Cooperation with the War Office and Ministry of Home Security (London, 1941). [0] Single leaf, printed on both sides. (There is a later issue, overprinted in red in the top left-hand corner, regarding the evacuation of invaded areas. Both issues dated 5/41) $400.

094a: SPEECH British Library of Information, New York, 1941. [0] Broadcast April 27. 7(8) pages $175.

095a: BROADCAST British Library of Information, New York, 1941. [0] Broadcast to the Polish people, May 3. 2 pages $150.

096a: ADDRESSES OF WINSTON CHURCHILL AND OTHERS AT NINETY-FIRST ANNUAL COMMENCEMENT OF THE UNIVERSITY OF ROCHESTER University of Rochester, Rochester, 1941. [1] Wraps $750.

097a: THE WAR IN THE MIDDLE EAST Ministry of Information, London, 1941. [0] Speech in the debate in the House of Commons, June 10. Printed in parallel texts (English and Chinese). 8 pages $300.

098a: FREEDOM'S CAUSE British Library of Information, New York, 1941. [0] Speech given on June 12. Together with Text of the Allied Resolution. 3(4) pages $250.

099a: SPEECH British Library of Information, New York, 1941. [0] Broadcast June 22. 4 pages $175.

100a: STATEMENT British Library of Information, New York, 1941. [0] Given to the House of Commons, June 29. 15(16) pages $175.

101a: THE ATLANTIC MEETING Ministry of Information, London, 1941. [0] Extracts from broadcast of August 24. 8 pages in card wraps $300.

102a: THE ASSURANCE OF VICTORY Ministry of Information, London, 1941. [0] Broadcast following his meeting with President Roosevelt. Printed in parallel texts (English and Chinese). 4 pages $200.

103a: SPEECH British Library of Information, New York (1941). [0] Broadcast of August 24. 7(8) pages $175.

104a: THE EUROPEAN WAR REVIEWED Ministry of Information, London, 1941. [0] Statement to the House of Commons, Sept. 9. Printed in parallel texts (English and Chinese). 6 pages $200.

105a: STATEMENT British Library of Information, New York, 1941. [0] Given to the House of Commons, September 30. 7(8) pages $200.

106a: SPEECH British Library of Information New York, 1941. [0] Given at the Mansion House, November 10. 4 pages (also published in 3 leaflets by the Political Warfare Exec., 1941) $200.

107a: SPEECH British Library of Information, New York, 1941. [0] Given in the House of Commons, November 12. 8 pages $200.

108a: ADDRESS British Library of Information, New York, 1941. [0] Given December 2. 10(12) pages $200.

109a: SPEECH British Library of Information, New York, 1941. [0] December 8th broadcast on the Far East War. 3(4) pages $200.

110a: SPEECH British Library of Information, New York, 1941. [0] Given to the House of Commons, December 11. 6(8) pages $200.

111a: ADDRESS British Library of Information, New York, 1941. [0] Given before the U.S. Congress, December 26. 6(8) pages. (Also printed by the Political Warfare Exec. in 1942) $300.

111b: ADDRESS ... BEFORE THE SENATE ... U.S. Government Printing Office, Washington, D. C., 1941. [] Senate Document No. 153. 9(12) pages $300.

111c: ADDRESS Overbrook Press, Stanford, Conn., 1942. [2] 1,000 cc. Red buckram with paper label on front board. Published January 4 $300.

111d: THE ADDRESS TO CONGRESS John Allen and Sons, Oxford (1942). [0] 16 pages in cream card wraps (some copies bound in dark brown suede wraps) $250.

THE MENACE OF LAND POLICY and ON HUMAN RIGHTS see entry 021

112a: WINSTON SPENCER CHURCHILL'S MESSAGE TO THE AMERICAN BOOKSELLERS American Bookseller's Association, no place or date [circa 1941]. [] Broadside, 11 x 13 1/2 inches (Pepper & Stern 8/93) $750.

113a: SPEECH British Library of Information, New York, 1942. [0] Given to the Canadian Parliament, December 30. 6(8) pages $200.

113b: CANADA AND THE WAR Director of Public Information, Ottawa, 1942. [0] 9(10) pages $175.

114a: WHAT KIND OF PEOPLE DO THEY THINK WE ARE? Daily Tele-graph and Morning Post, London (1942). [0] Contains 2 speeches (109a and 110a). 8 pages $175.

115a: ADDRESS Bermuda Press, Hamilton, 1942. [0] Given to the House Assembly, January 15. 4 pages $150.

116a: ADDRESS British Library of Information, New York, 1942. [0] Broadcast of February 15. 6(8) pages $150

117a: SPEECH British Library of Information, New York, 1942. [0] Broadcast of May 10. 8 pages $150.

118a: THE UNRELENTING STRUGGLE Cassell, London (1942). [1] 10,900 cc. Published September 24. Light blue cloth (*War Speeches*) $75/250

118b: THE UNRELENTING STRUGGLE Little, Brown, Boston (1942). [1] 15,000 cc. Published October 21 $50/150

119a: SPEECH British Library of Information, New York, 1942. [0] Broadcast given November 29. 7(8) pages $150.

120a: A FOUR YEARS PLAN FOR BRITAIN Times Publishing Co., London, 1943. [0] Speech broadcast March 22. 8 pages $250.

121a: ADDRESS U.S. Government Printing Office, Washington, D.C., 1943. [0] Given to Joint Session of Congress, May 19. 10(12) pages. Also noted on legal size pulpy paper. 18 pages headed "British Information Service, Release No. A-24" $300.

121b: AN ADDRESS BY WINSTON S. CHURCHILL PRIME MINISTER OF GREAT BRITAIN Overbrook Press, Stamford, Conn., 1943. [2] 600 cc. Published in September. Black paper-covered boards and red paper label $500.

121c: OUR CONTINENT REDEEMED Daily Telegraph, London, 1943. [0] 8 pages $150.

122a: THE END OF THE BEGINNING Cassell, London, (1943). [1] 16,000 cc. Published July 29. Light blue cloth (*War Speeches*) $60/200

122b: THE END OF THE BEGINNING Little, Brown, Boston (1943). [1] 6,000 cc. Published August 19. $50/150

123a: THE LAST DAYS OF MARLBOROUGH Times Publishing Co., London, 1943. [0] A broadsheet. 2 pages $200.

124a: LIBERALS' PART IN REBUILDING BRITAIN Liberal Publications Department, London, 1943. [0] Speech at the National Liberal Club. 4 pages $150.

124b: MR. CHURCHILL PAYS TRIBUTE TO THE LIBERAL PARTY Liberal Publications Department, London, 1943. [0] Excerpts from 121a. 1(2) pages $100.

125a: THE PRIME MINISTER'S SPEECH ON THE HOUSE OF COMMONS REBUILDING, 28 OCTOBER 1943 The University Press, Cambridge, 1944. [0] 12 pages in card wraps $350.

126a: PRIME MINISTER *A Selection from Speeches* British Information Service, New York, 1943. [1] "Published December 1943." Stapled wraps. 52 pages illustrated with photographs (Glenn Horowitz #16) $150.

127a: A SPEECH Kingsport Press, Tennessee, 1943. [2] ltd to 400 cc. Blue wraps with printed label on front cover. Speech given before Parliament of England, November 11. 36 pages $600.

128a: HIGHLIGHTS OF CHURCHILL Cassell, Sydney, no date [circa 1943]. [] 16 pp. in stiff pale green wraps with half-tone portrait of Churchill. Apparently a Christmas give- away. Prints excerpts from *In to Battle*, *The Unrelenting Struggle* and *End of the Beginning* laid out as blank verse (Adam Blakeney 2/93) $250.

129a: THE EVE OF ACTION W. & G. Baird (Belfast Telegraph), Belfast, 1944. [0] Speech to House of Commons, Feb. 22. 20 pages plus red card wraps $350.

130a: FOREIGN POLICY *The Prime Minister's Review* Times Publishing Co., London, 1944. [0] 12 pages $200.

131a: THE TIDE OF TRIUMPH British Legation Press Department, Berne, 1944. [0] Speech in the House of Commons, September 28. 24 pages $200.

132a: ONWARDS TO VICTORY Cassell, London, 1944. [1] 15,000 cc. Published June 29. Light blue cloth (*War Speeches*) $50/150

132b: ONWARDS TO VICTORY Little, Brown, Boston (1944). [1] 9,000 cc. Published July 13 $35/125

133a: ATLANTIC CHARTER AUGUST 12th 1941 Busy Bee (De Algemeene Vrije Illegale Drukkerij), Amsterdam (1944). [2] 100 cc. Wraps. ($1,193 at auction in Sotheby's sale of December 14, 1989) $1,750.

134a: COUNTRY BEFORE PARTY S. H. Benson, London, 1945. [] From a speech on March 15. 2 pages (3 variations at foot of p.2, "Vote Conservative", "Vote Unionist" or "Vote National") $100.

135a: OUR LAND OUR FOOD *Mr. Churchill's Declaration* S. H. Benson, London, 1945. [0] From speech to Conservative Party Congress, March 25. 4 pages $125.

135b: PREMIER'S PLEDGE TO FARMERS AND FARM WORKERS Conservative Party, London, 1945. [0] A shorter version of 128a. 2 pages $100.

136a: A TIMELY DELIVERANCE W. & G. Baird (Belfast Telegraph), Belfast, 1945. [0] Broadcast to the Nation, May 13. 10 pages $200.

136b: VICTORY IN EUROPE British Legation Press Department, Berne, 1945. [0] Adds speech by George VI $150.

137a: MR. CHURCHILL'S DECLARATION OF POLICY TO THE ELECTORS S. H. Benson, London, 1945. [0] General Election 1945. 16 pages $150.

138a: "HERE IS THE COURSE WE STEER" Conservative Party, London, 1945. [0] 12 pages plus pictorial paperwraps $250.

139a: THE DAWN OF LIBERATION Cassell, London (1945). [1] 14,250 cc. Published July 26. Light blue cloth (*War Speeches*) $35/125

139b: THE DAWN OF LIBERATION Little, Brown, Boston (1945). [1] 3,500 cc. Published August 12 $30/100

139c: THE DAWN OF LIBERATION McClelland & Steward, Toronto, 1945. [] (Ref.b) $15/75

140a: A TRUE PEOPLE'S PARTY Conservative Party, London, 1945. [0] 12 pages $175.

141a: SUBALTERN'S READING Times Publishing Co., London, 1945. [0] An extract from *My Early Life*. 2 pages $125.

142a: WE FIGHT FOR THE PEOPLE Conservative Party, London, 1945. [0] 16 pages $200.

143a: THE DAY WILL COME Conservative Party, London, 1946. [0] A speech at Edinburgh, April 29. 14(16) pages $200.

144a: VICTORY Cassell, London (1946). [1] 38,000 cc. Published June 27. Light blue cloth (*War Speeches*) $30/100

144b: VICTORY Little, Brown, Boston, 1946. [] 5,000 cc. Published August 7 $25/75

145a: WAR SPEECHES 1940-1945 Cassell, London (1946). [1] 20,000 cc. Published in July. Bound in white card wraps, printed black on a blue background $350.

146a: SECRET SESSION SPEECHES Cassell, London (1946). [1] 48,500 cc. Published September 26. Light blue cloth (some copies simultaneously issued in full blue morocco). In the first state of the dustwrapper, the proposed publication price of 7/6 net on the dustwrapper is blocked out, and the actual publication price of 6/-net substituted (Robert Temple 2/95) $30/100

146b: SECRET SESSION SPEECHES Simon and Schuster, New York, 1946. [0] 5,910 cc. Published in September. $25/75

147a: SPEECH Conservative Party, London, 1946. [] Speech given at Winter Gardes, Blackpool on October 5. 16 pages $150.

148a: UNITED EUROPE United Europe Movement, London, 1946. [0] A leaflet in the form of a letter from Churchill. 4 pages $250.

149a: A UNITED EUROPE: ONE WAY TO STOP A NEW WAR United Europe Movement, London, 1947. [0] 7(8) pages $250.

150a: MAXIMS AND REFLECTIONS Eyre and Spottiswoode, London (1947). [] Arranged and introduction by Colin Coote $25/100

150b: MAXIMS AND REFLECTIONS Houghton Mifflin, Boston, 1949. [1] $25/75

151a: THE PEOPLE'S PERIL - AND THE WAY OUT Conservative Party, London, 1947. [0] Speech in the House of Commons on March 12. 16 pages $175.

152a: "TRUST THE PEOPLE" Conservative Party, London, 1947. [0] A speech at Ayr, May 16. 16 pages $150.

153a: SET THE PEOPLE FREE Conservative Party, London, 1948. [0] A broadcast talk, February 14. 8 pages in card wraps $150.

154a: "THIS COUNTRY NEEDS A NEW PARLIAMENT" Conservative Party, London, 1948. [0] Wraps. Speech given April 21. 12 pages $175.

155a: THE GRAND DESIGN United Europe Movement, London, 1948. [0] Wraps. A speech at the Congress of Europe, May 7. 12 pages including cover $200.

156a: THE SECOND WORLD WAR Hougton Mifflin. 6 volumes. All volumes preceded the comparable British editions (from four to ten months earlier); and did not incorporate all of Churchill's corrections or include the folding maps which were in the Cassell edition:

Vol. I: THE GATHERING STORM Boston, 1948. [0] 75,000 cc. Published June 21. Red cloth, top edge yellow-brown, red and yellow imitation head and foot bands (a second state of this edition appeared without head and foot bands and without top edge stained).

Vol. II: THEIR FINEST HOUR Boston, 1949. [0] 35,000 cc. Published March 29. Red cloth, top edge yellow-brown, stars on title page inverted in this volume only.

(Woods comments: "It is noticeable that the print-run of this volume is at least half that of any of the others. It may possibly be of significance that this is also the only volume in which Americans could not read about themselves.")

Vol. III: THE GRAND ALLIANCE Boston, 1950. [0] 61,000 cc. Published April 24. Red cloth, top edge yellow-brown. (Stars inverted on dustwrapper of this volume only per Jeff Klaess.)

Vol. IV: THE HINGE OF FATE Boston, 1950. [0] 70,000 cc. Published November 27. Red cloth, top edge yellow-brown

Vol. V: CLOSING THE RING Boston, 1951. [0] 60,000 cc. Published November 23. Red cloth, top edge yellow-brown.

Vol. VI: TRIUMPH AND TRAGEDY Boston, 1953. [0] 60,000 cc. Published November 30. Red cloth, top edge yellow-brown.

The 6 volume set: $125/350

(Note: leather presentation binding offered by James Cummins 2/92 $4,000)

156b: THE SECOND WORLD WAR Cassell & Co. Ltd. 6 volumes:

Vol. I: THE GATHERING STORM London (1948). [1] 221,000 cc. Published October 4. Black cloth, top edge red. Unnumbered errata page and Corrigenda page tipped-in facing p.610, folding map facing p.496. This volume set in small type than all succeeding volumes.

Vol. II: THEIR FINEST HOUR London (1949). [1] 270,000 cc. Published June 27. Binding as Vol. I. Folding maps facing pages 78, 174 and 462.

Vol. III: THE GRAND ALLIANCE London (1950). [1] 300,000 cc. Published July 20. Binding as Vol. I. Folding maps facing pages 302, 366 and 526.

Vol. IV: THE HINGE OF FATE London (1951). [1] 275,000 cc. Published August 3. Binding as Vol.

I. Folding maps facing pages 174, 214 and 686. Folding facsimile of letter facing p.654.

Vol. V: CLOSING THE RING London (1952). [1] 275,000 cc. Published September 3. Binding as Vol. I. Folding maps facing pages 494, 526 and 558. Folding facsimile of minute facing p.78.

Vol. VI: TRIUMPH AND TRAGEDY London (1954). [1] 200,000 cc. Published April 26. Binding as Vol. I. Folding maps facing pages 22, 158, 160, 162, 246, 438, 454, 526, 542, 566 and (678).

The 6 volume set: $200/600

(Woods notes that there were 100 sets bound in full black pebble-grain morocco for presentation, offered in 1994 for $3,500.

156c: THE SECOND WORLD WAR Cassell, London (1959). [1] 25,000 cc. Published February 5. Abridged one volume edition with Epilogue on the years 1945 to 1957 $50/150

156d: THE SECOND WORLD WAR Educational Book Co., London, no date. [] 6 volumes. First Chartwell Edition and first illustrated edition. Half morocco (Buddenbrooks 7/93) $600.

156e: MEMOIRS OF THE SECOND WORLD WAR Houghton Mifflin, Boston, 1959. [1] (Ref.b) $25/75

156f: THE SECOND WORLD WAR Time, Chicago / New York, 1959. [0] Two volumess. In slipcase, with 10" recording of excerpts from Churchill's speeches (in pocket between the volumes). "By Winston Churchill and the Editors of *Life*" (Although the recording is not by Churchill) $75/100

157a: THE SINEWS OF PEACE Cassell, London (1948). [1] 10,000 cc. Published August 19. Post-War speeches, edited by Randolph S. Churchill. Orange-brown cloth $50/150

157b: THE SINEWS OF PEACE Houghton Mifflin, Boston, 1949. [0] 3,000 cc $40/125

157c: THE SINEWS OF PEACE *A Speech* Halcyon-Commonwealth Foundation, New York, 1965. [] Wraps. First separate edition with a preface by Harry S. Truman $125.

158a: PAINTING AS A PASTIME Odhams Press / Ernest Benn, London (1948). [1] 25,000 cc. Published in December. Fawn cloth $50/150

158b: PAINTING AS A PASTIME Whittlesey House, New York, 1950. [0] 20,000 cc. From sheets of 3rd printing of U.K. edition. Published February 10, 1950 $25/75

159a: THE RIGHT ROAD FOR BRITAIN Conservative Party, London, 1949. [0] Speech at Wolverhampton on July 23. 19(20) pages in card wraps $175.

160a: CHURCHILL'S VISIT TO NORWAY *Speeches ... Together with Addresses ...* Cappelens, Oslo, 1949. [] Pictorial wraps. Also noted in photographic wraps with "School Edition" on front (Glenn Horowitz #16) $100.

161a: EUROPE UNITE *Speeches 1947 and 1948* Cassell, London (1950). [1] 12,000 cc. Published February 3. Edited by Randolph S. Churchill. Dark green cloth $35/125

161b: EUROPE UNITE *Speeches 1947 and 1949* Houghton Mifflin, Boston, 1950. [0] 2,500 cc. From English sheets $30/100

162a: MR. CHURCHILL'S MESSAGE TO YOU Conservative Party, London, 1950. [0] 4 pages $125.

162b: MR. CHURCHILL'S MESSAGE TO YOU Conservative Party, London, 1950. [0] 1(2) pages $125.

163a: ELECTION ADDRESS Woodford Divisional Conservation Assoc., Woodford Green, 1950. [0] 4 pages $100.

164a: AN ADDRESS Overbrook Press, Stamford, Conn., 1950. [2] 1,000 cc only. Speech given in the House of Commons November 30, 1950. Printed for members of 82nd Congress $250.

165a: BROADCAST APPEAL ON BEHALF OF THE ROYAL AIR FORCE BENEVOLENT FUND R.A.F. Benevolent Fund, London, 1951. [0] 2 pages $100.

166a: IN THE BALANCE *Speeches 1949 and 1950* Cassell, London (1951). [] Uncorrected proof. In brown paperwraps (Heritage Book Shop 9/95) $750.

166b: IN THE BALANCE *Speeches 1949 and 1950* Cassell, London (1951). [1] 8,200 cc (2,000 used for 166d). Published October 18. Edited by Randolph S. Churchill. Dark blue cloth. First issue has first gathering bound so that last leaf of contents appears prior to half title (Glenn Horowitz #16) $75/125

166c: IN THE BALANCE *Speeches 1949 and 1950* Cassell, London (1951). [1] Second issue. Corrected. $25/75

166d: IN THE BALANCE *Speeches 1949 and 1950* Houghton Mifflin, Boston, 1952. [0] 2,000 cc from English sheets $35/100

167a: ELECTION SPEECH Woodford Divisional Conservative Association, Woodford Green, 1951. [0] 4 pages $100.

168a: THANKS TO THE BUNGLERS Charles Knight (Election Agent), Orpington (Kent), 1951. [0] 2 pages $75.

169a: THE MANIFESTO OF THE CONSERVATIVE AND UNIONIST PARTY Conservative Party, London, 1951. [0] 7(8) pages in paperwraps. Signed in facsimile at end of text $100.

170a: THE STATE OF THE NATION Conservative Party, London, 1952. [0] Broadcast of December 22. 8 pages in paperwraps $100.

171a: MR. CHURCHILL'S SPEECH TO THE CONGRESS OF THE UNITED STATES OF AMERICA, January 17th, 1952 H.M.S.O., London, 1952. [0] 8 pages $125.

172a: KING GEORGE VI Times Publishing Co, London, 1952. [0] Broadcast of February 7. 4 pages (issued unbound) $100.

172b: KING GEORGE VI Achille J. St. Onge, Worcester (Mass), 1952. [2] Ltd to 750 cc. Purple Nigerian goatskin, all edges gilt. Approximately 100 copies of total edition bound in red Nigerian Goatskin $450.

173a: THE WAR SPEECHES Cassell, London (1952). [1] (Definitive edition.) Compiled by Charles Eade. 3 volumes. 4,700 sets. Published September 3.

(Woods notes that the three volumes were intended to be published separately, but printing difficulties delayed Vol. I for a year) (assume no slipcase) $300.

173b: THE WAR SPEECHES Houghton Mifflin, Boston, 1953. [0] (Definitive Edition) Compiled by Charles Eade. 3 volumes. 500 sets from English sheets. In slipcase (George Houle 10/88) $300/350

174a: STEMMING THE TIDE *Speeches 1951 and 1952* Cassell, London (1953). [1] 5,500 cc. Published June 25. Edited by Randolph S. Churchill $35/125

174b: STEMMING THE TIDE *Speeches 1951 and 1952* Houghton Mifflin, Boston, 1954. [0] 1,850 cc. From the English sheets $30/100

175a: A CHURCHILL READER. Houghton Mifflin, Boston, 1954. [] The Wit & Wisdom with introduction by Colin R. Coote (Glenn Horowitz #16) $30/100

176a: DEFENCE THROUGH DETERRENTS Regional Information Office, Singapore, 1955. [0] Speech in House of Commons on March 1. 16 pages $150.

177a: ELECTION ADDRESS Woodford Divisional Conservative Assocication, Woodford Green, 1955. [0] 4 pages $100.

178a: THE WISDOM OF WINSTON CHURCHILL ... 1900-1955 George Allen & Unwin, London, 1956. [] $25/75

179a: I SUPPORT Conservative Central Office, London, 1956. [0] 1(2) pages $75.

180a: A HISTORY OF THE ENGLISH-SPEAKING PEOPLES 4 volumes:

Vol. I: THE BIRTH OF BRITAIN Cassell, London (1956). [1] 130,000 cc. Published April 23. Red buckram, top edge red.

Vol I: THE BIRTH OF BRITAIN Dodd, Mead, New York, 1956. [1] Published simultaneously with 168a. Did not see variant but assume there is one like the other volumes (see below).

Vol. II: THE NEW WORLD Cassell, London (1956). [1] 150,000 cc. Published November 26. Binding as in Vol. I.

Vol. II: THE NEW WORLD Dodd, Mead, New York, 1956. [0] Published December 3. Noted in two different bindings: (1) light to medium red panels on spine, bulking 42 mm; and (2) dark red panels, bulking 35 mm. Assume the first is first issue/state because the front dustwrapper flap did not have "BOMC" over printed, while the second did have BOMC printed on dustwrapper. Otherwise, no difference in dustwrappers. Both were priced.

Vol. III: THE AGE OF REVOLUTION Cassell, London (1957). [1] 150,000 cc. Published October 14. Binding as in Vol. I.

Vol. III: THE AGE OF REVOLUTION Dodd, Mead, New York, 1957. [1] Published September 23 (if this publication date is correct, than this precedes the U.K. edition). See Vol. II above. These bulked 42 mm vs. 33 mm.

Vol. IV: THE GREAT DEMOCRACIES Cassell, London (1958). [1] 150,000 cc. Published March 14. Binding as in Vol. I

Vol. IV: THE GREAT DEMOCRACIES Dodd, Mead, New York, 1958. [1] See Vol. II above. These bulked 45 mm vs. 38 mm.

The 4 U.K. volumes: $150/450
The 4 U.S. volumes: $100/300

Notes: (1) Uncorrected proofs of vols. III and IV were offered by two different English dealers in 1995 for $80 and $240, respectively. (2) There was an illustrated edition published simultaneously on a subscription basis, by The Educational Book Company Ltd. (8 guineas for the set). (3) A 12 volume "Blenheim" edition was issued by Cassell, 1965 and 1966. (4) Dodd Mead's "Presentation Edition" (on copyright page) was issued in black and gray cloth, in dustwrappers (Glenn Horowitz #16). (5) Cassell issued a set in publisher's leather presentation bindings (James Cummins 2/92). (6) Detering Book Gallery cataloged the Chartwell Edition (4 vols.) with a new preface for $400 in 1994, no publication date indicated in catalog.

181a: CATALOG OF AN EXHIBITION OF PAINTINGS BY RT. HON. SIR WINSTON CHURCHILL (Hallmark Cards, Kansas City, Mo.), 1958. [0] Foreword by Dwight Eisenhower. Hardcover issued in tissue wraps (Joel Sattler) $75

181b: CATALOG OF AN EXHIBITION OF PAINTINGS BY... (Hallmark Cards, Kansas City, Mo.), 1958. [] White wraps $35.

182a: ELECTION ADDRESS Woodford Divisional Conservative Association, Woodford, October, 1959. [] 4 pages $75.

183a: PAINTINGS BY THE RT. HON. SIR WINSTON CHURCHILL Royal Academy of Arts, London, 1959. [] Wraps (Dalian #49) $75.

184a: THE AMERICAN CIVIL WAR Cassell, London (1961). [1] 10,000 cc. Published March 23. "This Edition First Published 1961." From Vol. IV of *A History of The English-Speaking Peoples*. Adds Civil War photographs $35/125

185a: LETTER TO ANTHONY WEDGWOOD BENN H.E. Rogers, Briston, 1961. [0] 10,000 cc. 1(2) pages $75.

186a: THE UNWRITTEN ALLIANCE *Speeches 1953 to 1959* Cassell, London (1961). [0] 5,000 cc. Published April 27 $35/125

187a: FRONTIERS AND WARS (Eyre & Spottiswoode, London, 1962.) [] A condensation of Churchill's first four books (Glenn Horowitz #16) $15/75

187b: FRONTIERS AND WARS Harcourt Brace, New York (1962). [] A condensation of Churchill's first four books (Glenn Horowitz #16) $15/75

188a: SIR WINSTON CHURCHILL HONORARY CITIZEN OF THE UNITED STATES OF AMERICA Achille J. St. Onge, Worcester, Mass.,

1964. [2] 1500 cc. Miniature book in full leather. Includes the Act of Congress, April 9, 1963; the proclamation by John F. Kennedy, and Churchill's letter to President Kennedy. $125.

189a: THE ISLAND RACE Cassell, London (1964). [0] 42,500 cc. Published November 23. Abridged from *A History of The English-Speaking Peoples* $30/100

189b: THE ISLAND RACE Dodd, Mead, New York, 1964. [] 7,500 cc. From the English sheets. Published simultaneously $25/75

190a: THE WIT OF SIR WINSTON Publisher?, London, 1965. [] Compiled by Adam Sykes and Iain Spoat $15/50

191a: GREAT DESTINY Putnam, New York (1965). [1] "Sixty Years of Memorable Events... in His Own Words." Edited by F. W. Heath (ref.b) $25/75

192a: CHURCHILL *His Paintings* Hamish Hamilton, London (1967). [0] Catalog compiled by David Coombs, Foreword by Lady Spencer Churchill (ref.b) $25/75

192b: CHURCHILL *His Paintings* World Publishing, Cleveland (1967). [0] $20/60

193a: YOUNG WINSTON'S WARS Leo Cooper Ltd., London (1972). [0] 5,000 cc. Published July 20. Edited by Frederick Woods. Blue cloth $15/75

193b: YOUNG WINSTON'S WARS Viking, New York (1972). [1] "Published in 1972 by Viking" (actually published 3/30/73 at $8.95) $12/60

194a: COLLECTED WORKS Library of Imperial History, London (1973-1976). [2] 3,000 no. cc. (1,000 for American market were planned). Centenary Limited Edition. Edited by Frederick Woods, preface by Clementine Churchill. Each volume bound in full white vellum and in separate green leatherette slipcases. 38 volumes (Collected Works - 34 volumes plus 4 volumes of the Collected Essays). According to Richard Langworth's article in the January 16, 1989 issue of *The Antiquarian Bookman*, there were only about 2,000 sets of sheets printed, of which about 1,750 sets were bound and numbered as above. There are 20 sets bound in full red morocco and apparently one can order a set in morocco or in the original binding and slipcase. The original price in 1973 was $2,500 but it was raised to $3,000. (Ten sets bound in full red corrida leather with raised bands, gilt. David B. Mayou 3/95) $6,000.

195a: WINSTON S. CHURCHILL *The Complete Speeches 1897-1963* Chelsea House / Bowker, London / New York, 1974. [] 8 volumes (Glenn Horowitz #16) $500.

196a: THE COLLECTED ESSAYS Library of Imperial History, London, 1976. [2] 3,000 sets (2,000 for England, 1,000 for U.S.). "The Centenary Edition" 4 volumes. Noted in quarter blue morocco as well as "full vellum gilt, in green slipcases". "This was a separate issue of the final four volumes of *The Collected Works of Sir Winston Churchill.*" Buddenbrooks 7/95) $1,000.

197a: THE DREAM Churchill Foundation (London, New York, Australia, Canada, New Zealand, 1987). [2] 500 cc. Issued without dustwrapper $125.

JAMES CLAVELL

Clavell was born in England in 1924. When he was 17 years old he went into the Royal Artillery as a Captain. He was captured by the Japanese in Java and spent the last three years of the war in the Changi Camp in Singapore, where only 10,000 of the 150,000 prisoners survived. This experience was the basis for his first book. In the 1950s he was a writer in Hollywood, and a very successful one, which led to his writing the screenplay, producing and directing *To Sir, With Love*. He made it for $625,000 and it grossed over $25,000,000. His books haven't done badly either.

We thank Atheneum, Delacorte and Little, Brown for providing the quantities shown.

REFERENCES:

(a) Inventory.

(b) CUMULATIVE BOOK INDEX.

001a: KING RAT Little, Brown, Boston (1962).
[1] 7,500 cc $100/500

001b: KING RAT Michael Joseph, London (1963).
[] Uncorrected proof. In sky blue and gray wraps (Bev Chaney, Jr. 10/92) $150.

001c: KING RAT Michael Joseph, London (1963). [1] $30/150

002a: TAI-PAN *A Novel of Hong Kong* Michael Joseph, London, 1966. [] (Vagabond Books reports this precedes U. S. Edition.) $25/125

002b: TAI-PAN *A Novel of Hong Kong* Atheneum, New York, 1966. [1] Advance reading copy. Bound in dustwrapper (Reese #40) $200.

002c: TAI-PAN *A Novel of Hong Kong* Atheneum, New York, 1966. [1] 25,000 cc $40/200

003a: SHOGUN *A Novel of Japan* Atheneum, New York, 1975. [] Uncorrected proof. Two volumes in plain wraps with labels on front and spines (Antic Hay 12/91) $200.

003b: SHOGUN *A Novel of Japan* Atheneum, New York, 1975. [1] 50,000 cc $30/150

003c: SHOGUN *A Novel of Japan* Hodder & Stoughton, London, 1975. [] Wraps (ref.b) $50.

004a: NOBLE HOUSE *A Novel of Contemporary Hong Kong* Delacorte, New York (1980). [1] Manuscript proof pages in red 3-ring binder with label of "Localmedia" and title and author on front. According to publicity department there were 20 copies in this format for review: 4 were Xeroxed on one side of paper only and 16 on both sides. (Indicated an edition of 250,000 copies to be published 4/30/81) $250.

004b: NOBLE HOUSE *A Novel of Contemporary Hong Kong* Delacorte, New York (1980). [2] 500 sgd no. cc. Issued without dustwrapper. In slipcase $125/175

004c: NOBLE HOUSE *A Novel of Contemporary Hong Kong* Delacorte, New York (1980). [1] 247,000 cc. Also a "Complimentary Edition" in red cloth (Heritage Bookshop), "6456" on front dustwrapper flap, "0481" on back flap. These numbers also appear on the priced ($19.95) dustwrapper. Also noted with "Special Edition." Also a variant in black cloth with numbers and no price (Steven Temple) $15/60

004d: NOBLE HOUSE Hodder & Stoughton, London, 1981. [] Ref.b $15/60

005a: THE MAKING OF JAMES CLAVELL'S SHOGUN Delta/Dell, New York, 1980. [] Wraps (ref.b) $40.

005b: THE MAKING OF JAMES CLAVELL'S SHOGUN Cornet Books, London, 1981. [] Wraps (ref.b) $40.

006a: ART OF WAR Hodder & Stoughton, London, 1981. [] Wraps. A translation from the Chinese of Sun Tzu, edited by Clavell (British Books In Print, 1983) $60.

006b: ART OF WAR Delacorte, New York (1983). [1] Uncorrected proof. In peach colored printed wraps. Publication date: April, 1983 $125.

006c: ART OF WAR Delacorte, New York (1983). [1] 25,000 cc $15/75

007a: THE CHILDREN'S STORY Delacorte (New York, 1981). [1] 100,000 cc (a&b). Presumed first state brick orange-red colored dustwrapper (Almark Books). Also noted as a red dustwrapper with no front panel illustration and blank on the rear panel except for the Delacorte information and ISBN at the bottom. Same? (Sun, Moon, Bear Rare Books 11/96) $10/40

007b: THE CHILDREN’S STORY Delacorte (New York, 1981). [1] Presumed second state dustwrapper in blue with crayon drawing of a schoolhouse on front panel by Ivan Chermayeff and blurbs on the rear panel (Almark Books). The rear flap extends the author biography to include mention of the Mobil Showcase Theater version of this story (Johnnycake Books 10/96) $10/30

008a: THRUMP-O-MOTO Hodder & Stoughton, London (1986). [1] Reportedly precedes U.S. edition $10/50

008b: THRUMP-O-MOTO Delacorte, New York (1986). [1] Illustrated by George Sharp $7/35

009a: WHIRLWIND Morrow, New York (1986). [] Uncorrected proof. In decorated white wraps $150.

009b: WHIRLWIND Morrow, New York, 1986. [2] 75 sgd cc. "For Friends of the Publisher." Tipped-in leaf before half title. Red cloth ribbon. Issued in plain black cloth slipcase (Steven Temple 8/89) $150/200.

009c: WHIRLWIND Morrow, New York, 1986. [3] Also states "First Edition." 850,000 cc (*Publisher's Weekly*). (Published November 10, 1986 @ $22.95) $10/50

009d: WHIRLWIND Hodder & Stoughton, London / Sydney / Auckland / Toronto, (1986) [1] $10/40

009e: WHIRLWIND Macmillan of Canada, Toronto (1986?). [3] Also states "First published in U.S. in 1986 by William Morrow ..." $7/35

009f: WHIRLWIND Macmillan of Canada, Toronto (1986?). [3] Same as 009e except no price and the top edge yellow (Steven Temple 8/89) $7/35

010a: GAI-GIN Delacorte (New York, 1993). [3] Also states "June 1993." Published 6/93 @ $ 27.50_ $6/30

HARRY CREWS

Crews was born in Alma, Georgia in 1935. He received his B.A. and Ms. Ed. at the University of Florida, where he is currently teaching writing, one of his tamer pursuits.

We would like to thank Michael Hargraves for permission to use his excellent bibliography.

REFERENCES:

(a) Hargraves, Michael. HARRY CREWS *A Bibliography.* (Westport, Conn.): Meckler Publishing Corporation (1986).

(b) Inventory.

001a: THE GOSPEL SINGER Morrow, New York, 1968. [0] 4,000 cc $150/750

002a: NAKED IN GARDEN HILLS Morrow, New York, 1969. [0] 5,500 cc (a & b). Full green cloth. First issue dustwrapper with reviews of 001a on back. There is also light green simulated cloth binding, (Joseph The Provider 10/92 mentions this as the usual binding) but our copy of the first printing is in full medium to dark green cloth and our second printing is in the light green simulated cloth binding, which would indicate that the light green could be a second state/issue, although we have recently seen another copy with the simulated cloth in a first issue dustwrapper. $50/250

002b: NAKED IN GARDEN HILLS Morrow, New York, 1969. [0] Second issue dustwrapper with reviews of this book on back $50/150

Note: Second printing has two dots at foot of copyright page otherwise no difference

002c: NAKED IN GARDEN HILLS Charisma Books, London, 1973. [1] Wraps $75.

003a: THIS THING DON'T LEAD TO HEAVEN Morrow, New York, 1970. [0] 7,500 cc $40/200

004a: KARATE IS A THING OF THE SPIRIT Morrow, New York, 1971. [0] 5,942 cc $40/200

004b: KARATE IS A THING OF THE SPIRIT Secker & Warburg, London (1972). [1] $50/200

005a: CAR Morrow, New York, 1972. [0] Uncorrected proof. In white wraps (H.E. Turlington 9/90) $300.

005b: CAR Morrow, New York, 1972. [0] 5,005 cc $40/200

005c: CAR Car Productions, Los Angeles, 1972. [] A screenplay by Crews. 114 pages. Not produced (Pepper & Stern 5/90) $200.

005d: CAR Secker & Warburg, London (1973). [1] $30/150

006a: THE HAWK IS DYING Knopf, New York, 1973. [1] Approximately 5,000 cc $30/150

006b: THE HAWK IS DYING Secker & Warburg, London (1974). [1] $20/100

007a: THE GYPSY'S CURSE Knopf, New York, 1974. [1] 6,000 cc $30/100

007b: THE GYPSY'S CURSE Secker & Warburg, London (1975). [1] $20/100

008a: A FEAST OF SNAKES Atheneum, New York, 1976. [] Uncorrected proof. In green wraps (Ken Lopez 9/90) $200.

008b: A FEAST OF SNAKES Atheneum, New York, 1976. [1] 6,000 cc $30/150

008c: A FEAST OF SNAKES Secker & Warburg, London (1977). [1] The American edition dustwrapper was adapted for this somewhat taller English edition, causing the dustwrapper to appear over-trimmed (Bertram Rota 3/96) $25/100

009a: A CHILDHOOD *The Biography of a Place* Harper, New York (1978). [1] Uncorrected proof. In red wraps (Waverley Books 2/91) $250.

009b: A CHILDHOOD *The Biography of a Place* Harper, New York (1978). [3] Also states "First Edition." 6,500 cc $25/125

009c: A CHILDHOOD *The Biography of a Place* Secker & Warburg, London (1979) [1] $25/100

010a: BLOOD AND GRITS Harper, New York (1979). [3] Also states "First Edition." Uncorrected proof. In red wraps (Waverley Books 3/89) . $200.

010b: BLOOD AND GRITS Harper, New York (1979). [3] 6,500 cc. Also states "First Edition." (Somewhere we picked up the comment that the second printing of 2,000 copies corrects an error on the copyright page, however, we do not know what the error is) $25/125

011a: THE ENTHUSIAST Palaemon Press (Winston-Salem, 1981). [2] 50 sgd no. cc (Roman). Issued without dustwrapper or slipcase $225.

011b: THE ENTHUSIAST Palaemon Press (Winston-Salem, 1981). [2] 150 sgd no. cc. Also noted an out-of-series review copy (so stated on the front wrapper), signed but not numbered (Revere Books 11/96) $150.

012a: FLORIDA FRENZY University of Florida, Gainesville (1982). [0] 1,500 cc (ref.a), (2,070 cc according to publisher in correspondence with Steven Bernard 6/20/82). Wraps. First appearance of one essay, most of the others are first book appearances $75.

013a: 2 BY CREWS Lord John Press, Northridge, 1984. [2] 26 sgd ltr cc. Issued without dustwrapper or slipcase $300.

013b: 2 BY CREWS Lord John Press, Northridge, 1984. [2] 200 sgd no. cc. Issued without dustwrapper or slipcase $125.

014a: ALL WE NEED OF HELL Harper, New York (1987). [] Uncorrected proof. In printed red wraps $150.

014b: ALL WE NEED OF HELL Harper, New York (1987). [3] Also states "First Edition." (Published January 28, 1987 @ $14.95) $15/75

015a: BLOOD ISSUE *A Drama in Two Acts* No publisher or place, 1988. [] 107 page playscript. Loose Xeroxed paper in brads (Pepper & Stern 8/90) $150.

016a: THE KNOCKOUT ARTIST Harper, New York (1988). [] Uncorrected proof. First issue in printed yellow wraps with front and spine lettering unset. Shot from typescript and paginated to p. 382. (Ken Lopez 7/95) $150.

016b: THE KNOCKOUT ARTIST Harper, New York (1988). [] Second issue uncorrected proof in printed tan wraps with front and spine lettering typeset; paginated to p.247. (Ken Lopez 7/95) $125.

016c: THE KNOCKOUT ARTIST Harper, New York (1988). [3] Also states "First Edition." (Published April 1988 @ $17.95) $10/40

017a: BODY Poseidon Press (New York, 1990). [0] Advance uncorrected proof. Wraps. Includes an excerpt along with excerpts from books by Mary Gaitskill and Patrick McGrath $40.

017b: BODY Poseidon Press, New York (1990). [2] 10 sgd ltr cc in full leather. Issued by Ultramarine Press using Poseidon sheets $500.

017c: BODY Poseidon Press, New York (1990). [2] 40 sgd no. cc in decorated paper boards with leather spine. Issued by Ultramarine Press using Poseidon sheets $250.

017d: BODY Poseidon Press, New York (1990). [3] Signed on tipped in leaf (Waverley Books 4/92) $50/75

017e: BODY Poseidon Press, New York (1990). [3] $10/40

018a: MADONNA AT RINGSIDE Lord John Press, Northridge, 1991. [2] 26 sgd ltr cc $300.

018b: MADONNA AT RINGSIDE Lord John Press, Northridge, 1991. [2] 275 sgd no. cc $100.

019a: SCAR LOVER Poseidon Press, New York (1992). [] Uncorrected proof. In blue wraps $100.

019b: SCAR LOVER Poseidon Press, New York (1992). [3] (Published February 1992 @ $19.00) $7/35

020a: CLASSIC CREWS *A Harry Crews Reader* Poseidon Press, New York (1993). [3] Wraps. Collects *Car, The Gypsy's Curse, A Childhood*, and a selection of essays $40.

021a: THE MULCHING OF AMERICA Simon & Schuster, New York, 1995. [] Uncorrected proof. In yellow printed wraps (Waverley Books 9/95) $75

021b: THE MULCHING OF AMERICA Simon & Schuster, New York, 1995. [] Advance reading copy in glossy pictorial wraps (Waverley Books 7/95) $50.

021c: THE MULCHING OF AMERICA Simon & Schuster, New York, 1995. [] (Oracle Books 11/95) $5/25

022a: THE GOSPEL SINGER and WHERE DOES ONE GO WHEN THERE'S NO PLACE TO GO Gorse, London, 1995. [] Wraps. First publication of *Where Does One Go*... (Ian McKelvie 11/97) $20.

022b: WHERE DOES ONE GO WHEN THERE IS NO PLACE LEFT TO GO? Publisher? Place? 1997 [2] 26 sgd ltr cc (Vagabond Books 10/97) $200.

022c: WHERE DOES ONE GO WHEN THERE IS NO PLACE LEFT TO GO? Publisher? Place? 1997. [2] 400 sgd no. cc (Vagabond Books 10/97) $75.

023a: CELEBRATION Simon & Schuster, New York, 1998. [] Uncorrected proof. In printed yellow wraps (Bev Chaney, Jr. 5/98) $50.

023b: CELEBRATION Simon & Schuster (New York, 1998). [] Advance reading copy. Wraps (Ken Lopez 1/98) $40.

023c: CELEBRATION Simon & Schuster (New York, 1998). [3] Published at $23

JOAN DIDION

Didion was born in Sacramento, California in 1934. She received a B.A. from the University of California, Berkeley. She worked as a columnist or editor at *Vogue*, *Saturday Evening Post* and *The National Review*; and has written a number of film scripts. Didion is married to the writer, John Gregory Dunne.

REFERENCES:

(a) Bruccoli, Matthew J., and Clark, C. E. Frazer Jr. FIRST PRINTINGS OF AMERICAN AUTHORS. Volume 2. Detroit: Gale Research (1978).

(b) Inventory.

(c) CUMULATIVE BOOK INDEX.

(d) Dealer catalogs.

(e) BRITISH BOOKS IN PRINT - 1983.

001a: RUN RIVER Obolensky, New York (1963). [1] $30/150

001b: RUN RIVER Jonathan Cape, London (1964). [1] "Proof Only" on back dustwrapper flap. Dustwrapper about 1/2 inch taller than book. Publication date estimated at January 1, 1964 (ref.b) $25/125

001c: RUN RIVER Jonathan Cape, London (1964). [1] (Ref.b) $15/75

002a: SLOUCHING TOWARDS BETHLEHEM Farrar, Straus & Giroux, New York (1968). [] Uncorrected proof. In spiral bound wraps (Wm. Reese Co. 5/89) $250.

002b: SLOUCHING TOWARDS BETHLEHEM Farrar, Straus & Giroux, New York (1968). [1] $25/100

002c: SLOUCHING TOWARDS BETHLEHEM Deutsch (London, 1969). [] (Ref.c) $15/75

003a: PLAY IT AS IT LAYS Farrar, Straus, New York (1970). [] Uncorrected proof. In salmon colored ring bound wraps (Waverley Books #50) $150.

003b: PLAY IT AS IT LAYS Farrar, Straus, New York (1970). [1] $15/75

003c: PLAY IT AS IT LAYS Weidenfeld & Nicolson, London (1971). [1] (Ref.b) $12/60

003d: PLAY IT AS IT LAYS *A Screenplay* F. P. Films, New York/Los Angeles (1971). [0] 130 pages punch bound in printed wraps. Written with John Gregory Dunne (Joseph the Provider 9/89) $125.

004a: A BOOK OF COMMON PRAYER Simon & Schuster, New York (1977). [3] Uncorrected proof. In tall, printed pad-bound yellow wraps $100.

004b: A BOOK OF COMMON PRAYER Simon & Schuster, New York (1977). [3] $8/40

004c: A BOOK OF COMMON PRAYER Weidenfeld & Nicolson, London, no date [assume 1977]. [1] (U.S. plates.) "First Published in Great Britain By Weidenfeld..." Noted in two dustwrappers, one copper printed in light blue and black, the other pink printed in blue and dark pink (Arundel Press 10/91) $8/40

004d: A BOOK OF COMMON PRAYER Franklin Library, Franklin Center, 1981. [2] Sgd/ltd edition. In full leather. With special message from author $60.

005a: TELLING STORIES Friends of Bancroft Library, Berkeley, 1978. [] Wraps. "Not For Sale" (ref.d) $75.

006a: THE WHITE ALBUM Simon & Schuster, New York (1979). [3] (Ref.b) $7/35

006b: THE WHITE ALBUM Weidenfeld & Nicolson, London (1979). [] (Ref.e) $7/35

007a: SALVADOR Simon & Schuster, New York (1983). [3] Advance uncorrected proof. In yellow printed wraps (ref.b) $75.

007b: SALVADOR Simon & Schuster, New York (1983) [3] $10/40

007c: SALVADOR Chatto & Windus, London (1983). [] $7/35

007d: SALVADOR Chatto & Windus, London (1983). [] Simultaneous issue in wraps (Ken Lopez 7/96) 25.

008a: DEMOCRACY Simon & Schuster, New York (1984). [3] Advance uncorrected proof. In yellow printed wraps (ref.b) $75.

008b: DEMOCRACY Simon & Schuster, New York (1984) [3] (Ref.b.) Noted in two different dustwrappers, priority unknown: (1) metallic brown back-ground, title in turquoise, author's name in black; (2) pink, mulberry and blue , respectively $7/35

008c: DEMOCRACY Chatto & Windus / Hogarth, London (1984). [] (Ref.d) $7/35

008d: DEMOCRACY Dennys (Toronto, 1984). [0] (Ref.b) $6/30

009a: ESSAYS AND INTERVIEWS Ontario Review Press, Princeton, 1984. [] Edited by Ellen G. Friedman $10/40

010a: MIAMI Simon & Schuster, New York, nodate (cover). [0] Manuscript (8 1/2" x 11") sheets with black cloth spine. Reported to be limited to a few copies $100.

010b: MIAMI Simon & Schuster, New York (1987). [] Uncorrected proof. In yellow or ochre printed wraps $60.

010c: MIAMI Simon & Schuster, New York (1987). [] About 50,000 cc. (Published October 9, 1987 at $17.95) $7/35

010d: MIAMI Dennys, Toronto (1987). [] $6/30

010e: MIAMI Weidenfeld & Nicolson, London, 1988. [] (Ian McKelvie 11/92) $6/30

011a: SOME WOMEN *Photographs By Robert Mapplethorpe* Bulfinch Press, Boston (1989). [] Introduction by Didion (James S. Jaffe 11/95) $75/150

012a: AFTER HENRY Simon & Schuster, New York, 1992. [] Uncorrected proof. In yellow wraps $60.

012b: AFTER HENRY Simon & Schuster, New York, 1992. [] (Published May 1992 @ $22) $5/25

013a: THE LAST THING HE WANTED Alfred A. Knopf, New York, 1996. [] Uncorrected proof. In cream wraps (Bev Chaney, Jr. 12/96) $40.

013b: THE LAST THING HE WANTED Alfred A. Knopf, New York, 1996. [1] Advance reading copy in wraps. Signed by the author. In stiff paper slipcase $60.

JOHN DOS PASSOS
1896 - 1970

John (Roderigo) Dos Passos was born in Chicago. He received his B.A. degree "cum Laude" from Harvard in 1916. During WW1 he served with the Red Cross and U.S.A. Ambulance Services which gave him the material for his first book. During the 1920's he traveled around Spain, Mexico and the Middle East as a free-lance writer and journalist. In Paris he associated with e.e. cummings, Fitzgerald, Hemingway and other expatriates. Increasingly left wing in political views he became actively involved in social struggles and wrote articles and plays of social protest.

His literary success started with the first volume of the U.S.A. trilogy, *The 42nd Parallel*, in 1930. The trilogy won for him a reputation as one of the finest novelists of the 1930's.

By the end of the 1930's he had broken with communism and was disillusioned by the Spanish Civil War. He began to write critically of proletarianism and as time went on he started espousing conservatism.

We would like to thank Jeff Klaess for preparing the first draft of this guide; and Richard Layman for providing further details on first edition identification of the British editions (which were not covered at all in any of the other references).

REFERENCES:

(a) Potter, Jack. A BIBLIOGRAPHY OF JOHN DOS PASSOS. Chicago: Normandie House, 1950. Used for all entries, unless otherwise indicated, up to 1949.

(b) Bruccoli, Matthew J., and Clarke, C. E. Frazer, Jr. FIRST PRINTINGS OF AMERICAN AUTHORS. Volume 1. Detroit: Gale Research (1977). Used for all U.S. entries from 1950 to 1974 unless otherwise indicated.

(c) Sanders, David. JOHN DOS PASSOS *A Comprehensive Bibliography*. York: Garland Publishing Inc., 1987. Used for the quantities from 1950 to 1975, and as indicated.

(d) Information supplied by Richard Layman, inventory, dealer catalogs, etc.

001a: ONE MAN'S INITIATION - 1917 George Allen & Unwin Ltd., London (1920). [1] 750 cc (an additional 500 copies shipped to Doran for U.S. edition). Pale-blue mesh cloth. First state has a broken "d" and the word "flat" obliterated at p.35:32. Although not necessarily issued before second state in all cases as the sheets were used at random including those sent to the U.S. $150/750

001b: ONE MAN'S INITIATION - 1917 George Allen & Unwin Ltd., London (1920). [1] Pale blue mesh cloth. Second state has perfect "d" and "flat" at p.35:32 $100/600

001c: ONE MAN'S INITIATION - 1917 George H. Doran, New York, 1922. [0] 500 cc. Title page is a cancel on a stub, verso of title page blank. Shiny smooth maroon cloth, cream colored paper label on spine, top-edge trimmed and stained maroon (ref.b). Ref.d calls for red cloth. First state has broken "d" and obliterated "flat" at p.36:32 $150/750

001d: ONE MAN'S INITIATION - 1917 George H. Doran, New York, 1922. [0] Second state: perfect "d" and "flat" on p.35:32 $100/600

001e: FIRST ENCOUNTER Philosophical Library, New York (1945). [0] 2,000 cc. New title. Contains new introduction by Dos Passos $15/75

001f: ONE MAN'S INITIATION - 1917 Cornell University Press, Ithaca, New York (1969). [] 1,008 cc. Reprinted from the "Original uncorrected page proofs" per Dos Passos. Described by Publishers as "complete and unexpurgated." Contains a new 34 page introduction by Dos Passos, a 5 page publisher's note, and 6 drawings by Dos Passos (ref.b & c) $35/75

001g: ONE MAN'S INITIATION - 1917 Cornell University Press, Ithaca, New York (1970). [] 3,948 cc. Wraps (ref.c) $35.

002a: THREE SOLDIERS George H. Doran, New York (1921). [] Advance copy. In tan wraps $2,000.

002b: THREE SOLDIERS George H. Doran, New York (1921). [0] Approximately 2-3,000 copies printed (b to f). Publisher's colophon not found in any state of first printing. Three blank integral leaves at front, none at back, endpapers front and back (ref.b). "Signing" for "singing" at p.213:31. First state dustwrapper has publisher's blurb on front, spine and back (ref.a) $100/1,000

002c: THREE SOLDIERS George H. Doran, New York (1921). [0] Two blank integral leaves in front, none in back. Endpapers front and back. Pages 9-10 tipped onto pages 11-12 (ref.b. Not mentioned in ref.a); "signing" for "singing" p.213:31. Dustwrapper has a quotation from the *Brooklyn Daily Eagle* as last item on front panel (ref.a). In addition, we have had mixed states with various numbers of blank leaves in front and back $100/600

002d: THREE SOLDIERS George H. Doran, New York (1921). [0] Third state, like first, has three blank integral leaves in front and none in back, endpapers front and back, "signing" has been corrected to "singing." Dustwrapper same as 002c except the quote from the *Brooklyn Daily Eagle* has been replaced by one from *Stars and Stripes* (ref. a & b) $35/350

002e: THREE SOLDIERS George H. Doran, New York (1921). [0] Fourth state. Two integral blank leaves at front and three at back, no endpapers (the first and last leaves being pastedowns); "singing" at p.213:31. Dustwrapper as 002d but with price on spine blacked over (ref. a & b) $35/300

002f: THREE SOLDIERS George H. Doran, New York (1921). [0] Fifth state. Three blank integral leaves in front and four in back, endpapers in front and back (ref.b) $35/250

Note: Precedence of third, fourth and fifth states unknown (ref.b). Ref.a only mentions 002b and later state with "singing." Ref.c doesn't mention any states/points. Also noted with 3 blank integral leaves in front and two in back (Waiting For Godot 4/90)

002g: THREE SOLDIERS Hurst and Blackett, London (1922). [0] P.383 states "Printed by Anchor Press Ltd..." (ref.d) $100/400

002h: THREE SOLDIERS Modern Library, New York, 1932. [0] Modern Library edition. Contains a new introduction and minor textual revisions (ref. a & b) $15/75

003a: ROSINANTE TO THE ROAD AGAIN George H. Doran, New York (1922) [5] Yellow boards and dustwrapper. Quantity unknown. 2,359 cc sold $75/400

004a: A PUSHCART AT THE CURB George H. Doran, New York (1922). [5] 1,313 cc printed of which 544 were remaindered. Colored pictorial cloth, cream colored paper label on black cloth spine. (Two copies know with labels on front cover as well as on spine.) Cover painting and dustwrapper art by Dos Passos $100/450

005a: STREETS OF NIGHT George H. Doran, New York (1923). [5] Erratum: p.300:8 "horeshoe" for "horseshoe" (ref.a. Not mentioned in ref. b & c). Quantity unknown. 3,414 copies sold $75/350

005b: STREETS OF NIGHT Martin Secker, London (1923). [] $60/300

006a: MANHATTAN TRANSFER Harper & Bros., New York (1925). [1] 4,000 cc. "K-Z" on copyright page. Ref. a states the earliest copies have a perfect "p" in "Ferryship"; a perfect "2" in page number 298; and an almost obliterated "i" in "telling", p.328:22; although ref.c doesn't mention at all. There are two types of bindings and two dustwrappers: 1) yellow paper label on front cover and publishers device blind-stamped in lower right-hand corner, back cover plain, issued in dustwrapper with a montage of urban scenes on front panel; and 2) pasted over black cloth, a pictorial paper reproduction of N.Y. Harbor and skyline, on front and back covers, tips of corners black cloth, issued in matching pictorial dustwrapper. Artwork by Dos Passos. Of the 4,000 copies printed, 2,000 issued in each binding with no priority. All copies bound and issued simultaneously $150/750

006b: MANHATTAN TRANSFER Constable, London (1927). [1] (Ref.b) $60/300

007a: THE GARBAGE MAN Harper & Bros., New York (1926). [1] 1,000 cc. In first state of binding: chocolate brown boards, paper labels on front cover and spine, top-edge trimmed. Code "F-A" on copyright page. Dustwrapper art by Dos Passos $100/400

007b: THE GARBAGE MAN Harper & Bros., New York (1926). [1] 500 cc (balance of original printing) in second state binding: shiny dark blue cloth, paper label on spine only. Dustwrapper as in 007a $50/350

007c: THE GARBAGE MAN Constable, London, 1929. [] Excludes Author's Note on early productions of the play (ref.b) $50/250

007d: THE GARBAGE MAN Constable, London, 1929. [] In decorated wraps (Nicholas Pounder 6/90) $125.

008a: ORIENT EXPRESS Harper & Bros., New York (1927). [1] 1,000 cc. Issued in lavender boards and lavender paper label on shiny blue cloth spine, top-edge trimmed and stained wine-colored maroon. Code "M-A" on copyright page. 7 illustrations and dustwrapper art by Dos Passos $100/350

008b: ORIENT EXPRESS Harper & Bros., New York (1927). [1] 1,500 cc (balance of original printing) in second state binding: blue cloth with paper label on spine. Dustwrapper and illustrations remained the same $50/300

008c: ORIENT EXPRESS Jonathan Cape, London (1928). [1] "First issued in Traveler's Library" (ref.b, not mentioned in a or c) $30/200

008d: ORIENT EXPRESS Cape & Smith, New York, 1928. [0] Cape and Smith Traveller's Library (ref.d). Also noted in dustwrapper with imprint at bottom of spine of "Galaxy"? Remainder? $15/75

009a: FACING THE CHAIR Sacco Vanzetti Defense Committee, Boston, 1927. [0] Stiff olive drab wraps. (Facsimile publication by Decapo in 1970) $250.

010a: AIRWAYS, INC. Macaulay Co., New York (1928). [0] Approximately 1,000 - 1,500 cc printed (ref. a & b) $75/350

011a: METROPOLIS (T.S. Book Co.), New York, 1929. [0] Wraps. Translation of Manuel Maples Arce's work by Dos Passos (ref. a & b) $200.

012a: THE 42ND PARALLEL Harper & Bros., New York (1930). [1] 7,500 cc. Code "A-E" on copyright page. Variant bindings of paper covered boards but no priority. First volume of *U.S.A.* trilogy $100/450

012b: THE 42ND PARALLEL Constable, London (1930). [0] Also noted in wraps with dustwrapper as cover. Could have been an advance copy or simultaneous paperwraps issue (ref.d) $50/250

012c: THE 42ND PARALLEL Modern Library (New York, 1937). [] Adds introduction by Dos Passos $12/60

013a: PANAMA, OR THE ADVENTURES OF MY SEVEN UNCLES by Blaise Cendrars. Harper & Bros., New York, 1931. [2] 300 no. cc signed by Cendrars and Dos Passos (translation and introduction). In stiff cream colored pictorial wraps. Contains 12 reproductions of paintings by Dos Passos. In slipcase with title, author... and copy number on spine (not mentioned in any of the references) $200/350

013b: PANAMA, OR THE ADVENTURES OF MY SEVEN UNCLES by Blaise Cendrars. Harper & Bros., New York, 1931. [1] Code "M-E" on copyright page. Same as above without limitation page. Slipcase? $150.

014a: **1919** Harcourt, Brace, New York (1932). [1] 10,250 cc printed. Second volume of the *U.S.A.* trilogy $75/350

014b: **1919** Constable, London (1932). [1] Also noted in wraps with dustwrapper as cover. Could have been an advance copy or simultaneous paperwraps issue (ref.d) $50/200

015a: HARLAN MINERS SPEAK... Harcourt, Brace, New York (1932). [] A report on terrorism in Kentucky coal fields prepared for the defense of political prisoners. Contains "Continuity and Explanatory" paragraphs throughout by Dos Passos) $250.

016a: CULTURE AND CRISIS... League of Professional Groups for Foster and Ford, New York, 1932. [0] Wraps (ref.b) $250.

017a: IN ALL COUNTRIES Harcourt, Brace, New York (1934). [1] 1,500 cc printed $40/200

017b: IN ALL COUNTRIES Constable, London (1934). [1] (Ref.d) $25/125

018a: THREE PLAYS Harcourt, Brace, New York (1934). [0] 1,500 cc. This is the first appearance of *Fortune Heights* $60/250

018b: THREE PLAYS McLeod, Toronto, 1934. [] (Ref.c) $35/150

019a: THE BIG MONEY Harcourt, Brace, New York (1936) [1] 10,000 cc. Third volume of the *U.S.A.* trilogy $50/250

019b: THE BIG MONEY Constable (London, 1936). [1] Also noted in wraps with dustwrapper as cover. Could have been an advance copy of a simultaneous paperwraps issue (ref.d) $30/150

020a: THE VILLAGES ARE THE HEART OF SPAIN Esquire-Coronet, Chicago (1937). [2] 1,200 no. cc. Issued without dustwrapper $200.

021a: U.S.A. Harcourt, Brace, New York, no-date [1938]. [0] 5,200 cc. One volume trilogy (includes *The 42nd Parallel*, *1919*, and *The Big Money*). First appearance of short sketch by Dos Passos. Last copyright date 1937, but not published until January 1938. None of the references indicated this edition states "first edition" so, we assume it does not $35/175

021b: U.S.A. Constable, London (1938). [1] "Published... 1938" (ref.d) $25/125

021c: U.S.A. Houghton, Mifflin, Boston, 1946. [2] 365 no. copies signed by Dos Passos and Reginald

Marsh, the illustrator. 3 volumes in slipcase and paper and glassine dustwrappers (Heritage Book Shop 1/97, Beasley Books 1/97) $750/1000

021d: U.S.A. Houghton, Mifflin, Boston (1946). [0] 36 page prospectus for illustrated edition with one plate mounted on front cover (Watermark West 11/90) $75.

021e: U.S.A. Houghton, Mifflin, Boston, 1946. [0] 3 vols. Illustrated by Reginald Marsh. In cellophane and paper dustwrappers and slipcase $150/600

022a: JOURNEYS BETWEEN WARS Harcourt, Brace, New York (1938). [1] 2,500 cc $25/125

022b: JOURNEYS BETWEEN WARS Constable, London (1938). [1] (Ref.d) $25/100

023a: MAN WITH A WATCH IN HIS HAND Sherwood and Katharine Grover/Grabhorn Press, San Francisco, 1938. [2] 25 no. cc. (Reprinted from *The Big Money* where it was titled *The American Plan*) $500.

024a: ADVENTURES OF A YOUNG MAN Harcourt, Brace, New York (1939). [1] 10,000 cc. Ref.b mentions that the published reprinted this title in 1952 without date on title page but with "First Printing" on copyright page $25/125

024b: ADVENTURES OF A YOUNG MAN Constable, London (1939). [] (Ref.b.) First issue in purple buckram (Peter Jolliffe #36) $25/100

025a: THE BITTER DRINK Sherwood and Katharine, Grover (Grabhorn Press, San Francisco), 1939. [2] 35 no. cc. (Reprinted from *The Big Money*) ref.b. Ref.a has 25 copies, which we believe could be wrong as auction records also show 35 copies) $750.

026a: HENRY AND WILLIAM FORD AND HEARST... Sherwood and Katharine Grover / Grabhorn Press, San Francisco, 1940. [2] 35 cc. Wraps. (*Tin Lizzie* and *Poor Little Rich Boy* retitled and reprinted from *The Big Money.*) (Also noted in unbound sheets completely untrimmed) $750.

027a: THE LIVING THOUGHTS OF TOM PAINE Longmans Green, New York, 1940. [1] $35/175

027b: THE LIVING THOUGHTS OF TOM PAINE Cassell, London (1940). [] (Ref.b) $25/125

028a: THE GROUND WE STAND ON Harcourt, Brace, New York (1941). [1] 3,000 cc $25/125

028b: THE GROUND WE STAND ON Geo. Routledge, London (1942). [1] Adds an introduction by Dos Passos (ref.d) $25/125

029a: NUMBER ONE Houghton, Mifflin, Boston, 1943. [0] 15,000 cc. Date on title page. Rear panel of dustwrapper has statement by Dos Passos urging readers to buy War bonds. Ref.b mentions that the publisher reprinted the title in 1952 without a date on title page but with "First Printing" on copyright page $25/100

029b: NUMBER ONE Thomas Allen, Toronto, 1943. [] (Ref.c) $15/75

029c: NUMBER ONE Constable, London (1944). [1] (Ref.d) $15/75

029d: NUMBER ONE Dymock's, Sydney, 1944. [] First Australian edition (Todd's Books 11/95) $12/60

030a: STATE OF THE NATION Houghton, Mifflin, Boston, 1944. [0] 7,500 cc. Date on title page $15/75

030b: STATE OF THE NATION Routledge, London (1945). [1] (Ref.d) $15/75

030c: STATE OF THE NATION Thomas Allen, Toronto, 1945. [] (Ref.c) $15/60

FIRST ENCOUNTER see 001e

031a: TOUR OF DUTY [cover title only] Houghton Mifflin, Boston, 1946. [] Advance proof in blue wrappers. Issued without preliminaries and with cover-label serving as title page (Howard S. Mott 10/96) $250.

031b: TOUR OF DUTY Houghton Mifflin, Boston, 1946. [0] 8,000 cc. Date on title page $15/75

032a: THE GRAND DESIGN Houghton Mifflin, Boston, 1949. [0] 15,000 cc. Date on title page. Ref.b mentions that the publisher reprinted this title in 1952 without a date on the title page but with "First Printing" on copyright page $15/75

032b: THE GRAND DESIGN John Lehmann, London (1949). [1] (Ref.d) $12/60

032c: THE GRAND DESIGN Thomas Allen, Toronto, 1949. [] (Ref.c) $10/50

033a: THE PROSPECT BEFORE US Houghton Mifflin, Boston, 1950. [0] 5,000 cc. Date on title page. Ref.b identified two paper stocks, but no known priority $12/60

033b: THE PROSPECT BEFORE US John Lehmann, London (1951). [1] (Ref.d) $12/60

034a: LIFE'S PICTURE HISTORY OF WORLD WAR II Time / Simon & Schuster, New York, 1950. [0] (Each section has full-page article by Dos Passos.) Assume issued without dustwrapper $75.

035a: CHOSEN COUNTRY Houghton Mifflin, Boston, 1951. [0] 400 cc. With tipped-in "Complimentary Edition For the Book-sellers ... " and Dos Passos' signature $125/175

035b: CHOSEN COUNTRY Houghton Mifflin, Boston, 1951. [0] 10,000 cc (total a & b). Date on title page $12/60

035c: CHOSEN COUNTRY John Lehmann, London (1952). [1] "This Edition First Published in 1952" $10/50

035d: CHOSEN COUNTRY Thomas Allen, Toronto, 1952. [] (Ref.c) $10/50

036a: DISTRICT OF COLUMBIA Houghton Mifflin, Boston, 1952. [0] 3,000 cc. Date on title page. One volume edition containing *Adventures of a Young Man*, *Number One* and *The Grand Design* $25/100

037a: THE HEAD AND HEART OF THOMAS JEFFERSON Doubleday, Garden City, 1954. [1] $25/100

037b: THE HEAD AND HEART OF THOMAS JEFFERSON Robert Hale, London (1955). [1] (Ref.d) $15/75

038a: MOST LIKELY TO SUCCEED Prentice-Hall, New York (1954). [2] 1000 signed cc. Limitation printed on half-title $75/125

038b: MOST LIKELY TO SUCCEED Prentice-Hall, New York (1954). [0] Quantity is 7,539 per ref.c which we assume is for both a & b. Ref.a doesn't mention the signed copies $12/60

038c: MOST LIKELY TO SUCCEED Robert Hale, London (1955). [] $10/50

039a: THE THEME IS FREEDOM Dodd Mead, New York, 1956. [0] 3,000 cc $15/75

040a: THE MEN WHO MADE THE NATION Doubleday, Garden City, 1957. [1] $12/60

041a: THE GREAT DAYS Sangamore Press, New York (1958). [0] $15/75

041b: THE GREAT DAYS McClelland & Stewart, Toronto, 1958. [] $10/60

041c: THE GREAT DAYS Robert Hale, London (1959). [1] $10/50

042a: PROSPECTS OF A GOLDEN AGE Prentice-Hall, Englewood Cliffs, (1959). [0] 9,995 cc $15/75

043a: U.S.A. / A DRAMATIC REVUE Samuel French, New York (1960). [0] Wraps. Written with Paul Shyre. First has copyright of 1960, and $1.25 price on cover $40.

044a: MIDCENTURY Houghton Mifflin, Boston, 1961. [1] 10,000 cc $12/60

044b: MIDCENTURY Thomas Allen, Toronto, 1961. [] $10/60

044c: MIDCENTURY Deutsch (London, 1961). [1] (Ref.d) $10/50

045a: MR. WILSON'S WAR Doubleday, Garden City, 1962. [1] $12/60

045b: MR. WILSON'S WAR Hamish Hamilton, London (1963). [1] $10/50

046a: BRAZIL ON THE MOVE Doubleday, Garden City, 1963. [1] $25/100

046b: BRAZIL ON THE MOVE Sidgwick & Jackson, (London), 1963. [1] "First published ... 1964" (but it does have 1963 on title page) $15/75

047a: THOMAS JEFFERSON: THE MAKING OF A PRESIDENT Houghton Mifflin, Boston, 1964. [0] Date on title page. Two bindings: cloth 6,000 copies, and 4,000 copies in library binding. Assume both had dustwrappers (source: Houghton Mifflin records) $35/175

048a: OCCASIONS AND PROTESTS Henry Regnery, Chicago, 1964. [0] Uncorrected galley spiral bound in plain wraps (William Reese Co. 10/90) $125.

048b: OCCASIONS AND PROTESTS Henry Regnery, Chicago, 1964. [0] $10/50

049a: THE SHACKLES OF POWER: *Three Jeffersonian Decades* Doubleday, Garden City, 1966. [1] Edited by Lewis Gannett $12/60

050a: WORLD IN A GLASS Houghton Mifflin, Boston, 1966. [] "Revised" galley proofs. Spiral bound in printed wraps (William Reese Co. 10/92) $125.

050b: WORLD IN A GLASS Houghton Mifflin, Boston, 1966. [1] 3,500 cc (ref.c). Edited by Kenneth S. Lyon $25/75

051a: THE BEST OF TIMES *An Informal Memoir* New American Library, New York (1966). [1] Spiral bound uncorrected proof (Pepper & Stern 11/86) $100.

051b: THE BEST OF TIMES *An Informal Memoir* New American Library, New York (1966). [1] $8/40

051c: THE BEST OF TIMES *An Informal Memoir* Deutsch, London (1968). [] Deletes Author's Note $8/40

051d: THE BEST OF TIMES *An Informal Memoir* General Publishing Co., Toronto, 1968. [] $8/40

052a: THE PORTUGAL STORY *Three Centuries of Exploration and Discovery* Doubleday, Garden City, 1969. [1] $15/60

052b: THE PORTUGAL STORY *Three...* Robert Hale, London (1970). [1] $15/60

053a: AN INTERVIEW WITH JOHN DOS PASSOS Union College Press, Schenectady (1969).

[0] Pamphlet. Edited by Frank Gado. Verso of front cover has "Copyright 1969 by The Idol..." $50.

054a: EASTER ISLAND *Island of Enigmas* Doubleday, Garden City, 1971. [1] $12/60

055a: THE FOURTEENTH CHRONICLE *Letters and Diaries of John Dos Passos* Gambit, Boston, 1973. [] Edited by Townsend Ludington. Uncorrected proof in bright red wraps (Waiting For Godot #15) $75.

055b: THE FOURTEENTH CHRONICLE *Letters and Diaries of John Dos Passos* Gambit, Boston, 1973. [2] 300 sgd no. cc. Edited by Townsend Ludington. Signed by editor with facsimile of a Dos Passos' signed note $75/125

055c: THE FOURTEENTH CHRONICLE *Letters and Diaries of John Dos Passos* Gambit, Boston, 1973. [] Advance sampler in wraps (Nouveau 2/94) $30.

055d: THE FOURTEENTH CHRONICLE *Letters and Diaries of John Dos Passos* Gambit, Boston, 1973. [1] 10,000 cc. Edited by Townsend Ludington $8/40

055e: THE FOURTEENTH CHRONICLE ... Deutsch, London (1974). [] Edited by Townsend Ludington $8/40

056a: CENTURY'S EBB THE THIRTEENTH CHRONICLE Gambit, Boston, 1975. [1] 4,500 cc (ref.c) $8/40

057a: THE MAJOR NONFICTIONAL PROSE Wayne State Press, Detroit, 1988. [3] Wraps. Edited by Donald Pizer. Contains a number of previously uncollected pieces $40.

058a: AFTERGLOW AND OTHER UNDERGRADUATE WRITINGS Omnigraphics, Detroit, 1990. [0] Dos Passos first novel, a facsimile of the typescript and other early works from his Harvard days. Edited by Richard Layman. Issued without dustwrapper $100.

WILLIAM EASTLAKE

Eastlake was born in New York City in 1917. He served in the Army during WWII and then moved to an isolated area in New Mexico where he operated a small ranch. Although born in New York, his writing has been principally about his adopted region.

REFERENCES:

(a) Bruccoli, Matthew J., and Clark, C.E. Frazer, Jr., (editors). FIRST PRINTINGS OF AMERICAN AUTHORS. Volume 2. Detroit, Michigan: Gale Research Research Co., (1978).

(b) Inventory.

001a: GO IN BEAUTY Harper, New York (1956). [1] $60/300

001b: GO IN BEAUTY Secker & Warburg, London, 1957. [] $25/125

002a: THE BRONC PEOPLE Harcourt, New York (1958). [1] $40/200

002b: THE BRONC PEOPLE A. Deutsch, London, 1958. [] $25/100

003a: PORTRAIT OF AN ARTIST WITH TWENTY-SIX HORSES Simon & Schuster, New York, 1963. [1] $20/100

003b: PORTRAIT OF AN ARTIST WITH TWENTY-SIX HORSES Michael Joseph, London, 1965. [] $15/75

004a: CASTLE KEEP Simon & Schuster, New York (1965). [1] $12/60

004b: CASTLE KEEP Michael Joseph, London (1966). [] $10/50

005a: THE BAMBOO BED Simon & Schuster, New York (1969). [1] $15/75

005b: THE BAMBOO BED Michael Joseph, London (1970). [1] (Ref.b) $8/40

006a: A CHILD'S GARDEN OF VERSES FOR THE REVOLUTION Grove, New York (1970). [1] $10/50

007a: 3 BY EASTLAKE Simon & Schuster, New York (1970). [1] Wraps $30.

008a: DANCERS IN THE SCALP HOUSE Viking, New York (1975). [1] (Ref.b) $10/50

009a: THE LONG, NAKED DESCENT INTO BOSTON Viking, New York (1977). [] Unrevised proof in pictorial wraps (Wm. Reese Co. 5/92) $50.

009b: THE LONG, NAKED DESCENT INTO BOSTON Viking, New York (1977). [1] (Ref.b) $8/40

010a: JACK ARMSTRONG IN TANGIER Bamberger Books, Flint, Mich., 1984. [2] 50 sgd no. cc. Issued in cloth in dustwrapper. There were also 25 copies "Not For Sale" (ref.b) $70/100

010b: JACK ARMSTRONG IN TANGIER Bamberger Books, Flint, Mich., 1984. [2] 125 cc. Cloth in dustwrapper $35/60

010c: JACK ARMSTRONG IN TANGIER Bamberger Books, Flint, Mich., 1984. [2] 300 cc. Wraps $30.

011a: PRETTYFIELDS : A WORK IN PROGRESS Capra Press, Santa Barbara, 1987. [] Wraps. Bound with a Gerald Haslam title (Watermark West 12/89) $30.

F. SCOTT FITZGERALD
1896-1940

Fitzgerald was born in St. Paul, Minnesota. He attended Princeton and served in the Army during the teens. *This Side of Paradise* was published in 1920 and it was a great financial and critical success. He married Zelda the same year and they lived the "good" life, with homes on the Riviera, and in Paris, New York, Long Island and Washington.

He was very productive in the early 1920's, and by 1926 he had written seven of the nine books he would see published during his lifetime. After 1926, the financial and emotional demands on Fitzgerald increased as each year went by and as Zelda's mental state deteriorated.

The primary reference used for this guide is Matthew J. Bruccoli's bibliography which is an excellent one.

Ref.a is the source unless otherwise noted.

REFERENCE:

(a) Bruccoli, Matthew J. F. SCOTT FITZGERALD A DESCRIPTIVE BIBLIOGRAPHY. Revised Edition. (Pittsburgh): University of Pittsburgh Press, 1987.

001a: FIE! FIE! FI-FI! John Church Co., (Cincinnati / New York / London on cover) 1914. [0] Copyright notice on p.3 hand-corrected in ink "MCMXIV." White boards printed in black and orange. (Note: ref.a also notes (as Item A1) acting scripts in two volumes (Acts 1 & 2) in wraps with "Property of The Triangle Club Season 1914-15" which would precede this one volume edition) $2,000.

001b: FIE! FIE! FI-FI! *A Facsimile of the 1914 Acting Script and the Musical Score* University of South Carolina Press, Columbia, South Carolina, 1996. [2] 500 no. cc. Published at $49.95. There were also 50 out-of-series copies stamped "REVIEW COPY" (Southern First Editions 5/97) $50.

002a: THE EVIL EYE John Church Co., (Cincinnati / New York / London on cover), 1915. [0] White boards printed in black and orange. Some copies may have been bound in limp leather (ref.b) $2,250.

003a: SAFETY FIRST John Church Co., Cincinnati / New York / London (1916). [0] White boards printed in black, orange, red and blue $2,000.

004a: THIS SIDE OF PARADISE Charles Scribner's Sons, New York, 1920. [1] 3,000 cc. "Published April, 1920." Dustwrapper price: $1.75 also "$1.75 net" (ref.b). Priority undetermined. Green cloth. Scribner's seal on copyright page $1,000/10,000

004b: THIS SIDE OF PARADISE Charles Scribner's Sons, New York, 1920. [0] Approximately 500 cc (ref.b) with signed "Author's Apology" tipped in. This is 3rd printing: "Reprinted May 1920" $1,500/3,000

004c: THIS SIDE OF PARADISE W. Collins Sons, London (1921). [0] Blue cloth. Text varies unauthoritatively from the U.S. edition in some 850 readings $250/3,000

005a: FLAPPERS AND PHILOSOPHERS Charles Scribner's Sons, New York, 1920. [1] 5,000 cc. "Published September, 1920." Green linen-like grain cloth or vertical lines, priority undetermined. Scribner's seal on copyright page $750/10,000

005b: FLAPPERS AND PHILOSOPHERS W. Collins & Sons, London (1922). [0] Blue cloth. Numerous textual differences $300/1,500

006a: THE SAINT PAUL DAILY DIRGE (No-publisher, place, or date.) [0] Broadside written and privately printed as a joke. Distributed in 1922 in St. Paul, Minnesota $NVA

006b: THE SAINT PAUL DAILY DIRGE (Fitz-gerald Newsletter, Columbus, 1968.) [] 200 cc. Facsimile $100.

007a: THE BEAUTIFUL AND DAMNED Charles Scribner's Sons, New York, 1922. [1] 20,600 cc. "Published March, 1922." First printing of dustwrapper has book title on front in white outlined in black. Scribner's seal not on copyright page $400/6,000

007b: THE BEAUTIFUL AND DAMNED Charles Scribner's Sons, New York, 1922. [1] 19,750 cc. "Published March, 1922." Second printing has same title and copyright page except the latter has the Scribner seal. The second printing dustwrapper with the front title letters in black is a later dustwrapper per Bruccoli $100/1,750

007c: THE BEAUTIFUL AND THE DAMNED Copp, Clark Company, Toronto, 1922. [] First Canadian issue. Uses the American first printing sheets (Hugh Anson-Cartwright 4/97) $250/1,250

007d: THE BEAUTIFUL AND DAMNED W. Collins, London (1922). [0] Blue cloth $300/1,500

008a: TALES OF THE JAZZ AGE Charles Scribner's Sons, New York, 1922. [0] Dummy in green cloth with stylized "JAZZ" and blind-stamped saxophone player on front cover; in proof dustwrapper with blank flaps (Chapel Hill Rare Books 2/94) $7,500/15,000

008b: TALES OF THE JAZZ AGE Charles Scribner's Sons, New York, 1922. [1] 8,000 cc. "Published September, 1922." Green cloth. Scribner's seal on copyright page. There were three printings in 1922 and the only major difference was "and" for "an" at p.232:6 in the second and/or third printing (ref.b). Those printings were 3,000 copies each. There is confusion on this point because Ref.a appears to indicate that "and" was the first and changed to "an." (The sentence in question reads: “So you shall, an you give me pen, ink, a sheaf of paper, and a room to myself.”) We asked Mr. Bruccoli and his response was "copies with "an" and perfect type (at p.22:13, p.27:30, p.166:35, p.217:1, p.224:1 and p.252:1) are earlier than others. Therefore, this would imply that copies with "an" and battered type are second printings, and “and” and perfect type are third printings. $350/2,500

008c: TALES OF THE JAZZ AGE The Copp, Clark Company, Toronto, 1922. [] Green cloth. The copyright page erroneously carries the date "1902" (L & T Respess 11/95) $200/1,000

008d: TALES OF THE JAZZ AGE W. Collins, London / Glasgow... (1923). [0] Blue cloth $250/1,250

009a: THE VEGETABLE Charles Scribner's Sons, New York, 1923. [1] 7,650 cc. "Published April, 1923." Green cloth. Scribner's seal on copyright page $250/1,500

009b: THE VEGETABLE Charles Scribner's Sons, New York (1976). [3] Includes unpublished scenes and corrections (ref.b) $25/100

009c: THE VEGETABLE Charles Scribner's Sons, New York (1976). [3] Wraps $25.

010a: THE GREAT GATSBY Charles Scribner's Sons, New York, 1925. [0] 20,870 cc (a & b). Green cloth. First state of dustwrapper on back blurb (for *The Great Gatsby*) line 14 has lowercase "j" in "jay Gatsby" which is hand-corrected in ink in most copies; or over-stamped with a capital "J" which is obviously a different font. Front flap lists books by

Fitzgerald and back flap lists books by Lardner. First state of book includes the following differences: on p.60:16 "chatter" vs. "echolalia", p.119:22 "northern" vs. "southern", p.205:9-10 "sick in tired" vs. "sickantired", and p.211:7-8 "Union Street Station" vs. "Union Station." Scribner's seal on copyright page $1,250/25,000

010b: THE GREAT GATSBY Charles Scribner's Sons, New York, 1925. [0] Second state of dustwrapper has back blurb line 14 corrected to uppercase "J" in "Jay Gatsby," obviously reprinted in the same font $1,250/12,500

010c: THE GREAT GATSBY Charles Scribner's Sons, New York, 1925. [0] 3,000 cc. Second printing corrects the textual errors listed in 010a; otherwise, no difference in book. Dustwrapper has reviews on back flap and panel $250/5,000

010d: THE GREAT GATSBY Chatto & Windus, London (1926). [0] "Published 1926." Primary binding: dark blue cloth, spine stamped in gold. Also seen in tan cloth, stamped in black; also light blue cloth-like boards stamped in black, thought to be remainder binding. $500/5,000

010e: THE GREAT GATSBY Modern Library, New York (1934). [1] Approximately 5,000 cc. New introduction by author $30/150

010f: THE GREAT GATSBY Limited Editions Club, New York (1980). [2] 2,000 no. cc. signed by Fred Meyer (illustrator). Issued in slipcase $150/200

010g: THE GREAT GATSBY Arion Press, San Francisco, 1984. [2] 400 sgd no cc. Illustrated and signed by Michael Graves $400.

Note: Also see 048a

010h: THE GREAT GATSBY Scribner's, New York, 1991. [] First trade publication of the newly established critical text (Ian McKelvie 11/94) $10/35

011a: ALL THE SAD YOUNG MEN Charles Scribner's Sons, New York, 1926. [0] 10,100 cc. Green cloth. Earliest state of dustwrapper has woman's lips on front unbattered. Three printings in 1926 with no differences except type at p.38:6-9 (left), p. 248:21-24 (right) and the page number "90" is more battered on later printings. About 3,000 copies each in later printings $350/1,750

012a: JOHN JACKSON'S ARCADY Walter H. Baker, Boston (1928). [0] Wraps $1,500.

013a: TENDER IS THE NIGHT Charles Scribner's Sons, New York, 1934. [] Publisher's advance copy in stiff pictorial wraps (Heritage Book Shop 11/94) $7,500.

013b: TENDER IS THE NIGHT Charles Scribner's Sons, New York, 1934. [5] 7,600 cc. Green cloth. Dustwrapper (front flap) blurbs by Eliot, Mencken and Rosenfeld. Ref.b notes later dustwrapper with blurbs by Mary Colum, Gilbert Seldes and M. J. Rawlings. Terrell Wright noted a copy of the first edition in this later dustwrapper, which means it is a second issue dustwrapper (or somebody switched the dustwrapper) $500/6,500

013c: TENDER IS THE NIGHT Chatto & Windus, London, 1934. [0] Uncorrected proof bound in brown paperwraps. White label printed in black on front cover $3,500.

013d: TENDER IS THE NIGHT Chatto & Windus, London, 1934. [0] Blue cloth printed in yellow $150/1,500

013e: TENDER IS THE NIGHT Charles Scribner's Sons, New York, 1951. [0] 5,075 cc (d & e). With author's final revisions and preface by Malcolm Cowley. Copyright page has seal and 1948/51 dates but no "A". Tan cloth stamped in black and red. First state has the following errors: p.xi:18 "xett"; p.xiv:19 "tsandards"; p.xviii:23 "b each"; p.xviii:24 "accompanied". A publisher errata sheet was enclosed in review copies $75/300

013f: TENDER IS THE NIGHT Charles Scribner's Sons, New York, 1951. [0] Errors in text (see 013d) corrected on 3 cancel leaves. (One catalog {Puffer} noted a 1953 Scribner edition with all the errors but ref.a indicates this edition contained all the corrections) $30/150

013g: TENDER IS THE NIGHT The Grey Walls Press, London (1953). [0] "This new edition published in 1953." Pinkish-tan cloth or gold paper-covered boards. Priority undetermined. Contains Fitzgerald's final revisions and a preface by Malcolm Cowley. (Alice Robbins 11/94) $30/150

013h: TENDER IS THE NIGHT Limited Editions Club, New York, 1983. [2] 2,000 no cc signed by Fred Meyer (illustrator). Issued in slipcase $150/200

013i: TENDER IS THE NIGHT Samuel Johnson, London, 1995. [] Fewer than 30 cc. Spiral-bound wraps with clear acetate overlays. Text established by Matthew J. Bruccoli. "Reproduces the editor's marked copy of the first printing of *Tender is the Night*, providing the emendations necessary for a critical edition" (*i.e.* Fitzgerald's subsequent alterations and the editor's necessary corrections). Includes an appendix on the chronology of the novel. (Bertram Rota 10/95) $100.

013j: TENDER IS THE NIGHT Samuel Johnson, London, 1995. [] $6/30

014a: THE TRUE STORY OF APPOMATTOX (No publisher, place or date.) [0] A 38-line newspaper clipping made up for Fitzgerald by the *Baltimore Sun* in 1934 as a joke. May only be 3 copies (ref.b) $NVA

015a: TAPS AT REVEILLE Charles Scribner's Sons, New York, 1935. [5] 5,100 cc (a & b). Front flap unpriced or price rubber-stamped on front flap of some copies in two sizes: 3/16" and 1/8" high. First state pp.349-352 not canceled and p.351:29-30 reads "Oh, catch it - oh, catch it..." $450/2,000

015b: TAPS AT REVEILLE Charles Scribner's Sons, New York, 1935. [5] Dustwrapper price printed. Second state: pp.349-352 canceled; p.351:29-30 reads "Oh, things like that happen..." $150/1,500

016a: THE LAST TYCOON Charles Scribner's Sons, New York, 1941. [5] Blue cloth stamped in gold $100/750

016b: THE LAST TYCOON Grey Walls Press, London (1949). [1] Yellow cloth, spine stamped in gold $60/300

017a: THE CRACK-UP New Directions, no-place, (1945). [0] 2,520 cc. Paper covered boards with cloth spine. Title page printed in red-brown and black. Later printings have title page printed in black only and no colophon on p.348 $50/250

017b: THE CRACK-UP New Directions (no-place, or date). [0] First English issue of American copies. Paper label pasted on p.2 "This is a New Directions Book distributed through the British Empire..." $40/150

017c: THE CRACK-UP Penguin Books (Harmondsworth, 1965). [0] 35,000 cc. Wraps. "Published by Penguin Books 1965." Cover price: "3'6." First actual printing in England $35.

018a: THE PORTABLE F. SCOTT FITZGERALD Viking, New York, 1945. [1] "Published ... Sept. 1945." Selected by Dorothy Parker, introduction by John O'Hara. No new material $25/125

019a: THE DIAMOND AS BIG AS THE RITZ Armed Services Edition, New York (1946). [0] Wraps $200.

020a: THE STORIES OF F. SCOTT FITZGERALD Charles Scribner's, New York, 1951. [5] 7,510 cc. (28 stories.) Edited by Malcolm Cowley. First issue has Malcolm misspelled "Malcom" on spine $35/150

020b: THE STORIES OF F. SCOTT FITZGERALD Charles Scribner's, New York, 1951. [5] Second issue, "Malcolm" corrected $35/100

021a: BORROWED TIME Grey Walls Press, London, 1951. [1] Edited by Alan and Jennifer Ross. 9 stories $35/100

022a: THREE NOVELS *The Great Gatsby, Tender is the Night, The Last Tycoon* Charles Scribner's Sons, New York (1953). [] (Boston Book Company 10/95) $20/60

023a: BABYLON REVISITED AND WINTER DREAMS Kenkyusha, Tokyo (1955). [] Wraps. First separate edition with introduction and notes by Ikuo Uemura $150.

023b: BABYLON REVISITED ... Scribner, New York (1960). [5] "A-8.60 (C)." Wraps. No new material $60.

024a: AFTERNOON OF AN AUTHOR Princeton University Library, Princeton, 1957. [0] 1,500 cc $40/200

024b: AFTERNOON OF AN AUTHOR Charles Scribner's Sons, New York (1958). [5] "A-2.58 [MH]" $25/100

024c: AFTERNOON OF AN AUTHOR The Bodley Head, London (1958). [1] 5,000 cc $25/100

025a: THE BODLEY HEAD SCOTT FITZ-GERALD The Bodley Head, London, 1958-63. [] 6 vols. In dustwrappers (Boston Book Company 1/97) $150/450

026a: SIX TALES OF THE JAZZ AGE Scribner, New York (1960). [5] "A-1.60(H)." Includes *Stories from the Jazz Age* and *All the Sad Young Men.* No new material $25/125

027a: THE MYSTERY OF THE RAYMOND MORTGAGE Random House, New York, 1960. [2] 750 cc. Gray-blue wraps (Pepper & Stern 11/86) mentions publisher's letter and mailing envelope. Letter is dated September 2, 1960 - "An F. Scott Fitzgerald first edition..." $350.

028a: THE PAT HOBBY STORIES Charles Scribner's Sons, New York (1962). [] Uncorrected galley proofs. Loose sheets punched at top and string tied in plain wraps with printed label (Wm. Reese Co. 2/90) $1,250.

028b: THE PAT HOBBY STORIES Charles Scribner's Sons, New York (1962). [5] 8,000 cc. "A-6.62(V)" $20/100

028c: THE PAT HOBBY STORIES Penguin Books (Harmondsworth, 1967). [0] 30,000 cc. Wraps. "Published by Penguin Books 1967" Price: "4s 6d" $35.

029a: THE FITZGERALD READER Scribners, New York, 1963. [] Galley proof in plain wraps spiral bound at top (Wm. Reese Co. 5/92) $600.

029b: THE FITZGERALD READER Scribners, New York, 1963. [0] "3.63(H)." Edited by Arthur Mizener $25/100

030a: LETTER TO MAXWELL PERKINS (Scribner's, New York, 1963.) [0] Facsimile letter from Fitzgerald to Maxwell Perkins, 18 Sept. 1919.

Four leaves printed in blue ink on white wove paper. Promotion for item 031. See also items 037 and 055 $175.

031a: THE LETTERS OF F. SCOTT FITZGERALD Charles Scribner's Sons, New York (1963). [] Galley proof in two volumes spiral bound with paper label. Introduction by Andrew Turnbull laid in (Wm. Reese Co. 11/90) $750.

031b: THE LETTERS OF F. SCOTT FITZGERALD Charles Scribner's Sons, New York (1963). [5] 10,000 cc. "A-9.63(V)." Edited and introduction by Andrew Turnbull $25/100

031c: THE LETTERS OF F. SCOTT FITZGERALD Bodley Head, London (1964). [1] 4,000 cc $15/75

032a: TURKEY REMAINS (Cooper & Beatty, Toronto, 1965.) [0] 2,000 cc. Wraps $300.

033a: THE APPRENTICE FICTION OF F. SCOTT FITZGERALD 1909-1917 Rutgers University Press, New Brunswick (1965). [0] 5,000 cc $25/100

034a: THOUGHTBOOK OF FRANCIS SCOTT KEY FITZGERALD Princeton University Library, Princeton, 1965. [2] 300 cc. In glassine dustwrapper $250.

035a: LETTERS TO HIS DAUGHTER Scribners, New York (1965). [5] "A-8.65(V)." Introduction by Scottie Fitzgerald $25/100

036a: EXHIBITION CATALOGUE Ohio State University Library, no place, 1965. [2] 25 sgd no cc. Published in December 1965. An exhibition catalog marking the 25th anniversary of Fitzgerald's death. A single sheet folded twice to make 6 pages. Assume signed by Bruccoli since it is his collection. First printing of 4 Fitzgerald inscriptions $300.

036b: EXHIBITION CATALOGUE Ohio State University Library, no place, 1965. [2] 225 cc $75.

037a: LETTER TO PERKINS Charles Scribner's Sons, no place, 1967. [0] Broadside which prints facsimile of Fitzgerald letter to Maxwell E. Perkins, March 1920. Printed in black on gray wove paper. Distributed at fiftieth reunion of Fitzgerald's class. Not included in *The Letters...* (031). Also see 030 and 055 . $250.

038a: DEARLY BELOVED Windhover Press / University of Iowa, Iowa City, 1969. [2] 30 sgd no. cc. Signed by the artist, B. Burford. Copies numbered 1-30. Issued without dustwrapper $350.

038b: DEARLY BELOVED Windhover Press / University of Iowa, Iowa City, 1969. [2] 270 no. cc. Copies numbered 31-270. Issued without dustwrapper $150.

039a: "AND A FEW MISSING WORDS WOULD MEAN SO MUCH" Privately printed, London, 1970. [2] 200 sgd cc. Single sheet folded, signed (initialed) by Bruccoli $150.

040a: F SCOTT FITZGERALD IN HIS OWN TIME Kent State University Press, no place (1971). [1] 2,500 cc. Edited by M.J. Bruccoli and Jackson Bryer. Issued without dustwrapper $100.

041a: CRAZY SUNDAYS *F. Scott in Hollywood* Viking, New York, 1971. [1] By Aaron Latham. Includes previously unpublished material from letters, notes and scripts $25/100

041b: CRAZY SUNDAYS *F. Scott in Hollywood* Secker & Warburg, London (1972) $25/75

042a: DEAR SCOTT / DEAR MAX Chas. Scribner's Sons, New York (1971). [5] 6,000 cc. "A-10.71(H)." Edited by John Kuehl and Jackson Bryer $25/75

042b: DEAR SCOTT / DEAR MAX Cassell, London (1973). [1] 3,000 cc $15/60

043a: F. SCOTT FITZGERALD AND ERNEST HEMINGWAY IN PARIS *An Exhibition* Bruccoli-Clark, Bloomfield Hills / Columbia, 1972. [0] Wraps. Introduction by Scottie (Frances Scott Fitzgerald Smith) $75.

044a: AS EVER, SCOTT FITZ Lippincott, Philadelphia ./ New York (1972). [] 22 cc. In printed wraps for review. Edited by M.J. Bruccoli $350.

044b: AS EVER, SCOTT FITZ Lippincott, Philadelphia / New York (1972). [1] 5,000 cc. Edited by M.J. Bruccoli with Jennifer Atkinson. Foreword by Scottie Fitzgerald Smith $25/75

044c: AS EVER, SCOTT FITZ Woburn Press, London, 1973. [1] 2,000 cc $25/75

045a: THREE HOURS BETWEEN PLANES (Book Society of Canada, Ltd., no place, 1970). [0] Folio punched for loose leaf binding. Pages 1-3 text; p.4 teaching material. Accompanied by single-leaf commentary $NVA

046a: THE BASIL AND JOSEPHINE STORIES (Charles Scribner's Sons, New York, 1973.) [5] Wraps. Xeroxed galleys bound in very light blue-green wraps with white label on front printed in black $450.

046b: THE BASIL AND JOSEPHINE STORIES (Charles Scribner's Sons, New York, 1973.) [3] 10,000 cc. Edited and introduction by Jackson R. Bryer and John Kuehl $15/75

047a: F. SCOTT FITZGERALD'S LEDGER NCR / Microcard, Washington, D.C. (1972). [2] 1,000 no. cc. (Actually published September 1973 although

1972 stated.) Issued in coated black paper slipcase without dustwrapper. Introduction by Matthew J. Bruccoli $150.

048a: THE GREAT GATSBY: *A Facsimile of the Manuscript* Microcard Editions, Washington, DC, 1973. [2] 2,000 no cc. In white cloth slipcase with dustwrapper. Edited and introduction by M.J. Bruccoli $150/200.

049a: BITS OF PARADISE Bodley Head, London / Sydney / Toronto (1973). [1] 5,000 cc. Selected by M.J. Bruccoli and Scottie Fitzgerald, who also contributed a foreword $25/100

049b: BITS OF PARADISE Chas. Scribner's Sons, New York (1974). [3] 6,000 cc $25/100

050a: PREFACE TO THIS SIDE OF PARADISE Windhover Press, Iowa City, 1975. [2] 150 cc. Assume issued without dustwrapper $275.

051a: TRIMALCHIO Grolier Club, New York, 1975. [2] 300 cc. Long broadside printed on both sides reproducing a page of the galley proof of *The Great Gatsby* under original title on one side and Bruccoli's collection on the other side $125.

052a: THE CRUISE OF THE ROLLING JUNK Bruccoli Clark, Bloomfield Hills / Columbia, 1976. [0] 1,000 cc $35/125

053a: F. SCOTT FITZGERALD'S SCREENPLAY FOR THREE COMRADES Southern Illinois University Press, Carbondale / Edwardsville (1978). [0] By Erich Maria Remarque. 2,000 cc in cloth. $35/100

053b: F SCOTT FITZGERALD'S SCREENPLAY FOR THREE COMRADES Southern Illinois University Press, Carbondale / Edwardsville (1978). [0] 3,000 cc. Wraps. Published simultaneously $40.

054a: THE NOTEBOOKS OF F. SCOTT FITZGERALD Harcourt Brace / Bruccoli Clark, New York (1978). [4] 5,000 cc $15/75

055a: LETTER TO PERKINS (M.J. Bruccoli, Columbia, S.C., 1978.) [2] 500 cc. Single sheet printed on both sides. See also 030 and 037 $60.

056a: FROM THE NOTEBOOKS OF F. SCOTT FITZGERALD Harcourt, no place (1978). [] Single sheet printed on both sides (Waiting For Godot 6/94) $60.

057a: F. SCOTT FITZGERALD'S ST. PAUL PLAYS 1911-1914 Princeton University Library, Princeton, 1978. [0] 2,500 cc. Edited and introduction by Alan Margolies $15/75

058a: THE PRICE WAS HIGH Harcourt Brace / Bruccoli Clark, New York / London (1979). [] Uncorrected proof in printed blue wraps (Waiting For Godot 2/90) $200.

058b: THE PRICE WAS HIGH Harcourt Brace / Bruccoli Clark, New York / London (1979). [4] 15,000 cc. Edited by M.J. Bruccoli $10/50

058c: THE PRICE WAS HIGH Quartet Books, London / Melbourne / New York (1979). [1] 5,000 cc (c & d). First state: p.177 duplicated p.162 $20/60

058d: THE PRICE WAS HIGH Quartet Books, London / Melbourne / New York (1979). [1] Second state: corrects above error $6/40

059a: CORRESPONDENCE OF F. SCOTT FITZGERALD Random House, New York (1980). [] (Phoenix Bookshop) $10/50

060a: POEMS 1911-1940 Bruccoli Clark (Bloomfield Hills, 1981). [2] 100 sgd no cc. Edited and signed by James Dickey $250.

060b: POEMS 1911-1940 Bruccoli Clark (Bloomfield Hills, 1981). [] Trade edition $10/50

061a: CHRISTMAS RECALLED Arion Press, San Francisco, 1983. [] Single sheet folded, issued as Season's Greeting (Chloe's Books #27) $60.

062a: F. SCOTT FITZGERALD ON WRITING Scribner's, New York (1985). [] Edited by Larry Phillips. (Pepper & Stern List T) $10/40

062b: ON WRITING Equation, London, 1988 [] $10/50

063a: THE SHORT STORIES OF F. SCOTT FITZGERALD *A New Collection* Scribners, New York (1989). [] Edited by Matthew Bruccoli. Uncorrected proof in two volumes. Yellow-gold wraps (Waiting For Godot 2/92) $200.

063b: THE SHORT STORIES OF F. SCOTT FITZGERALD *A New Collection* Scribners, New York (1989). [] $10/40

063c: THE SHORT STORIES OF F. SCOTT FITZGERALD: *A New Collection* Scribners, London, 1989. [] Scribner proofs in blue wraps. "Printed in Great Britain" and giving provisional price in pounds (Alphabet Books 8/92) $150.

063d: THE SHORT STORIES OF F. SCOTT FITZGERALD: *A New Collection* Scribners, London, 1989. [] $10/40

064a: FANTASY AND MYSTERY STORIES... Hale, London (1991). [] Selected and introduced by Peter Haining $10/40

065a: THE LOVE OF THE LAST TYCOON *A Western* Cambridge University Press, Cambridge, 1993. [] A 1940 work edited by Matthew J. Bruccoli. (Published 12/93 at $34.95) $10/35

066a: A LIFE IN LETTERS Scribner's, New York, 1994. [] Uncorrected proof in yellow wraps (Waverley Books 5/94) $75.

066b: A LIFE IN LETTERS Scribner's, New York, 1994. [] (Published 7/94 at $30.00) $6/30

067a: LOVE IN THE NIGHT Ebury Press Limited, London?, 1994. [] $10/40

067b: LOVE IN THE NIGHT Clarkson Potter / Publishers, New York, 1995. [3] Also states "FIRST AMERICAN EDITION." Pictorial paper-covered boards with red ribbon ties. The book was issued sealed with a white paper band printed in red and blue. The band reads, in part: "This Greetings book is already wrapped for you to give. Undo the ribbons, remove this band, and write your greeting in the space provided on page 3. Then retie the ribbons in a bow, and your gift is complete." Issued without dustwrapper. Published at $10.00 $25.

068a: F. SCOTT FITZGERALD ON AUTHORSHIP University of South Carolina Press, Columbia, South Carolina, 1996? [] Published at $29.95 $6/30

IAN FLEMING
1908-1964

Fleming was born in London, educated at Eton College and the Royal Military Academy; and studied at the University of Munich and the University of Geneva.

He was Moscow Correspondent for Reuters and later *The Times* from 1929 to 1933. He worked for a firm of merchant bankers and as a stock broker from 1933 to 1939. He served as personal assistant to the Director of Naval Intelligence from 1939 to 1945.

After the war he worked as Foreign Manager for *Kemsley* (later *Thomson*) *Newspapers,* and from 1949 to 1964 published the *Book Collector* (London).

The continued interest in the Bond books may be based on the fact that the:

> "..novels are a perfect example of the right thing at the right time, as appropriate an expression and index of their age as, for example, the Sherlock Holmes stories or the novels of Dashiell Hammett... his powerful influence over writers who follow him, and his union of the fantastic and the absolutely real deserve serious and careful study... (which) may eventually establish Ian Fleming as one of the most appropriate writers of his time."
>
> -George Grella (ref.c)

(The movies haven't hurt either.)

REFERENCES:

(a) Penzler, Otto. "James Bond - Collecting Mystery Fiction" in *The Armchair Detective*, Fall 1984 (no first edition identification included).

(b) Campbell, Iain. IAN FLEMING: *A Catalogue of A Collection.*

(c) Reilly, John M. (editor). TWENTIETH CENTURY CRIME AND MYSTERY WRITERS. New York: St. Martin's Press (1985).

(d) Penzler, Otto. "Ian Fleming's James Bond- Collecting Mystery Fiction" in *The Armchair Detective*, Winter 1996, vol. 29, no. 1. A revision of ref.a.

We would also like to thank Mike Van Blaricum for sharing his knowledge on many of the issue points.

001a: CASINO ROYALE Cape, London (1953). [1] 4,750 cc. Bottom front flap of dustwrapper blank except for price (later printings had a review from the *Sunday Times*). First state of dustwrapper has two paragraph summary followed by "Jacket devised by the author" (Mordida Books 5/96) $500/7,500

001b: CASINO ROYALE Cape, London (1953). [] States "Second Printing" on copyright page. Dustwrapper adds "The Author" under drawing of Fleming on back panel and review from the *Sunday Times* on front flap $50/600

001c: CASINO ROYALE Macmillan, New York, 1954. [1] Dustwrapper front flaps are complete (the scarcer of the two states) (ref.d). Van Blaricom has Fleming's agent's copy which is clipped with the price of $2.75 at top, which looks as if it may have been stamped. His copy with the flaps unclipped is priced $2.75 at bottom of front flap, which would indicate to us that the clipped dustwrapper is actually the first issue. Ref.d assumes the clipped version is later. So, for either issue $150/1,250

001d: YOU ASKED FOR IT Popular Library, New York (1955). [] Wraps. New title $150.

002a: LIVE AND LET DIE Cape, London (1954). [] 50-150 cc (estimated by Steven Temple). Uncorrected proof in gray card cover wraps printed in black, with publisher's fact sheet tipped inside front cover (Steven Temple Books 6/95) $5,000.

002b: LIVE AND LET DIE Cape, London (1954). [1] 7,500 cc. First state dustwrapper does not credit dustwrapper artist or designer Kenneth Lewis on front flap (ref.d) $250/3,500

002c: LIVE AND LET DIE Cape, London (1954). [1] Second state dustwrapper with the words "Jacket devised by the author | and executed by Kenneth Lewis" on front flap in two lines approximately mid-way between the end of the dustwrapper blurb and the bottom of the front flap (ref.d, Hawthorn Books 1/96) $250/1,500

002c: LIVE AND LET DIE Cape, London (1954). [1] Third state of dustwrapper has the words "Jacket devised by the author | and executed by Kenneth Lewis" printed directly below the text on the front flap (ref.d) $250/750

002d LIVE AND LET DIE Macmillan, New York, 1955. [1] $100/600

003a: MOONRAKER Jonathan Cape, London (1955). [] Trial binding of light blue, lettered in silver. With "Jonathan Cape" at foot of spine rather than Cape logo. The book is slightly smaller than the published version and the top edges are stained yellow (Nigel Williams 10/96, a copy offered without dustwrapper). We assume trial dustwrapper also, although not reported $750/4,000

003b: MOONRAKER Cape, London (1955). [1] An "early state" in thinner binding with misprints p.10:31, "shoo" is the last word of the line; p.22:22, quotation marks missing before "well"; p.236:23, "a" vs. "all"; p.167:17, quotation marks missing before "It's" (Geir Andreassen). Spine measures 19 mm across spine (James M. Picard 7/97) $200/3,000

003c: MOONRAKER Macmillan, New York, 1955. [1] $150/750

003d: TOO HOT TO HANDLE Permabooks, New York, 1957. [] Wraps. New title. Text differs from 003a and b, as it was Americanized $200.

004a: DIAMONDS ARE FOREVER Cape, London (1956). [1] 12,500 cc $250/1,750

004b: DIAMONDS ARE FOREVER Macmillan, New York, 1956. [1] $75/500

005a: FROM RUSSIA WITH LOVE Cape, London (1957). [1] Noted with gilt lettering on spine (Edna Whiteson #118 "true first"). It normally has the title in red and name and Cape logo in silver, and we have never seen the one with gilt, nor could we find anyone else who had, so it must be rare and would be worth more $150/1,000

005b: FROM RUSSIA WITH LOVE Macmillan, New York, 1957. [1] $50/350

006a: THE DIAMOND SMUGGLERS Cape, London (1957). [1] Spine lettered in gilt (Maurice Neville 2/89) $75/250

006b: THE DIAMOND SMUGGLERS Cape, London (1957). [1] Spine lettered in white $25/175

006c: THE DIAMOND SMUGGLERS Macmillan, New York, 1958. [1] $30/150

007a: DR. NO Cape, London (1958). [] Uncorrected proof with standard Cape wraps with logo design $2,000.

007b: DR. NO Cape, London (1958). [] Uncorrected proof with woman's figure/silhouette on cover. "It was feared that this silhouette proof might be taken for a paperback so they abandoned it for a standard Cape proof format" (Ergo Books). However, Van Blaricum has both formats and believes this came after the standard proof $750.

007c: DR. NO Cape, London (1958). [1] Front cover stamped with woman's figure or blank, no clear priority. Ref.a states that both bindings occur on the later printings and the blank cover seems to be scarcer, while ref.b states that the silhouette is scarcer and later impressions all have plain front covers (at least one second printing has been seen with silhouette). $150/750

007d: DR. NO Macmillan, New York, 1958. [1] $50/250

008a: GOLDFINGER Cape, London, 1959. [] Uncorrected proof in greenish-yellow wraps, the Cape logo printed in white, with black lettering (ref.d) $1,250.

008b: GOLDFINGER Cape, London (1959)[1] $150/750

008c: GOLDFINGER Macmillan, New York, 1959. [1] Printed and bound in England (thus, for what it's worth, the Book Club is actually the first American printing!) $50/350

009a: THE EDUCATION OF A POKER PLAYER Cape, London, 1959. [1] Introduction by Fleming to Herbert Yardley's book $40/200

010a: FOR YOUR EYES ONLY *Five Secret Occasions in the Life of James Bond* Cape, London (1960). [1] $50/350

010b: FOR YOUR EYES ONLY *Five Secret Occasions in the Life of James Bond* Viking, New York, 1960. [1] "Published in 1960 by..." on copyright page $40/200

011a: THUNDERBALL Cape, London (1961). [] Uncorrected proof in greenish-yellow wraps, the

Cape logo printed in white, with black lettering (ref.d) $1,500.

011b: THUNDERBALL Cape, London (1961). [1] $50/300

011c: THUNDERBALL Viking, New York, 1961. [1] "Published in 1961 by.." $30/150

012a: GILT-EDGED BONDS Macmillan, New York, 1961. [1] Contains *Casino Royale*, *From Russia With Love*, and *Dr. No*. Introduction by Paul Gallico $25/125

013a: THE SPY WHO LOVED ME Cape, London (1962). [1] Uncorrected proof in wraps. "FLEMING" on title page correctly printed $1,000.

013b: THE SPY WHO LOVED ME Cape, London (1962). [1] First issue with "FLEMING" on title page correctly printed. "Published in 1962 by ..." (ref.d) $50/300

013c: THE SPY WHO LOVED ME Cape, London (1962). [1] Later issue with printer's error on title page. Line between "e" and "m" in "Fleming." Proof copies do not have error (ref.d). $25/200

013d: THE SPY WHO LOVED ME Viking, New York (1962). [1] $20/100

014a: AIRLINE DETECTIVE Collins, London, 1962. [0] Donald Fish's first book. Foreword by Fleming $15/75

014b: THE LAWLESS SKY Putnam, New York (1962). [1] Fish's book, new title $12/60

015a: ON HER MAJESTY'S SECRET SERVICE Cape, London (1963). [2] 250 sgd no. cc. In black cloth with a white leather spine, issued in plain plastic/acetate dustwrapper without a slipcase. Note: There were also a few copies specially bound and signed by the author and reserved for friends of the author and publisher. These are identical to the edition of 250 sgd no cc issued at the same time except they are marked" For Presentation" (Detering Book Gallery 12/94) $4,500.

015b: ON HER MAJESTY'S SECRET SERVICE Cape, London (1963). [1] $40/200

015c: ON HER MAJESTY'S SECRET SERVICE New American Library (New York, 1963). [1] $20/100

016a: THRILLING CITIES Cape, London (1963). [0] Erratum slip tipped in at end $25/100

016b: THRILLING CITIES New American Library (New York, 1964). [1] $25/75

017a: ALL NIGHT AT MR. STANYHURST'S Cape, London, 1963. [] Reissue of Hugh Edward's book with introduction by Fleming $15/75

017b: ALL NIGHT AT MR. STANYHURST'S Macmillan, New York (1963). [1] English sheets without price on dustwrapper $10/50

018a: THE IVORY HAMMER *The Year at Sotheby's* Longmans Green (London, 1963). [1] "The Property of a Lady" a specially commissioned James Bond story is included. Issued in dustwrapper (story is included in the Signet edition of *Octopussy*. See 023c) $40/125

018b: THE IVORY HAMMER *The Year at Sotheby's* Holt, New York (1964). [1] $30/100

019a: YOU ONLY LIVE TWICE Cape, London (1964). [1] First issue with "First published 1964" (ref.d) $35/150

019b: YOU ONLY LIVE TWICE Cape, London (1964). [1] Second issue with "First published in March 1964" (ref.d) $15/100

019c: YOU ONLY LIVE TWICE New American Library (New York, 1964). [1] $15/75

020a: CHITTY-CHITTY-BANG-BANG *The Magical Car Adventure* Number 1 (Cape, London, 1964.) [1] $25/125

020b: CHITTY-CHITTY-BANG-BANG *The Magical Car Adventure* Number 2 Jonathan Cape, London, 1964. [] Corrected proof in stapled wraps utilizing the trimmed dustwrapper of the published book (Alphabet Bookshop 7/95) $750.

020c: CHITTY-CHITTY-BANG-BANG *The Magical Car Adventure* Number 2 (Cape, London, 1964.) [1] $25/125

020d: CHITTY-CHITTY-BANG-BANG *The Magical Car Adventure* Number 3 (Cape, London, 1965.) [1] $25/125

The three volumes together: $100/400

020e: CHITTY-CHITTY-BANG-BANG Random House, New York (1964). [1] 3 volumes in one. Presumed first issue in red cloth stamped in gold, with pictorial endpapers. "A Random House Book" on back of dustwrapper. 6-line entry on copyright page and 21-line dedication including "PS." Dustwrapper priced $3.50. There are reprints without "First Printing" on copyright page $25/125

020f: CHITTY-CHITTY-BANG-BANG Random House, New York (1964). [1] Presumed second issue/printing in red cloth stamped in either gold or black. Priced at either $3.50 or $3.95. 5 or 6-line entry on copyright page (no Library of Congress) and 16-line dedication without "PS." Still states "First Printing" on copyright page $15/75

020g: THE COMPLETE ADVENTURES OF THE MAGICAL CAR (Cape, London, 1971.) [1] "Omnibus Edition First Published 1971" $15/75

021a: THE MAN WITH THE GOLDEN GUN Cape, London, 1965. [] Uncorrected proof in white wraps printed in light olive-green and black (Robert Temple 2/93, "Campbell does not mention a proof") $500.

021b: THE MAN WITH THE GOLDEN GUN Cape, London (1965). [1] With gilt embossed gun on front cover said to be rarest of all Bond first editions. It is reported that 1,000 copies in this binding were produced for export to South Africa and Australia (ref.d) $3,500/3,600

021c: THE MAN WITH THE GOLDEN GUN Cape, London (1965). [1] Second issue without gun on front cover, patterned green and white endpapers and title in one line on half-title $25/75

021d: THE MAN WITH THE GOLDEN GUN Cape, London (1965). [1] Presumed third issue with white endpapers and title in two lines on half title (Steven Temple 12/88). The proof had the title in one line on the half title and have seen second printings with half title in two lines, so assume this would be a third issue $10/50

021e THE MAN WITH THE GOLDEN GUN New American Library (New York, 1965). [1] $12/60

022a: MORE GILT-EDGES BONDS Macmillan, New York (1965). [1] Contains *Live and Let Die*, *Moonraker* and *Diamonds Are Forever* $25/75

023a: BONDED FLEMING... Viking, New York (1965). [1] "Published in 1965 by Viking." Contains *For Your Eyes Only*, *Thunderball* and *The Spy Who Loved Me* $10/50

024a: IAN FLEMING INTRODUCES JAMAICA Deutsch (London, 1965). [1] Edited by Morris Cargill $15/75

024b: IAN FLEMING INTRODUCES JAMAICA Hawthorne, New York (1966). [0] Edited by Morris Cargill $15/75

025a: OCTOPUSSY AND THE LIVING DAYLIGHTS Cape, London (1966). [] Uncorrected proof in printed wraps in dustwrapper. "Proof Only" with provisional publication date of 6/23/66 (Michael Thompson 7/91) $450.

025b: OCTOPUSSY AND THE LIVING DAYLIGHTS Cape, London (1966). [1] Sticker price of "16s in UK only 80p net" was added later. Also noted with sticker reading "J Cape Net UK Only £4.95" (Colophon Book Shop 4/96) $8/50

025c: OCTOPUSSY New American Library (New York, 1966) $8/50

025d: OCTOPUSSY Pan, Toronto, 1967, [] Wraps. First edition to add "The Property of a Lady" $60.

025e: OCTOPUSSY Signet Books, New York, 1967. [] Wraps. Also contained first U.S. book appearance of "The Property of a Lady" $50.

026a: A JAMES BOND OMNIBUS Cape, London, 1973. [1] Includes *Live and Let Die*, *Diamonds Are Forever* and *Dr. No* $25/75

027a: (FLEMING) OMNIBUS EDITION Heinemann / Octopus, London, 1978. [] Includes *Moonraker*, *From Russia With Love*, *Dr. No*, *Goldfinger*, *Thunderball*, and *On Her Majesty's Secret Service* $25/50

027b: (FLEMING) OMNIBUS EDITION Heinemann / Octopus (New York, 1980). [1] Includes *Casino Royale, From Russia With Love, Live and Let Die, Dr. No*, and *Goldfinger* $20/40

027c: JAMES BOND 007 Avenel, New York, 1988. [] Contains six books. Assume reprint of 027b $15/30

For the "Bond" completist, James Bond "books" are noted:

Amis, Kingsley THE JAMES BOND DOSSIER Cape, London (1965).

Markham, Robert (Kingsley Amis). COLONEL SUN Cape, London / Harper, New York 1968

John Gardner. (Cape/Hodder & Stoughton, London. Or Putnam, New York)

(1) LICENSE RENEWED 1981
(2) FOR SPECIAL SERVICES 1982
(3) ICEBREAKER 1983
(4) ROLE OF HONOUR 1984
(5) NOBODY LIVES FOREVER 1986
(6) NO DEALS MR. BOND 1987
(7) SCORPIUS 1988
(8) WIN, LOSE OR DIE 1989
(9) BROKEN CLAW 1990
(10) THE MAN FROM BARBAROSSA 1991
(11) DEATH IS FOREVER 1992
(12) NEVER SEND FLOWERS 1993
(13) SEAFIRE Putnam 1994 (8/94 @ $18.95)
(14) GOLDENEYE 1995
(15) COLDFALL 1996

DICK FRANCIS

Francis was born in Temby, Pembrokeshire, England in 1920. He served as a flying officer in the Royal Air Force during World War II. He was an Amateur National Hunt steeplechase jockey from 1946 to 1948, when he turned professional. Francis was a professional jockey from 1948 to 1957 and then Racing Correspondent of the London *Sunday Express* from 1957 to 1973. The number of people collecting Francis first editions has increased considerably in recent years.

001a: THE SPORT OF QUEENS Michael Joseph, London (1957). [1] $200/1,000

001b: THE SPORT OF QUEENS Michael Joseph, London (1957). [1] Second issue dustwrapper with reviews of this book printed on the front flap (Nigel Williams 7/96) $200/750

001c: THE SPORT OF QUEENS Michael Joseph, London (1968). [1] "This Revised Edition 1968" $50/250

001d: THE SPORT OF QUEENS Harper, New York (1969). [1] $50/250

001e: THE SPORT OF QUEENS Pan, London (1974). [] Wraps. Second revised edition $50.

001f: THE SPORT OF QUEENS Penzler, New York (1993). [2] 100 sgd no. cc. Issued without dustwrapper. In slipcase $50/125

002a: DEAD CERT Michael Joseph, London (1962). [1] $600/6,000

002b: DEAD CERT Holt, New York (1962). [1] $250/1,500

002c: DEAD CERT The Armchair Detective, New York, 1989. [2] 26 sgd ltr cc (Buckingham Books 4/91) $300/350

002d: DEAD CERT The Armchair Detective, New York, 1989. [2] 100 sgd no. cc. Issued in slipcase (Vagabond 9/89) $150/200

003a: NERVE Michael Joseph, London (1964). [1] First printing dustwrapper has only one paragraph (13 lines) on front flap. (Second printing dustwrapper has three paragraphs) $250/1,250

003b: NERVE Harper, New York (1964). [1] $150/600

003c: NERVE The Armchair Detective, New York, 1990. [2] 26 sgd ltr cc. Issued without dustwrapper. In slipcase $250/300

003d: NERVE The Armchair Detective NY 1990 [2] 100 sgd no. cc Issued without dustwrapper. In slipcase $100/150

004a: FOR KICKS Michael Joseph, London (1965). [1] $250/1,250

004b: FOR KICKS Harper, New York (1965). [1] $100/400

004c: FOR KICKS The Armchair Detective, New York, 1990. [2] 26 sgd ltr cc. Issued without dustwrapper. In slipcase. New introduction by Stephen Dobyns (also signed by him) $200/250

004d: FOR KICKS The Armchair Detective, New York, 1990. [2] 100 sgd no. cc. Issued without dustwrapper. In slipcase. New introduction by Stephen Dobyns (also signed by him) $50/100

005a: ODDS AGAINST Michael Joseph, London (1965). [] Uncorrected proof in buff wraps (Robert Temple 12/90) $1,000.

005b: ODDS AGAINST Michael Joseph, London (1965). [1] $150/750

005c: ODDS AGAINST Harper, New York (1966). [1] First printing dustwrapper does not have 3 reviews on front flap (Else Fine List 21) $60/300

005d: ODDS AGAINST The Armchair Detective, New York, 1991. [2] 26 sgd ltr cc. Introduction by Robert Reeves, also signed by him $150/200

005e: ODDS AGAINST The Armchair Detective, New York, 1991. [2] 100 sgd no. cc. Introduction by Robert Reeves, also signed by him $50/100

006a: FLYING FINISH Michael Joseph, London (1966). [1] $100/500

006b: FLYING FINISH Harper, New York (1967). [] Uncorrected proof in blue printed wraps with plastic spiral spine (Serendipity 5/89) $250.

006c: FLYING FINISH Harper, New York (1967). [1] $50/250

006d: FLYING FINISH The Armchair Detective, New York, 1991. [2] 100 sgd no. cc $50/100

007a: THE WILL TO WIN Doubleday, Garden City, 1966. [1] Book by Jane McIlvaine. Foreword by Dick Francis $25/100

008a: BEST RACING AND CHASING STORIES Volume I. Faber, London (1966). [1] Edited by Francis and John Welcome. (Published 9/1/66 @ 21 shillings per review slip) $25/125

009a: BLOOD SPORT Michael Joseph, London (1967). [1] $60/400

009b: BLOOD SPORT Harper, New York (1967). [1] $40/200

009c: BLOOD SPORT The Armchair Detective, New York, 1992. [2] 100 sgd no. cc. Issued without dustwrapper. In slipcase $50/75

010a: FORFEIT Michael Joseph, London (1968). [] $75/500

010b: FORFEIT Harper NY 1969 [1] Correct first issue with the code "A-T". Black endpapers (Malcolm and Christine Bell 5/98) $30/150

010c: FORFEIT Harper, NY, 1969 [1] Presumed second issued noted with the code "D-T" "Harper Suspense" endpapers $5/25

011a: ENQUIRY Joseph, London (1969). [1] $60/350

011b: ENQUIRY Harper, New York, 1969. [1] $25/125

012a: BEST RACING AND CHASING STORIES Volume II. Faber, London (1969) [1] Edited by Francis and John Welcome $25/125

013a: THE RACING MAN'S BEDSIDE BOOK Faber, London (1969). [1] Edited by Francis and John Welcome $25/125

014a: THREE TO SHOW Harper, New York (1969). [1] Includes *Dead Cert*, *Nerve* and *Odds Against* $25/75

015a: RAT RACE Michael Joseph, London (1970). [1] Noted in wrap-around band announcing that Francis won an Edgar Award (James Pepper 10/96) $50/200

015b: RAT RACE Harper, New York (1971). [1] Also has series of numbers "71 72 73 74 10 ...1" on last blank page $25/125

016a: BONECRACK Joseph, London (1971). [1] $40/200

016b: BONECRACK Harper, New York (1972). [1] Also has series "72....321" on last page. (Published May 1972 @ $5.95) $20/100

017a: SMOKESCREEN Michael Joseph, London (1972). [1] Noted in wrap-around band (David Rees 6/96) $30/150

017b: SMOKESCREEN Harper, New York (1973). [1] Also has numbers on back page "...76 77 10 9...1" $20/100

018a: SLAY-RIDE Michael Joseph, London (1973). [1] $25/125

018b: SLAY RIDE Harper, New York, 1974. [] Uncorrected proof in blue wraps $150.

018c: SLAY RIDE Harper, New York (1974). [1] Also has numbers on back page "...76 77 10 9...1." Also noted in wrap-around band with quote from *Time* magazine (Pepper & Stern 11/93) $15/75

019a: KNOCK DOWN Michael Joseph, London (1974). [1] $25/100

019b: KNOCKDOWN Harper, New York (1975). [] Uncorrected proof in red wraps $100.

019c: KNOCKDOWN Harper, New York (1975). [3] Also states "First Edition." Published April 1975 @ $6.95 $15/75

020a: HIGH STAKES Michael Joseph, London (1975). [1] $25/100

020b: HIGH STAKES Harper, New York (1976). [] Uncorrected proof in red wraps (Waverley Books 1/89) $150.

020c: HIGH STAKES Harper, New York (1976). [3] Also states "First Edition." Noted with both red endpapers and blue endpapers. Front dustwrapper flap has "0576" $15/75

021a: ACROSS THE BOARD Harper, NY (1975). [1] Includes *Flying Finish*, *Blood Sport* and *Enquiry* $10/50

022a: IN THE FRAME Michael Joseph, London (1976). [1] $25/100

022b: IN THE FRAME Harper, New York (1976). [3] Also states "First U.S. Edition" $12/60

023a: THREE WINNERS Michael Joseph, London (1977). [1] Collects *Dead Cert, Nerve* and *For Kicks* $25/75

024a: RISK Michael Joseph, London (1977). [1] $25/100

024b: RISK Harper, New York, 1978. [] Uncorrected proof in red wraps (J. Chryk 3/93) $125.

024c: RISK Harper, New York (1978). [3] Also states "First U.S. Edition." (Published May 1978 @ $8.95) $12/60

025a: THREE FAVOURITES Michael Joseph, London (1978). [1] collects *Odds Against, Flying Finish* and *Blood Sport* $25/75

026a: TRIAL RUN Michael Joseph, London (1978). [1] $25/100

026b: TRIAL RUN Harper, New York, 1979. [] Uncorrected proof in dark beige wraps $125.

026c: TRIAL RUN Harper, New York, 1979. [3] Also states "First U.S. Edition" $12/60

027a: WHIP HAND Michael Joseph, London (1979). [1] $15/75

027b: WHIP HAND Harper, New York (1980). [3] (Copyright in 1979 but published April 1980 @ $9.95.) Also states "First U.S. Edition" $10/50

028a: REFLEX Michael Joseph, London (1980). [] Uncorrected proof in printed boards (Ronald Levine 6/89) $125.

028b: REFLEX Michael Joseph, London (1980). [1] $15/75

028c: REFLEX Putnam, New York (1981). [0] 50,000 cc $10/50

029a: TWICE SHY Michael Joseph, London (1981). [1] $15/75

029b: TWICE SHY Putnam, New York (1982). [0] 60,000 cc $8/40

030a: BANKER Michael Joseph, London (1982). [1] $12/60

030b: BANKER Putnam, New York (1983). [1] 75,000 cc $8/40

031a: TWO BY FRANCIS Harper, New York (1983 [1982?]). [3] Includes *Forfeit* and *Slay Ride* $8/40

032a: THE DANGER Michael Joseph, London (1983). [1] $12/60

033b: THE DANGER Putnam, New York (1984). [] Uncorrected proof in green printed wraps (Buddenbrooks 3/95) $60.

033c: THE DANGER Putnam, New York (1984). [0] 100,000 cc $7/35

034a: DICK FRANCIS FOUR COMPLETE NOVELS Avenel, New York (1984). [] Includes *Odds Against, Flying Finish, Blood Sport* and *Rat Race* (Jim Chryk 9/93) $10/40

035a: PROOF Michael Joseph, London, 1984. [1] Noted with edges stained sand-colored and unstained $10/50

035b: PROOF Putnam, New York (1985). [3] 110,000 cc $7/35

036a: BREAK IN Joseph, London (1985). [1] $10/50

036b: BREAK IN Putnam, New York (1986). [3] $/7/35

037a: LESTER *The Official Biography* Michael Joseph, London (1986). [2] 1000 sgd no. cc. Red leather. In slipcase (Nigel Williams 7/93) $250/300

037b: LESTER *The Official Biography* Michael Joseph, London (1986). [1] $12/60

037c: A JOCKEY'S LIFE *The Biography of Lester Piggott* Putnam, New York (1986). [3] $10/50

038a: BOLT Michael Joseph, London (1986). [1] $10/50

038b: BOLT Putnam, New York (1986). [] Uncorrected proof in printed white wraps (Bev Chaney 9/89) $50.

038c: BOLT Putnam, NY (1987). [3] 140,000 cc $7/35

039a: DICK FRANCIS Heinemann/Secker & Warburg / Octopus, London, 1987. [1] "This Edition Published 1987." Includes *For Kicks* and *Flying Finish* (James Chryk-9/93) $10/40

040a: HOT MONEY Michael Joseph, London (1987). [] Uncorrected proof in white wraps (Alphabet Books 11/91) $75.

040b: HOT MONEY Michael Joseph, London (1987). [1] $10/50

040c: HOT MONEY Putnam, New York (1988). [3] Uncorrected proof in flint gray printed wraps $60.

040d: HOT MONEY Putnam, New York (1988). [3] Advance reading copy in pictorial wraps $35.

040e: HOT MONEY Putnam, New York (1988). [2] 250 sgd no. cc. Issued without dustwrapper. In slipcase. (Published March 1988 @ $75.) $200/250

040f: HOT MONEY Putnam, New York (1988). [3] 155,000 cc. (Published March 1988 @ $17.95) $6/30

041a: THE EDGE Michael Joseph, London (1988). [1] $10/50

041b: THE EDGE Putnam, New York, 1989. [] Advance reading copy in pictorial wraps $30.

041c: THE EDGE Putnam, New York (1989). [3] 60,000 cc (*Publisher's Weekley*). (Published February 1989 @ $18.95) $6/30

042a: STRAIGHT Michael Joseph, London, 1989. [2] 500 sgd no. cc. Issued without dustwrapper. In slipcase (Mordida Books 7/90) $125/175

042b: STRAIGHT Michael Joseph, London (1989). [1] $10/50

042c: STRAIGHT Putnam, New York (1989). [3] Uncorrected proof in red wraps $50.

042d: STRAIGHT Putnam, New York (1989). [3] 225,000 cc. (Published November 1989 @ $18.95) $6/30

043a: LONGSHOT Michael Joseph, London (1990). [1] $10/50

043b: LONGSHOT Putnam, New York (1990). [3] Uncorrected proof in orange-yellow wraps. (Yellow decorated wraps [Books, Inc. 6/95]) $40.

043c: LONGSHOT Putnam, New York (1990). [2] 250 sgd no. cc. In full leather. Published for Waldenbooks Preferred Readers. This is a second printing Putnam edition with "2 3 4 5 6 7 8 9 10" on © page $100.

043d: LONGSHOT Putnam, New York (1990). [3] (Published October 17, 1990 @ $19.95) $5/25

044a: COMEBACK Michael Joseph, London, 1991. [1] $10/50

044b: COMEBACK Putnam, New York (1991). [3] Uncorrected proof in red wraps $40.

044c: COMEBACK Putnam, New York (1991). [3] (Published 10/18/91 @ $21.95) $5/25

045a: DRIVING FORCE Michael Joseph, London (1992). [1] $8/45

045b: DRIVING FORCE Putnam, New York (1992). [] Uncorrected proof in dark blue-gray wraps $35.

045c: DRIVING FORCE Putnam, New York (1992). [3] (Published October 1992 @ $21.95) $5/25

046a: DECIDER Michael Joseph, London, 1993. [] Uncorrected proof in red wraps $60.

046b: DECIDER Michael Joseph, London (1993). [1] Also noted in a dustwrapper which lacks the title of the book on both the front panel and spine $8/40

046c: DECIDER Putnam, New York, 1993. [] Uncorrected proof in blue wraps $30.

046d: DECIDER Putnam, New York, 1993. [] (Published 10/93 @ $22.95) $5/25

047a: WILD HORSES Scorpion Press, Bristol, 1994. [2] 20 sgd ltr cc. Signed by the author and H. R. F. Keating who provides *An Appreciation of Dick Francis.* Quarter bound in goat skin with raised bands on spine, and marbled boards. In transparent dustwrapper $600.

047b: WILD HORSES Scorpion Press, Bristol, 1994. [2] 99 sgd no. cc (of an edition of 119 cc). In glassine dustwrapper. Issued without slipcase $250.

047c: WILD HORSES Michael Joseph, London (1994). [1] $7/35

047d: WILD HORSES Putnam, New York (1994). [3] Uncorrected proof in printed red wraps (Kugelman & Bent 19/95) $30.

047e: WILD HORSES Putnam, New York (1994). [3] $5/25

048a: COME TO GRIEF Michael Joseph, London, 1995. [] (David Rees 9/95) $7/35

048b: COME TO GRIEF Putnam, New York (1995). [] Uncorrected proof in gold wraps (Oracle Books 11/95) $30.

048c: COME TO GRIEF Putnam, New York (1995). [3] Published @ $23.95 $5/25

049a: TO THE HILT Scorpion Press, Blakeney (1996). [2] 15 sgd ltr cc. Signed by Francis and Margaret Yorke. Deluxe copies for private distribution. Quarter leather with raised bands $500.

049b: TO THE HILT Scorpion Press, Blakeney (1996). [2] 99 sgd no. cc. In acetate dustwrapper. Issued without slipcase (Buckingham Books 9/96) $150.

049c: TO THE HILT Michael Joseph, London (1996). [1] Published September 1996 @ £15.99 $7/35

049d: TO THE HILT Putnam, New York (1996). [3] Uncorrected proof in yellow wraps, printed in black $30.

049e: TO THE HILT Putnam, New York (1996). [3] Published @ $24.95 $5/25

050a: 10 LB. PENALTY Putnam (New York, 1997). [] Published at $24.95 $45.

Robert Frost

ROBERT FROST
1874-1963

Robert Frost was born in San Francisco but moved to his grandfather's house in Lawrence, Massachusetts after his father's death. He graduated from the local high school in 1892. A few of his poems had appeared in the high school bulletin, but his first published poem was "My Butterfly" in the *New York Independent* in 1894.

He studied at Dartmouth and Harvard without graduating. He worked in Lawrence at a woolen mill, on a newspaper and at other odd jobs, but continued to write poems. In 1900, Frost settled on a farm in Derry, New Hampshire and taught at the Academy there. He sold the farm in 1912 and moved his family to England where his first two books were published.

The first two books brought him recognition on both sides of the Atlantic and upon his return to New Hampshire in 1915, he found himself in demand for public readings and teaching positions.

Frost taught at Amherst from 1926 to 1938, Harvard from 1939 to 1943, Dartmouth from 1943 to 1949 and finally received a permanent appointment at Amherst.

He was award Pulitzer Prizes in 1924, 1931, 1937 and 1943; and is, or course, well remembered by our generation as the poet at the inauguration of President Kennedy.

Note on Pricing:

- Prices before 1920 are for very good to fine copies without dustwrapper

- Prices estimated for 1920 and later are for very good copies without/with dustwrapper

- **Christmas cards are in wraps and would normally have one estimated price, but as the quantities differ so much, we have used a range showing an estimate of the card with the imprint that has the largest quantity to the imprint that has the smallest quantity**

REFERENCES:

(a) Clymer, W.B.; Green, Shubrick and Charles B. ROBERT FROST *A Bibliography.* Jones Library, Amherst (1937). Used through *Selected Poems* in 1936, unless otherwise noted.

(b) Crane, Joan St. C. ROBERT FROST *A Descriptive Catalogue of Books and Manuscripts In The Clifton Waller Barrett Library University of Virginia.* Charlottesville: University Press of Virginia, 1974. Used from 1936 through 1962 unless otherwise noted.

(c) Broccoli & Clarke. FIRST PRINTINGS OF AMERICAN AUTHORS. Volume 1. Detroit: Gale Research, (1977). Used from 1963 through 1972, unless otherwise noted.

(d) Inventory or dealer catalogs.

001a: TWILIGHT (American Printing House (?), Lawrence, Mass., 1894.) [0] 2 cc printed (one destroyed by Frost, one known to survive). Wraps $60,000.

001b: TWILIGHT Clifton Waller Barrett Library / Reynolds Co., University of Virginia, 1966. [2] 20 cc on handmade Maidstone paper for presentation. Facsimile. Wraps (Robert Frost Books 5/91) $350.

001c TWILIGHT Clifton Waller Barrett Library / Reynolds Co., University of Virginia, 1966. [2] 150 no. cc. Wraps. Facsimile (ref.b) $250.

002a: A BOY'S WILL David Nutt, London, 1913. [0] (Estimated at 1,000 to 1,100 copies for A through E.) First issue, binding A: bronzed-brown pebbled cloth. Gilt stamped $6,000.

002b: A BOY'S WILL David Nutt, London, 1913. [0] First issue, binding B: cream vellum-paper boards stamped in red (including border rule) $2,750.

002c: A BOY'S WILL David Nutt, London, 1913. [0] Second issue, binding C: cream linen-paper wraps, stamped in black without a border rule. 70 copies rubber-stamped on p. iv (ref.b) $1,750.

002d: A BOY'S WILL David Nutt, London, 1913. [0] Second issue, binding D: cream linen-paper wraps, stamped in black. The difference is 4-petaled flowers (preceding bindings have 8-petaled flowers) (ref.b) $1,500.

002e: A BOY'S WILL David Nutt, London, 1913, [2] 135 sgd no. cc in wraps. (Binding D) (ref.b) $2,000.

002f: A BOY'S WILL Henry Holt, New York, 1915. [0] Blue fine linen cloth and white endpapers (later copies in coarse blue linen cloth with buff endpapers). "Aind" for "And" on last line of p.14. (corrected in second printing). Glassine dustwrapper in ref.b, but we've had three in regular dustwrappers and two of the second printing in glassine, so believe issued both ways $600/3,000

002g: A BOY'S WILL Henry Holt, New York, 1915. [0] Second printing with "and" correct $250.

003a: NORTH OF BOSTON David Nutt, London (1914). [1] 350 cc. There were 1,000 sets of sheets printed and from 1914 to 1923. These sets were bound in various bindings. First issue, binding A: coarse green cloth measuring 195 x 154 mm $3,000.

003b: NORTH OF BOSTON Henry Holt, New York, 1914. [1] 150 cc. The UK sheets with Holt title page. Binding B: drab gray-brown boards backed with brown cloth. (Actually sold in 1915) $2,500.

003c: NORTH OF BOSTON David Nutt, London (1914). [1] 200 cc. Binding C: fine green cloth measuring 189 x 145 mm (first issue sheets bound about 1917) (ref.b) $1,750.

003d: NORTH OF BOSTON David Nutt, London (1914). [1] 41 cc. Binding D: blue cloth (first issue sheets bound about 1922) (ref.b) $1,250.

003e: NORTH OF BOSTON David Nutt, London (1914). [1] 59 cc. Re-bound 003c in binding E: coarse green cloth, rubber-stamp on p.iv (first issue sheets bound about 1923). 200 x 145 mm (ref.b) $1,000.

003f: NORTH OF BOSTON David Nutt, London (1914). [1] 200 cc. Binding F: coarse green cloth, rubber-stamp on p.iv (first issue sheets bound in about 1923). 195 x 150 mm (ref.b) $1,000.

003g: NORTH OF BOSTON Henry Holt, New York, 1915. [0] "Second Edition, 1915." 1,300 cc. Includes one poem "Good Hours" not in first (not included in Contents) $350.

003h: NORTH OF BOSTON Henry Holt, New York, no-date [1919]. [0] 500 cc. First Illustrated Edition $350/750

004a: MOUNTAIN INTERVAL Henry Holt, New York (1916). [0] 4,000 cc (a & b). First state: p.88:6 and 7 repeated lines; "'Come'" for "'Gone'" p.93 line 6 from bottom $350/1,750

004b: MOUNTAIN INTERVAL Henry Holt, New York (1916). [0] Second state: errors corrected $150/1,500

005a: MY NOVEMBER GUEST (Poet's Guild, New York, 1922.) [] 5 x 7 1/2 inch broadside. Fewer than 300 copies (Pharos 7/85) $175.

006a: A HILLSIDE THAW (Poet's Guild, New York, 1922.) [] 5 x 7 1/2 inch broadside. About 200 copies (Pharos 7/92) $200.

007a: SELECTED POEMS Henry Holt, New York, 1923. [0] 1,025 cc. "March, 1923" on copyright page $200/1,000

007b: SELECTED POEMS Heinemann, London (1923). [1] $150/600

008a: NEW HAMPSHIRE Henry Holt, New York, 1923. [2] 350 sgd no. cc. Issued in white slipcase. Pulitzer Prize in Poetry for 1924 $800/1,000

008b: NEW HAMPSHIRE Henry Holt, New York, 1923. [0] 5,350 cc $150/500

008c: NEW HAMPSHIRE Grant Richards, Ltd., London, 1924. [0] 150 cc of the US sheets with cancel title page $150/750

008d: NEW HAMPSHIRE New Dresden Press, Hanover, NH, 1955. [2] 750 sgd and no. cc. First separate edition of the poem. In semitransparent rough white Japanese paper dustwrapper $450/500

009a: AN OLD MAN'S WINTER NIGHT Hampshire Bookshop, Northampton, 1924. [2] 175 cc. Folded sheet $350.

010a: SEVERAL SHORT POEMS Henry Holt (New York, 1924). [0] 2,000 cc. Wraps $500.

011a: SELECTED POEMS Henry Holt, New York (1928). [1] 3,475 cc. Revised/Expanded of the 1923 [007a] edition $100/450

011b: SELECTED POEMS Henry Holt, New York (1934). [] "Third Edition" on title page and dustwrapper. Adds 16 poems $50/150

012a: WEST-RUNNING BROOK Henry Holt, New York (1928). [0] 8,400 cc (estimated). Lacks "First Edition" statement. Ref.a assumes the publisher ran off most of the copies before noticing the omission of the "First Edition" statement $60/300

012b: WEST-RUNNING BROOK Henry Holt, New York (1928). [1] 1,000 cc (estimated). States "First Edition" $40/200

012c: WEST-RUNNING BROOK Henry Holt, New York (1928). [2] 1,000 no. cc signed by Frost, and frontis and 3 plates pencil signed by artist J.J. Lankes. Slipcase. This issue used entirely different type and pagination than the trade edition $400/500

013a: A WAY OUT *A One Act Play* Harbor Press New York 1929 [2] 485 sgd no. cc. Issued without dustwrapper $500.

014a: THE LOVELY SHALL BE CHOOSERS Random House, New York, 1929. [2] 475 cc. Wraps. Sold in a set in slipcase with 11 other poet's work as *The Poetry Quartos*) $150.

015a: THE COW'S IN THE CORN *A One-Act Irish Play In Rhyme* Slide Mountain Press, Gaylordsville, 1929. [2] 91 sgd and no. cc. In flexible paper covered boards. Issued without dustwrapper. Noted with tipped in errata slip (Robert Frost Books 10/95) $2,000.

016a: CHRISTMAS TREES (Spiral Press, New York, 1929.) [0] 275 cc. Wraps. The first of the Christmas cards with four imprints (quantities vary from 50 to 100) $500-750.

016b: CHRISTMAS TREES Henry Holt and Company, New York (1990). [3] Published @ $14.95. Assume issued in wraps or without dustwrapper $20.

017a: COLLECTED POEMS OF ROBERT FROST Random House, New York, 1930. [2] 1,000 sgd no. cc. Ref.a & b do not mention a dustwrapper. Van Allen Bradley (*Handbook of Values* 1982 edition) shows with dustwrapper. Plain unprinted glassine dustwrapper (Bert Babcock 5/ 88) $750.

017b: COLLECTED POEMS OF ROBERT FROST Henry Holt, New York (1930). [1] 3,870 cc. "First Trade Edition." Pulitzer Prize for Poetry for 1931" $100/350

017c: COLLECTED POEMS OF ROBERT FROST Longmans, Green, London, 1930. [] 1,000 cc. Holt's sheets with Longmans, Green title page. Also noted with Book Society wrap-around band (Hawthorn Books 4/90) $100/300

018a: WILFRED DAVISON MEMORIAL LIBRARY BREAD LOAF (Middlebury College, Middlebury, VT) 1930. [] 16 page pamphlet published as *Bread Loaf Folder No. 8* $450.

019a: THE FOUR BELIEFS (Dartmouth College, 1931.) [] 250 cc. One sheet folded $350.

020a: EDUCATION BY POETRY - A MEDITATIVE MONOLOGUE Amherst, 1931. [0] 16 page pamphlet issued as supplement to Alumni Council News $350.

021a: TWO LETTERS WRITTEN ON HIS UNDERGRADUATE DAYS AT DARTMOUTH COLLEGE IN 1892 The Printer's Devil Press, Hanover. 1931. [2] 10 no. cc. Wraps (ref.b) $2,750.

022a: THE AUGUSTAN BOOKS OF POETRY ROBERT FROST Benn, London (1932). [0] Wraps $200.

022b: THE AUGUSTAN BOOKS OF POETRY ROBERT FROST Benn, London (1932). [0] Wraps. Binding "B" with dull red simulated linen paper wrap pasted over original self-wraps with a panel cut in the front cover exposing only "ROBERT FROST" of the original cover-title lettering (Robert Frost Books 10/95) $175.

023a: THE LONE STRIKER (Knopf, New York, 1933.) [0] 2,000 cc. Wraps. Issued in envelope. (Some used as a Christmas card by Frost) $100.

024a: TWO TRAMPS IN MUD-TIME (Spiral Press, New York) 1934. [0] 775 cc. Wraps. (Christmas poem: 6 imprints with quantities varying from 25 to 200 copies) $300-600

025a: THREE POEMS Baker Library Press, Hanover (1935). [2] 125 no. cc. Wraps $750.

026a: THE GOLD HESPERIDEE (Bibliophile Press, Cortland, 1935.) [] Tan wraps. 500 cc printed, all but 37 copies were withdrawn. Colophon page has "Cortland NY/A." P.7 second line from bottom "Twas Sunday and Square Hale was dressed for meeting." Unnumbered on limitation page. Leaves measure 162x114 mm $1,000.

026b: THE GOLD HESPERIDEE (Bibliophile Press, Cortland, 1935.) [2] 200 no. cc. Colophon page has "Cortland NY/B." Yellow wraps. Line noted in 021a has been reset so that "for meeting" is on separate line. Leaves measure 183x127 mm $500.

026c: THE GOLD HESPERIDEE (Bibliophile Press, Cortland, 1935.) [] Reportedly 67 cc. Same as 026a but in pale yellow wraps with the word "English" stamped under "copy number" on p.2 $600.

027a: NEITHER OUT FAR NOR IN DEEP (Spiral Press, New York) 1935. [0] 1,235 cc. Wraps. (Christmas poem: 8 imprints with quantities varying from 25 to 450 copies) $100-250

028a: FROM SNOW TO SNOW Henry Holt, New York (1936). [0] 300 cc. Light-tan mottled wraps with a 4 page insert before half-title from The Hampshire Bookshop. Paper watermarked "Champlain / Text" (later watermarked "Warren's / Olde Style") (Some copies issued in envelope with "...Compliments of Henry Holt and Company" printed in gray) $350.

028b: FROM SNOW TO SNOW Henry Holt, New York (1936). About 1,200 copies. Bound in rough tan line cloth lettered in dark brown. Issued without dustwrapper $250.

028c: FROM SNOW TO SNOW Henry Holt, New York (1936). [0] 3,000 cc. Second printing in fine green linen cloth stamped in silver, issued in dustwrapper. (There was also another printing of 1,200 copies which may be exactly the same) $35/125

029a: A FURTHER RANGE Henry Holt, New York (1936). [2] 803 sgd and no. cc. Issued in glassine dustwrapper in slipcase $400/500

029b: A FURTHER RANGE Henry Holt, New York (1936). [1] 4,000 cc. Pulitzer Prize for Poetry in 1937 $30/150

029c: A FURTHER RANGE Jonathan Cape, London (1937). [1] $25/125

030a: SELECTED POEMS Jonathan Cape, London (1936). [1] Contains comments by Auden, Engle, C. Day-Lewis and Muir $50/250

030b: SELECTED POEMS Henry Holt (1937). [] "In this latest edition there have been included sixteen additional poems." Not sure if this is the same selection as 030a (not in ref.a) or the next printing after 011b $25/75

031a: EVERYBODY'S SANITY Dahlstrom, Los Angeles, 1936 (on front cover). [0] About 100-150 cc. Wraps $400.

032a: TO A YOUNG WRETCH (Spiral Press, New York, 1937.) [0] 820 cc. Wraps. (Christmas poem: 7 imprints with quantities varying from 25 to 275 copies) $150-250

032b: TO A YOUNG WRETCH (Barrett Library, University of Virginia, Charlottesville, no-date [1970]). [0] Wraps $40.

033a: CARPE DIEM (Spiral Press, New York, 1938.) [0] 230 cc. Wraps. (Christmas poem: 3 imprints, quantities of 30, 50 and 150) $200-350

034a: WHAT BECAME OF NEW ENGLAND? Oberlin College, 1938. [0] One sheet folded to make 4 pages. Reprinting Frost's June 1937 commencement address, which had been published in the Oberlin alumni magazine for May 1938. First separate edition (Black Sun 5/87) $250.

035a: COLLECTED POEMS OF ROBERT FROST Henry Holt, New York, 1939. [1] 3,750 cc (a & b) $50/250

035b: COLLECTED POEMS OF ROBERT FROST Henry Holt, New York, 1939. [1] Signed on tipped-in sheet $250/350

035c: COLLECTED POEMS OF ROBERT FROST Longmans, Green, London (1939). [] American sheets (ref.c). Not listed in ref.b $50/250

036a: A CONSIDERABLE SPECK (Boston, 1939.) [0] Printer's proof. Early state of proof printing poem text and border only (Heritage Book Shop 9/95) $1,500.

036b: A CONSIDERABLE SPECK (Colonial Society of Massachusetts, Boston, 1939.) [0] Proof, identical to published state except the words "Original Proof" printed in lower right corner of page 1 (Heritage Book Shop 9/95) $1,500.

036c: A CONSIDERABLE SPECK (Colonial Society of Massachusetts, 1939.) [0] Less than 100 cc. Single sheet folded to 4 pages $1,250.

037a: TRIPLE PLATE (Spiral Press, New York, 1939.) [0] 1,825 cc. Wraps. Decorated by Fritz Eichenberg (Christmas poem: 8 imprints with quantities varying from 25 to 900 copies) $75-300

038a: OUR HOLD ON THE PLANET (No publisher or place), 1940. [0] 975 cc. Wraps. (Christmas poem: 3 imprints, quantities of 125, 250 and 600 copies) $100-350

039a: I COULD GIVE ALL TO TIME (No publisher or place), 1941. [0] 1,000 cc. Wraps. (Christmas poem: 3 imprints, quantities of 150, 180 and 770 copies) $150-350

040a: A WITNESS TREE Henry Holt, New York (1942). [2] 735 sgd no cc. In slipcase $300/400

040b: A WITNESS TREE Henry Holt, New York (1942). [1] 8,500 cc. Pulitzer Prize for 1943 $25/125

040c: A WITNESS TREE Jonathan Cape, London (1943). [1] $25/125

041a: THE GIFT OUTRIGHT (No publisher or place), 1942. [0] 1,250 cc. Wraps. (Christmas poem: 3 imprints, quantities of 100, 150 and 1,000 copies) 100/350

042a: THE TESTING TIME FOR LOYALTIES Dartmouth College (Hanover, New Hampshire), 1942 [] Wraps (Bromer Books 6/93) $350.

043a: COME IN AND OTHER POEMS Henry Holt, New York (1943). [1] Edited by Louis Untermeyer $25/125

043b: COME IN AND OTHER POEMS Jonathan Cape, London (1944). [1] $25/100

044a: THE GUARDEEN (Ward Ritchie, Los Angeles), 1943. [2] 96 no. cc. Wraps. Printed for Earle J. Bernheimer $500.

045a: TWO LEADING LIGHTS (Ward Ritchie, Los Angeles), 1944. [2] 52 no. cc. Wraps. Printed for Earle J. Bernheimer $750.

046a: FIFTY YEARS OF ROBERT FROST Hanover, 1944. [] Boards. Includes first appearance of "In England" (Pharos 5/90) $250.

046b: FIFTY YEARS OF ROBERT FROST Hanover, 1944. [] Wraps. Regular issue (Pharos 1988) $150.

047a: THE FOUR BELIEFS Dartmouth College, Hanover, New Hampshire, 1944. [] Wraps. 250 cc (Robert Frost Books 11/93) $250.

048a: AN UNSTAMPED LETTER IN OUR RURAL LETTER BOX (Spiral Press, New York), 1944. [0] 2,050 cc. Wraps. (Christmas Poem: 6 imprints, quantities vary from 100 to 1,250 copies) $75-200

049a: A MASQUE OF REASON Henry Holt, New York (1945). [2] 800 sgd no. cc. Issued without dustwrapper in slipcase $300/400

049b: A MASQUE OF REASON Henry Holt, New York (1945). [1] 15,000 cc $15/75

049c: A MASQUE OF REASON, A MASQUE OF MERCY and STEEPLE BUSH Jonathan Cape, London (1948). [1] $15/75

050a: A MOOD APART Duke University, 1945. [] Broadside (Heritage Bookshop 6/92) $350.

051a: ON MAKING CERTAIN ANYTHING HAS HAPPENED (Spiral Press, New York, 1945.) [0] 2,600 cc. Wraps. (Christmas poems: 8 imprints, quantities vary from 100 to 1,050 copies) $60/200

052a: THE COURAGE TO BE NEW Orris Manning Memorial, Ripton, 1946. [0] Broadside $250.

053a: THE POCKET BOOK OF ROBERT FROST'S POEMS Pocket Books, New York (1946). [] Wraps. Enlarged edition of *Come in...*, Edited by Louis Untermeyer (ref.c) $50.

054a: THE POEMS OF ROBERT FROST Modern Library, New York (1946). [1] With introductory essay: *The Constant Symbol* $25/100

055a: A YOUNG BIRCH (Spiral Press, New York), 1946. [0] 3,445 cc. Wraps. (Christmas poems: 10 imprints, quantities vary from 50 to 1,160 copies) $60-200

056a: STEEPLE BUSH Henry Holt, New York (1947). [2] 751 sgd and no. cc. Issued without dustwrapper. In slipcase $300/400

056b: STEEPLE BUSH Henry Holt, New York (1947). [0] 7,500 cc. (See 049c for English publication) $25/100

057a: A MASQUE OF MERCY Henry Holt, New York (1947). [2] 751 sgd and no. cc. Issued without dustwrapper. In slipcase $300/400

057b: A MASQUE OF MERCY Henry Holt, New York (1947). [1] 7,500 cc. (See 049c for English publication) $25/100

058a: TWO POEMS ON REVOLUTION... Bookbuilders, Boston, 1947. [0] about 25-30 cc. Wraps. (About 32 copies-Robert Frost Books, 6/93.) Also includes poem by Oscar Williams $5,000.

059a: A SERMON Rockdale Temple, Cincinnati (1947). [2] 500 cc. Wraps $450.

060a: ONE STEP BACKWARD TAKEN (Spiral Press, New York, 1947.) [0] 3,050 cc. Wraps. (Christmas poem: 10 imprints, quantities vary from 50 to 1,200 copies.) (Also a unique trial proof, with substantial differences, in pale yellow wraps catalogued by George Houle in 1988 for $1,250.) $60-250

061a: THE FALLS (Ward Ritchie, Los Angeles, 1947.) [] "First Proof" in stapled pale blue wraps printed in red (Glenn Horowitz 3/91) $850.

061b: THE FALLS (Ward Ritchie, Los Angeles, 1947.) [2] 60 no. cc. Wraps. Printed for Earle J. Bernheimer $750.

062a: ON THE INFLATION OF THE CURRENCY Earle J. Bernheimer, 1948. [2] 60 no. cc. Wraps $750.

063a: CLOSED FOR GOOD (Spiral Press, New York, 1948.) [0] 2,275 cc. Wraps. (Christmas poems: 8 imprints, quantities vary from 75 to 1,050 copies) $60-175

064a: GREECE Black Rose Press, Chicago (1948). [2] 47 no. cc were printed but only 26 sent out $1,000.

065a: ON A TREE FALLEN ACROSS THE ROAD (Spiral Press, New York, 1949.) [0] 3,060 cc. Wraps. (Christmas poem: 14 imprints plus 50 copies left blank for Lesley Frost. Quantities vary from 50 to 935 copies) $60-200

066a: COMPLETE POEMS OF ROBERT FROST 1949 Henry Holt, New York (1949). [2] 500 sgd and no. cc. Issued in glassine dustwrapper. In slipcase $500/600

066b: COMPLETE POEMS OF ROBERT FROST 1949 Henry Holt, New York (1949). [1] 7,325 cc $35/175

066c: COMPLETE POEMS OF ROBERT FROST 1949 Limited Editions Club, New York, 1950. [2] 1,500 sgd no. cc. 2 volumes. In slipcase $600/750

066d: COMPLETE POEMS OF ROBERT FROST 1949 Jonathan Cape, London (1951). [1] $30/150

067a: DOOM TO BLOOM (Spiral Press, New York, 1950.) [0] 3,750 cc. Wraps. (Christmas poems: 16 imprints, quantities vary from 75 to 1,050 copies) $50-175

068a: HARD NOT TO BE KING House of Books, New York, 1951. [2] 300 sgd no. cc $500.

069a: THE ROAD NOT TAKEN Henry Holt, New York (1951). [0] Further enlargement of *Come In* and *The Pocket Book...* with new title (ref.c). Edited by Louis Untermeyer $15/75

070a: A CABIN IN THE CLEARING (Spiral Press, New York, 1951.) [0] 3,750 cc. Wraps. (Christmas poem: 14 imprints, quantities vary from 75 to 1,325 copies) $50-175

071a: DOES NO ONE AT ALL... (Spiral Press, New York, 1952.) [0] 3,875 cc. Wraps. (Christmas poem: 14 imprints, quantities vary from 50 to 1,300 copies.) Beige wraps with design in dark green. Variant in light blue gray wraps with design in dark red $50-250

072a: AMHERST COLLEGE AMHERST, MASSACHUSETTS 1953 Amherst College, Amherst, 1953. [] New Year's greeting card from Frost (Robert Frost Books 5/91) $200.

073a: ONE MORE BREVITY (Spiral Press, New York), 1953. [0] 4,501 cc. Wraps. (Christmas poem: 15 imprints, quantities vary from 75 to 1,575 copies) $50-175

074a: AFORESAID Henry Holt, New York (1954). [2] 650 sgd no. cc. Issued without dustwrapper. In slipcase. No trade edition. $450/550

075a: FROM A MILKWEED POD (Spiral Press, New York, 1954.) [0] 5,076 cc. Wraps. (Christmas poem: 18 imprints, quantities vary from 32 to 1,767 copies) $50-250

076a: ROBERT FROST SELECTED POEMS Penguin Books, Harmondsworth (1955). [1] Wraps. Penguin Poets D 27. Introduction by C. Day Lewis $50.

NEW HAMPSHIRE see item 008d

077a: SOME SCIENCE FICTION (Spiral Press, New York, 1955.) [0] 5,650 cc. Wraps. (Christmas poem: 17 imprints, quantities vary from 50 to 2,000 copies.) Variant in gray laid paper (Robert Frost Books 5/91) $40-200

078a: KITTY HAWK (Spiral Press, New York, 1956.) [0] 7,000 cc. Wraps. (Christmas poem: 21 imprints, quantities vary from 25 to 2,950 copies) $40-250

079a: A TALK FOR STUDENTS Fund for the Republic, New York (1956). [0] Wraps $100.

080a: MY OBJECTION TO BEING STEPPED ON (Spiral Press, New York, 1957.) [0] 8,290 cc. Wraps. (Christmas poem: 21 imprints, quantities vary from 70 to 3,675 copies.) Page 3 either has a red-orange floral ornament or an olive green 8-pointed star, no priority $40-175

081a: AWAY! (Spiral Press, New York, 1958.) [0] 9,155 cc. Wraps (Christmas poem: 22 imprints, quantities vary from 35 to 4,550 copies) $50-250

082a: A REMEMBRANCE COLLECTION OF NEW POEMS (Henry Holt, New York, 1959.) [2] 150 cc. Wraps (ref.d). First appearance of all 8 poems (Robert Frost Books 5/91) $275.

083a: YOU COME TOO Henry Holt, New York (1959). [1] Specially Bound publisher's copy with burgundy-colored endpapers, fine linen brown covers, leather backstripping at spine and corners, tooled leather spine, stamped in decorated in gilt (Robert Frost Books 10/95) $200.

083b: YOU COME TOO Henry Holt, New York (1959). [1] $15/75

083c: YOU COME TOO Bodley Head, London (1964). [] Advance uncorrected proof in blue wraps (Dalian Books 7/91) $100.

083d: YOU COME TOO Bodley Head, London (1964). [] Ref.c (not in ref.b) $15/75

084a: FRESHMAN DAYS... Dartmouth (Hanover), 1959. [0] Off-print in pictorial stapled wraps, from the March 1959 alumni magazine (Waiting For Godot 2/87) $150.

085a: A-WISHING WELL (Spiral Press, New York, 1959.) [0] 10,760 cc. Wraps. (Christmas poem: 20 imprints, quantities vary from 50 to 6,870 copies) $40-200

086a: ROBERT FROST READING HIS POEMS Library of Congress (Washington, D.C.), 1960. [0] Wraps. One leaf folded to make four pages. A program for his reading at the Cooledge Auditorium May 2, 1960. Printed by the Government Printing Office. Includes excerpts from a number of his poems $100.

087a: ACCIDENTALLY ON PURPOSE (Spiral Press, New York) 1960. [0] 10,600 cc. Wraps. (Christmas poem: 20 imprints, quantities vary from 50 to 6,600 copies) $40-150

088a: THE WOOD-PILE (Spiral Press, New York), 1961. [0] 15,060 cc. Wraps. (Christmas poem: 21 imprints, quantities vary from 50 to 10,265 copies) $40-150

089a: MY BUTTERFLY. AN ELEGY California Friends of Robert Frost (Huntington Library?), Pasadena, no-date [1960s?]. [] 14" x 18" broadside. First separate edition of Frost's first published poem for pay (Waiting For Godot 10/90) $100.

090a: SIX POEMS New York Public Library, New York, 1961. [0] Wraps. Includes three poems by Frost and three by Carl Sandburg $60.

091a: DEDICATION THE GIFT OUTRIGHT THE INAUGURAL ADDRESS Washington, D.C., 1961. [2] 250 no. cc of total printing of 500 (numbered 1-250). The Inaugural Address. "Printed for the friends of Holt, Rinehart..." on p.4. Ref.a notes a "pamphlet edition from the1992 same type was later printed by Holt as a keepsake for the dinner..." later given to Frost $500.

091b: DEDICATION THE GIFT OUTRIGHT THE INAUGURAL ADDRESS Washington, D.C., 1961. [2] 250 no. cc of total printing of 500 (numbered 251-500). "Printed for friends of the Spiral Press..." on p.4 $500.

091c: DEDICATION THE GIFT OUTRIGHT THE INAUGURAL ADDRESS [Washington, D.C.], The Spiral Press, no place [New York], 1961. [] 800 cc in wraps. Printed for Henry Holt and Company as a keepsake for the dinner Robert Frost was given by President Kennedy's Cabinet (Robert Frost Books 10/95.) (See note in 091a above) $250.

092a: IN THE CLEARING Holt, Rinehart & Winston, New York (1962). [1] Tall spiral bound uncorrected proof in light blue wraps (Pharos Books 1/90) $400.

092b: IN THE CLEARING Holt, Rinehart & Winston, New York (1962). [2] 1,500 sgd and no. cc. Issued without dustwrapper. In slipcase $200/300

092c: IN THE CLEARING Holt, Rinehart & Winston, New York (1962). [1] Back panel of dustwrapper noted in two states: white with black lettering; and black with white lettering. Priority unknown (Am Here Books 6/89) $12/60

092d: IN THE CLEARING Holt, Rinehart & Winston, New York (1962). [] First Edition, second printing, specially bound copies in brown leather-like material stamped in gilt and blind; top edges gilt; silk-like endpapers. In slipcase made of same material as binding. Reportedly, a limited number of these were made up to celebrate the book's success (Robert Frost Books 10/95) $200.

092d: IN THE CLEARING Holt, Rinehart & Winston, London (1962). [1] Introduction by Robert Graves not in U.S. edition $15/75

093a: THE PROPHETS REALLY PROPHESY AS MYSTICS THE COMMENTATORS MERELY BY STATISTICS (Spiral Press, New York), 1962. [0] 17,055 cc. Wraps. (Christmas poem: 21 imprints, quantities vary from 50 to 12,500 copies) $35-175

094a: THE CONSTANT SYMBOL Cornelia & Waller Barrett, 1962. [0] 500 cc. Wraps. Printed by Spiral Press, New York $100.

095a: ROBERT FROST ON "EXTRAVAGANCE" Dartmouth, (Hanover), 1963. [] An off-print, in printed wraps, from the alumni magazine (Waiting For Godot 2/87) $125.

096a: THE LETTERS OF ROBERT FROST TO LOUIS UNTERMEYER Holt, Rinehart & Winston, New York (1963). [1] Uncorrected proof in spiral bound pink printed wraps (Wm. Reese Co. 6/92) $150.

096b: THE LETTERS OF ROBERT FROST TO LOUIS UNTERMEYER Holt, Rinehart & Winston, New York (1963). [1] Edited by Louis Untermeyer $10/50

096c: THE LETTERS OF ROBERT FROST TO LOUIS UNTERMEYER Jonathan Cape, London (1964). [1] $12/60

097a: ROBERT FROST: FARM POULTRYMAN Dartmouth Publications, Hanover, New Hampshire, 1963. [0] $12/60

098a: ROBERT FROST AND JOHN BARTLETT *The Record of a Friendship* Holt, Rinehart & Winston, New York (1963). [1] $15/75

099a: ROBERT FROST : HIS AMERICAN SEND-OFF - 1915 Stinehour Press, Lunenburg, Vt. (1963). [] Wraps $125.

100a: IN MEMORY OF ROBERT FROST Amherst, 1963. [0] Wraps. Memorial service at the Johnson Chapel on February 17, 1963 with 11 poems by Frost. 10 pages including cover $125.

101a: WILD GRAPES Scott, Foreman & Co., (Chicago, 1963). [0] Wraps. The poem with questions for students and short biography $75.

102a: SELECTED POEMS OF ROBERT FROST Holt, Rinehart & Winston, New York (1963). [0] Introduction by Robert Graves $25/100

103a: SELECTED LETTERS OF ROBERT FROST Holt, Rinehart & Winston, New York (1964). [] Galley proofs in two spiral bound volumes (Wm. Reese Co. 6/92) $175.

103b: SELECTED LETTERS OF ROBERT FROST Holt, Rinehart & Winston, New York (1964). [1] Edited by Lawrence Thompson $15/75

103c: SELECTED LETTERS OF ROBERT FROST Jonathan Cape, London (1965). [1] $15/75

104a: ROBERT FROST SPEAKS DEPARTMENTALLY Robert Frost Library/ Spiral Press, Amherst, 1965. [] Wraps. (Polyanthos 2/94) $50.

105a: AN UNCOMPLETED REVISION OF "EDUCATION BY POETRY" (Dartmouth, Hanover, 1966.) [] Wraps. Facsimile of Frost's holograph corrections to text, with a note by Edward Connery Lathem $75.

0106a: INTERVIEWS WITH ROBERT FROST Holt, Rinehart & Winston, New York (1966). [] Uncorrected proof in plastic spiral binding (Waiting For Godot Books 2/95) $100.

106b: INTERVIEWS WITH ROBERT FROST Holt, Rinehart & Winston, New York (1966). [1] Edited by Edward Connery Lathem $12/60

106c: INTERVIEWS WITH ROBERT FROST Jonathan Cape, London (1967). [] $12/60

107a: ROBERT FROST AND THE LAWRENCE, MASS. "HIGH SCHOOL BULLETIN..." Grolier Club, New York, 1966. [] Edited by Lathem and Thompson $100.

108a: SELECTED PROSE OF ROBERT FROST Holt, Rinehart & Winston, New York (1966). [1] Edited by Hyde Cox and Edward Connery Lathem $10/50

109a: FROST: THE POET AND HIS POETRY Holt, Rinehart & Winston, New York (1967). [0] Wraps with record by Frost in back pocket. Edited by David Sohn and Richard Tyre $75.

110a: THE POETRY OF ROBERT FROST Holt, Rinehart & Winston, New York (1969). [1] Edited by Edward Connery Lathem. Two volumes $35/75

110b: THE POETRY OF ROBERT FROST Holt, Rinehart & Winston, New York (1969). [1] One volume in dustwrapper priced $10.95, and with "1169" at bottom of text on front flap (also noted without price or "1169" on front flap, assume book club edition) $10/50

110c: THE POETRY OF ROBERT FROST Imprint Society, Barre, Massachusetts, 1971. [2] 1,950 sgd cc. Signed by the designer, Ruzicka. Two volumes. New introduction by Edward Connery Lathem $150/200

111a: ONE FAVORED ACORN Middlebury College, Ripton, 1969. [2] 400 cc. Wraps (ref.b) $150.

112a: STOPPING BY THE WOODS ON A SNOWING EVENING Castalia Press, Easthampton, 1970. [2] 40 cc. Broadside. First separate printing (In Our Time, 1988) $350.

113a: HOLIDAY GREETINGS FROM ROBERT FROST New Hampshire Historical Society, Concord, 1971. [2] 750 cc. Wraps. Reprints Frost's first Christmas poem/card "Christmas Trees" and briefly describes the various poems/cards issued between 1929 and 1963 $50.

114a: FAMILY LETTERS OF ROBERT AND ELINOR FROST State University of New York Press, Albany, New York, 1972. [1] Foreword by Lesley Frost, edited by Arnold Grade $10/50

115a: ROBERT FROST: POETRY AND PROSE Holt, Rinehart & Winston, New York (1972). [0] Edited by Edward Lathem and Lawrance Thompson $15/50

116a: ROBERT FROST ON WRITING Rutgers University Press, New Brunswick (1973). [0] Edited by Elaine Barry $15/50

117a: A TIME TO TALK CONVERSATIONS & INDISCRETIONS Robson (London, 1973). [1] Recorded by Robert Francis (Robert Loren Link 6/90) $10/40

118a: ROBERT FROST 1874-1963 A REMEMBRANCE Amherst College, 1974. [0] 500 cc. Wraps with facsimile of a handwritten fragment $75.

119a: TRIBUTE TO E.A. ROBINSON Godine, Boston, 1974. [2] 1,000 cc. Wraps. Facsimile of the original holograph manuscript (ref.d) $40.

120a: HOW TO READ A POEM (New England Books, Lancaster, New Hampshire, 1975.) [2] 1000 cc. In printed wraps. Prints interview with Frost by Myron Magnet and George Trow (Waiting For Godot Books 2/95) $50.

121a: THE POETRY OF ROBERT FROST Holt, Rinehart, New York (1976). [] (ref.d) $8/40

122a: FOREST FLOWERS Amherst College Library, Amherst, 1978. [2] 400 cc. Wraps. Laid-in is one sheet with history and first form of this poem as "Tutelary Elves" $75.

123a: ROBERT FROST AND SIDNEY COX FORTY YEARS OF FRIENDSHIP University Press of New England, Hanover, 1981. [0] The letters with a foreword by James M. Cox. Connecting text by William R. Evans $10/50

124a: EARLY POEMS BY ROBERT FROST Avenel Books, New York, 1981. [] (Robert Frost Books 10/95) $7/35

125a: PROSE JOTTINGS OF ROBERT FROST Stinehour Press, Lunenburg (1982). [] Quarter cloth in slipcase. Edited by Edward Connery Lathem and Hyde Cox $100/125

126a: AN INTERLUDE WITH ROBERT FROST The Private Press of Frederic Brewer, Bloomington, Indiana, 1982. [2] 110 cc. Correspondence between Frost and J. Albert Robbins (Robert Frost Books 10/95) $75/125

127a: [set of five poems] COME IN, DUST OF SNOW, ONCE BY THE PACIFIC, THE PASTURE, and STOPPING BY THE WOODS Prometheus Press, Grasse [France], 1982. [2] 5 sgd ltr cc (signed by Prokosch and lettered in Greek, alpha-epsilon). Stiff green wraps, front covers with holograph paper labels, variously colored silk ties. Each with tipped-in original watercolor illustration by Frederic Prokosch (George Houle 5/96) $1,250.

128a: [set of five poems] MOWING; NEITHER FAR OUT; THE MIDDLENESS OF THE ROAD; STORM FEAR and DESIGN Prometheus Press, Grasse, 1983. [2] Wraps. Each pamphlet limited to 5 copies signed and illustrated by Frederick Prokosch. Sold originally as a set $1,200.

129a: THE BUTTERFLY Prometheus Press, Grasse, 1984. [2] 5 sgd ltr cc (lettered in Greek letters from alpha to epsilon; and signed by the artist, Frederic Prokosch). Tan wraps with handwritten label. Each copy hand-written by the artist, signed, with an original water-color tipped in. Sixteen-line poem handwritten in pink and black (Bromer Booksellers 3/96) $300.

130a: I WENT TO TURN Prometheus Press, Grasse, 1984. [2] 5 sgd ltr cc (lettered in Greek letters from alpha to epsilon; and signed by the artist, Frederic Prokosch). Tan wraps with handwritten label. Each copy hand-written on yellow paper by the artist, signed, with an original water-color tipped in. Sixteen-line poem hand-written in pink and black (Bromer Booksellers 3/96) $300.

131a: LOVE AT THE LIPS Prometheus Press, Grasse, 1984. [2] 5 sgd ltr cc (lettered in Greek letters from alpha to epsilon; and signed by the artist, Frederic Prokosch). Tan wraps with handwritten label. Each copy hand-written by the artist, signed, with an original watercolor tipped in. Sixteen-line poem handwritten in pink and black (Bromer Booksellers 3/96) $300.

132a: NOW NO JOY Prometheus Press, Grasse, 1984. [2] 5 sgd ltr cc (lettered in Greek letters from alpha to epsilon; and signed by the artist, Frederic

Prokosch). Tan wraps with handwritten label. Each copy handwritten by the artist, signed, with an original watercolor tipped in. Sixteen-line poem hand-written in pink and black (Bromer Booksellers 3/96) $300.

133a: THE ROAD NOT TAKEN Prometheus Press, Grasse, 1984. [2] 5 sgd ltr cc (lettered in Greek letters from alpha to epsilon; and signed by the artist, Frederic Prokosch). Tan wraps with handwritten label. Each copy hand-written on yellow paper by the artist, signed, with an original water-color tipped in. Sixteen-line poem hand-written in pink and black (Bromer Booksellers 3/96) $300.

134a: BIRCHES Henry Holt, New York, 1988. [] $10/40

135a: ROBERT FROST *Toward the Source, Against the Stream* Writers in Performance, New York, 1990. [2] 350 cc. Wraps $40.

136a: TWO WINTERY POEMS Brookhaven Press, no place or date. [] Illustrated folded card (Chloe's Books) $30.

137a: SOME PEOPLE SEEM TO THINK Quintessence Press, no place or date. [] Illustrated broadside $30.

138a: SWEET AND BITTER BARK... The Nature Company, Berkeley, 1992. [] Dark blue cloth with cream colored cover label. Issued without dustwrapper? (Sun Moon Bear Rare Books 9/96) $25.

William Goyen

WILLIAM GOYEN
(1915-1984)

Goyen was born in Trinity, Texas. He was educated at Rice University and then served in the U.S. Navy throughout World War II. He was a critic and reviewer for the *New York Times* from 1950 to 1965, and senior editor at McGraw Hill from 1966 to 1972. During and after this period he taught at various universities.

Ref.c includes 10 plays adapted by Goyen from his own or other writers works which have not been included herein. These are mimeographed sheets for the most part and we have only seen one set catalogued, that was "Christy" (New York, 1964) by Glenn Horowitz, Catalog 11 at $225.

REFERENCES:

(a) Lepper, Gary M. A BIBLIOGRAPHICAL REFERENCE TO SEVENTY-FIVE MODERN AMERICAN AUTHORS. Berkeley: Serendipity Books, 1976.

(b) Bruccoli & Clark. FIRST PRINTINGS OF AMERICAN AUTHORS. Detroit: Gale Research (1979). Volume 4.

(c) Wright, Stuart. WILLIAM GOYEN *A Descriptive Bibliography, 1938-1985*. Westport, Conn.: Meckler Publishing (1986).

001a: THE HOUSE OF BREATH Random House, New York (1950). [1] 4,000 cc (quantity-ref.c). One of Greene's *Fifty Best Books on Texas*. (A variant with top edge gray noted by Wm. Reese Co. Cat. 63) $25/125

001b: THE HOUSE OF BREATH Chatto & Windus, London, 1951. [0] 3,000 cc (quantity-ref.c) $15/75

001c: THE HOUSE OF BREATH Random House / Bookworks, New York / Berkeley (1975). [2] 1,500 copies. Adds note by Goyen, 25th Anniversary Edition, quantity stated on copyright page $20/50

001d: THE HOUSE OF BREATH Random House / Bookworks, New York / Berkeley (1975). [2] 7,500 cc. Wraps. Issued simultaneously. Quantity stated on copyright page $25.

002a: GHOST AND FLESH STORIES AND TALES Random House, New York (1952). [1] 2,000 cc (quantity-ref.c) $25/100

003a: THE LAZY ONES New Directions (Norfolk, 1952). [0] Translation of Cossery's book (ref.b) $15/75

003b: THE LAZY ONES Peter Owen, London, 1952. [] Published simultaneously with 003a (ref.c) $15/75

004a: A SHAPE OF LIGHT Southwest Review, no place, 1952. [] Off-print from Winter issue. Stapled on left margin (H. E. Turlington 9/90) $60.

005a: THE PEOPLE OF JOSEPH GLASSCO C. Viviano, New York (1953). [0] Wraps. All text by Goyen $75.

006a: IN A FARTHER COUNTRY Random House, New York (1955). [0] 2,500 cc (quantity-ref.c) $20/100

006b: IN A FARTHER COUNTRY Peter Owen, London (1962). [1] $12/60

006c: IN A FARTHER COUNTRY Peter Owen, London (1962). [0] about 100 cc of 006b. Stamped "...Dufour Editions.." on copyright page and distributed in U.S. $25/75

007a: THE FACES OF BLOOD KINDRED Random House (New York, 1960). [1] $12/60

008a: THE FAIR SISTER Doubleday, Garden City (1963). [1] $12/60

008b: SAVATA, MY FAIR SISTER Peter Owen, London (1963). [0] New title $10/50

009a: SHORT STORIES Vandenhoeck & Ruprecht Gottingen (Germany, 1964). [0] Includes first publication of "The Thief Coyote" $75

010a: JOTTINGS FROM A DUBLIN JOURNAL (Show, no place, 1965.) [0] 4 page off-print from magazine (H. E. Turlington 6/91) $60.

011a: MY ANTONIA *A Critical Commentary* American R.D.M., New York (1966). [0] Wraps $50.

012a: RALPH ELLISON'S INVISIBLE MAN *A Critical Commentary*. American R.D.M., New York (1966). [0] Yellowish-green, light-grayish blue and white wraps. (Second printing in red, white and black wraps {ref.c}) $50.

013a: THE THIEF COYOTE Southwest Review, place?, 1971. (Summer.) [] Wraps. Off-print (H. E. Turlington 12/94) $50.

014a: A BOOK OF JESUS Doubleday, Garden City, 1973. [] Long printer's galley proofs (H. E. Turlington 9/90) $200.

014b: A BOOK OF JESUS Doubleday, Garden City, 1973. [1] Uncorrected proof in mustard card covers, ring-bound and with cover label (Serendipity Books #40) $100.

014c: A BOOK OF JESUS Doubleday, Garden City, 1973. [1] 5,500 cc (quantity-ref.c). Also noted with wrap-around band (H. E. Turlington 9/90) $10/40

015a: SELECTED WRITINGS OF WILLIAM GOYEN Random House, New York / Berkeley (1974). [] Uncorrected proof in string tied signatures. Laid in sample dustwrapper (H. E. Turlington 9/90) $75/125

015b: SELECTED WRITINGS OF WILLIAM GOYEN Random House, New York (1974). [] Uncorrected proof in white wraps (Anacapa Books 3/95) $75.

015c: SELECTED WRITINGS OF WILLIAM GOYEN Random House, New York / Berkeley (1974). [1] 1,500 cc (quantity on copyright page) $12/60

015d: SELECTED WRITINGS OF WILLIAM GOYEN Random House, New York / Berkeley (1974). [1] Wraps. 7,500 cc (quantity on copyright page) $25.

016a: COME, THE RESTORER Doubleday, Garden City, 1974. [] Uncorrected proof in spiral-bound wraps (Anacapa Books 3/95) $100

016b: COME, THE RESTORER Doubleday, Garden City, 1974. [1] 6,000 cc (quantity-ref.c). (Published 10/4/74 @ $5.95) $10/40

017a: THE COLLECTED STORIES OF WILLIAM GOYEN Doubleday, Garden, 1975. [] Long sheets of galley proofs (H. E. Turlington 9/90) $100.

017b: THE COLLECTED STORIES OF WILLIAM GOYEN Doubleday, Garden City, 1975. [] Uncorrected proof in red wraps $75.

017c: THE COLLECTED STORIES OF WILLIAM GOYEN Doubleday, Garden City, 1975. [1] (Ref.b.) 4,000 cc (ref.c) $10/50

018a: NINE POEMS Albondocani, New York, 1976. [2] 26 sgd ltr cc. Wraps (ref.b) $150.

018b: NINE POEMS Albondocani, New York, 1976. [2] 200 sgd no. cc. Wraps (ref.b) $60.

019a: WHILE YOU WERE AWAY - A Talk Delivered By Wm. Goyen at Houston Public Library…

Houston Public Library (Houston, 1978). [0] Wraps (ref.b) $60.

020a: SIMON'S CASTLE AND OTHER STORIES Deutscher..., Munich (1978). [] Wraps. English and German text (H. E. Turlington 9/90) $50.

021a: ARTHUR BOND Palaemon Press (Winston-Salem, 1979). [2] 30 cc. Marbled wraps. Numbered in Roman. For distribution by author and publisher (out of 230 copies). (Ref.c states 226 copies in total were issued so perhaps this was only 26 cc) $100.

021b: ARTHUR BOND Palaemon Press (Winston-Salem, 1979). [2] 200 sgd no. cc (out of 230 cc.) Wraps (ref.c) $50.

022a: WONDERFUL PLANT Palaemon Press (Winston-Salem, 1980). [2] 60 sgd no. cc (Roman numerals). Not For Sale. Issued in acetate dustwrapper without slipcase (ref.c) $100.

022b: WONDERFUL PLANT Palaemon Press (Winston-Salem, 1980). [2] 100 sgd no. cc. Issued in acetate dustwrapper (ref.c) $60.

023a: PRECIOUS DOOR Red Ozier Press, no place, 1981. [2] 115 sgd no. cc. Issued without dustwrapper or slipcase. Signed by Goyen and the artist John DePol (ref.c) $200.

024a: NEW WORK AND WORK IN PROGRESS Palaemon Press (Winston-Salem, 1983). [2] 40 sgd no. cc. Issued without dustwrapper. Signed by Goyen and Reginald Gibbons (interviewer) (ref.c) $100.

024b: NEW WORK AND WORK IN PROGRESS Palaemon Press (Winston-Salem, 1983). [2] 160 sgd cc (not numbered) $40.

025a: ARCADIO Potter, New York (1983). [] Uncorrected proof in pumpkin wraps (Bev Chaney 9/91) $60.

025b: ARCADIO Potter, New York (1983). [3] Also states "First Edition" $8/40

026a: HAD I A HUNDRED MOUTHS Potter, New York (1985). [] Uncorrected proof in gray wraps $60.

026b: HAD I A HUNDRED MOUTHS Potter, New York (1985). [3] Also states "First Edition." New and selected stories 1947-1983 with introduction by Joyce Carol Oates. $10/40

026b: HAD I A HUNDRED MOUTHS Potter, New York (1985). [3] Also states "First Edition." Pictorial wrappers (Bev Chaney, Jr. 3/97) $15.

027a: HALF A LOOK OF CAIN *A Fantastical Narrative* Triquarterly Books / Northwestern University Press, Evanston (1994). [] (Between the Covers 8/95) $6/30

Zane Grey.

ZANE GREY
(1872 - 1939)

Zane Grey was born in Zanesville, Ohio in 1872 and graduated from the University of Pennsylvania in 1896. He was a prolific writer of adventure stories taking place in the West and Southwest. All of his stories contain vivid topographical detail. Grey is best known for *Riders of The Purple Sage* (1912).

While we have not included the following three books as having been Grey's, we feel they should be noted.

> *Cruise of the Fisherman*, New York: Harper, 1929. [1] Written by Grey's son Romer (at an early age, which leads many to believe this book was written with a great deal of help from his father). We would value this title at $500/750.
>
> *The "Fisherman" Under the Southern Cross*, New York: Harper, 1930. [] Also written by Grey's son Romer (again, probably with the help of his father). Scarce. We would value this title at $750/1,500.
>
> *Adventures of a Deep-Sea Angler*, New York: Harper, 1930. [1] Written by Grey's brother R.C. Grey (believed to have been heavily edited by Zane Grey). $500/750.

The prices before 1920 in this guide are for fine copies without dustwrappers as dustwrappers before 1920 are rare. Nice copies in dustwrappers would probably be two to five times the prices shown.

We wish to thank Edward and Judith Myers of Country Lane Books for allowing us to use their bibliographic work in the preparation of this guide; James Vickers, a past president of the Zane Grey's West Society; and Ric Olmsted of W.R. Olmsted Sporting Books in British Columbia, Canada, for their assistance.

REFERENCES:

(a) Myers, Edward and Judith. A BIBLIOGRAPHICAL CHECK LIST AND PRICE GUIDE FOR THE WRITINGS OF ZANE GREY. New Hartford, Conn.: Country Lane Books, 1995.

(b) Eppard, Philip B. (editor). FIRST PRINTINGS OF AMERICAN AUTHORS. Volume 5. Detroit: Gale Research (1987). Used for English editions; however, no first edition identification was provided.

(c) Wheeler, Dr. Joe L. ZANE GREY'S WEST. Volume I through Volume VII. (Texas / Annapolis): 1989-1991.

001a: BETTY ZANE Charles Francis Press, New York (1903). [0] No mention of the edition on the title page. Issued in glassine dustwrapper $3,500.

001b: BETTY ZANE Charles Francis Press, New York (1903). [] States "Second Edition" in small letters near the center of the title page. Issued in glassine dustwrapper $1,000.

001c: BETTY ZANE Hodder & Stoughton, London, 1920. [] $200/1,000

001d: BETTY ZANE Saalfield, Akron (1940). [] Abridged edition (George Houle 11/89) $50.

002a: THE SPIRIT OF THE BORDER A.L. Burt, New York (1906). [0] With 4 pages of advertisements and Burt's address listed as 52-58 Duane Street on each page (ref.a). Ref.b states earliest copies have ads at back headed "Good fiction worth reading." First page begins "Colonial Free Lance." Second page begins "Darnley." Third page begins "Guy Fawkes." Fourth page begins "Winsor Castle." Also, first page lists 5 books, other pages no more than 3 books. Ed Myers (11/92) stated that he believed the “R” in “Remembered” in last line on p. 8 is the important point. It was dropped in later printings--also grayish-green cloth vs. light blue in later. $750.

002b: THE SPIRIT OF THE BORDER Laurie, London (1921). [] (Although ref.c shows 1920 using U.S. sheets) $150/750

002c: THE SPIRIT OF THE BORDER Hodder & Stoughton, London, no date. [0] (James Vickers' collection) $150/750

003a: TARPON THE SILVER KING (New York and Cuba Mail Steamship Co., New York, 1906.) [0] Wraps. Grey's name on third page at bottom (ref.c). Not in ref. a $1,000.

004a: THE LAST OF THE PLAINSMEN Outing Publishing Co., New York, 1908. [0] $450.

004b: THE LAST OF THE PLAINSMEN Hodder & Stoughton, London, 1908. [] Ref.b had 1909 but assume ref.c is correct as 1908 $300.

004c: THE LAST OF THE PLAINSMEN A.C. McClurg, New York, 1909. [0] With “Outing” on spine $200.

004d: THE LAST OF THE PLAINSMEN A.C. McClurg, New York, 1911 [] “Second Edition” on title page. McClurg on title page and on spine $150.

005a: THE LAST TRAIL A.L. Burt, New York (1909). [0] With two pages of advertisements listing 52-58 Duane Street as Burt's address. The address would also appear on dustwrapper (ref.a). Ref.b & c call for six pages of ads with page 1 beginning with "Abner Daniel," page 2 "The Circle," page 3 "The House on Cherry Street," page 4 "Max," page 5 "The Reconstructed Marriage," page 6 "Susan Clegg..." and ends with "The Younger Set." Ref.b & c go on to identify the second printing as having 9 pages of ads and the third printing having 11 pages of ads. Ed Myers believes that the address on Duane Street is important as Burt moved about 1910. James Vickers believes the issue with 6 pages of ads was after they moved. $600.

005b: THE LAST TRAIL Laurie, London (1920). [] $150/750

005c: THE LAST TRAIL Hodder & Staughton, London, no date. [0] (James Vickers collection) $150/750

006a: NASSAU CUBA YUCATAN MEXICO A PERSONAL NOTE OF APPRECIATION OF THESE NEARBY FOREIGN LANDS New York and Cuba Mail Steam Ship Co., New York, 1909. [0] Wraps. (Not in ref.a) $1,000.

006b: NASSAU CUBA YUCATAN MEXICO A PERSONAL NOTE OF APPRECIATION OF THESE NEARBY FOREIGN LANDS Zane Grey Collector, Williamsport, Md., 1976. [] 500 cc. Wraps. A facsimile edition edited by G.M. Farley $50.

007a: THE SHORT STOP A.C. McClure, New York, 1909. [1] "Published June, 1909" $600.

007b: THE SHORT STOP Laurie, London (1920). [] $150/750

008a: THE HERITAGE OF THE DESERT Harper & Bros., New York, 1910. [1] "Published September 1910." No code letters on copyright page $400.

008b: THE HERITAGE OF THE DESERT Nelson, London, no date [1918]. [0] James Vickers collection) $100.

008c: DESERT HERITAGE World, London, 1965. [] Wraps. New title $35.

009a: THE YOUNG FORESTER Harper & Bros., New York, 1910. [1] "Published October 1910." No code letters on copyright page $500

009b: THE YOUNG FORESTER Nelson, London, no date [circa 1922]. [] $100/500

010a: THE YOUNG PITCHER Harper & Bros., New York, 1911. [1] "Published March, 1911." No code letters on copyright page $600.

010b: THE YOUNG PITCHER Lloyds, London (1919). [] $200.

011a: THE YOUNG LION HUNTER Harper & Bros., New York, 1911. [1] "Published October 1911." No code letters on copyright page $500.

011b: THE YOUNG LION HUNTER Lloyds, London (1919). [1] "Published October, 1911" $200.

012a: RIDERS OF THE PURPLE SAGE Harper & Bros., New York, 1912. [] "Advance copy for private distribution. Not for sale." Red boards with printed label on cover and binding sample glued to back of front cover. (George R. Minkoff 11/90) $2,500.

012b: RIDERS OF THE PURPLE SAGE Harper & Bros., New York, 1912. [1] "Published January 1912." No code letters on copyright page. (Noted with "H-M" on copyright page but this is a later printing). A copy in chipped, stained, and repaired dustwrapper brought $6,000 at auction in 1993) $1,500.

012c: RIDERS OF THE PURPLE SAGE Harper & Bros., New York (1921). [0] Contains code letters "K-V." Color plates by W. Herbert Dunton $250/1,250

012d: RIDERS OF THE PURPLE SAGE Nelson, London, no date [1921]. [0] (James Vickers collection) $150/750

013a: KEN WARD IN THE JUNGLE Harper & Bros., New York, 1912. [1] "Published September 1912." Code letters "H-M" on copyright page $500.

013b: KEN WARD IN THE JUNGLE Nelson, London (1919). [] $150.

014a: DESERT GOLD Harper & Bros., New York, 1913. [0] Code letters [0] "C-N" on copyright page $300.

015a: THE LIGHT OF WESTERN STARS Harper & Bros., New York, 1914. [1] "Published January 1914" and code letters "M-N" on copyright page $275.

015b: THE LIGHT OF WESTERN STARS Nelson, London (1918). [] $100.

016a: THE LONE STAR RANGER Harper & Bros., New York, 1915. [1] "Published January 1915" and code letters "M-O" on copyright page. Variant in reddish-brown pictorial cloth (Country Lane Books-11/92) $250.

017a: THE RAINBOW TRAIL Harper & Bros., New York (1915). [1] "Published August 1915" and code letters "F-P" on copyright page $250.

018a: THE BORDER LEGION... Harper & Bros., New York (1916). [1] "Published May 1916" and code letters "E-Q" on copyright page $250.

019a: WILDFIRE Harper & Bros., New York (1917). [1] "Published January 1917" and code letters "L-Q" on copyright page $200.

019b: WILDFIRE Nelson, London (1920). [] $50/300

020a: THE U.P. TRAIL Harper & Bros., New York (1918). [1] "Published January 1918" and code letters "A-S" on copyright page. Olive-green cloth. Also noted, a variant in emerald green cloth with a somewhat rougher vertical grain (Country Lane Books 10/96.) Also an issue with correct codes in red flexible leatherette. Possibly an Armed Services edition like 072b (James Vickers collection $150.

020b: THE ROARING U.P. TRAIL Hodder & Stoughton, London (1918). [] $125.

021a: THE DESERT OF WHEAT Harper & Bros., New York (1919). [1] "Published January 1919" and code letters "A-T" on copyright page $100.

021b: THE DESERT OF WHEAT Hodder & Stoughton, London (1919). [] $75.

022a: TALES OF FISHES Harper & Bros., New York (1919). [1] 50 copies bound in quarter leather for presentation (quantities provided by Olmsted from Harper and Zane Grey correspondence) $1,500.

022b: TALES OF FISHES Harper & Bros., New York (1919). [1] "Published June 1919" and code letters "F-T" on copyright page $200.

022c: TALES OF FISHES Hodder & Stoughton, London (1920) [] $200/750

023a: GREAT GAME FISHING AT CATALINA Santa Catalina Island Co., 1919 [0] 32 pages in stiff pictorial wraps. Issued in envelope $1,000.

024a: THE MAN OF THE FOREST Harper & Bros., New York (1920). [1] "Published January 1920" and code letters "A-U" on copyright page $125/600

025a: THE REDHEADED OUTFIELD AND OTHER STORIES Grosset & Dunlap, New York (1920). [0] Copies have been noted with and without a frontis, but Myers believes that copies with the frontispiece are later. 11 titles should be listed on first page of ads with the last being *The Last of The Great Scouts*. 18 titles on rear of dustwrapper excluding *Tales of Fishes* and *The Man of The Forest*. Bindings have been noted in both tan and green cloth. Also noted a copy without the frontis and with 11 titles listed on first page of ads, however the rear panel of dustwrapper lists 20 titles (Kugelman & Bent 10/96) $150/750

026a: THE MYSTERIOUS RIDER Harper & Bros., New York (1921). [1] "Published January 1921" and code letters "I-U" on copyright page $125/600

026b: THE MYSTERIOUS RIDER Hodder & Stoughton, London (1921). [] $50/250

027a: TO THE LAST MAN Harper & Bros. NY (1921) [1] Also has code letters "K-V" on copyright page $75/450

027b: TO THE LAST MAN Hodder & Stoughton, London (1922). [] $50/250

028a: THE DAY OF THE BEAST Harper & Bros., New York (1922). [1] Also has code letters "G-W" on copyright page $200/1,000

029a: TALES OF LONELY TRAILS Harper & Bros., New York (1922). [1] Few copies bound in quarter leather and signed by Grey in purple ink for presentation (Country Lane Books 11/92) $1,000/1,500

029b: TALES OF LONELY TRAILS Harper & Bros., New York (1922). [1] Also contains code letters "G-W" on copyright page (the same letter code as the previous title) 125/600

029c: TALES OF LONELY TRAILS Hodder & Stoughton, London (1922). [] $50/250

030a: FISHING IN THE GULF STREAM Miami Angler's Club, Miami, no date [1922]. [] 31 pages in stiff pictorial wraps. (Olmsted catalogued as "only one known copy" in 1996) $1,250

031a: THE BONEFISH BRIGADE Zane Grey, (Pasadena,) 1922. [0] Stiched wraps with tassel. "Christmas 1922" on title page. Illustrated by Bessie Bethal Crank $1,250.

032a: WANDERER OF THE WASTELAND Harper & Bros., New York (1923). [1] Also contains code letters "L-W" on copyright page. There is also a printing stating first edition, with the code letters "A-X" (The published year) but this is later $75/400

032b: WANDERER OF THE WASTELAND Hodder & Stoughton, London (1923). [] $50/250

033a: TAPPAN'S BURRO Harper & Bros., New York (1923). [1] Also contains code letters "I-X" on copyright page $75/400

033b: TAPPAN'S BURRO Hodder & Stoughton, London (1923). [] $50/200

034a: CALL OF THE CANYON Harper & Bros., New York, 1924. [1] Also contains code letters "K-X" on copyright page $75/400

035a: ROPING LIONS IN THE GRAND CANYON Harper & Bros. New York (1924). [0] Code letters "B-Y" on copyright page $150/600

035b: ROPING LIONS IN THE GRAND CANYON Hodder & Stoughton, London (1924). [0] $75/300

036a: TALES OF SOUTHERN RIVERS Harper & Bros., New York (1924). [1] Fewer than 12 copies bound in quarter leather for presentation. (Olmsted 1997) $1,500/2,000

036b: TALES OF SOUTHERN RIVERS Harper & Bros., New York (1924). [1] Also contains code letters "H-Y" on copyright page $175/650

036c: TALES OF SOUTHERN RIVERS Hodder & Stoughton, London (1924). [0] "H-Y" on copyright page. U.S. sheets $125/400

037a: THE THUNDERING HERD Harper & Bros., New York, 1925. [1] Also contains code letters "L-Y" on copyright page $100/500

037b: THE THUNDERING HERD Hodder & Stoughton, London (1925). [] $35/150

038a: THE VANISHING AMERICAN Harper & Bros., New York, 1925. [1] Also contains code letters "I-Z" on copyright page $60/300

038b: THE VANISHING INDIAN Hodder & Stoughton, London (1926). [] $30/150

039a: TALES OF FISHING VIRGIN SEAS Harper & Bros., New York, 1925. [1] Also contains code letters "K-Z" on copyright page. There was also a publisher's presentation binding in three-quarters morocco (Detering Book Gallery 12/92) $175/650

039b: TALES OF FISHING VIRGIN SEAS Hodder & Stoughton, London (1926). [] $125/400

040a: UNDER THE TONTO RIM Harper & Bros., New York, 1926. [1] Also contains code letters "F-A" on copyright page $60/300

040b: UNDER THE TONTO RIM Hodder & Stoughton, London, no date [1927]. [] $25/125

041a: TALES OF AN ANGLER'S ELDORADO Harper & Bros., New York / New Zealand, 1926. [] About 100 deluxe uncut copies in quarter red morocco bound by Harper exclusively for Grey's use. Included special color frontis painting not in trade edition (Olmsted 1997) $1,500/2,000

041b: TALES OF AN ANGLER'S ELDORADO Harper & Bros., New York / New Zealand, 1926. [1] Also contains code letters "G-A." $175/650

041c: TALES OF AN ANGLER'S ELDORADO Hodder & Stoughton, London, 1926. [] (J & J House Books--11/92) $125/400

042a: TALES OF SWORDFISH AND TUNA Harper & Bros., New York, 1927. [] Presentation copies bound in quarter morocco with two special frontis paintings (Olmsted 1997) $1,500/2,000

042b: TALES OF SWORDFISH AND TUNA Harper & Bros., New York, 1927. [1] Also contains code letters "H-B" on copyright page $250/750

042c: TALES OF SWORDFISH AND TUNA Hodder & Stoughton, London (1927). [] $150/400

043a: FORLORN RIVER Harper & Bros., New York, 1927. [1] Also contains code letters "H-B" on copyright page $60/300

043b: FORLORN RIVER Hodder & Stoughton, London (1928). [] $25/125

044a: NEVADA Harper & Bros., New York, 1928. [] Publisher's dummy. 2 pp. publisher's synopsis, 4 pp. text; in dustwrapper (George Houle 6/91) $350/750

044b: NEVADA Harper & Bros., New York, 1928. [1] Also contains code letters "B-C" on copyright page $75/350

044c: NEVADA Hodder & Stoughton, London, 1928. [] $30/150

045a: TALES OF FRESH WATER FISHING Harper & Bros., New York, 1928. [1] Code letters "F-C." About 50 copies bound in quarter leather for presentation (Olmsted 1997) $1,500/2,000

045b: TALES OF FRESH WATER FISHING Harper & Bros., New York, 1928. [1] Code letters "F-C" $250/750

045c: TALES OF FRESH WATER FISHING Hodder & Stoughton, London (1928). [] $150/500

046a: WILD HORSE MESA Harper & Bros., New York, 1928. [1] Also contains code letters "G-C" $75/350

046b: WILD HORSE MESA Hodder & Stoughton, London (1928). [] $25/125

047a: DON THE STORY OF A LION DOG Harper & Bros., New York, 1928. [1] Also has code letters "G-C" $150/600

048a: ZANE GREY: THE MAN AND HIS WORK Harper & Bros., New York (1928). [] 8vo. Gilt stamped leatherette. Published for Friends of the Author. Issued without dustwrapper (Olmsted 1997). $250.

048b: ZANE GREY: THE MAN AND HIS WORK Harper, New York (1928). [] Trade edition in stiff yellow wraps stamped in green (Olmsted 1997) $250.

049a: FIGHTING CARAVANS Harper & Bros., New York, 1929. [1] Also has code letters "H-D" $75/350

049b: FIGHTING CARAVANS Hodder & Stoughton, London (1930). [] $25/125

050a: THE WOLF TRACKER Harper & Bros., New York, 1930. [1] Code letters "C-E $250/750

051a: THE SHEPHERD OF GUADALOUPE Harper & Bros., New York, 1930. [1] Also has code letters "C-E". Noted with green wrap-around band: "With the publication of this book will be celebrated the Twentieth Anniversary of Zane Grey's association with Harper..." (George Houle 5/96). There was also a 4-page pamphlet laid in some copies "Celebrating 20 years …" which would add to value if present $75/350

051b: THE SHEPHERD OF GUADALOUPE Hodder & Stoughton, London (1930). [] $30/150

052a: ZANE GREY'S BOOK OF CAMPS AND TRAILS Harper & Bros., New York, 1931. [0] Code letters "G-F" $300/1,000

053a: TALES OF TAHITIAN WATERS Harper & Bros. New York, 1931. [1] Also has code letters "I-F." At least 10 different binding states. Gilt stamped turquoise cloth is first (Olmsted 1997) $300/1,000

053b: TALES OF TAHITIAN WATERS Harper & Bros. New York, 1931. [1] Other bindings $250/900

053c: TALES OF TAHITIAN WATERS Hodder & Stoughton, London (1931). [] $200/750

054a: SUNSET PASS Harper & Bros., New York, 1931. [1] Also has code letters "K-F" $75/350

054b: SUNSET PASS Hodder & Stoughton, London (1931). [] $30/150

055a: ARIZONA AMES Harper & Bros., New York, 1932. [1] Also has code letters "I-F" $75/350

055b: ARIZONA AMES Hodder & Stoughton, London (1932). [] $25/125

056a: ROBBER'S ROOST Harper & Bros., New York, 1932. [1] Also has code letters "F-G" $75/350

056b: ROBBER'S ROOST Hodder & Stoughton, London (1932). [] $25/125

056c: THIEVES' CANYON World London, 1965. [0] Wraps. New title $30.

057a: THE DRIFT FENCE Harper & Bros., New York, 1933. [1] Also has code letters "K-G" $60/300

057b: THE DRIFT FENCE Hodder & Stoughton, London, 1933. [1] $25/125

058a: THE HASH KNIFE OUTFIT Harper & Bros., New York, 1933. [1] Also has code letters "G-H" $60/300

058b: THE HASH KNIFE OUTFIT Hodder & Stoughton, London (1933). [] $30/150

059a: THE GREAT MAKO American Museum of Natural History, New York, 1934. [] Offprint of article from Vol. 34 No. 3 of *Natural History* with eleven black and white photos by Grey. Issued in lime white paperwraps stapled on left (Olmsted 1997) $100.

060a: THE CODE OF THE WEST Harper & Bros., New York, 1934. [1] Also has code letters "B-I" $50/250

060b: THE CODE OF THE WEST Hodder & Stoughton,, London, (1934). [] $25/125

061a: THUNDER MOUNTAIN Harper & Bros., New York, 1935. [1] Also has code letters "B-K" $50/250

061b: THUNDER MOUNTAIN Hodder & Stoughton, London (1935). [] $25/125

061c: THUNDER MOUNTAIN Grosset & Dunlap, New York, no date. [] Signed edition. Issued in slipcase (Dinkytown Antiquarian Books 1/96) $175/250

062a: THE TRAIL DRIVER Harper & Bros., New York, 1936. [1] Also has code letters "M-K" $60/300

062b: THE TRAIL DRIVER Hodder & Stoughton, London (1936). [] $25/125

063a: FLY FISHING Ibbotson Horrocks, New York, 1936. [] 7 page story in wraps $350.

064a: THE LOST WAGON TRAIN Harper & Bros., New York, 1936. [1] Also has code letters "G-L" $60/300

064b: THE LOST WAGON TRAIN Hodder & Stoughton, London (1936). [] $25/125

065a: AN AMERICAN ANGLER IN AUSTRALIA Harper & Bros., New York, 1937. [1] Fewer than 10 copies bound in quarter morocco for presentation (Olmstead 1997) $2,500/3,000

065b: AN AMERICAN ANGLER IN AUSTRALIA Harper & Bros., New York, 1937. [1] Also has code letters "B-M" $250/750

065c: AN AMERICAN ANGLER IN AUSTRALIA Hodder & Stoughton, London (1937). [] $200/500

066a: WEST OF THE PECOS Harper & Bros., New York, 1937. [1] Also has code letters "C-M" $75/350

066b: WEST OF THE PECOS Hodder & Stoughton, London (1937). [] $30/150

067a: RAIDERS OF SPANISH PEAKS Harper & Bros., New York, 1938. [1] Also has code letters "D-N" $50/250

067b: RAIDERS OF SPANISH PEAKS Hodder & Stoughton, London (1938). [] $25/125

068a: KNIGHTS OF THE RANGE Harper & Bros., New York, 1939. [1] Also has code letters "M-N" $50/250

068b: KNIGHTS OF THE RANGE Hodder & Stoughton, London (1939). [] $25/125

069a: WESTERN UNION Harper & Bros., New York, 1939. [1] Also has code letters "I-O" $50/250

069b: WESTERN UNION Hodder & Stoughton, London (1939). [] $25/125

070a: THIRTY THOUSAND ON THE HOOF Harper & Bros., New York (1940). [1] Also has code letters "G-P" $50/250

070b: THIRTY THOUSAND ON THE HOOF Hodder & Stoughton, London (1940). [] $25/125

071a: TWIN SOMBREROS Harper & Bros., New York (1940). [1] Also has code letters "C-Q" $50/250

071b: TWIN SOMBREROS Hodder & Stoughton, London (1942). [] $30/150

072a: MAJESTY'S RANCHO Harper & Bros., New York (1942). [1] Also has code letters "C-R." (Note: copyrighted in 1938 but published in 1942 $50/250

072b: MAJESTY'S RANCHO Harper & Bros., New York (1942). [1] Variant of first on thinner paper. First stated. "Service Edition" on front panel of plain printed dustwrapper $50/175

073a: ZANE GREY OMNIBUS Harper & Bros., New York (1943). [0] Code letters "B-S." Issued without dustwrapper $300.

073b: ZANE GREY OMNIBUS Harper & Bros., New York (1943). [0] Code letters "C-S." The second edition issued as a textbook for the schools. Also issued without dustwrapper $125.

073c: ZANE GREY ROUND UP Grosset & Dunlap, New York (1943). [0] New title with pictorial dustwrapper $25/100

074a: STAIRS OF THE SAND Harper & Bros., New York (1928 [1943]). [1] Also has code letters "C-S." Actually published in 1943 $50/250

074b: STAIRS OF THE SAND Hodder & Stoughton, London (1943). [] $25/125

075a: THE WILDERNESS TREK Harper & Bros., New York (1944). [1] Also has code letters "E-T" $50/250

075b: THE WILDERNESS TREK Hodder & Stoughton, London (1945). [] $25/125

076a: SHADOW ON THE TRAIL Harper & Bros., New York (1946). [1] Also has code letters "A-V" $40/200

076b: SHADOW ON THE TRAIL Hodder & Stoughton, London (1947). [] $20/100

077a: VALLEY OF WILD HORSES Harper & Bros., New York (1947). [1] Also has code letters "B-W" $40/200

077b: VALLEY OF WILD HORSES Hodder & Stoughton, London (1947). [] $20/100

078a: KING OF THE ROYAL MOUNTED and GHOST GUNS OF ROARING RIVER Whitman Racine (Wisconsin, 1946). [0] "Based on famous newspaper strip" $25/100

079a: ROGUE RIVER FEUD Harper & Bros., New York (1930 [1948]). [0] Code letters "C-X." Mr. Myers notes that this is rarely seen. Actually published in 1948 $60/300

079b: ROGUE RIVER FEUD Hodder & Stoughton, London (1949). [] $25/125

080a: THE DEER STALKER Harper & Bros., New York (1925 [1949]). [1] Also has code letters Actually published in 1949. "D-Y." First issue dustwrapper without *Christian Herald* announcement (Country Lane Books 11/90) $30/150

080b: THE DEER STALKER Harper & Bros., New York (1925 [1949]) [1] Second issue dustwrapper with *Christian Herald* announcement $30/100

080c: THE DEER STALKER Hodder & Stoughton, London (1950). [] (1949 per Hawthorn Books; probably © 1949) $15/75

081a: THE MAVERICK QUEEN Harper & Bros., New York (1950). [1] Also has code letters "D-Z" $30/150

082a: THE DUDE RANGER Harper & Bros., New York (1951). [1] Also has code letters "F-A" $30/150

082b: THE DUDE RANGER Hodder & Stoughton, London (1952). [] $15/75

083a: CAPTIVES OF THE DESERT Harper & Bros., New York (1926 [1952]). [0] Code letters "B-B." Actually published in 1952 $50/200

083b: CAPTIVES OF THE DESERT Hodder & Stoughton, London (1953). [] $30/150

084a: ZANE GREY'S ADVENTURES IN FISHING Harper & Bros., New York (1952). [1] Also has code letters "I-B." Edited by Ed Zern (Ref.b has 1953 but code would indicate this was wrong) $75/250

085a: WYOMING Harper & Bros., New York (1932 [1953]). [1] Also has code letters "F-C." Actually published in 1953 $25/125

085b: WYOMING Hodder & Stoughton, London (1954). [] $12/60

086a: LOST PUEBLO Harper & Bros., New York (1954). [1] Also has code letters "H-D" $25/125

086b: LOST PUEBLO Hodder & Stoughton, London (1955). [] $12/60

087a: BLACK MESA Harper & Bros., New York (1955). [1] Also has code letters "H-E" $25/125

087b: BLACK MESA Hodder & Stoughton, London (1956). [] $12/60

088a: STRANGER FROM THE TONTO Harper & Bros., New York (1956). [0] Code letters "G-F" $25/125

088b: STRANGER FROM THE TONTO Hodder & Stoughton, London (1957). [] $12/60

089a: THE FUGITIVE TRAIL Harper & Bros., New York (1957). [0] No code letters $25/125

089b: THE FUGITIVE TRAIL Hodder & Stoughton, London (1958). [] $12/60

090a: ARIZONA CLAN Harper & Bros., New York (1958). [1] Also has code letters "H-H" $25/100

090b: ARIZONA CLAN Hodder & Stoughton, London (1959). [] $12/60

091a: HORSE HEAVEN HILL Harper & Bros., New York (1959). [1] Also has code letters "F-I" $25/125

091b: HORSE HEAVEN HILL Hodder & Stoughton, London (1960). [] $12/60

092a: THE RANGER AND OTHER STORIES Harper & Bros., New York (1958 [1960]). [1] Also has code letters "E-K." Actually published in 1960 $25/125

092b: THE RANGER AND OTHER STORIES Hodder & Stoughton, London (1963) [] $10/50

092c: THE RANGER AND OTHER STORIES Franklin Library, Franklin Center, 1979. [] Dark brown leather binding, gilt edges, ribbon markers (Waverley Books 6/95) $60.

093a: BLUE FEATHER AND OTHER STORIES Harper & Bros., New York (1961). [1] Also has code letters "I-L" $25/125

093b: BLUE FEATHER AND OTHER STORIES Hodder & Stoughton, London (1962) [] $12/60

094a: BOULDER DAM Harper & Bros., New York (1963). [1] Also has code letters "G-N" $25/125

094b: BOULDER DAM Hodder & Stoughton, London (1965). [] $12/60

095a: THE ADVENTURES OF FINSPOT D.J. Books, San Bernardino, 1974. [2] 950 cc. Tipped in color plates. Edited by G. M. Farley and Betty Zane Grosso $125/300

096a: THE RUSTLERS OF PECOS COUNTY and SILVERMANE Belmont Tower, New York (1974). [0] Wraps $35.

097a: ZANE GREY'S SAVAGE KINGDOM Belmont Tower, New York (1975). [0] Wraps. Edited by Loren Grey (ref.b) $35.

098a: SHARK! ZANE GREY'S TALES OF MAN-EATING SHARKS Belmont Tower, New York (1976). [0] Wraps. Edited by Loren Grey (ref.b) $50.

099a: THE TRAIL OF THE JAGUAR Zane Grey Collector, Williamsport, MD (1976). [1] 500 cc. Wraps. Edited by G.M. Farley (ref.b) $75.

100a: THE ZANE GREY COOKBOOK Prentice-Hall, Englewood Cliffs, NJ (1976). [3] Book is by Barbara and George Reiger. With 18 pages of photos of Grey at end $25/75

101a: THE WESTERNER Belmont Tower, New York (1977). [0] Wraps. Edited by Loren Grey (ref.b) $35.

102a: THE REEF GIRL Harper, New York (1977). [3] Also states "First Edition" $10/50

103a: THE BUFFALO HUNTER Belmont, New York (1978). [0] Wraps. Edited by Loren Grey $35.

104a: ZANE GREY: OUTDOORSMAN Prentice-Hall, Englewood Cliffs, N.J. (1972). [] Edited by George Reiger $25/75

105a: ZANE GREY'S GREATEST ANIMAL STORIES Belmont Tower, New York (1975). [] Wraps. Edited by Loren Grey $35.

106a: ZANE GREY'S GREATEST WESTERN STORIES Belmont Tower, New York (1975). [] Wraps. Edited by Loren Grey $35.

107a: ZANE GREY'S GREATEST INDIAN STORIES Belmont Tower, New York (1975). [] Wraps. Edited by Loren Grey $35.

108a: ROUND-UP Manor Books (New York, 1976). [] Wraps. Edited by Loren Grey $30.

109a: YAQUI AND OTHER GREAT INDIAN STORIES Belmont Tower, New York (1976). [] Wraps. Edited by Loren Grey $30.

110a: THE BIG LAND Belmont Tower, New York (1976). [] Wraps. Edited by Loren Grey $30.

111a: TENDERFOOT Belmont Tower, New York (1977). [] Wraps. Edited by Loren Grey $30.

112a: TALES FROM A FISHERMAN'S LOG (Hodder & Stoughton, Auckland, 1978.) [1] New material from an old diary and recently discovered photographs of Grey's second visit to New Zealand in 1927 (Country Lane Books 11/92). $25/125

112b: TALES FROM A FISHERMAN'S LOG (Hodder & Stoughton, Auckland, 1978.) Seven copies in quarter red morocco $1,500.

113a: THE CAMP ROBBER Walter J. Black, Roslyn, New York (1979). [] Edited by Loren Grey $10/50

114a: LORD OF LACKAWAXEN CREEK (Lime Rock Press, Salisbury, Ct., 1981.) [2] A miniature book illustrated and signed by Catryna Ten Eyck (2 7/8" x 2 1/2") $100.

115a: ANGLER'S ELDORADO, ZANE GREY IN NEW ZEALAND Roslyn, NY (1982). [1] Adds several chapters to *The Tales of an Angler's Eldorado* (See item 40) $75/125

115b: ANGLER'S ELDORADO, ZANE GREY IN NEW ZEALAND A. H. and A. W. Reed, New Zealand (1982). [1] Stiff paperwraps. Published simultaneously $40.

115c: ZANE GREY IN THE SOUTH PACIFIC Angus & Robertson, Sydney (1982). [1] New title. Published simultaneously $25/75

116a: AMBER'S MIRAGE +++ Publisher?, New York, 1983. [] Wraps. First book publication of one story. *Amber's Mirage* first appeared as a magazine serial in the *Ladies' Home Journal* beginning in May, 1929 $30.

117a: THE UNDISCOVERED ZANE GREY FISHING STORIES... Winchester Press, no place (1983). [ ] States "11 12 13..." DeLuxe edition. In publisher's pictorial box. Foreword by James Michener (Country Lane Books 10/95) $75/100

117b: THE UNDISCOVERED ZANE GREY FISHING STORIES... Winchester Press, no place (1983). [] States "11 12 13..." Cloth. Issued in dustwrapper $15/50

118a: THE WESTERN MOTION-PICTURE Arundel Press, London, 1984. [2] 25 numbered large paper copies on handmade paper with check signed by Grey tipped in back. Bound in 1/2 morocco (Pepper & Stern 12/89) $500.

118b: THE WESTERN MOTION-PICTURE Arundel Press, Los Angeles, 1984. [2] 100 cc. Signed frontispiece by D/Ambrosio (George Houle) 100.

119a: ZANE GREY FISHING LIBRARY Derrydale Press Lyon, Mississipppi 1990-91 [2] 2500 sgd no. cc (signed by Loren Grey) 10 vols.: 8 fishing titles, Romor's book, Biography by Loren Grey (Authors of the West 12/92) Publ. @ $450 $650.

120a: THE MANY FACES OF ZANE GREY Silver Spruce, Flagstaff (1993). [2] 125 numbered copies. Issued without dustwrapper. In slipcase. Written by George Farley with an introduction by James Vickers. Contains some poems by Grey $50/75

121a: GEORGE WASHINGTON, FRONTIERSMAN University Press of Kentucky (Lexington, 1994). [0] Edited by Carleton Jackson (including reconstruction of some passages that were missing) and with introduction by Carleton Jackson $6/30

Note: There were a number of "King of the Royal Mounted" and "Tex Thorne" titles published by the Whitman Publishing Co. as "Big Little Books" but there are so many copies of them that the value is nominal.

MARTHA GRIMES

Martha Grimes, a native of Garrett County, Maryland, taught English at Montgomery College in Takoma Park, Maryland. She occasionally teaches detective fiction at Johns Hopkins University and lives in Washington, D.C. The following information is from our personal collection with the quantities supplied by Little Brown, one of the few cooperative publishers.

001a: THE MAN WITH A LOAD OF MISCHIEF Little, Brown, Boston (1981). [] Uncorrected proof in white printed wraps (Antic Hay Books 5/95) $600.

001b: THE MAN WITH A LOAD OF MISCHIEF Little, Brown, Boston (1981). [1] 5,171 cc. Noted with two different dustwrappers (priority unknown)

1) ISBN number on back panel in black letters, backed in white, the initials "FPT" on upper left corner and "00001545" in lower left corner of front flap; and

2) ISBN number printed in white on back panel, "FPT" or "00001545" not on front flap. 75/350

001b: THE MAN WITH A LOAD OF MISCHIEF Michael O'Mara, London (1990). [1] "First published in Great Britain in 1990" $15/75

002a: THE OLD FOX DECEIV'D Little, Brown, Boston (1982). [1] Uncorrected advance proof. In printed red wraps $300.

002b: THE OLD FOX DECEIV'D Little, Brown, Boston (1982). [1] 7,328 cc. (Published August 1982 @ $13.95) $50/250

002c: THE OLD FOX DECEIV'D Michael O'Mara, (London, 1990). [1] $10/50

003a: THE ANODYNE NECKLACE Little, Brown, Boston (1983). [1] Uncorrected advance proof. In printed flint gray wraps announcing a price of $13.95 $200.

003b: THE ANODYNE NECKLACE Little, Brown, Boston (1983). [1] 8,546 cc. (Published June 27, 1983.) $14.95 price on dustwrapper $30/150

003c: THE ANODYNE NECKLACE Michael O'Mara, London, 1989. [] $10/50

004a: THE DIRTY DUCK Little, Brown, Boston (1984). [1] Uncorrected advance proof. In printed dark green wraps $175.

004b: THE DIRTY DUCK Little, Brown, Boston (1984). [1] 20,075 cc. (Published April 26, 1984 @ $14.95) $20/100

004c: THE DIRTY DUCK Michael O'Mara, (London) no-date (lists US copyright of 1984). [1] "First Published in Great Britain..." $8/40

005a: JERUSALEM INN Little, Brown, Boston (1984). [1] Uncorrected advance proofs. In printed dark-green wraps calling for price of $14.95 $150.

005b: JERUSALEM INN Little, Brown, Boston (1984). [1] 24,766 cc. (Published November 7, 1984.) Dustwrapper price of $15.95 $12/60

005c: JERUSALEM INN Michael O'Mara, London, 1987. [] $8/40

006a: HELP THE POOR STRUGGLER Little, Brown, Boston (1985). [1] Uncorrected advance proof. In printed green wraps $125.

006b: HELP THE POOR STRUGGLER Little, Brown, Boston (1985). [1] 24,839 cc. (Published May 1, 1985 @ $15.95) $12/60

006c: HELP THE POOR STRUGGLER Michael O'Mara, London (1988). [] $10/50

007a: THE DEER LEAP Little, Brown, Boston (1985). [1] Uncorrected advance proof. In printed orange-brown wraps $100.

007b: THE DEER LEAP Little, Brown, Boston (1985). [1] 27,566 cc. (Published November 6, 1985 @ $15.95) $10/50

007c: THE DEER LEAP Michael O'Mara, London, 1988. [] $10/50

008a: THE MARTHA GRIMES READER Dell, New York (1985) [0] Wraps. Sales promotion item with excerpts from Grimes' novels. Bound dos-a-dos with *The Robert Bernard Reader* (Janus Books 10/96) $20.

009a: I AM THE ONLY RUNNING FOOTMAN Little, Brown, Boston (1986). [1] Uncorrected advance proof. In printed dark green wraps $100.

009b: I AM THE ONLY RUNNING FOOTMAN Little, Brown, Boston (1986). [1] 31,954 cc. (Published November 4, 1986 @ $15.95) $8/40

009c: I AM THE ONLY RUNNING FOOTMAN Michael O'Mara, (London) no-date (has U.S. copyright of 1986). [1] "First published in Great Britain..." $7/35

010a: MARTHA GRIMES SAMPLER Dell, New York (1986). [0] Wraps $25.

011a: THE FIVE BELLS AND BLADEBONE Little, Brown, Boston (1987). [1] Uncorrected advance proof. In printed orange-brown wraps $100.

011b: THE FIVE BELLS AND BLADEBONE Little, Brown, Boston (1987). [1] (Published August 25, 1987 @ $15.95) $8/40

011c: THE FIVE BELLS AND BLADEBONE Michael O'Mara, London (1988). [] $8/40

012a: THE OLD SILENT Little Brown, Boston, 1989. [] Advance reading copy. In pictorial Wraps $40.

012b: THE OLD SILENT Little Brown, Boston, 1989. [1] 100,000 cc (*Publisher's Weekly*). (Published September 1989 @ $16.95) $6/30

012c: THE OLD SILENT Headline (London, 1990). [3] Also says "First published in Great Britain..." $6/30

013a: SEND BYGRAVES Putnam, New York (1989). [] Advance reading copy. In pictorial wraps $30.

013b: SEND BYGRAVES Putnam, New York (1989). [3] 36,000 cc (*Publisher's Weekly*). (Published November 1989.) Illustrated by Devis Grebu. Issued without dustwrapper $25.

014a: THE OLD CONTEMPTIBLES Little, Brown, Boston (1991). [] Advance reading copy. In pictorial wraps $50.

014b: THE OLD CONTEMPTIBLES Little, Brown, Boston (1991). [3] Also states "First Edition." (Published January 1991 @ $19.95) $6/30

015a: THE END OF THE PIER Knopf, New York, 1992. [] Uncorrected proof. In gray wraps $60.

015b: THE END OF THE PIER Knopf, New York, 1992. [] Uncorrected proof. In pictorial wraps $35.

015c: THE END OF THE PIER Knopf, New York, 1992. [1] 100,000 cc (*Publisher's Weekly*). (Published April 1992 @ $20) $6/30

016a: THE HORSE YOU CAME IN ON Knopf, New York, 1993. [1] Uncorrected proof. In gray wraps (Monroe Stahr Books 9/95) $40.

016b: THE HORSE YOU CAME IN ON Knopf, New York, 1993. [1] 100,000 cc (*Publisher's Weekly*). (Published 7/93 @ $21.00) $5/25

016c: THE HORSE YOU CAME IN ON Headline, London, 1993. [] $6/30

017a: RAINBOW'S END Knopf, New York, 1995. [] Uncorrected proof. In blue wraps (Oracle Books 11/95) $30.

017b: RAINBOW'S END Knopf, New York, 1995. [] (Published 6/95 @ $23.00) $5/25

018a: HOTEL PARADISE Knopf, New York, 1996. [1] $5/25

018b: HOTEL PARADISE Headline (London, 1996). [3] $6/30

DORIS GRUMBACH

Doris Grumbach was born in New York City in 1918. She graduated from New York University in 1939 and received a masters degree from Cornell University in 1940. Since that time, in addition to being a novelist and biographer and mother of four, she has been active as a writer and educator. She was a Professor of English at the College of St. Rose until 1972, literary editor for the New Republic from 1972 to 1974, Professor at American University from 1974 to 1983, and taught at Johns Hopkins. During this period, she also worked as a columnist/critic/reviewer for various newspapers/news shows including the *Washington Star*, *Washington Post*, *L.A. Times*, *Chicago Tribune*, *New York Times Book Review*, *Fine Print*, *Saturday Review*, National Public Radio and MacNeil-Lehrer News Hour. In her spare time, she has taught at Empire State and the Iowa Writer's Workshop. Doris and her long time friend, Sybil Pike, maintain a residence in Washington, D.C. but spend much of their time at their home in Sargentsville, Maine where they run an antiquarian bookstore, Wayward Books.

001a: THE SPOIL OF THE FLOWERS Doubleday, Garden City, New York, 1962. [1] 2,000 cc (per the author) $40/200

002a: THE SHORT THROAT, THE TENDER MOUTH Doubleday, Garden City, New York, 1964. [1] 3,000 cc (per the author) $40/200

003a: LORD, I HAVE NO COURAGE Venerini Publications, Worcester (1964). [0] Heavy (cardboard) cover with label on front. The author believes there were about 500 copies. The life story of Rosa Venerini who established a school for women in the early 18th Century. Prepared for "young readers" $350.

004a: THE COMPANY SHE KEPT Coward McCann, New York (1967). [0] A portrait of Mary McCarthy $15/75

004b: THE COMPANY SHE KEPT Bodley Head, London (1967). [1] $10/50

005a: LETTER TO A WOULD-BE WRITER *Fiction I* Empire State College, Saratoga Springs, 1973. [0] Wraps. 8"x11" sheets in clamp binder (easily reproduced) $125.

006a: LETTER TO A WOULD-BE WRITER - *Journalism III* Empire State College, Saratoga Springs, 1973. [0] Wraps. 8"x11" sheets in clamp binder (easily reproduced) $125.

Note: written for use in class. William Kennedy wrote *Fiction II* and *Journalism IV*

007a: CHAMBER MUSIC Dutton, New York (1979). [] Uncorrected proof in tall gray wraps (Second Life Books 3/90) $125.

007b: CHAMBER MUSIC Dutton, New York (1979). [3] Also states "First Edition." Advance reading copy. In pictorial wraps $60

007c: CHAMBER MUSIC Dutton, New York (1979). [3] $15/75

007d: CHAMBER MUSIC (Hamish Hamilton, London), no date. [0] Advance uncorrected proof. In gray printed wraps $75.

007e: CHAMBER MUSIC Hamish Hamilton, London (1979). [1] $12/60

008a: THE MISSING PERSON Putnam, New York (1981). [0] Uncorrected proof. In blue printed wraps $75.

008b: THE MISSING PERSON Putnam, New York (1981). [0] (Published March 31, 1981 @ $11.95) $6/30

008c: THE MISSING PERSON Hamish Hamilton, London (1981). [1] $8/40

009a: THE LADIES Dutton, New York (1984). [3] Also states "First edition". Advance uncorrected proof. In tan wraps with picture from subsequent dustwrapper on front panel $60.

009b: THE LADIES Dutton, New York (1984). [3] (Published September 27, 1984 @ $14.95) $7/35

009c: THE LADIES Hamish Hamilton, London (1985). [1] $7/35

010a: THE MAGICIAN'S GIRL Macmillan, New York (1987). [3] Uncorrected proof. In printed creme colored wraps $60.

010b: THE MAGICIAN'S GIRL Macmillan, New York (1987). [3] (Published January 5, 1987 @ $16.95) $6/30

010c: THE MAGICIAN'S GIRL Hamish Hamilton, London (1987). [1] $7/35

011a: COMING INTO THE END ZONE: *A Memoir* Norton, New York (1991). [3] Also States "First Edition" $6/30

012a: EXTRA INNINGS *A Memoir* Norton, New York, 1993. [3] (Published 11/93 @ $22.00) $5/25

013a: FIFTY DAYS OF SOLITUDE Beacon Press, Boston (1994). [] Advance reading copy. In pictorial wraps $40.

013b: FIFTY DAYS OF SOLITUDE Beacon Press, Boston (1994). [3] $5/25

014a: THE BOOK OF KNOWLEDGE Norton, New York (1995). [] Uncorrected proof. In wraps (Ampersand Books 11/95) $35.

014b: THE BOOK OF KNOWLEDGE Norton, New York (1995). [3] Also states "First Edition" (Alice Robbins 6/96) $5/25

015a: LIFE IN A DAY Beacon Press, Boston, 1996. [3] Advance reading copy. In wraps (Watermark West 11/96) $40.

015b: LIFE IN A DAY Beacon Press, Boston (1996). [3] $5/25

016a: AUTOBIOGRAPHY OF AN ELDERLY WOMAN Pushcart Press (Wainscott, 1995). [0] Originally published anonymously in 1911. Afterword by Grumbach $6/30

016a: AUTOBIOGRAPHY OF AN ELDERLY WOMAN Pushcart Press (Wainscott, 1995). [0] Wraps $20.

017a: THE MINUTES OF THE LEAD PENCIL CLUB Pushcart Press, Wainscott (1996). [0] Edited by Bill Henderson. Afterword by Grumbach $5/25

017b: THE MINUTES OF THE LEAD PENCIL CLUB Pushcart Press, Wainscott (1996). [0] Wraps $15.

JIM HARRISON

Harrison was born in Grayling, Michigan in 1937. He received a B.A. and M.A. in comparative literature from Michigan State University. He was an Assistant Professor of English at the State University of New York, Stony Brook for a time before resigning to write full time.

001a: PLAIN SONG Norton, New York (1965). [] Uncorrected galley proof. In plastic spiral-bound printed green covers; 7½ x 11 inch sheets, unnumbered and printed on rectos only (Robert Wendler 2/96) $1,500.

001b: PLAIN SONG Norton, New York (1965). [1] 1,500 cc $75/450

001c: PLAIN SONG Norton, New York (1965). [1] 1,500 cc. Wraps. Issued simultaneously $100.

002a: WALKING Pym Randall Press, Cambridge (1967). [2] 26 sgd ltr cc $1,500.

002b: WALKING Pym Randall Press, Cambridge (1967). [2] 100 sgd no. cc. Oblong wraps $750.

003a: LOCATIONS Norton, New York (1968). [3] 1,250 cc $75/350

003b: LOCATIONS Norton, New York (1968). [3] 1,250 cc. Wraps $100.

004a: FIVE BLIND MEN Sumac Press, Fremont, 1969. [2] 26 sgd ltr cc. Harrison is one of five poets. Issued without dustwrapper $750.

004b: FIVE BLIND MEN Sumac Press, Fremont, 1969. [2] 100 cc. Harrison has indicated that none were numbered (although called for) in correspondence with Steven C. Bernard, but numbered copies have been seen — $250.

004c: FIVE BLIND MEN Sumac Press, Fremont, 1969. [] 1,000 cc. Wraps. Issued simultaneously (Pettler & Lieberman 8/88) — $60.

005a: OUTLYER AND GHAZALS Simon & Schuster, New York (1971). [1] Scarcest trade book — $100/500

005b: OUTLYER AND GHAZALS Simon & Schuster, New York (1971). [1] Wraps — $100.

006a: WOLF Simon & Schuster, New York (1971). [] Uncorrected proof. In tall pad-bound yellow wraps. — $1,250.

006b: WOLF Simon & Schuster, New York (1971). [1] — $50/250

006c: WOLF Flamingo, London, 1993. [] Wraps. Not issued in hardcover in Britain — $40.

007a: A GOOD DAY TO DIE Simon & Schuster, New York, 1973. [] Uncorrected proof. In yellow wraps. — $1,250

007b: A GOOD DAY TO DIE Simon & Schuster, New York, 1973. [3] — $100/450

007c: A GOOD DAY TO DIE W.H. Allen, London, 1975. [] — $50/250

008a: LETTERS TO YESENIN Sumac Press, Fremont (1973). [2] 26 sgd ltr cc — $1,500.

008b: LETTERS TO YESENIN Sumac Press, Fremont (1973). [2] 100 sgd no. cc — $750.

008c: LETTERS TO YESENIN Sumac Press, Fremont (1973). [] 1,000 cc. Wraps. Also see 011b — $100.

009a: SERGE, YESENIN 1895-1925 Sumac Press, Fremont, no date. [] 33 cc (quantity based on an inscribed copy with "1 of 33 handset" [Phoenix Bookshop #210]). Small (6" x 9") broadside. We assume it was issued around time of *Letters...* (008a) $350.

010a: FARMER Viking, New York (1976). [] Uncorrected proof. In dark-blue green wraps (Books, Inc. 6/95) $400

010b: FARMER Viking, New York (1976). [1] 7,500 cc (b&c). First issue binding with the spine not glued and the board measuring 5 1/16 inches from spine cloth to edge The publisher requested that these be destroyed, due to the inferior production quality, and they supplied replacement copies to all accounts (Ken Lopez 3/95) $75/200

010c: FARMER Viking, New York (1976). [1] 7,500 cc. Second issue binding measuring 4 7/8 inches from spine to cloth edge. Also, a few copies perfect bound, priority unknown (Lame Duck Books 4/94) $30/150

010d: FARMER Flamingo, London, 1993. [] Wraps. No U.K. hardcover issue $35.

011a: RETURNING TO EARTH Ithaca House (Berkeley, 1977). [0] Stapled wraps. "A Court Street Chapbook." Reportedly only 500 copies $400.

011b: LETTERS TO YESENIN and RETURNING TO EARTH POEMS Center Publishers (Los Angeles), 1979. [0] 35 sgd cc (Watermark West #2). Assume unnumbered. Wraps $200.

011c: LETTERS TO YESENIN and RETURNING TO EARTH POEMS Center Publishers (Los Angeles), 1979. [0] Wraps. $100.

012a: LEGENDS OF THE FALL Delacorte, New York (1979). [] Advance uncorrected proof. White wraps, pad-bound. Fewer than 15 cc (Beasley Books #31) $600.

012b: LEGENDS OF THE FALL Delacorte, New York (1979). [] Uncorrected proof. In printed red wraps (Beasley Books #31) $300.

012c: LEGENDS OF THE FALL (Esquire Magazine, New York, 1979.) [] Offprint of title novella on newsprint, stapled (Ken Lopez 1/94) $200.

012d: LEGENDS OF THE FALL, REVENGE, and THE MAN WHO GAVE UP HIS NAME Delacorte (New York, 1979). [2] 250 sgd no. cc. Signed in first volume. Three volumes of this collection of novellas, issued without dustwrappers. In slipcase $600/750

012e: LEGENDS OF THE FALL Delacorte, New York (1979). [1] 1,000 cc. Three volumes issued without dustwrappers. In slipcase $125/250

012f: LEGENDS OF THE FALL Delacorte, New York (1979). [1] 15,000 cc. One volume edition $25/125

012g: LEGENDS OF THE FALL Collins, London, 1980. [1] $15/75

013a: WARLOCK Delacorte (New York, 1981). [] Uncorrected proof in yellow wraps. Laid in proof dustwrapper (Ken Lopez 7/91) $200/300

013b: WARLOCK Delacorte (New York, 1981). [2] 250 sgd no. cc. Issued without dustwrapper. In slipcase $200/250

013c: WARLOCK Delacorte (New York, 1981). [1] 19,000 cc. (Published October 1981 @ $13.95) $15/75

013d: WARLOCK Collins, London, 1981. [] Uncorrected proof. In beige wraps (Ken Lopez 4/93) $100

013e: WARLOCK Collins, London, 1981. [1] Printed in U.S. $10/50

014a: NEW AND SELECTED POEMS 1961-1981 Delacorte (New York, 1982). [] Uncorrected proof. In gray wraps $150.

014b: SELECTED AND NEW POEMS 1961-1981 Delacorte (New York, 1982). [2] 250 sgd no. cc. Issued without dustwrapper. In slipcase $200/250

014c: SELECTED AND NEW POEMS 1961-1981 Delacorte (New York, 1982). [1] 2,500 cc $15/75

014d: SELECTED AND NEW POEMS 1961-1981 Delacorte (New York, 1982). [1] Wraps. Issued simultaneously $30.

015a: NATURAL WORLD A BESTIARY. Open Book (Barrytown, New York, 1981.) [2] 100 sgd no. cc. Poems by Harrison and photos of sculptures by Diana Guest. Signed by both. Issued without dustwrapper or slipcase. (We have also seen copies catalogued as one of 250 signed copies; and told that there may have been 350 copies in total, but only 100 for sale) $400.

016a: SUNDOG Dutton, New York (1984). [] Uncorrected proof. In orange wraps $150.

016b: SUNDOG Dutton, New York (1984). [2] 250 sgd no. cc. Issued without dustwrapper. In slipcase $200/250

016c: SUNDOG Dutton, New York (1984). [3] Also states "First Edition" $12/60

016d: SUNDOG Heinemann, London (1985). [1] $10/50

017a: THE THEORY AND PRACTICE OF RIVERS Winn Books, Seattle, 1986. [2] 350 sgd cc (of which 175 copies were signed by Harrison and Chatham and issued with a portfolio of prints by Russell Chatham; and 175 copies, signed only by

Harrison were issued without the prints) (Joe Spitz 2/97). Illustrated by Russell Chatham. Issued without dustwrapper. In slipcase. Published with a portfolio of Chatham works at $350 and sold separately at $85. The publisher has indicated in a letter that none of the copies were numbered. Yet, copies have been catalogued with the indication that they are numbered copies. We assume this is an error in cataloging or perhaps a person or persons unknown have sophisticated these copies. Also noted, a copy lacking the limitation page, but signed by Harrison; same binding and slipcase (Bert Babcock 4/95)

With portfolio of illustrations: $700/750
Without portfolio of illustrations: $150/200

017b: THE THEORY AND PRACTICE OF RIVERS Winn Books, Seattle, 1986. [4] 3,000 cc. Wraps. Issued in dustwrapper $35/75

018a: DALVA Dutton, New York (1988). [] Uncorrected proof. In printed tan wraps $100.

018b: DALVA Dutton, New York, 1988. [] Numbered copies in wraps (limitation not stated, but no. 208 offered by Rob Warren 3/95). Advance excerpt consisting of one stapled signature taken from the uncorrected proofs (Ken Lopez 10/96, had No. 227) $75.

018c: DALVA Dutton, New York (1988). [3] (Published March 1988 @ $18.45) $10/40

018d: DALVA Jonathan Cape, London (1989). [] Uncorrected proof. In reddish-brown wraps (Books, Inc. 6/95) $100.

018d: DALVA Jonathan Cape, London, 1989. [] $10/40

019a: BETWEEN WARS Columbia Pictures, Burbank, 1989. [] A screenplay. In printed studio wraps $175.

020a: THEORY AND PRACTICE OF RIVERS AND NEW POEMS Clark City Press, Livingston, Montana (1989). [1] Illustrated by Russell Chatham. "First Clark City Press Edition July 1989" on copyright page $12/60

020b: THEORY AND PRACTICE OF RIVERS AND NEW POEMS Clark City Press, Livingston, Montana (1989). [1] Wraps $25.

021a: THE WOMAN LIT BY FIREFLIES Houghton Mifflin, Boston, 1990. [] Uncorrected proof. In yellow wraps $100.

021b: THE WOMAN LIT BY FIREFLIES Houghton Mifflin, Boston, 1990. [2] 225 sgd no. cc. Issued without dustwrapper. In slipcase $175/225

021c: THE WOMAN LIT BY FIREFLIES Houghton Mifflin, Boston, 1990. [3] 20,000 cc. (Published August 1990 @ $19.95) $8/40

021d: THE WOMAN LIT BY FIREFLIES Weidenfeld & Nicholson, London, 1991. [] $8/40

022a: BOOK FOR SENSEI Big Bridge Press, Pacifica, Calif., 1990. [2] 26 sgd ltr cc. Signed by Harrison, Rothenberg, McClure, Whalen, Kyger, Codrescu, and the illustrator, Nancy Davis. In slipcase $500.

022b: BOOK FOR SENSEI Big Bridge Press, Pacifica, Calif., 1990. [2] 74 no. cc. Issued in boards. In slipcase $250.

023a: KOBUN *A Poem* Dim Gray Bar Press (1990). [2] 100 sgd no. cc. 11"x13" broadside $60.

024a: JUST BEFORE DARK *The Collected Nonfiction* Clark City Press, Livingston, Montana 1991 [] Uncorrected proof. In glossy illustrated wraps (Lame Duck Books 12/94) $75.

024b: JUST BEFORE DARK *The Collected Non-fiction* Clark City Press, Livingston, Montana (1991). [2] 26 sgd ltr cc. Issued without dustwrapper. In cloth-covered slipcase $400/500

024c: JUST BEFORE DARK *The Collected Non-fiction* Clark City Press, Livingston, Montana (1991). [2] 250 sgd no. cc. Issued without dustwrapper. In slipcase. Some copies seen signed but not numbered (Else Fine Books 3/94) $100/175

024d: JUST BEFORE DARK *The Collected Non-fiction* Clark City Press, Livingston, Montana (1991). [1] Trade $8/40

025a: THE RAW & THE COOKED Dim Gray Bar Press, New York, 1992. [2] 26 sgd ltr cc. Bound in quarter morocco $350.

025b: THE RAW & THE COOKED Dim Gray Bar Press, New York, 1992. [2] 100 sgd no. cc $175.

026a: SKETCH FOR A JOB APPLICATION BLANK (Houghton Mifflin, Boston, 1992.) [0] Broadside, 9 x 13 inches. Printed by Okeanos. Text from *Just Before Dark.* Only a handful of these were prepared for sales representatives and friends to coincide with the publication of the paperback edition (Bev Chaney, Jr.) $75.

027a: JULIP Houghton Mifflin, Boston, 1994. [] Uncorrected proof. In printed bright green wraps. Some copies noted signed with autopen facsimile of Harrison's signature (Bev Chaney, Jr. 2/96) $75.

027b: JULIP Houghton Mifflin, Boston, 1994. [2] 200 sgd no. cc. Issued without dustwrapper. In slip-case $150/200

027c: JULIP Houghton Mifflin, Boston, 1994. [ ] 21,000 cc. (Published 4/94 @ $21.95) $7/35

027d: JULIP Flamingo, London, 1994. [] Uncorrected proof. In glossy wrap $75.

028a: AFTER IKKYU Shambala, Boston, 1996. [] 1,000 cc (also reported as 500 copies [Vagabond Books 12/96]) $15/50

028b: AFTER IKKYU Shambala, Boston, 1996. [] Wraps. Simultaneous issue $20.

029a: COYOTE NO. 1 The Alternative Press, Ann Arbor, no date. [] A postcard poem. Printed on tan card stock. Illustrated by Ann Mikolowski (Lame Duck Books 12/96) $40.

030a: THE SUMAC READER Michigan State University Press, East Lansing, 1997. [2] 26 sgd ltd cc (signed by Harrison, Gerber, and Bednarek). Issued without dustwrapper. Published at $200

030b: THE SUMAC READER Michigan State University Press, East Lansing, 1997. [2] 100 sgd no. cc (signed by Harrison, Gerber and Bednarek). Issued without dustwrapper. Published at $150

030c: THE SUMAC READER Michigan State University Press, East Lansing, 1997. [] Wraps. Published at $17.95

ROBERT HEINLEIN
(1907 - 1988)

Robert Heinlein was born in Butler, Missouri, one of seven children. He attended high school in Kansas City, Missouri and college at the U.S. Naval Academy in Annapolis, Maryland, graduating in 1929. From 1929 to 1934 he served on aircraft carriers and destroyers but was retired in the latter year due to physical disabilities. He started graduate school at UCLA, studying mathematics and physics, but his health never allowed him to finish. He worked at various jobs including real estate, mining and architecture until 1939 when he began writing full time. His writing career was interrupted by the war which he spent as a mechanical engineer at the Naval Aircraft factory in Philadelphia.

He wrote for magazines, radio, television, and motion pictures in addition to his books. The winner of four Hugo Awards, among many awards during his lifetime, he was always highly regarded in the field. In 1954, the *New York Herald Tribune* wrote of *The Star Beast*: "Regularly every year Robert Heinlein produces the best juvenile science fiction novel - and in so doing creates a work more satisfying than ninety per cent of adult science fiction."

His own view - "My stories have been speculations about the future and what mankind will make of it...My writing has been strongly affected by Rudyard Kipling, Winston Churchill, H.G. Wells, et al... I enjoy life and believe man will live forever and spread out through the universe." (*Contemporary Novelists*, St. Martin's Press, New York, 1976)

REFERENCES:

(a) Currey, L.W. SCIENCE FICTION AND FANTASY AUTHORS. Boston: G.K. Hall (1979).

(b) Smith, Curtis C. (Editor). TWENTIETH-CENTURY SCIENCE FICTION WRITERS. New York: St. Martin's Press

(1981). Used for titles printed in Great Britain not covered in Ref.a.

(c) The information provided by Joel Sattler, would apply to all entries after 1980. Also includes a few entries derived from inventory or dealer catalogs.

Note: We have included the published prices on the Scribner books, because it is probable the publisher printed new dustwrappers with higher prices; and certainly the publisher price clipped some jackets and rubber stamped new prices, which would indicate books that were sold later, although still first edition books and dustwrappers.

The order of publications within each year is arbitrary as we have not looked up the publication dates and do not have an accurate chronological list of the titles.

We wish to thank Joel Sattler, John Knott and particularly Lloyd Currey, the preeminent science fiction bibliographer not only for ref.a, but also for providing updated information on a number of the entries.

001a: THE DISCOVERY OF THE FUTURE... Speech Delivered by Guest of Honor at Third World Science Fiction Convention. A Novacious Publication (Los Angeles, 1941). [2] Stapled wraps. "Limited First Edition (200)" on front wrapper. Printed in green ink. Issued in mailing envelope $1,750.

001b: THE DISCOVERY OF THE FUTURE... A Novacious Publication (LA 1941) [2] Wraps. Adds "Reprint (100)" under original limitation. Second printing with peach colored front cover, 18 pp. including covers (ref.c) $650.

002a: ROCKET SHIP GALILEO Scribner's, New Year (1947). [5] Also has publisher's seal on copyright page. Illustrated by Thomas W. Voter. Published at $2.00 $200/1,000

002b: ROCKET SHIP GALILEO New English Library, London, 1971. [] Wraps. Ref.b $30/75

003a: SPACE CADET Scribner's, New York (1948). [5] Also has publisher's seal on copyright page. Illustrated by Clifford N. Geary. Published at $2.50 $150/750

003b: SPACE CADET Gollancz, London, 1966. [1] (Ref.c) $40/200

004a: BEYOND THIS HORIZON Fantasy Press, Reading, PA, 1948. [2] 500 sgd no. cc. Brick red cloth $1,250.

004b: BEYOND THIS HORIZON Fantasy Press, Reading, PA, 1948. [1] Brick red cloth. In 4-color dustwrapper $125/500

004c: BEYOND THIS HORIZON Fantasy Press, Reading, PA, 1948. [1] Medium blue cloth. In blue dustwrapper $75/250

005a: RED PLANET Scribner's, New York, 1949. [5] Also has seal on copyright page. Illustrated by Clifford N. Geary. Published at $2.50 $125/600

005b: RED PLANET Gollancz, London, 1963. [0] Copy seen had "I-5.61[V]" on copyright page. Red cloth (simulated?) stamped in gold on spine $40/200

006a: SIXTH COLUMN Gnome Press, New York (1949). [1] $100/500

006b: THE DAY AFTER TOMORROW (Mayflower Books, London, 1962.) [] New title (ref.b) $40/200

007a: THE MAN WHO SOLD THE MOON Shasta, Chicago (1950). [1] Signed on tipped-in page. (Reportedly about 200 copies) $450/650

007b: THE MAN WHO SOLD THE MOON Shasta, Chicago (1950). [1] His Future History Series. Introduction by John W. Campbell, Jr. $75/350

007c: THE MAN WHO SOLD THE MOON New American Library (New York, 1951). [1] Wraps. "First printing, March 1951." Signet #847 at 25 cents. Abridged edition $35.

007d: THE MAN WHO SOLD THE MOON Sidgwick & Jackson, London (1953). [] $25/100

008a: FARMER IN THE SKY Scribner's, New York, 1950. [5] Also has publisher's seal on copyright page. Illustrated by Clifford N. Geary. Published at $2.50. "Published in condensed form in *Boy's Life* magazine under the title: Satellite Scout" $100/500

008b: FARMER IN THE SKY Gollancz, London, 1962. [0] Illustrated by Clifford N. Geary. Red cloth printed in gold on spine $30/150

009a: WALDO AND MAGIC, INC. Doubleday, Garden City, 1950. [1] Published at $2.50 $75/350

009b: WALDO AND MAGIC INC. Pan Books, London, 1969. [] (Pan Science Fiction. Ref.c) $25/125

010a: UNIVERSE Dell, New York (1951). [0] Dell Book 36 (10 cents). Pictorial wraps. *Adventure on A Gigantic Spaceship* at head of title $125.

011a: BETWEEN PLANETS Scribner's, New York, 1951. [5] Also has publisher's seal on copyright page. Illustrated by Clifford N. Geary. Published at $2.50. "A condensed version under the title Planets In Combat appeared in ... the *Blue Book* magazine". Also noted, a later state dustwrapper priced $2.95 (L. W. Currey 11/95) $100/500

011b: BETWEEN PLANETS Gollancz, London, 1968. [] Illustrated by Clifford N. Geary (ref.b) $25/125

012a: THE GREEN HILLS OF EARTH Shasta, Chicago (1951). [1] Signed on tipped-in page. (Reportedly 200 copies) $450/650

012b: THE GREEN HILLS OF EARTH Shasta, Chicago (1951). [1] (Ref.c) $60/300

012c: THE GREEN HILLS OF EARTH Sidgwick & Jackson, London, 1954. [1] (Ref.c) $25/125

013a: THE PUPPET MASTERS Doubleday, Garden City, 1951. [1] (Doubleday Science Fiction.) Published at $2.75 $125/500

013b: THE PUPPET MASTERS Science Fiction Club (Museum Press Ltd., London, 1953). [] (L. W. Currey 4/97) $25/125

013c: THE PUPPET MASTERS Pan Books, London (1969). [] Assume wraps $35.

014a: TOMORROW, THE STARS Doubleday, Garden City, 1952. [1] A science fiction anthology edited by Heinlein and including his preface $35/175

015a: THE ROLLING STONES Scribner's, New York (1952). [5] Also has publisher's seal on copyright page. Illustrated by Clifford N. Geary. Published at $2.50. "A condensed version ... was published in *Boy's Life* under the title Tramp Space Ship" $125/500

015b: SPACE FAMILY STONE Gollancz, London, 1969. [0] New title (ref.b) $40/200

016a: REVOLT IN 2100 Shasta, Chicago (1953). [1] Signed on tipped-in page. (Reportedly 200 to 300 copies) $450/650

016b: REVOLT IN 2100 Shasta, Chicago (1953). [1] $60/300

016c: REVOLT IN 2100 Gollancz, London (1964). [] $30/150

017a: ASSIGNMENT IN ETERNITY Fantasy Press, Reading, PA, (1953) [2] 500 no. cc. Signed on tipped-in page $450/650

017b: ASSIGNMENT IN ETERNITY Fantasy Press, Reading, PA, (1953) [1] First binding: brick red cloth, gilt. "Heinlein" 3 mm. high on spine. $75/350

017c: ASSIGNMENT IN ETERNITY Fantasy Press, Reading, PA (1953). [1] Second binding (Greenberg variant): green boards, spine lettered in black. Also noted in blue cloth lettered in gilt, and "Heinlein" 3 mm high on spine (Captain's Bookshelf 3/95) $50/250

017d: ASSIGNMENT IN ETERNITY Fantasy Press, Reading, PA (1953). [1] Third binding (Grant variant): red cloth, and "Heinlein" 2 mm. high on spine. Also noted in dark blue cloth stamped in black (Beasley Books 4/90) $30/150

017e: ASSIGNMENT IN ETERNITY Science Fiction Club (Museum Press), London (1955). [1] (Ref.b) $40/200

Also see 031a

018a: STARMAN JONES Scribner's, New York (1953). [5] Also has publisher's seal on copyright page. Illustrated by Clifford N. Geary. Published at $2.50 $75/400

018b: STARMAN JONES Sidgwick & Jackson, London (1954). [1] (Ref.b) Blue cloth printed in dark blue on spine $35/175

019a: THE STAR BEAST Scribner's, New York (1954). [5] Also has publisher's seal on copyright page. Published at $2.50. Also noted in price clipped dustwrapper and rubber stamped price increase to "$2.75" (L. W. Currey 5/95) $75/400

020a: TUNNEL IN THE SKY Scribner's, New York (1955). [5] Published at $2.50 $75/400

020b: TUNNEL IN THE SKY Gollancz, London, 1965. [] (Ref.b) $25/125

021a: DOUBLE STAR Doubleday, Garden City, 1956. [1] Heinlein's scarcest juvenile. Winner of the 1956 Hugo (his first). Published at $2.95 $250/1,250

021b: DOUBLE STAR Joseph, London (1958). [1] Black cloth lettered in white on spine $60/300

022a: TIME FOR THE STARS Scribner's, New York (1956). [5] "A-8.56[v]." Published at $2.75 $75/350

022b: TIME FOR THE STARS Gollancz, London, 1963. [1] (Ref.c) $20/100

023a: CITIZEN OF THE GALAXY Scribner's, New York (1957). [5] "A:7.57v." Published at $2.95 $75/350

023b: CITIZEN OF THE GALAXY Gollancz, London, 1969. [] (Ref.b) $20/100

024a: THE DOOR INTO SUMMER Doubleday, Garden City, 1957. [1] Published at $2.95 $150/750

024b: THE DOOR INTO SUMMER Panther, London, 1960. [] Assume wraps (ref.b) $35.

024c: THE DOOR INTO SUMMER Gollancz, London, 1967. [] First U.K. hardback (Robert Gavora 5/91) $30/150

025a: A ROBERT HEINLEIN OMNIBUS The Science Fiction Book Club by arrangement with Sidgwick & Jackson, London, 1958. [0] Collects *The Man Who Sold The Moon* and *The Green Hills of Earth*. On copyright page: ("This Science Fiction

Book Club edition was produced in 1958 for sale to it's members only") $15/75

026a: METHUSELAH'S CHILDREN Gnome Press, Hicksville, NY (1958) [0] 7,500 cc for all issues but many were probably never bound. Rear panel of dustwrapper lists 35 titles and publisher's address as "80 East 11th St., NY 3." Black boards, spine printed in red (Currey 4/90) $75/400

026b: METHUSELAH'S CHILDREN Gnome Press, Hicksville, NY (1958). [0] Gray cloth, spine printed in red. Second issue dustwrapper lists 35 titles but "3" is dropped from address on rear panel (Currey 4/90) $40/200

026c: METHUSELAH'S CHILDREN Gnome Press, Hicksville, NY (1958). [0] Red boards, spine printed in black. May have a third dustwrapper which lists 32 titles on rear panel and has publisher's address as "Box 161, Hicksville, NY" $25/125

026d: METHUSELAH'S CHILDREN Gnome Press, Hicksville, NY (1958). [0] Lime green boards, spine printed in black (Currey 4/90) $25/125

026e: METHUSELAH'S CHILDREN Gnome Press, Hicksville, NY (1958). [0] Red cloth (not seen) (Currey 4/90) $25/125

026f: METHUSELAH'S CHILDREN Gollancz, London, 1963. [0] Red cloth stamped in gold on spine (ref.b) $30/150

027a: HAVE SPACE SUIT - WILL TRAVEL Scribner's, New York (1958). [5] 1958 Hugo Nominee. Illustrated. 276 pp., 21 cm. "A.9-58 [MJ]." Published at $2.95 $100/500

027b: HAVE SPACE SUIT - WILL TRAVEL Gollancz, London, 1970. [] (Ref.b) $25/125

028a: STARSHIP TROOPERS Putnam, New York (1959). [0] "A much abridged version...was published in *Fantasy and Science Fiction* magazine under the title Starship Soldier." Won Hugo in 1960 $250/1,250

028b: STARSHIP TROOPERS (New English Library, London, 1961.) [] (Ref.b). Assume hardback $30/150

029a: THE MENACE FROM EARTH Gnome Press, Hicksville, NY (1959). [1] $100/400

029b: THE MENACE FROM EARTH Dennis Dobson, London (1966). [] (L. W. Currey 5/96) $20/100

030a: THE UNPLEASANT PROFESSION OF JONATHAN HOAG Gnome Press, Hicksville, NY (1959). [1] Reissued by Pyramid Books in 1961 as "6xH" $50/250

030b: THE UNPLEASANT PROFESSION OF JONATHAN HOAG D. Dobson, London (1964) [1] $20/100

031a: LOST LEGACY Brown, Watson, London (1960). [0] Pictorial wraps. Digit Books D386 (2/-). Reprints two stories from *Assignment in Eternity* $50.

032a: STRANGER IN A STRANGE LAND Putnam, New York (1961). [0] 1962 Hugo winner. Dustwrapper priced $4.50. P.408 has "C22" (Currey 4/90) $350/1,500.

032b: STRANGER IN A STRANGE LAND New English Library, London, 1965. [] Wraps $60.

032c: STRANGER IN A STRANGE LAND New English Library (London, 1975). [1] First U.K. hardback edition. Green cloth $60/300

032d: STRANGER IN A STRANGE LAND *The Original Uncut Version* Putnam, New York, 1990. [] Uncorrected proof. In blue wraps $150.

032e: STRANGER IN A STRANGE LAND *The Original Uncut Version* Putnam, New York, 1990. [] The 30th Anniversary Edition with 50,000 words restored. (Published January 1991 @ $24.95) $7/35

032f: STRANGER IN A STRANGE LAND Ace / Putnam (The Science Fiction Book Club), New York (1991). [2] Bound in full red leather. First "Limited Edition," first authorial text edition (expands original edition of 160,000 words to 220,000 words), but assume same as 032e. Issued without dustwrapper (Barry R. Levin 12/94) $75.

033a: PODKAYNE OF MARS *Her Life and Times* Putnam, New York (1963). [0] Dustwrapper flap "POM | $3.50 | YA" (Currey 4/90) $125/650

033b: PODKAYNE OF MARS New English Library, London, 1969. [] Wraps (ref.b) $40.

033c: PODKAYNE OF MARS New English Library (London, 1977). [] First U.K. hardcover edition (L.W. Currey 3/96) $8/40

034a: GLORY ROAD Putnam, New York (1963). [0] $150/850

034b: GLORY ROAD New English Library (London, 1965). [] (Ref.b.) Assume hardback $30/150

035a: ORPHANS OF THE SKY Gollancz, London, 1963. [0] Precedes American publication. Issued with wrap-around band. Reportedly the brown cloth preceded the red (Hawthorn Books 1/91) $150/750

035b: ORPHANS OF THE SKY Putnam, New York (1964). [1] Note: the Book Club also has "First American Edition" on the copyright page $75/450

036a: FARNHAM'S FREEHOLD Putnam, New York (1964). [0] "A short version of this novel ...

appeared in *Worlds of Science Fiction* magazine, 1964." Published at $4.95 $125/600

036b: FARNHAM'S FREEHOLD Dobson, London (1965). [1] (Ref.c) $30/100

037a: THREE BY HEINLEIN Doubleday, Garden City, 1965. [0] Code "G39" at base of page 426 $15/75

037b: A HEINLEIN TRIAD Gollancz, London, 1966. [0] $15/75

038a: THE MOON IS A HARSH MISTRESS Putnam, New York (1966). [0] Hugo Award for 1967 $250/1,250

038b: THE MOON IS A HARSH MISTRESS Dobson, London, 1967. [] (Ref.b) 75/400

039a: THE WORLDS OF ROBERT A. HEINLEIN Ace Books, New York (1966). [0] Wraps. Ace Book F-375 (40 cents). First thus $35.

039b: THE WORLDS OF ROBERT A. HEINLEIN New English Library (London, 1970). [] Wraps (ref.c) $35.

040a: THE PAST THROUGH TOMORROW Putnam, New York (1967). [0] Reprint collection of "Future History" stories $60/300

040b: THE PAST THROUGH TOMORROW New English Library (London, 1977). [1] Two volumes. Black cloth (simulated?) $35/125

041a: I WILL FEAR NO EVIL Putnam, New York (1970). [0] $40/200

041b: I WILL FEAR NO EVIL New English Library (London, 1971). [0] Dark blue cloth stamped in gold on spine $20/100

042a: TIME ENOUGH FOR LOVE Putnam, New York (1973). [0] $30/150

042b: TIME ENOUGH FOR LOVE New English Library, London, 1974. [] (Ref.b) $15/75

043a: THE BEST OF ROBERT HEINLEIN Sidgwick & Jackson, London (1973). [1] Edited by Angus Wells $12/60

044a: ARE YOU A 'RARE BLOOD?' Horizon, no place, 1976. [] Off-print from *Horizon Magazine*, stapled sheets (Barry Levin 1/90) $250.

045a: THE NOTEBOOKS OF LAZARUS LONG Putnam, New York (1978). [0] Written with D.F. Vassallo (illuminations). Pictorial wraps $60.

046a: DESTINATION MOON Gregg Press, Boston, 1979. [] With a new introduction by David G. Hartwell. [The Gregg Press Science Fiction Series]; "...photographic reprint of *Destination Moon* and his article "Shooting Destination Moon," which originally appeared in *Astounding Science Fiction*, July 1950. Issued without dustwrapper (ref.c) $75.

047a: EXPANDED UNIVERSE *The New Worlds of Robert A. Heinlein.* Grosset & Dunlap, New York (1980). [1] (Ref.c) $25/75

047b: EXPANDED UNIVERSE... Grosset & Dunlap, New York (1980). [1] Wraps. Simultaneously issued (ref.c) $30.

048a: THE NUMBER OF THE BEAST New English Library (London, 1980). [1] $15/75

048b: THE NUMBER OF THE BEAST Fawcett Columbine, New York (1980). [] First US hard cover edition. Reportedly published in small quantity and sold only to US library market. US text is different and adds illustrations by Richard M. Powers $15/75

048c: THE NUMBER OF THE BEAST Fawcett Columbine, New York, 1980. [] Wraps. Illustrated by Richard M. Powers $20.

048d: THE NAMES OF THE BEAST IN *The Number of the Beast* No publisher, place or date [Robert A. Heinlein, Santa Cruz, 1980]. [0] A single leaf, 8½ x 11 inches. Authorial photocopy typescript, typed mostly single spaced. Sent by Heinlein to a small number of friends, he lists all the anagrams in his book, *The Number of the Beast,* and reveals some other secrets in the text (Barry R. Levin 6/96, catalogued @ $1,650). $NVA.

049a: FRIDAY Holt, Rinehart, Winston, New York (1982). [2] 500 sgd no. cc. Issued without dustwrapper. In slipcase $150/250

049b: FRIDAY Holt, Rinehart, Winston, New York (1982). [3] Also states "First Edition" $8/40

050a: JOB *A Comedy of Justice* Del Ray/Ballantine Books, New York (1984). [] Uncorrected proof. In white wraps $150.

050b: JOB *A Comedy of Justice* Del Ray/Ballantine Books, New York (1984). [2] 26 sgd ltr cc (Barry Levin 11/91) $500/600

050c: JOB *A Comedy of Justice* Del Ray/Ballantine Books, New York (1984). [2] 750 sgd and no. cc. Issued without dustwrapper. In slipcase $150/225

050d: JOB *A Comedy of Justice* Del Ray/Ballantine Books, New York (1984). [3] Also states "First Edition - September 1984" $7/35

050e: A COMEDY OF JUSTICE New English Library (London, 1984). [] Note: Mistitled. Advance copy (uncorrected proof). Printed wraps $75.

050f: JOB *A Comedy of Justice* New English Library (London, 1984). [] $7/35

051a: THE CAT WHO WALKS THROUGH WALLS Putnam, New York (1985). [] Uncorrected proof. In blue wraps (Metropolitan Book Auction 6/95) $100.

051b: THE CAT WHO WALKS THROUGH WALLS Putnam, New York (1985). [2] 350 sgd no. cc. Issued without dustwrapper. In slipcase $200/300

051c: THE CAT WHO WALKS THROUGH WALLS Putnam, New York (1985). [3] 115,000 cc (b & c). First issue with text in line 3 starting "Enterprise ..." on p.300 and erratum slip laid in $35/60

051d: THE CAT WHO WALKS THROUGH WALLS Putnam, New York (1985). [3] Second state: Error on p.300 corrected so that line 3 starts "Ignate universes ..." $7/35

051e: THE CAT WHO WALKS THROUGH WALLS New English Library, London, 1985. [] $8/40

052a: TO SAIL BEYOND THE SUNSET Ace / Putnam, New York (1987). [3] 115,000 cc. (Published 7/7/87 at $18.95) $6/30

052b: TO SAIL BEYOND THE SUNSET Michael Joseph, London, 1987. [] $6/30

053a: GRUMBLES FROM THE GRAVE Ballantine / Del Rey, New York (1990). [3] Also states "First Edition , January 1990" $6/30

054a: REQUIEM *New Collected Works By and Tributes To The Grand Master* Tor/St. Martin's Press, New York (1992). [] Uncorrected proof. In white wraps with image of dustwrapper on front cover $60.

054b: REQUIEM *New Collected Works By and Tributes To The Grand Master* Tor / St. Martin's

Press, New York (1992). [1] "First Edition, February 1992." (Published February 1992 @ $21.95) $5/25

055a: TRAMP ROYALE Berkeley/Ace, New York (1992). [3] Also states "First Edition, April 19, 1992." (Published April 1992 @ $18.95) $5/25

JOSEPH HELLER

Heller was born in Brooklyn in 1923. He received his B.A. from New York University, his M.A. from Columbia University and attended Oxford University on a Fulbright Scholarship. He served in the Army Air Force during WWII and taught and worked in advertising and promotion for *Time*, *Look* and *McCall's* before becoming a full time writer.

REFERENCES:

(a) Lepper, Gary M. A BIBLIOGRAPHICAL REFERENCE TO SEVENTY-FIVE MODERN AMERICAN AUTHORS. Berkeley: Serendipity Books, 1976.

(b) Inventory.

(c) Bruccoli & Clark. FIRST PRINTINGS OF AMERICAN AUTHORS Volume 2. Detroit: Gale Research (1977).

001a: CATCH-22 Simon & Schuster, New York, 1961. [] Galley proofs in tall spiral bound pink wraps (Pharos #6) $1,500.

Note: the first chapter appeared as a novel in progress in *New World Writing* under the title Catch 18. New American Library (New York, 1955). [1] Wraps $100.

001b: CATCH-22 Simon & Schuster, New York, 1961. [] Advance review copy. In white pictorial wraps printed in blue. (Publisher's prospectus laid in some copies {Joseph The Provider #31}) $1,000.

001c: CATCH-22 Simon & Schuster, New York, 1961. [1] Presumed advance issue with publisher's logo on first page rather than after two blank leaves as in normal trade editions. In first issue dustwrapper without reviews on back (Waiting For Godot 10/90) $350/1,350

001d: CATCH-22 Simon & Schuster, New York, 1961. [1] In first issue dustwrapper without reviews on back $250/1,250

001e: CATCH-22 Simon & Schuster, New York, 1961. [1] In second issue dustwrapper with reviews by Algren, Jones, Shaw, et al on back $250/350

001f: CATCH-22 Jonathan Cape, London (1961?). [] Pre-publication extract. In 16 page booklet in green printed wraps (Dalian Books 11/88) $150.

001g: CATCH-22 Jonathan Cape, London (1962). [1] With top edge stained green. Presumed first issue (Robert Dagg 11/89) in dustwrapper with blurb about book on back $60/300

001h: CATCH-22 Jonathan Cape, London (1962). [] Presumed second issue dustwrapper with blurbs by leading authors on back $60/150

001i: CATCH-22 *A Dramatization* French, New York (1971). [0] Wraps $40.

001j: CATCH-22 *A Dramatization* Delacorte, New York (1973). [1] New foreword by Heller $25/125

001k: CATCH-22 Franklin Press, Franklin Center, 1978. [2] Signed "Limited Edition." In decorated full leather $125.

001l: CATCH-22 Simon & Schuster, New York, 1994. [2] 750 sgd no. cc. Issued in slipcase. Contains a five-page introduction by Heller written for this edition reflecting upon the history of the novel over the years (James Pepper Rare Books, Inc. 2/97) $150/250

002a: WE BOMBED IN NEW HAVEN (Privately printed, New York), 1968. [] Xeroxed copies for production "in a Theatre in New York" $75.

002b: WE BOMBED IN NEW HAVEN Knopf, New York, 1968. [1] $15/75

002c: WE BOMBED IN NEW HAVEN Jonathan Cape, London, 1969. [] (Ref.c) $10/50

002d: WE BOMBED IN NEW HAVEN Dell, New York (1970). [1] Wraps. Revised (ref.b) $25.

003a: CLEVINGER'S TRIAL French, New York (1973). [0] Wraps (ref.c) $100.

004a: SOMETHING HAPPENED Knopf, New York, 1974. [] Uncorrected proof. In mustard colored wraps (Waiting For Godot 10/90) $75.

004b: SOMETHING HAPPENED Knopf, New York, 1974. [2] 350 sgd no. cc. Issued in cream colored dustwrapper. In slipcase $125/200

004c: SOMETHING HAPPENED Knopf, New York, 1974. [1] $8/40

004d: SOMETHING HAPPENED Jonathan Cape, London (1974). [1] (Ref.b) $8/40

005a: DIRTY DINGUS MAGEE Metro-Goldwyn-Mayer, New York (1978). [] Folio wraps. Screenplay written with Tom and Frank Waldman (Joseph the Provider 8/90) $200.

006a: GOOD AS GOLD Simon & Schuster, New York (1979). [] Uncorrected proofs. In printed yellow wraps (H.E. Turlington #28) $75.

006b: GOOD AS GOLD Simon & Schuster, New York (1979). [2] 500 sgd no. cc. Issued in acetate dustwrapper. In slipcase $100/150

006c: GOOD AS GOLD Simon & Schuster, New York (1979). [2] 1,000 cc. "Specially bound for friends..." Issued in acetate dustwrapper $40.

006d: GOOD AS GOLD Simon & Schuster, New York (1979). [3] $6/30

006e: GOOD AS GOLD Jonathan Cape, London (1979). [1] $8/40

006f: GOOD AS GOLD Franklin Press, Franklin Center, 1979. [2] Signed "Limited Edition" with Special Message by Heller. Issued in decorated full leather $60.

007a: GOD KNOWS Knopf, New York, 1984. [] Uncorrected proof. In yellow wraps (Bert Babcock 5/89) $75.

007b: GOD KNOWS Franklin Library, Franklin Center, 1984. [2] "Limited Signed" edition with Special Message by Heller. Issued in decorated full leather $75.

007c: GOD KNOWS Knopf, New York, 1984. [2] 350 sgd no. cc. Issued in special dustwrapper. In slipcase $100/150

007d: GOD KNOWS Knopf, New York, 1984. [1] (Published October 8, 1984 @ $16.95) $7/35

007e: GOD KNOWS Jonathan Cape L (1984) [1] Uncorrected proof. In printed red wraps. "Provisional publication date 11/1/84 @ £8.95." (Also noted in rust colored wraps. Assume the same) $75.

007f: GOD KNOWS Jonathan Cape, London (1984). [1] $8/40

008a: NO LAUGHING MATTER Putnam, New York, 1986. [] Uncorrected proof. In tan wraps (Metropolitan Book Auction 6/95) $60.

008b: NO LAUGHING MATTER Putnam, New York, 1986. [] Written with Speed Vogel. (Published @ $18.95) $7/35

008c: NO LAUGHING MATTER Jonathan Cape, London (1986). [] $8/40

009a: PICTURE THIS Putnam, New York, 1988. [] Uncorrected proof. In printed red wraps $60.

009b: PICTURE THIS Putnam, New York, 1988. [2] 250 sgd no. cc. Issued in slipcase $100/150

009c: PICTURE THIS Putnam, New York, 1988. [] 86,000 cc. (Published September, 1988 @ $19.95) $6/30

009d: PICTURE THIS Macmillan, London (1988). [0] 24 pages in paper wraps. A "sample." Around 500 copies (Nicholas Burrows 1/89) $30.

009e: PICTURE THIS Macmillan, London (1988). [2] 50 no. cc Uncorrected proof. In publisher's printed wraps (Ian McKelvie 2/93) $75.

009f: PICTURE THIS Macmillan, London (1988). [] $8/40

010a: CONVERSATIONS WITH JOSEPH HELLER University of Mississippi Press, Jackson, 1993. [] (Published 5/93 @ $32.95) $20/40

010b: CONVERSATIONS WITH JOSEPH HELLER University of Mississippi Press, Jackson, 1993. [] Wraps. (published 5/95 @ $14.95) $25.

011a: CLOSING TIME Franklin Library, Franklin Center (1994). [2] Signed "Limited Edition." Issued in decorated full leather $75.

011b: CLOSING TIME Simon & Schuster, New York (1994). [] Uncorrected proof. In printed wraps. (Joseph the Provider 1/95) $50.

011c: CLOSING TIME *The Sequel to Catch-22* Simon & Schuster, New York, 1994. [] Uncorrected proof. In pictorial wraps $75.

011d: CLOSING TIME ... Simon & Schuster, New York, 1994. [2] 750 sgd no. cc. In slipcase $50/100

011e: CLOSING TIME ... Simon & Schuster, NY, 1994. [] 200,000 cc (PW). (Publ. 10/94 @ $24.00) $5/25

011f: CLOSING TIME ... Simon & Schuster, London, 1994. [] Proof in glossy wraps. Noted a copy numbered "0149" on inside front wrap. Produced from the American sheets (Nicholas and Helen Burrows 4/97) $50.

012a: NOW AND THEN Alfred A. Knopf, New York, 1998. [] Uncorrected proof. First issue in white or beige wraps (Ken Lopez 6/98) $50.

012b: NOW AND THEN Alfred A. Knopf, New York, 1998. [] Second issue: same as 012a but with black and white mock-up of dustwrapper pasted or stapled to front cover (Ken Lopez 6/98) $50.

012c: NOW AND THEN Alfred A. Knopf, New York, 1998. [] Third issue: in non-glossy wraps with the black and white cover of 012b as cover and back blank (Ken Lopez 6/98) $40.

012d: NOW AND THEN Franklin Library, Franklin Center, 1998. [2] Sgd ltd edition. In full leather $60.

012e: NOW AND THEN Alfred A. Knopf, New York, 1998. [1] Published at $24

012f: NOW AND THEN Simon & Schuster (U.K.), London, 1998. [] $7/35

ZORA NEALE HURSTON
1891 - 1960

Zora Neale Hurston was born in Eatonville, Florida, the first incorporated Black town in America. Her first years are described in *Dust Tracks on a Road.* After her mother died she characterized her life as "a series of wanderings" until she enrolled as a full-time student at Baltimore's Morgan Academy. She moved to Washington, D.C. in 1918 and became a part-time student at Howard University and began to write. Hurston moved to New York in 1925 and broadened her contacts with the major figures of the Harlem Renaissance and the white literary community. She received a scholarship to Barnard College where she studied Cultural Anthropology. After graduating in 1928 she spent four years doing research on folklore in the South which she used in a number of her books.

Hurston's standing as a major writer has endured to the present although she herself withdrew from public life by the 1950's. Her argument that the pressure for integration denied the value of existing black institutions and other views did not endear her to many people. She spent the last years of her life in ill health and poverty and died in Port Pierce, Florida.

The bibliographical information herein was based on the collection of Charles Dickison, whom we thank for his assistance; and Bruccoli / Clark's FIRST PRINTINGS OF AMERICAN AUTHORS, Volume I, 1978.

001a: JONAH'S GOURD VINE Lippincott, Phila., 1934. [0] $600/6,000

001b: JONAH'S GOURD VINE Duckworth, London, 1934. [] $400/2,000

002a: MULES AND MEN Lippincott, Phila., 1935. [0] Illustrated by Miguel Covarrubias. Introduction by Franz Boaz $400/2,000

002b: MULES AND MEN Kegan, Paul, London, 1936. [] $200/1,000

003a: THEIR EYES WERE WATCHING GOD Lippincott, Phila. (1937). [0] $350/2,500

003b: THEIR EYES WERE WATCHING GOD Dent, London, 1938. [] $150/750

Also noted, a reference to "First Cheap Edition"

004a: TELL MY HORSE Lippincott, Phila. (1938). [0] $250/1250

004b: VOODOO GODS *An Inquiry Into Native Myths and Magic in Jamaica and Haiti* Dent, London (1939). [1] New title (Kelmscott Bookshop) $200/1,000

005a: MOSES, MAN OF THE MOUNTAINS Lippincott, Phila. (1939). [1] Reddish-brown cloth $250/1,250

005b: MOSES, MAN OF THE MOUNTAINS Lippincott, Phila. (1939). [1] Green cloth $200/1,000

005c: THE MAN OF THE MOUNTAIN Dent, London (1941). [1] $100/500

006a: DUST TRACKS ON A ROAD *An Autobiography* Lippincott, Phila. (1942). [1] $150/750

006b: DUST TRACKS ON A ROAD, *An Autobiography* Hutchinson, London, 1944. [] $100/500

006c: DUST TRACKS ON A ROAD *An Autobiography* Virago (London, 1986). [1] Wraps. "Published by Virago..." "several chapters restored that were either substantially altered or cut from the original." New introduction by Dellita Martin $50.

007a: SERAPH ON THE SUWANEE Scribner, New York, 1948. [5] Uncorrected proof. In blue printed wraps. "Published October 11, 1948 @ $3.00". $1,000.

007b: SERAPH ON THE SUWANEE Scribner, New York, 1948. [5] Advance review copy. In beige wraps (Waverley Books 2/93) $750.

007c: SERAPH ON THE SUWANEE Scribner, New York, 1948. [5] $150750

008a: I LOVE MYSELF WHEN I'M LAUGHING Feminist Press (Old Westbury, NY), 1979. [] A Hurston reader edited by Alic Walker (James Jaffe 2/92) $150/750

008b: I LOVE MYSELF WHEN I'M LAUGHING Feminist Press (Old Westbury, NY), 1979. [] Wraps $100.

009a: THE SANCTIFIED CHURCH Turtle Island, Berkeley, 1981. [0] Cloth. In acetate dustwrapper $250.

009b: THE SANCTIFIED CHURCH Turtle Island, Berkeley, 1981. [0] Wraps $75.

010a: SPUNK SELECTED SHORT STORIES Turtle Island, Berkeley (1985). [0] Wraps $75.

011a: THE GILDED SIX-BITS Redpath Press, Minn. (1986). [0] Wraps. 5,000 copies. Issued in envelope $50.

012a: MULE BONE *A Comedy of Negro Life* Harper Perennial, New York (1991). [] Written with Langston Hughes. Includes the original Hurston short story *The Bone Of Contention*, on which the play was based, together with letters from Hurston and Hughes. Published primarily as a paperback, this hardbound issue was done in a very small edition with most copies going primarily to libraries. Not issued in dustwrapper? (Joseph the Provider Books 5/95) $200.

012b: MULES AND MEN *A Comedy of Negro Life* Harper Perennial, New York (1991). [] Wraps. Written with Langston Hughes (Joseph the Provider Books 5/95) $50.

013a: THE COMPLETE STORIES OF ZORA NEALE HURSTON Harper Collins, New York, 1994. [] (Published 5/94 @ $ 25.00) $10/40

014a: ZORA NEALE HURSTON NOVELS AND STORIES Library of America, New York, 1995. [] (Waverley Books 4/95) Published @ $35.00 $15/40

015a: FOLKLORE, MEMOIRS, AND OTHER WRITING Library of America, New York, 1995. [] Issued in slipcase (A Tale of Two Sisters 7/96) $15/40

JOHN IRVING

Irving was born in 1942 in Putney, Vermont. He graduated from the University of New Hampshire, received an M.F.A. from the University of Iowa and studied further at the University of Pittsburgh and the University of Vienna. The latter experience (or at least the area) was used in his first book, which received some good critical but not public attention. The latter acclaim was reserved for *The World According To Garp*, which put him "on the map" so to speak.

The information in this guide on the American firsts was based on information provided by Jackson Bryer, whom we thank for his assistance; and "A John Irving Bibliography" by Edward C. Reilly in the *Bulletin of Bibliography*, Vol. 42, No. 1, March, 1985. The latter was used for the British editions, but provided only the publisher and date, therefore, we assumed the first book by Corgi was in wraps. The quantities sold for the first three books were obtained from Scott Haller's "John Irving's Bizarre World" which appeared in *Saturday Review*, September 1981. This article did not state if these quantities covered more than one printing or if they included remainder sales.

We would also like to thank David Potter of St. Petersburg for providing additional listings and information.

001a: SETTING FREE THE BEARS Random House, New York (1968). [1] 6,228 cc sold. Review slip indicated the book was actually published in January 1969 (Joseph the Provider Books 9/92) $150/750

001b: SETTING FREE THE BEARS Corgi Books, London, 1968. [] Wraps $100.

001c: SETTING FREE THE BEARS Bloomsbury Classics, London, 1991. [] First British hardcover edition (Nicholas Burrows 11/94) $15/75

002a: THE WATER METHOD MAN Random House, New York (1972). [4] 6,906 cc sold. Although the quantity would indicate that this title would be more common than item 003a, this does not seem to be case, in fact it seems scarcer to us. $75/400

002b: THE WATER METHOD MAN Corgi Books, London, 1980. [] Wraps $50.

003a: THE 158-POUND MARRIAGE Random House, New York (1974). [4] 2,560 cc sold $50/250

003b: THE 158-POUND MARRIAGE Corgi (London, 1980). [1] Wraps. "First published in Great Britain." $50.

003c: THE 158 POUND MARRIAGE Bloomsbury Classics, London, 1993. [] First British Hardcover edition. Small format (Nicholas Burrows 11/94) $10/50

004a: THE WORLD ACCORDING TO GARP Dutton, New York (1978). [3] Uncorrected proof. In bright yellow-green wraps indicating a first printing of 25,000 copies. Also noted, a "first issue proof" in mustard colored , tall wraps (Ken Lopez 12/94) $600.

004b: THE WORLD ACCORDING TO GARP Dutton, New York (1978). [3] Uncorrected proof. In blue-green wraps (Serendipity Books and Monroe Stahr Books 1/96) $400.

004c: THE WORLD ACCORDING TO GARP Dutton, New York (1978). [3] 1,500 cc. Advance copy. In white wraps with red letters. Erratum slip laid in (Lame Duck Books 12/94) $250.

004d: THE WORLD ACCORDING TO GARP Dutton, New York (1978). [3] 25,000 cc. Also states "First Edition" $25/125

004e: THE WORLD ACCORDING TO GARP Gollancz, London, 1978. [] Advance Excerpt consisting of the first chapter. In stapled wraps (Ken Lopez Books 1/93) $75.

004f: THE WORLD ACCORDING TO GARP Gollancz, London, 1978. [0] $25/100

004g: THE WORLD ACCORDING TO GARP Hutchinson of Australia / Victor Gollancz, Australia, 1978. [] Australian issue using the English sheets (Larsen Books 10/96) $25/100

004h: THE WORLD ACCORDING TO GARP The Modern Library, New York (1998). [3] New Introduction by the author. Published at $18.50

005a: THREE BY IRVING Random House, New York (1980). [1] The first three novels $25/75

006a: THE PENSION GRILLPARZER (Tale Blazer, Perfection Form Co., Logan, 1980.) [] Stapled wraps. First separate edition (Lame Duck Books 12/94) $60.

007a: THE HOTEL NEW HAMPSHIRE Dutton, New York (1981). [3] Uncorrected proof in tan wraps. Dates "July 2, 1978" and "August 6, 1980" not typeset and author corrections can be seen $250.

007b: THE HOTEL NEW HAMPSHIRE Dutton, New York (1981). [3] Uncorrected proof. In tan wraps with contents typeset (priority assumed). Also Ken Lopez, 5/97, had later issue proof with pages 1 and 1A tipped in.

Also perfect bound in white card binding duplicating dustwrapper on front. Appeared to be a photocopy of an uncorrected proof, perhaps for use in Canada {Steven Temple 6/92}). Also bound signatures in plain gray wraps with end sheets of printed book (Ken Lopez Books 10/92). Ken Lopez has seen corrected proof copy shot from the typescript and reproducing holographic corrections throughout, including numerous word changes, deletions of sentences and even whole paragraphs (some of the original text remaining visible). Dated "6 August 1980." We believe these forms may have been for some special internal use and not distributed $175.

007c: THE HOTEL NEW HAMPSHIRE Dutton, New York (1981). [2] 550 sgd no. cc. In full leather. Issued without dustwrapper. In slipcase $250/300

007d: THE HOTEL NEW HAMPSHIRE Dutton, New York (1981). [3] 175,000 cc. Also states "First Edition." Variant with sheets bulking 2.8 cm vs. 3.0 cm, price clipped but otherwise identical. Purchased in Vancouver, B.C. , Canada (Wm. Reese Co. 9/92) $8/40

007e: THE HOTEL NEW HAMPSHIRE Jonathan Cape, London (1981). [1] Black boards stamped in gold on spine $8/40

008a: HOW TO SPELL (International Paper Co., New York, 1983.) [] 11" x 8 1/4" broadside printed on both sides with three photos of Irving. There may also be a 11" x 17" format (David Potter) $60.

009a: THE CIDER HOUSE RULES Morrow, New York (1985). [0] Uncorrected proof. In yellow wraps $200.

009b: THE CIDER HOUSE RULES Morrow, New York (1985). [0] Advance copies. "Special Signed Edition" in beige boards and dark brown cloth spine (Bev Chaney 11/89). Glassine dustwrapper (Between the Covers Books 12/92) $150.

009c: THE CIDER HOUSE RULES Franklin Library, Franklin, PA, 1985. [2] Signed limited edition in full leather, reportedly preceding other editions $150.

009d: THE CIDER HOUSE RULES Morrow, New York (1985). [2] 250 sgd no. cc. Issued in glassine dustwrapper. In slipcase $400/450

009e: THE CIDER HOUSE RULES Morrow (Offered by the Book-of-the-Month Club), New York (1985). [2] 795 sgd no. cc. Off-yellow spine, dark green boards in glassine jacket. In dark green slipcase (David Potter). We have no idea where this fits in chronologically. This placement is arbitrary $200/250

009f: THE CIDER HOUSE RULES Morrow, New York (1985). [0] With signed tipped-in leaf (Watermark West #2) $75/125

009g: THE CIDER HOUSE RULES Morrow, New York (1985). [0] 250,000 cc. (Published June 17, 1985 @ $18.95) $8/40

009h: THE CIDER HOUSE RULES Jonathan Cape, London (1985). [] Uncorrected proof. In red printed wraps ("Provisional publication date: 20 June 1985"). (Dalian #46 included an advance uncorrected proof in brown printed wraps?) $100.

009i: THE CIDER HOUSE RULES Jonathan Cape, London (1985). [1] Black cloth stamped in gold on spine $10/50

010a: A PRAYER FOR OWEN MEANY Dennys (Toronto, 1989). [] Reportedly preceded U.S. editions $12/60

010b: A PRAYER FOR OWEN MEANY Franklin Library, Franklin Center, 1989. [2] Signed "limited edition." In decorated full leather $125.

010c: A PRAYER FOR OWEN MEANY Morrow, New York, 1989. [2] 250 sgd no. cc. Issued in acetate dustwrapper. In slipcase. (Published price was $150) $200/350

010d: A PRAYER FOR OWEN MEANY Morrow, New York, 1989. [3] 300,000 cc (PW). (Published March 1989 @ $19.95) $8/40

010e: A PRAYER FOR OWEN MEANY Bloomsbury, London (1989). [] "Uncorrected Book Proof." In glossy pictorial wraps (Waiting For Godot 4/90) $60.

010f: A PRAYER FOR OWEN MEANY Bloomsbury (London, 1989). [] $10/50

011a: MASS APPEAL LETTER FROM NARAL Naral, 1989. [] Wraps. Issued in envelope $75

012a: TRYING TO SAVE PIGGY SNEED Alfred A. Knopf Canada (Toronto, 1993). [1] "First Canadian Edition." True First (Waverley Books 7/95) $25/100

012b: TRYING TO SAVE PIGGY SNEED Bloomsbury (London, 1993). [1] "This Collection First Published 1993." Contains eight stories / memoirs $15/75

012c: TRYING TO SAVE PIGGY SNEED Bloomsbury (London, 1993). [1] Simultaneous issue in wraps. "This Collection First Published 1993" $25.

012d: TRYING TO SAVE PIGGY SNEED Arcade, New York, 1995. [] Uncorrected manuscript. 8½ x 11 inches. In ring-bound plastic cover, dated 6/19/95 (Gordon Beckhorn 1/96) $150.

012e: TRYING TO SAVE PIGGY SNEED Arcade, New York (1995). [3] Also states "FIRST U.S. EDITION." Advance Excerpt. In perfect-bound decorative wraps. 40 pp. Contains two essays from the author's upcoming collection which was originally published in Canada (Waverley Books 7/95). Ken Lopez 5/97 states "includes the title essay and one work of fiction. The contents page lists a slated essay on Kurt Vonnegut that did not appear in the final volume." $100.

012f: TRYING TO SAVE PIGGY SNEED Arcade, New York (1995). [3] Also states "FIRST U.S.

EDITION". Uncorrected Proof. In pictorial wraps (Gordon Beckhorn 1/96) $100.

012g: TRYING TO SAVE PIGGY SNEED Arcade, New York (1996). [3] Also states "First U. S. Edition." Contains 12 stories/memoirs $6/30

013a: A SON OF THE CIRCUS Franklin Library, Franklin Center, 1994. [2] "Limited Edition." In brick-red decorated leather (Waverley Books 1/95) $125.

013b: A SON OF THE CIRCUS Random House, New York (1994). [] uncorrected proof. First page contains the Random House catalog describing the book and the author. Most copies of this proof had this page excised at the author's insistence (Cultured Oyster Books 4/96) $150.

013c: A SON OF THE CIRCUS Random House, New York (1994). [] Uncorrected proof. First page excised (Ken Lopez 5/95) $100.

013d: A SON OF THE CIRCUS Random House, New York (1994). [] (Published 9/94 @ $25.00) $5/25

013e: A SON OF THE CIRCUS Random House, Toronto, 1994. [] (Ken Lopez 5/97) $6/30

013f: A SON OF THE CIRCUS Bloomsbury (London, 1994). [] Uncorrected proof. In wraps (Ken Lopez 2/95) $60.

013g: A SON OF THE CIRCUS Bloomsbury (London, 1994). [] $8/40

014a: THE IMAGINARY GIRLFRIEND Alfred A. Knopf Canada, Toronto, 1996. [] Issued simultaneously in the U.K. and Canada (Ken Lopez 6/96) $10/60

014b: THE IMAGINARY GIRLFRIEND Bloomsbury, London, 1996. [] Uncorrected proof. In oversize proof dustwrapper with £13.99 price. The book was eventually issued at £9.99 (Nicholas and Helen Burrows 9/96) $50/100

014c: THE IMAGINARY GIRLFRIEND Bloomsbury (London, 1996). [] (Agathon Books 5/96) $8/40

015a: A WIDOW FOR ONE YEAR Bloomsbury, London, 1998. [2] 1,000 no. cc (numbered on a book plate affixed to the free front endpaper). Cloth. Issued without dustwrapper. True first (Ed Smith Books 5/98) $125.

015b: A WIDOW FOR ONE YEAR Bloomsbury, London, 1998. [] (Nicholas and Helen Burrows 5/98) $8/40

015c: A WIDOW FOR ONE YEAR Random House, New York (1998). [] Advance reading copy. In illustrated wraps (Bev Chaney, Jr. 5/98) $50.

015d: A WIDOW FOR ONE YEAR Random House, New York (1998). [4] Published at $27.97

015e: A WIDOW FOR ONE YEAR Unicycle Press, Media, Pa., 1998. [2] Approximately 1,200 sgd no. cc (the publisher indicates the print run will depend upon the number of copies ordered but will not exceed 1,200 copies). Adds introduction not in trade edition. Full leather. Published June 1998 at $120. $150.

WILLIAM KENNEDY

Kennedy was born in 1928 and worked as a movie critic and reporter for the Albany Times Union. His book *Ironweed*, which was reportedly rejected by a number of publishers, won the Pulitzer Prize in 1984.

001a: THE INK TRUCK Dial, New York, 1969. [1] $125/600

001b: THE INK TRUCK Macdonald & Co., London (1970). [1] Published price £1.50 or 30s. Black cloth stamped in silver on spine only $40/200

001c: THE INK TRUCK Viking, New York (1984). [] 13,000 cc. Reissue with short author's note $8/40

002a: LETTER TO A WOULD-BE WRITER - *Fiction II* Empire State College, Saratoga Springs, 1973. [0] Wraps. 8"x 11" sheets in clamp binder (easily reproduced) $NVA

003a: LETTER TO A WOULD-BE WRITER - *Journalism IV* Empire State College, Saratoga Springs, 1973. [0] Wraps. 8" x 11" sheets in clamp binder (easily reproduced) $NVA

Note: written for use in class. Doris Grumbach wrote *Fiction I* and *Journalism III*

004a: LEGS Coward-McCann, New York (1975). [0] $50/250

004b: LEGS Jonathan Cape, London (1976). [1] $25/125

005a: BILLY PHELAN'S GREATEST GAME Viking, New York (1978). [1] 9,000 cc $40/200

005b: BILLY PHELAN'S GREATEST GAME Penguin (London, 1984). [1] Wraps. "Published...in Great Britain 1984" $50.

006a: IRONWEED Viking, New York (1983). [] Uncorrected proof. In yellow wraps (Lame Duck 9/91) $350.

006b: IRONWEED Viking, New York (1983). [1] 6,500 cc. P.205:22 "perceivced" vs. "perceived." Assume all copies (error still in fifth printing - Jeff Klaess). Winner of Pulitzer Prize in 1984 $50/250

006c: IRONWEED Viking, New York (London, 1983). [1] Same as Viking New York edition with two changes: "Printed in Great Britain" on copyright page and price of £7.95 added at bottom of front dustwrapper flap, which still has $14.95 on upper corner $25/100

Note: The first copies actually sold in England were later Viking New York printings with the price sticker "£7.95"

006d: IRONWEED Viking, New York (London, 1983). [1] Same as 006b with £7.95 clipped and sticker with £8.95 pasted at bottom of dustwrapper $25/75

007a: O ALBANY Viking, New York, 1983. [0] Unpublished proof. In blue printed wraps $200.

007b: O ALBANY Viking Press, New York, 1983. [0] 5,000 cc $20/100

008a: CHARLEY MALARKEY AND THE BELLY BUTTON MACHINE Atlantic Monthly

Press, Boston (1986). [1] Written with his son Brendan. Illustrated by Glen Baxter. (Published September 1986 @ $10.95) $6/30

008b: CHARLEY MALARKEY AND THE BELLY BUTTON MACHINE Jonathan Cape, London, 1987. [] Laminated pictorial boards. Issued without dustwrapper $40.

009a: THE COTTON CLUB St. Martin's Press, New York (1986). [3] Wraps. Also states "First U.S. Edition. "Reproduces original script by Kennedy and Francis Coppola" $100.

010a: THE MAKING OF IRONWEED (Movie) Viking, New York. 1988. [] Uncorrected proof. In stapled wraps with eight pages of photographs from the movie $75.

010b: THE MAKING OF IRONWEED (Movie) Viking, New York, 1988. [] Wraps. Introduction and afterword by Kennedy as well as text for screenplay to go along with the 100+ photographs $75.

011a: QUINN'S BOOK Viking (New York, 1988). [1] Unrevised and unpublished proof. In dark green wraps $75.

011b: QUINN'S BOOK Viking (New York, 1988). [2] 500 sgd no. cc. Issued without dustwrapper. In slipcase $50/75

011c: QUINN'S BOOK Viking (New York, 1988). [1] 150,000 cc (PW). (Published May 1988 @ $18.95) $5/25

011d: QUINN'S BOOK Jonathan Cape, London (1988). [1] $7/35

012a: VERY OLD BONES Viking, New York, 1992. [] Uncorrected proof. In tan-gray wraps $50.

012b: VERY OLD BONES Viking, New York, 1992. [] 60,000 cc (PW). (Published April 1992 @ $23.) $5/25

013a: RIDING THE YELLOW TROLLEY CAR Viking (no place, 1993). [0] Uncorrected proof. In wraps printed overall in gold-yellow, lettering in black $50.

013b: RIDING THE YELLOW TROLLEY CAR Viking, New York (1993). [] $5/25

014a: CHARLEY MALARKEY AND THE SINGING MOUSE Viking (New York, 1994). [] Laminated pictorial boards. In dustwrapper $5/25

016a: THE FLAMING CORSAGE Viking (no place, 1996). [] Uncorrected proof. In pictorial wraps (Bev Chaney, Jr. 5/96) $40.

016b: THE FLAMING CORSAGE Viking (no place, 1996). [3] Also states "First published in 1996..." $5/25

016c: THE FLAMING CORSAGE Franklin Library, Franklin Center, 1996. [2] Signed "limited edition." In decorated full leather (Waverley Books) $75.

017a: CONVERSATIONS WITH WILLIAM KENNEDY University Press of Mississippi, Jackson (1997). [] (Bev Chaney, Jr. 5/98 $45.

017b: CONVERSATIONS WITH WILLIAM KENNEDY University Press of Mississippi, Jackson (1997). [] Wraps $20.

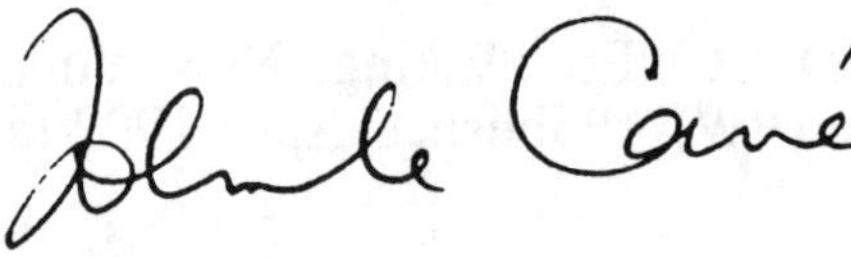

JOHN LeCARRE

John LeCarre is the pseudonym for David John Moore Cornwell. He was born in Poole, Dorset, England in 1931. LeCarre was a member of the British Foreign Service from 1959-64 serving as the Second Secretary at the Bonn Embassy from 1961-64.

001a: A CALL FOR THE DEAD Gollancz, London, 1961. [0] $600/5,000

001b: A CALL FOR THE DEAD Walker, New York, 1962. [1] Issued in white pictorial dustwrapper. Note: the edition without date on title page and in color printed dustwrapper, which also states "First published by Walker in 1962," is a later printing $300/2,000

001c: THE DEADLY AFFAIR Penguin, London, 1966. [] Wraps. New title. This title exists only in the sixth printing of Penguin C2066. Prior and subsequent printings were under the original title, *A Call for the Dead* (American Dust Company 4/97) $40.

002a: A MURDER OF QUALITY Gollancz, London, 1962. [0] Red cover. Variant in brown issued for libraries (Bell, Book & Radmall 6/92) $250/3,500

002b: A MURDER OF QUALITY Walker, New York (1963). [1] $200/1,000

002c: A MURDER OF QUALITY Hodder & Stoughton, London, 1990. [] "Lamplighter" edition with new preface by the author (David Rees 2/96) $8/40

002d: A MURDER OF QUALITY *The Novel and the Screenplay* Hodder & Stoughton, London

(1991). [1] Wraps. "This edition first published in Great Britain in 1991." Novel and complete film script, with new introduction by author $50.

003a: THE SPY WHO CAME IN FROM THE COLD Gollancz, London, 1963. [0] Noted in Book Society wrap-around band (Maggs Brothers Ltd. 3/95). Also noted a variant in brown cloth (Ken Lopez 12/95). "The variant brown publisher's binding probably precedes the usual blue binding as the blue version was retained in all reprints of the first edition. Possibly a trial binding" (Nigel Williams 11/96) $150/750

003b: THE SPY WHO CAME IN FROM THE COLD Coward-McCann, New York (1963). [] The English edition with Coward-McCann label pasted over Gollancz on title page, assume advance copy (Firsts & Co. 1986) $600.

003c: THE SPY WHO CAME IN FROM THE COLD Coward-McCann, New York (1964). [] Uncorrected proof. In blue wraps (Chapel Hill Rare Books 6/91) $500.

003d: THE SPY WHO CAME IN FROM THE COLD Coward-McCann, New York (1964). [1] First edition priced at $4.50 and without "W" on copyright page (Booksearch - AB ad). First issue dustwrapper with only three blurbs on rear panel (Joseph Dermont 3/90). Also noted with orange wrap-around band with Graham Green blurb: "The best spy story I have ever read." $50/250

003e: THE SPY WHO CAME IN FROM THE COLD Hodder & Stoughton, London, 1990. [] New introduction by LeCarre $8/40

004a: THE LeCARRE OMNIBUS Gollancz, London, 1964. [0] Contains *Call For The Dead* and *A Murder of Quality* $50/250

004b: THE INCONGRUOUS SPY Walker, New York (1964). [1] States "First published in U.S..." under each title $25/125

005a: THE LOOKING GLASS WAR Heinemann, London (1965). [1] (Dustwrapper spine usually faded) $35/175

005b: THE LOOKING GLASS WAR Coward McCann, New York (1965). [] Uncorrected proof. In spiral bound wraps (Ken Lopez 12/91) $350.

005c: THE LOOKING GLASS WAR Coward McCann, New York (1965). [1] $20/100

006a: A SMALL TOWN IN GERMANY Heinemann, London (1968). [0] $20/100

006b: A SMALL TOWN IN GERMANY Coward McCann, New York (1968). [2] 500 sgd no. cc. In tissue dustwrapper (Maurice Neville List 0) $400.

006c: A SMALL TOWN IN GERMANY Coward McCann, New York (1968). [1] Noted with spine lettering on author, title and publisher in pink, white and blue, respectively; or, in red, yellow and green, respectively. Priority unknown $15/75

006d: A SMALL TOWN IN GERMANY Hodder & Stoughton, London, 1990? [] New introduction by LeCarre $7/35

007a: PHILBY *The Spy Who Betrayed a Generation* Andre Deutsch (London, 1968). [1] Book by Bruce Page, David Leitch and Phillip Knightly with 15 page introduction by LeCarre $20/100

008a: THE NAIVE AND SENTIMENTAL LOVER Hodder & Stoughton, London (1971). [1] $25/100

008b: THE NAIVE AND SENTIMENTAL LOVER Knopf, New York, 1972. [] Uncorrected proof. In tall red wraps (Ken Lopez 9/91) $250.

008c: THE NAIVE AND SENTIMENTAL LOVER Knopf, New York, 1972. [1] $15/75

009a: TINKER, TAILOR, SOLDIER, SPY Hodder & Stoughton, London (1974). [1] $25/125

009b: TINKER, TAILOR, SOLDIER, SPY Knopf, New York, 1974. [1] $12/60

010a: THE HONOURABLE SCHOOLBOY (Hodder & Stoughton, London, 1977.) [] Uncorrected proof. In white glazed card wraps with map endpapers tipped to flys (Alan Smith 2/91) $200.

010b: THE HONOURABLE SCHOOLBOY Hodder & Stoughton, London (1977). [] 120,000 cc (Nicholas Burrows 5/92) $15/75

010e: THE HONOURABLE SCHOOLBOY Franklin Library, Franklin Center, 1977. [2] Decorated full leather. Contains “Special Message” from LeCarre not in trade edition. First American edition (Mordida Books 2/95). Reportedly, precedes the Knopf edition $100.

010f: THE HONOURABLE SCHOOLBOY Knopf, New York, 1977. [1] 10/50

011a: SMILEY’S PEOPLE Franklin Library, Franklin Center, 1979. [2] Limited edition. In decorated full leather. Contains an introduction not printed in subsequent editions (Pepper & Stern 11/94) $125.

011b: SMILEY'S PEOPLE Hodder & Stoughton, London (1980). [1] Noted with printed price of £5.95, as well as unpriced. The latter probably for export $20/100

011b: SMILEY'S PEOPLE Knopf, New York, 1980. [1] With signed tipped in leaf $125/150

011c: SMILEY'S PEOPLE Knopf, New York, 1990. [] Presentation Issue in leather (Ken Lopez 6/93) $500.

011d: SMILEY'S PEOPLE Knopf, New York, 1980. [1] $8/40

012a: QUEST FOR KARLA Hodder & Stoughton, London, 1982. [1] Includes *Tinker...*, *Honourable...* and *Smiley's...* $15/75

012b: QUEST FOR KARLA Knopf, New York, 1982. [1] $10/50

013a: THE LITTLE DRUMMER GIRL Knopf, New York (1983). [] Uncorrected proof. In blue wraps (Waiting For Godot 10/90) $100.

013b: THE LITTLE DRUMMER GIRL Knopf, New York, 1983. [1] With an extra leaf signed by author. About 200 cc (Mordida Books 5/90) $100/125

013c: THE LITTLE DRUMMER GIRL Knopf, New York, 1983. [1] $8/40

013d: THE LITTLE DRUMMER GIRL (Book of Month Club), New York, 1983. [2] 1,048 sgd no. cc. Green cloth with tan buckram spine. In acetate dustwrapper in slipcase. Issued by BOMC $250/300

013e: THE LITTLE DRUMMER GIRL Hodder & Stoughton, London, 1983. [] Uncorrected proof. In blue printed wraps (Alphabet Books 10/94) $100.

013f: THE LITTLE DRUMMER GIRL Hodder & Stoughton, London (1983). [2] 739 sgd cc. Pre-publication copy. In white wraps signed by author on upper cover (R. A. Gekoski) $200.

013g: THE LITTLE DRUMMER GIRL Hodder & Stoughton, London, 1983. [1] "Reproduced from original setting by Knopf." Noted with top edge stained either gray or dark brown. Priority uncertain but Alphabet Books believes gray is first (5/92) $15/75

014a: JOHN LE CARRE *Three Complete Novels* Avenel Books, New York, 1983. [] Omnibus edition containing *The Spy Who Came in From the Cold, A Small Town in Germany* and *The Looking Glass War* (Mordida Books 2/95) $25/75

015a: A PERFECT SPY Hodder & Stoughton, London (1986). [2] 250 sgd no. cc. Specially bound for London Limited Editions. Issued in glassine dustwrapper (no slipcase) $250/300

015b: A PERFECT SPY Hodder & Stoughton, London (1986). [1] $12/60

015c: A PERFECT SPY Knopf, New York, 1986. [] Uncorrected proof. First in white wraps $125.

015d: A PERFECT SPY Knopf, New York, 1986. [] Uncorrected proof. Second issue in red wraps $75.

015e: A PERFECT SPY Knopf, New York, 1986. [1] Signed on tipped in leaf $100/125

015f: A PERFECT SPY Knopf, New York, 1986. [1] (Copies without printed price on dustwrapper are for export to Canada, unless they have a Book-of-the-Month stamp on back cover) $7/35

015g: A PERFECT SPY Viking, Toronto, 1986. [] (Annex Books 4/96) $7/35

016a: THE CLANDESTINE MUSE Seluzicki Fine Books, Portland, Oregon (1986). [2] 250 sgd no. cc. Issued in stiff wraps (plus 10 copies Hors Commerce) $350.

017a: JOHN LeCARRE SAMPLER (Bantam, New York, 1987.) [3] Wraps. No title page but complete copyright page. Excerpts from seven novels $15.

018a: THE RUSSIA HOUSE Knopf, New York, 1989. [1] Uncorrected proof. In cream (tan, buff Monroe Stahr Books 5/95) colored wraps $125.

Note: Reportedly, the U.S. edition of RUSSIA HOUSE was published three weeks before the English edition (Monroe Stahr 6/92)

018b: THE RUSSIA HOUSE Knopf, New York, 1989. [1] With signed tipped in leaf. (Approximately 400 copies - Ken Lopez 12/91) $125/150

018c: THE RUSSIA HOUSE Knopf, New York, 1989. [1] 350,000 cc (PW). (Published June 9, 1989 @ $19.95) $7/35

018d: THE RUSSIA HOUSE Hodder & Stoughton, London (1989). [] Uncorrected proof. In white or tan wraps (Monroe Stahr 3/90). Priority uncertain. Pictorial wraps (David Rees 5/94) $125.

018e: THE RUSSIA HOUSE Hodder & Stoughton, London, and Limited Editions, London (1989). [2] 250 sgd no. cc. In tissue dustwrapper $275.

018f: THE RUSSIA HOUSE Hodder & Stoughton, London (1989). [1] About 500 special bound (not signed) copies. In gray cloth with leather spine. In slipcase (Ken Lopez 9/89) $100/125

018g: THE RUSSIA HOUSE Hodder & Stoughton, London (1989). [1] Noted in promotional wrap-around band (Nicholas and Helen Burrows 2/96) $8/40

019a: THE SECRET PILGRIM Knopf, New York, 1991. [] Uncorrected proof. First state in tan wraps with 1990 date on cover; announcing 250,000 cc (Pepper & Stern 11/94). Precedes U.K., but reportedly the Sydney, Australia edition was published on December 10, 1990 (Monroe Stahr 5/91) $125.

019b: THE SECRET PILGRIM Knopf, New York, 1991. [] Uncorrected proof. Second state in blue wraps with 1991 on front cover and title page and 1990 on copyright page. First printing announced as 350,000 cc (Ken Lopez 2/95) $75.

019c: THE SECRET PILGRIM Knopf, New York, 1991. [1] Signed tipped in page. (About 700 copies - Ken Lopez 3/92) $75/100

019d: THE SECRET PILGRIM Knopf, New York, 1991. [1] 350,000 cc (PW). (Published January 1991 @ $21.95) $7/35

019e: THE SECRET PILGRIM Hodder & Stoughton, London, 1991. [] Uncorrected proof. First issue in white printed wraps, lacking full British cataloging data. In proof dustwrapper without author photograph on back. (About 80 copies - Hartley Moorhouse 4/92.) (65 copies - Pepper & Stern 11/94) $100/150

019f: THE SECRET PILGRIM Hodder & Stoughton, London, 1991. [] Uncorrected proof. Second issue in bound signatures without covers. Laid in proof dustwrapper with author's picture on back $50/100

019g: THE SECRET PILGRIM Hodder & Stoughton, London, 1991. [] (Published January 17, 1991) $8/40

020a: THE UNBEARABLE PEACE Granta, London, 1991. [] Pictorial Wraps (Buckingham Books 9/92) $50.

020b: THE UNBEARABLE PEACE Viking Penguin, New York, 1991. [] Wraps (Mordida Books 2/95) $40.

021a: THE NIGHT MANAGER Knopf, New York, 1993. [] Uncorrected Proof. In gray-brown wraps (Bev Chaney, Jr. 6/93); gray wraps (Waiting For Godot Books); tan wraps (Bev Chaney, Jr. 10/94?); mauve wraps (Monroe Stahr Books 5/95). This is our "Eye of the beholder" entry (Carl Hahn) $75.

021b: THE NIGHT MANAGER Knopf, New York, 1993. [1] Advance reading copy. In pictorial wraps in larger format (Monroe Stahr Books 6/95) $35.

021c: THE NIGHT MANAGER Knopf, New York, 1993. [1] Sgd by author on a publisher's tipped-in leaf $50/75

021d: THE NIGHT MANAGER Knopf, New York, 1993. [1] 450,000 cc (quantity stated on proof and per *Publishers Weekly*). (Published 7/93 @ $24.00) $5/25

021e: THE NIGHT MANAGER Hodder & Stoughton, London, 1993. [] Uncorrected proof. In glossy wraps. Small quantity issued (Andrew Sclanders 6/93) $75.

021f: THE NIGHT MANAGER Hodder & Stoughton, London (1993). [] $6/30

022a: OUR GAME Hodder & Stoughton, London, 1995. [] Uncorrected proof. In blue photographic wraps (David Rees 6/95) $75.

022b: OUR GAME Hodder & Stoughton, London (1995). [3] 1,000 cc? An export issue. First impression with different paper, binding and dustwrapper from the second impression. Black binding; the dustwrapper is dark gray lettered in gold, with raised silhouettes on the front panel. An unknown number of copies, perhaps no more than 1,000 were printed and bound for airport and overseas sales. The edition number series begins with "1" (David Rees 6/95) $75/150

022c: OUR GAME Hodder & Stoughton, London (1995). [3] Second impression, the first on general sale, and the first thus. The number series starts with "2" rather than 1, due to an error, the publishers say. Dark gray binding; quarter bound in maroon cloth. The dustwrapper has a small illustration of a figure in silhouette seen through an open door, with a backdrop of snow, mountains and red sky (David Rees 6/95). This may come after U.S. edition (see 022f below) $6/30

022d: OUR GAME Franklin Library, Franklin Center, 1995. [2] Signed limited edition of unknown limitation. In decorated full leather. Contains the author's specially written introduction for this edition (Waiting For Godot Books 2/97) $75.

022e: OUR GAME Knopf, New York, 1995. [] Uncorrected proof. In light green wraps, black tape on spine, 8½ x 11" format (Beasley Books 3/95) $75.

022f: OUR GAME Knopf NY 1995 [1] Uncorrected Proof. In red wraps. Proof gives date of publication, quantity, and price as listed below (022h) (Monroe Stahr Books 5/95). Also noted with trial dustwrapper tipped in and later changed. "This is the true first edition. The first UK edition was withdrawn after limited distribution to Europe." (Bev Chaney, Jr. 10/95) $75.

022g: OUR GAME Knopf, New York, 1995. [1] Advance copy. Publisher's complimentary label on front panel of dustwrapper and rear panel without bar code. Precedes English edition (Mordida Books 11/95) $10/50

022h: OUR GAME Knopf, New York, 1995. [1] 350, 000 cc (Publ. 3/ 10/95 @ $24.00) $5/25

023a: THE TAILOR OF PANAMA Hodder and Stoughton, London (1996). [] Published October 1996 @ £16.99 $7/35

023b: THE TAILOR OF PANAMA Knopf, New York, 1996. [1] "A Special Presentation Copy" in

8½ x 11 inch sheets tape bound with tan card stock covers stating "to be published October 20, 1996 Uncorrected." Also noted with typescript of speech LeCarre gave at a sales conference two months prior to publication (Ken Lopez 2/97) $100.

023c: THE TAILOR OF PANAMA Knopf, New York, 1996. [1] "Advance Reader's Edition" in glossy white printed wraps $50.

023d: THE TAILOR OF PANAMA Knopf, New York, 1996. [1] $5/25

024a: [ACCEPTANCE SPEECH FOR THE PRESIDENCY OF THE MORRAB LIBRARY] No publisher, Penzance, 1997. [0] 13-page speech printed on cream laid paper, stapled at the top. It is thought that Le Carre signed around 200 of these, most of which would have gone to library subscribers (Nicholas and Helen Burrows 6/97)

Signed: $75.
Unsigned: $40.

THE LIMITED EDITIONS CLUB

LIMITED EDITIONS CLUB

The Limited Editions Club (LEC) was founded in 1929 by George Macy, to publish finely printed and well illustrated books for a small number of members (1,500). To select texts the membership would consider worth republishing, edit them, contract with sympathetic typographers, and successful illustrators, have them printed and bound by the best available craftsmen, and turn out 12 books a year was not an easy task. However, the LEC was successful until 1971, under George Macy and his wife Helen who ran the business after his death.

From 1971 to 1978 the ownership changed five times and by the end of the decade the club was left in the red and without the Heritage Press which had published the "trade editions" of the books; and presumably made more money for Macy than the LEC (Heritage had been sold off in the mid-1970's to raise money).

During the first few years of the 1980's the club stayed with the 2,000 copy printing, which the various owners had moved to in the 1970's, but by 1983 the club was back to the quantity of 1,500 copies, which had been used throughout the Macy's tenure. And by 1986, the quantity had moved down to 1,000 copies or less.

We believe that the LEC produced and still produces beautiful books. we've always been amazed that people are paying $40 or more for leather bound Franklin Press books "limited" to 4,000 to 15,000 copies (our best guess based on the few titles on which we've been able to obtain the quantities), when the LEC books, limited to 1,500 signed and numbered copies, were selling for under $40 in the 1970's. The recent ones, we admit have gotten much more expensive, but the current owners seem to be moving toward more expensive artist books with small limitations.

We have arranged this guide chronologically, but have included an alphabetical index of the authors, illustrators, etc. for your convenience. All titles were issued in boxes or slipcases. Nearly all of the books are signed by the illustrator, and occasionally by the author or others.

Estimated value is based on fine copies, with unfaded and clean spines, in slipcases. If the slipcase is lacking, prices would probably be lowered 10-20% on the more valuable ones and perhaps as much as 40-50% on the less valuable ones.

All are limited to 1,500 numbered copies unless otherwise stated. In some instances, the date of publication may not be in proper chronological order as we assume that they experienced printing delays after the publications were announced. We kept this guide in the same order as the primary reference through 1985. All were issued with slipcases unless noted otherwise, and estimated prices assume both the books and slipcases are in fine condition.

We wish to thank Robert Garvey for his help identifying the recent titles.

NOTE: for your convenience, an index of the authors, illustrators, etc. follows the Limited Editions Club entries.

REFERENCES:

(a) BIBLIOGRAPHY OF THE FINE BOOKS PUBLISHED BY THE LIMITED EDITIONS CLUB 1929-1985. (New York: Limited Editions Club, 1985.)

(b) Haveles, Paul J. & David P. LIMITED EDITIONS CLUB GUIDE. (Danielson, Conn.: Extensive Search Service, 1976.)

(c) Prospectus from the LEC were used from 1985 to date.

(d) Inventory, dealer catalogs, etc. were necessary, as the first three references were deficient in many ways for our purposes.

001: Swift, Jonathan THE TRAVELS OF LEMUEL GULLIVER New York, 1929. Signed and illustrated by Alexander King. Introduction by Shane Leslie $400.

002: Whitman, Walt LEAVES OF GRASS Mt. Vernon, NY, 1929. Signed by Frederic Warde, the designer. Introduction by Carolyn Wells $200.

003: Raspe, Rudolphe E. THE TRAVELS OF BARON MUNCHAUSEN Chicago, 1929. Signed and illustrated by John Held, Jr. Introduction by Carl Van Doran $175.

004: Whittier, John Greenleaf SNOW-BOUND New York, 1930. Signed by Purlington Rollins, the designer. Introduction by George S. Bryan; vignette by Alice Hubbard Stevens $125

005: Poe, Edgar Allen THE NARRATIVE OF ARTHUR GORDON PYM Portland, 1930. Signed by Rene Clarke, the designer. Introduction by Joseph Wood Krutch $200.

006: Stevenson, Robert Louis TWO MEDIEVAL TALES (New York, 1929.) Signed and illustrated by C .B. Falls. Introduction by Clayton Hamilton $125.

007: Boccaccio, Giovanni THE DECAMERON New York, 1930. 2 vols. Signed by T .M. Cleland, the designer and illustrator. Translated by Frances Winwar, introduction by Burton Rascoe $250.

008: Irving, Washington RIP VAN WINKLE New York, 1930. Signed by Frederic Goudy, the designer. Introduction by Mark Van Doren $150.

009: Daudet, Alphonse TARTARIN OF TARASCON Westport, 1930. 2 vols. Signed by W.A. Dwiggins, the designer and illustrator. Translation and introduction by Jacques Le Clercq $125.

010: LaMotte-Fouque, F. de UNDINE New York, 1930. Signed by Allen Lewis, the illustrator. Translated by Edmund Gosse $100.

011: Defoe, Daniel ROBINSON CRUSOE New York, 1930. Signed by Edward A. Wilson, the illustrator. Introduction by Ford Madox Ford $200.

012: La Fontaine, Jean De THE FABLES OF JEAN DE LA FONTAINE New York, 1930. 2 vols. Signed by Rudolph Ruzicka, the illustrator. Translated and with introductions by Joseph Auslander and Jacques Le Clercq $150.

013: Hugo, Victor NOTRE-DAME DE PARIS Paris, 1930. 2 vols. Originally published in wraps, most copies rebound by the publisher. Signed by Masereel, the illustrator. Translated by Jessie Haynes, introduction by Andrew Lang. G. Macy noted that upon reception of their copies many, many members felt "cheated because the two volumes were paperbound. We had to bind in hard cases, American fashion, most of the copies."

Paperbound copies: $500.
Hardbound copies: $250.

014: DeQuincey, Thomas CONFESSIONS OF AN ENGLISH OPIUM EATER Oxford, 1930. 1,520 cc. Signed by Zhenya Gay, the illustrator and B. H. Newdigate, the printer. Introduction by William Bolitho $200.

015: Homer THE ODYSSEY Haarlem, 1930. Signed by J. Van Drimpen, the designer. Translated by Alexander Pope, introduction by Carl Van Doren $200.

016: Moliere TARTUFFE, or THE HYPOCRITE Leipzig, 1930. Signed by Hugo Steiner-Prag, the illustrator. Translated by Curtis Hidden Page, introduction by Brander Matthews $125.

017: THE LITTLE FLOWERS OF SAINT FRANCIS OF ASSISI New York, 1930. Signed by Paolo

Molnar, the illustrator. The first English translation (1864), revised, by Dom Roger Hudleston. Introduction by Arthur Livingston $200.

018: Carlyle, Thomas SARTOR RESARTUS London, 1931. Signed by Oliver Simon, the printer. Introduction by Bliss Perry $75.

019: AUCASSIN & NICOLETTE Prague, 1931. Signed by Vojtech Preissig, the designer and illustrator. Translation and introduction by Andrew Lang $100.

020: Grimm, J. L. and W. K. GRIMM'S FAIRY TALES Offenbach, 1931. Signed by Fritz Kredel, the illustrator and Rudolf Koch, the designer. Introduction by Harry Hansen $175.

021: Loti, Pierre AN ICELAND FISHERMAN Stockholm, 1931. Signed by Yngve Berg, the illustrator. Introduction by Guy Endore $75.

022: Thackeray, William Makepeace VANITY FAIR Oxford, 1931. 2 vols. Signed by John Austen, the illustrator. Introduction by G. K. Chesterton $150.

023: Hawthorne, Nathaniel MARBLE FAUN or THE ROMANCE OF MONTE BENI Zurich, 1931. 2 vols. Signed by Carl Straus, the illustrator. Introduction by Herbert Gorman $75.

024: Homer ILIAD Haarlem, 1931. Signed by J. Van Krimpen, the designer. Introduction by Alexander Pope. Note by Carl Van Doren $275.

025: Fielding, Henry HISTORY OF TOM JONES New York, 1931. Signed by Alexander King, the illustrator. Introduction by J. B. Priestley $150.

026: Franklin, Benjamin THE AUTOBIOGRAPHY OF BENJAMIN FRANKLIN San Francisco, 1931. Signed by John Henry Nash, the printer. Introduction and marginal glosses by Edward F. O'Day $250.

027: Dickens, Charles THE CHIMES London, 1931. Signed by Arthur Rackham, the illustrator. Introduction by Edward Wagenknecht $750.

028: Surtees, R. S. THE JAUNTS & JOLLITIES OF MR. JOHN JORROCKS Boston, 1932. Signed by Gordon Ross, the illustrator. Introduction by A. Edward Newton $125.

029: Balzac, Honore de DROLL STORIES (30 Tales) Portland, 1932. 3 vols. Signed by W.A. Dwiggins, the designer. Translation and preface by Jacques Le Clercq $150.

030: Goethe, Johann Wolfgang von FAUST *A Tragedy* New York, 1932. Signed by Rene Clarke, the illustrator. Translation by Alice Raphael, introduction by Mark Van Doren $100.

031: Hearn, Lafcadio KWAIDAN Tokyo, 1932. Signed by Yasumasa Fujita, the illustrator. Introduction by Oscar Lewis $500.

032: Reade, Charles CLOISTER AND THE HEARTH New York, 1932. 2 vols. Signed by Lynd Ward, the illustrator. Introduction by Hendrik Willem van Loon $100.

033: Cooper, James Fenimore THE LAST OF THE MOHICANS Rochester, 1932. Signed by E. A. Wilson, the illustrator. Introduction by Edward Everett Hale. Designed by Will Ransom $125.

034: Douglas, Norman SOUTH WIND New York, 1932. Signed by Carlotta Petrina, the illustrator. Introduction by Carl Van Doren $75.

035: Maran, Rene BATOUALA New York, 1932. Signed by Miguel Covarrubias, the illustrator. Translated and introduction by Alvah C. Bessie $300.

036: Carroll, Lewis (Charles L. Dodgson) ALICE'S ADVENTURES IN WONDERLAND New York, 1932. Approximately 1,200 of the 1,500 copies were signed by Alice Hargreaves, the original "Alice." Introduction by Henry Seidel Canby, illustrations by John Tenniel (ABPC Vol. 95 states 500 copies signed)

Signed: $1,250.
Unsigned: $400.

(Also see 065)

037: Apuleius, Lucius GOLDEN ASSE New York, 1932. Signed by Percival Goodman, the illustrator. Translated and introduction by Jack Lindsay $125.

038: Dumas, Alexandre THE THREE MUSKETEERS Maastricht, 1932. 2 vols. Signed by Pierre Falke, the illustrator. Translated by Wm. Robson, introduction by Ben Ray Redman $100.

039: THE FOUR GOSPELS *According to Matthew, Mark, Luke & John* Leipzig, 1932. Signed by Emil Rudolf Weiss, the illustrator $200.

040: Twain, Mark THE ADVENTURES OF HUCKLEBERRY FINN New York, 1933. Signed by Carl Purington Rollins, the designer. Introduction by Booth Tarkington, includes the original illustrations by E. W. Kemble $175.

041: Alighieri, Dante THE DIVINE COMEDY Verona, 1932. Signed by Hans Mardersteig, the designer and printer. Translated and annotated by Melville Best Anderson, introduction by Arthur Livingston $300.

042: Confucius THE ANALECTS OF CONFUCIUS Shanghai, 1933. Translated with an introduction by Lionel Giles. In special Chinese redwood box $350.

043: Villon, Francois THE LYRICS OF FRANCOIS VILLON New York, 1933. Signed by Howard Simon, the illustrator. Translations by Swinburne, Rossetti, Henley, Payne, and Leonie Adams. Introduction by Leonie Adams $125.

044: Shakespeare, William THE TRAGEDY OF HAMLET, PRINCE OF DENMARK (High Wycombe, 1933.) Signed by Eric Gill, the illustrator. Introduction by Gilbert Murray $600.

045: Dickens, Charles THE POSTHUMOUS PAPERS OF THE PICKWICK CLUB Oxford, 1933. 2 vols. Signed by John Austen, the illustrator. Introduction by G. K. Chesterton $150.

046: Tolstoy, Leo ANNA KARENIA Moscow, 1933. 2 vols. Signed by Nikolas Piskariov, the illustrator. Translated by Constance Garnett, edited by Bernard Guilbert Guerney and Gustavus Spett, introduction by Anatole Lunacharsky $125.

047: AESOP'S FABLES Oxford, 1933. Signed by Bruce Rogers, the designer and illustrator. Translation by Samuel Croxall, bibliographical note by Victor Scholderer $250.

048: Cervantes, Miguel de ON QUIXOTE OF LA MANCHA Barcelona,1933. 2 vols. Signed by Enric-Cristobal Ricart, the illustrator. Translated and introduction by John Ormsby $200.

049: France, Anatole AT THE SIGN OF QUEEN PEDAUQUE Chicago, 1933. Signed by Sylvain Sauvage, the illustrator. Translated by Mrs. Wilfrid Jackson, introduction by Ernest Boyd $75.

050: Dostoevsky, Fyodor THE BROTHERS KARAMAZOV Boston, 1933. 3 vols. Signed by

Alexander King, the illustrator. Translation of Constance Garnett revised by and with an introduction by Avrahm Yarmolinsky $175.

051: Dickens, Charles THE CRICKET ON THE HEARTH Oxford, 1933. Illustrated by Hugh Thomson, introduction by Walter de la Mare $200.

052: Longus THE PASTORAL LOVES OF DAPHNIS AND CHLOE New York, 1934. Signed by Ruth Reeves, the illustrator. Translated and introduction by George Moore $125

053: Shelley, Mary Wollstonecraft FRANKENSTEIN, or THE MODERN PROMETHEUS New York, 1934. Signed by Everett Henry, the illustrator. Introduction by Edmund Lester Pearson $300.

054: Butler, Samuel EREWHON New York, 1934. Signed by Rockwell Kent, the illustrator. Introduction by Aldous Huxley $200.

055: de Coster, Charles THE GLORIOUS ADVENTURES OF TYL ULENSPEIGL Haarlem, 1934. Signed by Richard Floethe, the illustrator. Translated by Allan Ros MacDougall, introduction by Romain Rolland $75.

056: Marco Polo THE TRAVELS OF MARCO POLO New York, 1934. 2 vols. Signed by Nikolai Fyodorovitch Lapshin, the illustrator. The Marsden translation revised and edited, with an introduction by Manuel Komroff $175.

057: Aristophanes LYSISTRATA Westport, 1934. Signed by Pablo Picasso, the illustrator. Translated and introduction by Gilbert Seldes. 150 copies also had a set of 6 proofs of the original Picasso etchings, each signed by Picasso (ref.b)

With the six proofs: $10,000.
Without the six proofs: $5,000.

058: Sheridan, Richard Brinsley THE SCHOOL FOR SCANDAL Oxford, 1934. Signed by Rene Ben Sussan, the illustrator. Introduction by Carl Van Doren $125.

059: THE BOOK OF THE THOUSAND NIGHTS AND A NIGHT New York, 1934. 6 vols. Signed by Valenti Angelo, the illustrator. Translation, notes, introduction (etc.) by Sir Richard Burton. Edited by Emile Van Vliet $200.

060: Emerson, Ralph Waldo THE ESSAYS OF RALPH WALDO EMERSON The First and Second Series. San Francisco, 1934. Signed by John Henry Nash, the printer. Introduction by Edward F. O'Day $150.

061: Dickens, Charles A CHRISTMAS CAROL Boston, 1934. Signed by Gordon Ross, the illustrator. Introduction by Stephen Leacock $150.

062: Chaucer, Geoffrey THE CANTERBURY TALES London, 1934. 2 vols. Signed by George Jones, the printer. Introduction by Frank Ernest Hill $175.

063: Hudson, W. H. GREEN MANSIONS New York, 1935. Signed by Edward A. Wilson, the illustrator. Introduction by William Beebe $75.

064: More, Sir Thomas UTOPIA New York, 1934. Signed by Bruce Rogers, the printer. Introduction by H. G. Wells $175.

065: Carroll, Lewis THROUGH THE LOOKING-GLASS New York, 1935. Most of the 1,500 copies were signed by Alice Hargreaves, the original "Alice." Introduction by Carl Van Doren, illustrations by John Tenniel. (Ref.b states that only 200 copies were signed by Hargreaves, which does not appear to be correct)

Signed: $1,250.
Unsigned: $400.

(Also see 036)

066: Hawthorne, Nathaniel THE HOUSE OF THE SEVEN GABLES New York, 1935. Signed by Valenti Angelo, the illustrator. Introduction by Van Wyck Brooks $100.

067: Henry, O. (Wm. Sydney Porter) THE VOICE OF THE CITY New York, 1935. Signed by George Grosz, the illustrator. Introduction by Clifton Fadiman $500.

068: Hoffman, Dr. Heinrich SLOVENLY PETER New York, 1935. Translated into English jingles by Mark Twain. Foreword by Clara Clemens, introduction by Philip Hofer, illustrated by Fritz Kredel $300.

069: Melville, Herman TYPEE *Romance of South Seas* New York, 1935. Signed by Miguel Covarrubias, the illustrator. Introduction by Raymond Weaver $300.

070: Sterne, Laurence THE LIFE & OPINIONS OF TRISTRAM SHANDY, GENTLEMAN New York, 1935. 2 vols. Signed by T. M. Cleland, the illustrator. Introduction by Christopher Morley $125.

071: Joyce, James ULYSSES New York, 1935. All copies signed by Henri Matisse, the illustrator. 250 copies (ref.b) were also signed by Joyce. Introduction by Stuart Gilbert

Signed by Joyce and Matisse: $15,000.
Signed by Matisse: $5,000.

072: Smollett, Tobias THE ADVENTURES OF PEREGRINE PICKLE Oxford, 1935. 2 vols. Signed by John Austen, the illustrator. Introduction by G. K. Chesterton $100.

073: THE HOLY BIBLE: THE KING JAMES VERSION New Haven (1935-1936). 5 vols. Volumes I, II, and III dated (1935); Volumes IV, and V dated (1936). Designed by George Macy $250.

074: Khayyam, Omar THE RUBAIYAT OF OMAR KHAYYAM (Westport), 1935. Signed by Valenti Angelo. Definitive text selected from the five editions of Edward Fitzgerald's translation $200.

075: Butler, Samuel THE WAY OF ALL FLESH New Haven, 1936. 2 vols. Signed by Robert Ward Johnson, the illustrator. Introduction by Theodore Dreiser $125.

076: Landor, Walter Savage IMAGINARY CONVERSATIONS Verona, 1936. Signed by Giovanni Mardersteig, the designer-printer. Introduction by R. H. Boothroyd $200.

077: Borrow, George LAVENGRO London, 1936. 2 vols. Signed by Barnett Freedman, the illustrator. Introduction by Hugh Walpole $100.

078: Thoreau, Henry David WALDEN, or LIFE IN THE WOODS New York, 1936. Signed by Edward Steichen, the photographer. Introduction by Henry Seidel Canby $1,000.

079: Hale, Edward Everett THE MAN WITHOUT A COUNTRY New York, 1936. Signed by Edward A. Wilson, the illustrator. Introduction by Carl Van Doren $100.

080: Rostand, Edmond CYRANO DE BERGERAC Windham, 1936. Signed by Sylvain Sauvage, the illustrator. Translated, with an introduction by Brian Hooker $125.

081: Sterne, Laurence A SENTIMENTAL JOURNEY THROUGH FRANCE AND ITALY High Wycombe, 1936. Signed by Denis Tegetmeier, the illustrator and Eric Gill, the designer $250.

082: Rabelais, Francois GARGANTUA AND PANTAGRUEL Portland, 1936. 5 vols. Signed by W.A. Dwiggins, the designer and decorator. Introduction by Jacques Le Clercq $175.

083: Malory, Sir Thomas LE MORTE DARTHUR London, 1936. 3 vols. Signed by Robert Gibbings, the illustrator. Preface by William Caxton, bibliographical note by A. W. Pollard. Printed by the Golden Cockerel Press $350.

084: Milton, John PARADISE LOST and PARADISE REGAIN'D San Francisco, 1936. Signed by Carlotta Petrina, the illustrator. Introduction by William Rose Benet. Designed by John Henry Nash $150.

085: Aristophanes THE FROGS Haarlem, 1937. Signed by John Austen, the illustrator. Translated by William James Hickie, introduction by Gilbert Seldes $100.

086: Cellini, Benvenuto THE LIFE OF BENVENUTO CELLINI Verona, 1937. Signed by Fritz Kredel, the illustrator. Translated by John Addington Symonds, introduction by Thomas Craven. Printed by Hans Mardersteig $200.

087: Wilde, Oscar THE BALLAD OF READING GAOL New York, 1937. Signed by Zhenya Gay, the illustrator. Introduction by Burton Rascoe $125.

088: Collodi, Carlo PINOCCHIO, THE ADVENTURES OF A MARIONETTE New York, 1937. Signed by Richard Floethe, the illustrator. Introduction by Carl Van Doren $150.

089: Lewis, Sinclair MAIN STREET Chicago, 1937. Signed by Grant Wood, the illustrator. Contains a special introduction by the author $750.

090: Gay, John THE BEGGAR'S OPERA Lyon, 1937. Signed by Mariette Lydis, the illustrator. Preface by A. P. Herbert $100.

091: Dickens, Charles GREAT EXPECTATIONS Edinburgh, 1937. Signed by Gordon Ross, the illustrator. With the original "honest ending" (original ending which had not appeared in book form previously). Preface by Bernard Shaw $200.

092: Burton, Richard F. THE KASIDAH OF HAJI ABDU EL-YEZDI New Haven, 1937. Signed by Valenti Angelo, who did the designs, decorations and hand-illuminations $150.

093: Dumas, Alexandre CAMILLE London, 1937. Signed by Marie Laurencin, the illustrator. Translation and introduction by Edmund Gosse $750.

094: Allen, Hervey ANTHONY ADVERSE Mount Vernon, 1937. 3 vols. Signed by Edward A. Wilson, the illustrator. Special introduction by the author $125.

095: Collier, John Payne PUNCH AND JUDY New York, 1937. Introduction by Paul McPharlin, illustrated by George Cruikshank $175.

096: France, Anatole THE CRIME OF SYLVESTRE BONNARD New York, 1937. Signed by Sylvain Sauvage, the illustrator. Translated by Lafcadio Hearn, introduction by A .S. W. Rosenbach $125.

097: Stowe, Harriet Beecher UNCLE TOM'S CABIN New York, 1938. Signed by Miguel Covarrubias, the illustrator. Introduction by Raymond Weaver $600.

098: Le Sage, Alain Rene THE ADVENTURES OF GIL BLAS OF SANTILLANE Oxford, 1937. 2 vols. Signed by John Austen, the illustrator. Translated by Tobias Smollett, introduction by J. B. Priestley $125.

099: Maugham, W. Somerset OF HUMAN BONDAGE New Haven, 1938. 2 vols. Signed by John Sloan, the illustrator. Introduction by Theodore Dreiser $650.

100: Peattie, Donald Culross AN ALMANAC FOR MODERNS Washington, 1938. Signed by Asa Cheffetz, the illustrator. Special introduction by the author $75.

101: Flaubert, Gustave MADAME BOVARY Zurich, 1938. Signed by Gunter Böhmer, the illustrator. Translated by Eleanor Marx Aveling, introduction by Andre Maurois $125.

102: THE SONG OF ROLAND Windham, 1938. Signed by Valenti Angelo, the illustrator. Translated by C. K. Scott-Moncrieff, introduction by Hamish Miles $150.

103: Boswell, James THE LIFE OF SAMUEL JOHNSON, LL.D. London, 1938. 3 vols. Designed by Oliver Simon. Introduction by Edward Fletcher $250.

104: Wilde, Oscar SALOME Paris/London, 1938. 2 vols. Signed by Andre Derain, the illustrator. First volume is the original French version, the second volume is the English version translated by Lord Alfred Douglas, introduction by Holbrook Jackson with illustrations by Aubrey Beardsley (contains 4 not in first edition) $600.

105: Tolstoy, Leo WAR AND PEACE Glasgow, 1938. 6 vols. Signed by Barnett Freedman, the illustrator. Introduction by Aylmer Maude $350.

106: Gray, Thomas ELEGY WRITTEN IN A COUNTRY CHURCH-YARD London, 1938. Signed by Agnes Miller Parker, the illustrator. Introduction by Hugh Walpole $300.

107: Stevenson, Robert Louis KIDNAPPED New York, 1938. Signed by Hans Alexander Mueller, the illustrator. Introduction by Christopher Morley $100.

108: Hugo, Victor LES MISERABLES Mount Vernon, 1938. 5 vols. Signed by Lynd Ward, the illustrator. Introduction by Andre Maurois $300.

109: Wharton, Edith ETHAN FROME Portland, 1939. Signed by Henry Varnum Poor, the illustrator. Introduction by Clifton Fadiman $250.

110: Dreiser, Theodore SISTER CARRIE New York, 1939. Signed by Reginald Marsh, the illustrator. Introduction by Burton Rascoe $300.

111: Browne, Sir Thomas RELIGIO MEDICI Univ. of Oregon, 1939. Signed by John Henry Nash, designer and printer. Introduction by Geoffrey Keynes $125.

112: Shaw, Bernard BACK TO METHUSELAH New York, 1939. Signed by John Farleigh, the illustrator. New introduction by the author $125.

113: Chaucer, Geoffrey TROILUS AND CRESSIDA London, 1939. Signed by George W. Jones, the designer. Rendered in modern English verse by George Philip Krapp $125.

114: Twain, Mark THE ADVENTURES OF TOM SAWYER Cambridge, 1939. Signed by Thomas Hart Benton, the illustrator. Introduction by Bernard De Voto $750.

115: Austen, Jane PRIDE AND PREJUDICE Boston, 1940. Signed by Helen Sewell, the illustrator. Preface by Frank Swinnerton $200.

116: Casanova, Jacques THE MEMOIRS OF JACQUES CASANOVA DE SEINGALT Edinburgh, 1940. 8 vols. Translated by Arthur Machen, introduction by Francis Meynell $150.

117: Baudelaire, Charles LES FLEURS DU MAL / FLOWERS OF EVIL Paris/London, 1940. 2 vols. The French original, illustrated by Auguste Rodin, preface by Camille Mauclair; and the English version, illustrated by Jacob Epstein, and foreword by James Laver. (Distribution of the French volume was delayed until 1947 by W.W.II)

Both volumes: $300.
French version alone: $125.
English version alone: $125.

118: Shakespeare, William THE COMEDIES, HISTORIES & TRAGEDIES OF WILLIAM SHAKESPEARE New York, 1939-1940. 37 vols. 1,950 copies. Signed by Bruce Rogers. Illustrated by various artists $1,750.

(Also see 122)

119: Cooper, James Fenimore THE PRAIRIE New York, 1940. Signed by John Steuart Curry, the illustrator. Introduction by Harry Hansen $150.

(Also see special editions at end of listing)

120: Scott, Sir Walter IVANHOE New York, 1940. 2 vols. Signed by Allen Lewis, the illustrator. Introduction by the author $250.

121: Brooks, Van Wyck FLOWERING OF NEW ENGLAND Boston, 1941. Signed by Raymond J. Holden, the illustrator. Introduction by M. A. DeWolfe Howe. Some copies also signed by author

Signed by both: $150.
Signed only by Holden: $100.

122: Shakespeare, William POEMS AND SONNETS New York, 1941. 2 vols. Signed by Bruce Rogers, the designer. Introduction by Louis Untermeyer

Two vols.: $250.
With 37 vols. of Plays (118, above): $2,000.

123: Stevenson, Robert Louis TREASURE ISLAND New York, 1941. Illustrated with a signed lithograph frontispiece by Edward A. Wilson, introduction by the author $200.

124: Merimee, Prosper CARMEN New York, 1941. Signed by Jean Charlot, the illustrator. Introduction by Konrad Bercovici $250.

125: Poe, Edgar Allan TALES OF MYSTERY AND IMAGINATION Baltimore, 1941. Signed by William Sharp, the illustrator. Introduction by Vincent Starrett $250.

126: Bellamy, Edward LOOKING BACKWARD Los Angeles (1941). Signed by Elise (Cavanna), the illustrator. Introduction by Irwin Edman $125.

127: Dumas, Alexandre THE COUNT OF MONTE CRISTO Mount Vernon, 1941. 4 vols. Signed by Lynd Ward, the illustrator. Introduction by Andre Maurois $250.

128: Plutarch THE LIVES OF THE NOBLE GRECIANS AND ROMANS Portland, 1941. 8 vols. Signed by W.A. Dwiggins, the designer. Introduction by Emil Ludwig $350.

129: Bunyan, John THE PILGRIM'S PROGRESS New York, 1941. Introduction by Geoffrey Keynes, illustrated by William Blake $300.

130: Bennett, Arnold THE OLD WIVES' TALE Oxford, 1941. 2 vols. Signed by John Austen, the illustrator. Preface by the author, introduction by Frank Swinnerton $125.

131: Hawthorne, Nathaniel THE SCARLET LETTER New York, 1941. Signed by Henry Varnum Poor, the illustrator. Introduction by Dorothy Canfield $200.

132: Twain, Mark ADVENTURES OF HUCKLEBERRY FINN (New Haven), 1942. Signed by Thomas Hart Benton, the illustrator. Introduction by Bernard De Voto $600.

133: Adams, Henry THE EDUCATION OF HENRY ADAMS Boston, 1942. Signed by Samuel Chamberlain, the illustrator. Introduction by Henry Seidel Canby $125.

134: Masters, Edgar Lee SPOON RIVER ANTHOLOGY New York, 1942. Signed by the author and Boardman Robinson, the illustrator. New introduction by the author $300.

135: Pepys, Samuel THE DIARY OF SAMUEL PEPYS Mt. Vernon, 1942. 10 vols. Signed by William Sharp, the illustrator. Introduction by Henry B. Wheatley $250.

136: Stephens, James THE CROCK OF GOLD New York, 1942. Signed by Robert Lawson, the illustrator. Introduction by Clifton Fadiman $125.

137: Lincoln, Abraham THE LITERARY WORKS OF ABRAHAM LINCOLN New York, 1942. Signed by John Steuart Curry, the illustrator. Introduction and notes by Carl Van Doren $250.

138: Andersen, Hans Christian FAIRY TALES New York, 1942. 2 vols. Signed by Fritz Kredel, the illustrator and Jean Hersholt, the translator $300.

139a: Hemingway, Ernest FOR WHOM THE BELL TOLLS Princeton, 1942. Uncorrected Proof in plain blue wraps $1,000.

139b: Hemingway, Ernest FOR WHOM THE BELL TOLLS Princeton, 1942. 15 copies for presentation by the author, stating "One of 15 Presentation Copies Out of Series." $6,000.

139c: Hemingway, Ernest FOR WHOM THE BELL TOLLS Princeton 1942. Signed by Lynd Ward, the illustrator. Introduction by Sinclair Lewis. $500.

140: Diaz del Castillo, Bernal THE DISCOVERY AND CONQUEST OF MEXICO 1517-1521 Mexico City, 1942. Signed by Miguel Covarrubias, the illustrator. Also signed by Harry Block, the editor and Rafael Loera Y Chavez, the printer $450.

141: Whitman, Walt LEAVES OF GRASS New York, 1942. 2 vols. Signed by Edward Weston, the photographer. Introduction by Mark Van Doren $1,000.

142: Thackeray, William Makepeace THE ROSE AND THE RING New York, 1942. Illustrated by Fritz Kredel. Dedicatory introduction by George Macy $100.

143: Flaubert, Gustave THE TEMPTATION OF SAINT ANTHONY New York, 1943. Signed by Warren Chappell, the illustrator. Translated by Lafcadio Hearn $175.

144: Erasmus, Desiderius THE PRAISE OF FOLLY (MORIAE ENCOMIUM) Harrisburg, 1943. Signed by Lynd Ward, the illustrator. Translated by Harry Carter, introduction by Hendrik Willem van Loon $250.

145: Fielding, Henry THE HISTORY OF THE LIFE OF THE LATE MR. JONATHAN WILD THE GREAT New York 1943. Signed by T. M. Cleland, the illustrator. Introduction by Louis Kronenberger $150.

146: Hoffman, Ernest THE TALES OF HOFFMANN New York, 1943. Signed by Hugo Steiner-Prag, the illustrator. Introductory essay by Arthur Ransom $200.

147: Puskin, Alexander EUGENE ONEGIN New York, 1943. Signed by Fritz Eichenberg, the illustrator. Translation by Babette Deutsch, introduction by Avrahm Yarmolinsky $175.

148: Melville, Herman MOBY DICK, or THE WHALE Brattleboro, 1943. 2 vols. Signed by Boardman Robinson, the illustrator. Introduction by Clifton Fadiman $500.

149: Parkman, Francis THE OREGON TRAIL Brattleboro, 1943. Signed by Maynard Dixon, the illustrator. Introduction by Mason Wade $175.

150: Cable, George Washington OLD CREOLE DAYS Together with "The Scenes of Cable's Romances" by Lafcadio Hearn New York, 1943. Signed by John O'Hara Cosgrave, the illustrator $150.

151: Bierce, Ambrose TALES OF SOLDIERS AND CIVILIANS New York, 1943. Signed by Paul Landacre, the illustrator. Introduction by Joseph Henry Jackson $150.

152: Hudson, W. H. FAR AWAY AND LONG AGO Buenos Aires, 1943. Signed by Raul Rosarivo, the illustrator and Alberto Kraft, the designer. Issued without slipcase and was shipped in a rough gray cardboard box of poor quality $250.

153: Poe, Edgar Allan THE POEMS OF EDGAR ALLAN POE New York, 1943. 1,100 cc. Signed by Hugo Steiner-Prag, the illustrator. Commentary by Louis Untermeyer $250.

154: Gautier, Theophile MADEMOISELLE DE MAUPIN New York, 1943. Signed by Andre Dugo, the illustrator. Introduction by Jacques Barzun $75.

155: Crane, Stephen THE RED BADGE OF COURAGE New York, 1944. 1,000 cc. Signed by John Steuart Curry, the illustrator. Introduction by Carl Van Doren $300.

156: Stevenson, Robert Louis A CHILD'S GARDEN OF VERSES New York, 1944. 1,100 cc.

Signed by Roger Duvoisin, the illustrator. Introduction by William Rose Benet $200.

157: Bacon, Sir Francis THE ESSAYES OF FRANCIS BACON New York, 1944. 1,100 cc. Signed by Bruce Rogers, the designer. Introduction by Christopher Morley, bibliographical note by A. S. W. Rosenbach $250.

158: Twain, Mark LIFE ON THE MISSISSIPPI New York, 1944. 1,200 cc. Signed by Thomas Hart Benton, the illustrator. Introduction by Edward Wagenknecht. Adds a number of previously suppressed passages printed for the first time $750.

159: Willkie, Wendell L. ONE WORLD New York, 1944. 1,500 cc. Signed by Willkie. Illustrated with photographs $75.

160: Harte, Bret TALES OF THE GOLD RUSH New York, 1944. 1,200 cc. Signed by Fletcher Martin, the illustrator. Introduction by Oscar Lewis $100.

161: Plato THE REPUBLIC New York, 1944. 2 vols. 1,200 sets (ref.b states 1,500 sets, book states 1,200). Signed by Fritz Kredel, the illustrator and Bruce Rogers, the designer. Translation, introduction, etc. by Benjamin Jowett $300.

162: Longfellow, Henry Wadsworth THE POEMS OF HENRY WADSWORTH LONGFELLOW Brattleboro, 1944. 1,100 cc. Signed by Boyd Hanna, the illustrator. Commentary by Louis Untermeyer $150.

163: Virgil THE AENEID Brattleboro, 1944. 1,100 cc. Signed by Carlotta Petrina, the illustrator. Translated and introduction by John Dryden $125.

164: Gogol, Nikolai CHICHIKOV'S JOURNEYS (DEAD SOULS) New York, 1944. 2 vols. 1,200 sets. Signed by Lucille Corcos, the illustrator. Translated by Bernard Guilbert Guerney, introduction by Avrahm Yarmolinsky $125.

165: Hughes, Richard THE INNOCENT VOYAGE (A HIGH WIND IN JAMAICA) Brattleboro, 1944. Signed by Lynd Ward, the illustrator. Introduction by Louis Untermeyer $150.

166: Beckford, William VATHEK, AN ARABIAN TALE New York, 1945. Signed by Valenti Angelo, the designer. Translated and introduction by Herbert Grimsditch $125.

167: Untermeyer, Louis THE WONDERFUL ADVENTURES OF PAUL BUNYAN New York, 1945. Retold and with a foreword by Untermeyer. Signed by Everett Gee Jackson, the illustrator $125.

168: Emerson, Ralph Waldo THE POEMS OF RALPH WALDO EMERSON New York, 1945. Signed by Richard and Doris Beer, the illustrators. Commentary by Louis Untermeyer $150.

169: Hamilton, Alexander and James Madison and John Jay THE FEDERALIST New York, 1945. 2 vols. Signed by Bruce Rogers, the designer. Introduction by Carl Van Doren $300.

170: Coleridge, Samuel Taylor THE RIME OF THE ANCIENT MARINER New Haven, 1945. Signed by Edward A. Wilson, the illustrator. Introduction by John Livingston Lowes $125.

171: Whittier, John Greenleaf THE POEMS OF JOHN GREENLEAF WHITTIER New York, 1945. Signed by Raymond J. Holden, the illustrator. Commentary by Louis Untermeyer $100.

172: Addison, Joseph with Richard Steele and Eustace Budgell THE SIR ROGER DE COVERLEY PAPERS New York, 1945. Signed by Gordon Ross, the illustrator. Prefatory notes by William Makepeace Thackeray $100.

173: THE BOOK OF JOB New York, 1946. 1,950 cc. Signed by Arthur Szyk, the illustrator. Introduction by Mary Ellen Chase $450.

174: Gibbon, Edward THE HISTORY OF THE DECLINE AND FALL OF THE ROMAN EMPIRE Brattleboro, 1946. 7 vols. $250.

175: Chaucer, Geoffrey THE CANTERBURY TALES London, 1946. Signed by Arthur Szyk, the illustrator. Put into modern English verse by Frank Ernest Hill $450.

176: Montaigne, Michel de THE ESSAYS OF MICHEL DE MONTAIGNE New York, 1946. 4 vols. Signed by T. M. Cleland, the designer. Introduction by Andre Gide and a Handbook to the Essays by Grace Norton $200.

177: Bryant, William Cullen THE POEMS OF WILLIAM CULLEN BRYANT New York, 1947. Signed by Thomas W. Nason, the illustrator. Commentary by Louis Untermeyer $100.

178: Nordoff, Charles and James Norman Hall MUTINY ON THE BOUNTY New York, 1947. Signed by Fletcher Martin, the illustrator. With a preface by the authors and an appendix containing the true story of Peter Heywood $300.

179: Morier, J .J. THE ADVENTURES OF HAJJI BABA OF ISPAHAN New York, 1947. 2 vols. Signed by Honore Guilbeau, the illustrator. Introduction by E.G. Browne $125.

180: Stendhal (Marie-Henri Beyle) THE RED AND THE BLACK New York, 1947. Signed by Rafaello Busoni, the illustrator. Translated by C. K. Scott-Moncrieff, introduction by Hamilton Basso $125.

181: France, Anatole PENGUIN ISLAND New York, 1947. Signed by Malcolm Cameron, the illustrator. Translated by A. W. Evans, introduction by Carl Van Doren $100.

182: Kingsley, Charles WESTWARD HO! New York, 1947. 2 vols. Signed by Edward A. Wilson, the illustrator. Introduction by John T. Winterich $100.

183: Epicurus THE EXTANT REMAINS OF THE GREEK TEXT New York, 1947. Signed by Bruce Rogers, the designer. Translation by Cyril Bailey, introduction by Irwin Edman $300.

184: THE BOOK OF RUTH New York, 1947. 1,950 cc (ref.b). Signed by Arthur Szyk, the illustrator. Preface by Mary Ellen Chase $450.

185: Dana, Richard Henry TWO YEARS BEFORE THE MAST New York, 1947. Signed by Hans Alexander Mueller, the illustrator. Introduction by William McFee $125.

186: Browning, Elizabeth Barrett SONNETS FROM THE PORTUGUESE New York, 1948. Signed by Valenti Angelo, the illustrator. Introduction by Louis Untermeyer $150.

187: Walton, Izaak and Charles Cotton THE COMPLEAT ANGLER New York, 1948. Signed by Douglas Gorsline, the illustrator. Introduction by James Russell Lowell $300.

188: Zola, Emile NANA New York, 1948. Signed by Bernard Lamotte, the illustrator. Translated by E. A. Vizetelly, preface by Henry James (from the first English edition) and a new introduction by Lewis Galantiere $100.

189: Dostoevsky, Fyodor CRIME AND PUNISHMENT Brattleboro, 1948. 2 vols. Signed by Fritz Eichenberg, the illustrator. Translated by Constance Garnett, introduction by Laurence Irving $200.

190: Balzac, Honore de OLD GORIOT London, 1948. Signed by Rene ben Sussan, the illustrator. Translated by Ellen Marriage, introduction by Francois Mauriac $100.

191: Chuan, Shui Hu ALL MEN ARE BROTHERS New York, 1948. 2 vols. Signed by Miguel Covarrubias, the illustrator. English version by Pearl Buck, introduction by Lin Yutang $250.

192: Benet, Stephen Vincent JOHN BROWN'S BODY London, 1948. Introduction by Douglas Southall Freeman, illustrated by John Steuart Curry $100.

193: *The Evergreen Tales* New York, 1948. 3 vols. (Series I) 2,000 cc.

ALADDIN AND THE WONDERFUL LAMP Retold by Jean Hersholt. Illustrated by Fritz Kredel

Southey, Robert THE THREE BEARS Edited by Jean Hersholt, illustrated by William Moyers

THE STORY OF JOSEPH AND HIS BROTHERS Edited by Jean Hersholt, illustrated by Arthur Szyk
The three: $175.

(Also see 202, 203, 222, 228)

194: Browning, Robert THE RING AND THE BOOK Los Angeles, 1949. 2 vols. Signed by Carl Schultheiss, the illustrator. Introduction by Edward Dowden $100.

195: Anderson, Hans Christian THE COMPLETE ANDERSEN New York (1949). 6 vols. 168 stories. Signed by Fritz Kredel and Jean Hersholt, the translator $450.

196: Clemens, Samuel Langhorne (Mark Twain) A CONNECTICUT YANKEE IN KING ARTHUR'S COURT New York, 1949. Signed by Honore Guilbeau, the illustrator. Introduction by Carl Van Doren $100.

197: Dostoevsky, Fyodor THE BROTHERS KARAMAZOV Brattleboro, 1949. 2 vols. Signed by Fritz Eichenberg, the illustrator. Translation by Constance Garnett revised and introduced by Avrahm Yarmolinsky $300.

198: THE SEVEN VOYAGES OF SINDBAD THE SAILOR New York, 1949. Signed by Edward A. Wilson, the illustrator. Introduction by C. S. Forester $200.

199: James, Henry THE TURN OF THE SCREW Los Angeles, 1949. Introduction by Carl Van Doren, Illustrated by Mariette Lydis $125.

200: France, Anatole CRAINQUEBILLE New York, 1949. Signed by Bernard Lamotte, the illustrator. Translation and introduction by Jacques Le Clercq $100.

201: Brillat-Savarin, Jean Anthelme THE PHYSIOLOGY OF TASTE New York, 1949. Translated by M. F. K. Fisher, illustrations by Sylvain Sauvage $250.

202: *The Evergreen Tales* New York, 1949. 3 vols. (Series II), 2,000 cc.

SAINT GEORGE AND THE DRAGON Retold by William H. G. Kingston, illustrated by Edward Shenton

Beaumont, Mme. Le Prince de BEAUTY AND THE BEAST Translated by P. H. Muir, illustrated by Edy Legrand

DICK WHITTINGTON AND HIS CAT Retold and illustrated by Robert Lawson. Signed by him and Jean Hersholt, the editor.

The three: $175.

(Also see 193, 203, 222, 228)

203: *The Evergreen Tales* New York, 1949. 3 vols. (Series III). 2,000 cc.

THE TALE OF ALI BABA AND THE FORTY THIEVES Translated into English by E. Powys Mathers, illustrated by Edward Ardizzone

Perrault, Charles THE SLEEPING BEAUTY IN THE WOOD Translated by P. H. Muir, illustrated by Sylvain Sauvage

Andersen, Hans Christian THE UGLY DUCKLING Translated by Jean Hersholt, illustrated by Everett Gee Jackson

The three: $175.

(Also see 193, 202, 222, 228)

204: Swift, Jonathan A VOYAGE TO LILLIPUT BY DR. LEMUEL GULLIVER New York, 1950. A miniature book 2 1/4 x 3 1/2 inches. In compartmented slipcase with A VOYAGE TO BROBDINGNAG MADE BY LEMUEL GULLIVER (13 1/4 x 18 1/2 inches). Designed by Bruce Rogers $500.

205: Pushkin, Alexander THE GOLDEN COCKEREL New York, no date [1949]. Signed by Edmund Dulac, the illustrator $275.

206: Flaubert, Gustave MADAME BOVARY New York, 1950. Signed by Pierre Brissaud, the illustrator. Introduction by Jacques de Lacretelle $100.

207: Doyle, Arthur Conan THE ADVENTURES OF SHERLOCK HOLMES Mount Vernon, 1950. 3 vols. Illustrated by Frederic Dorr Steele, Sidney Paget, and others. Introduction by Vincent Starrett $400.

208: Frost, Robert THE COMPLETE POEMS OF ROBERT FROST New York, 1950. 2 vols. Signed by Frost and Thomas W. Nason, the illustrator. Designed by Bruce Rogers $750.

209: Cervantes Saavedra, Miguel de DON QUIXOTE, THE INGENIOUS GENTLEMAN OF LA MANCHA Mexico City, 1950. 2 vols. Translated by John Ormsby, introduction by Irwin Edman, illustrated by Edy Legrand $250.

210: Apuleius, Lucius THE MARRIAGE OF CUPID AND PSYCHE New York, 1951. Signed by Edmund Dulac, the illustrator. Retold by Walter Pater $300.

211: Scott, (Sir) Walter IVANHOE New York, 1951. 2 vols. Signed by Edward A. Wilson, the illustrator $75.

212: Turgenev, Ivan FATHERS AND SONS New York, 1951. Signed by Fritz Eichenberg, the illustrator. Translated by Constance Garnett, preface by John T. Winterich $175.

213: Tolstoy, Leo ANNA KARENINA London, 1951. 2 vols. Signed by Barnett Freedman, the illustrator. Introduction by Lionel Trilling $150.

214: Shakespeare, William THE LIFE OF KING HENRY V New York, 1951. Illustrated by Fritz Kredel. Introduction by Herbert Arthur Evans. Prefatory note by Mark Van Doren $100.

215: Wister Owen THE VIRGINIAN Los Angeles, 1951. Signed by William Moyers, the illustrator. Introduction by Struthers Burt $100.

216: Schiller, Johann Christoph Friedrich von WILLIAM TELL Zurich, 1951. Signed by Charles Hug, the illustrator. Introductory essay by Thomas Carlyle $100.

217: Manzoni, Alessandro THE BETROTHED (I PROMESSI SPOSI) Verona, 1951. Signed by Bruno Bramanti, the illustrator and Giovanni Mardersteig, the printer. Introduction by Ronald H. Boothroyd $175.

218: Stevenson, Robert Louis STRANGE CASE OF DR. JEKYLL AND MR. HYDE New York, 1952. Signed by Edward A. Wilson, the illustrator. Introduction by John Mason Brown $150

219: Dumas, Alexandre THE BLACK TULIP Haarlem, 1951. Signed by Jan van Krimpen, the designer and Frans Lammers the illustrator. Introduction by Ben Ray Redman $125.

220: Fielding, Henry THE HISTORY OF TOM JONES, A FOUNDLING New York, 1952. 2 vols. Signed by T.M. Cleland, the illustrator. Introduction by Louis Kronenberger $125.

221: Raspe, Rudolph and others THE SINGULAR ADVENTURES OF BARON MUNCHAUSEN New York, 1952. Signed by Fritz Kredel, the illustrator. Introduction by John Carswell $125.

222: *The Evergreen Tales* New York, 1952. 3 vols. (Series IV), 2,000 cc.

Anderson, Hans Christian THE EMPEROR'S NEW CLOTHES Translated by Jean Hersholt, illustrated by Ervine Metzl. Signed by both

Hawthorne, Nathaniel PANDORA'S BOX Illustrated and signed by Rafaello Busoni

Hawthorne, Nathaniel KING MIDAS AND THE GOLDEN TOUCH Illustrated and signed by Fritz Eichenberg

The three: $200.

(Also see 193, 202, 203, 228)

223: Doyle, Arthur Conan THE LATER ADVENTURES OF SHERLOCK HOLMES New York, 1952. 3 vols. Illustrated by Frederic Dorr Steele, Sidney Paget and others. Introductions by Elmer Davis, Fletcher Pratt and Rex Stout $350.

(Also see 207 and 224, the companion volumes)

224: Doyle, Arthur Conan THE FINAL ADVENTURES OF SHERLOCK HOLMES New York, 1952. 2 vols. Illustrated by Frederic Dorr Steele, Sidney Paget and others. Introductions by Christopher Morley and Anthony Boucher $300.

The set (207, 223 and 224): $1,000.

225: BEOWUF New York, 1952. Translated, with introduction, by William Ellery Leonard. Illustrated by Lynd Ward. Not signed $150.

226: Maupassant, Guy de A WOMAN'S LIFE (UNE VIE) New York, 1952. Signed by Edy Legrand, the illustrator. Translated by Marjorie Laurie. Introduction by Edmond Jaloux $75.

227: Dickenson, Emily POEMS OF EMILY DICKINSON New York, 1952. Signed by Helen Sewell, the illustrator. Commentary by Louis Untermeyer $200.

228: *The Evergreen Series* New York, 1952. 3 vols. (Series V), 2,000 cc.

Perrault, Charles BLUEBEARD Translated by Arthur Quiller-Couch, illustrated by Hans Bendix. Signed by Jean Hersholt, editor

Grimm, Jacob and Wilhelm HANSEL AND GRETEL Translated by P. H. Muir, illustrated by Henry C. Pitz. Signed by Jean Hersholt, editor

JACK AND THE BEANSTALK Retold by Jean Hersholt, illustrated by Malcolm Cameron. Signed by Jean Hersholt, editor

The three: $250.
Set of all Evergreens (193, 202, 203, 222, 228): $1,000.

229: Virgil (Publius Virgilius Maro) THE GEORGICS Verona, 1952. Signed by Bruno Bramanti, the illustrator and Giovanni Mardersteig, the printer. Translated by John Dryden, introduction by George F. Whicher $175.

230: Tennyson, Alfred Lord IDYLLS OF THE KING New York, 1952. Introduction by Henry Van Dyke, illustrated and signed by Lynd Ward $150.

231: Doughty, Charles M. TRAVELS IN ARABIA DESERTA New York, 1953. Introduction by T. E. Lawrence, illustrated by Edy Legrand. Not signed. Text abridged and arranged by Edward Garnett $250.

232: Tegner, Esaias FRITHIOF'S SAGA Stockholm, 1953. Signed by Eric Palmquist, the illustrator. General introduction by Bayard Taylor $75.

233: Voltaire, Francois Marie Arouet THE HISTORY OF ZADIG OR DESTINY Paris, 1952. Translated by R. Bruce Boswell. Introduction by Rene de Messieres. Illustrated by Sylvain Sauvage. Note: the artist died shortly after he finished the illustrations, and the book was not published until after his death $150.

234: Spenser, Edmund THE FAERIE QUEENE Oxford, 1953. 2 vols. Signed by Agnes Miller Parker, the illustrator. Introduction by John Hayward $250.

235: Eliot, George SILAS MARNER, THE WEAVER OF RAVELOE London, 1953. Signed by Lynton Lamb, the illustrator. Introduction by John T. Winterich $100.

236: Jonson, Ben VOLPONE, or THE FOX Oxford, 1952. Signed by Rene Ben Sussan, the illustrator. Introduction by Louis Kronenberger $150.

237: Dumas, Alexandre THE THREE MUSKETEERS New York, 1953. Illustrated by Edy Legrand. Translated by William Robson $100.

238: Sheridan, Richard Brinsley THE RIVALS London, 1953. Signed by Rene Ben Sussan, the illustrator. Introduction by John Mason Brown $100.

239: France, Anatole THE REVOLT OF THE ANGELS New York, 1953. Translated by Mrs. Wilfrid Jackson. Introduction by Desmond MacCarthy. Illustrated by Pierre Watrin $75.

240: Rostand, Edmond CYRANO DE BERGERAC New York, 1954. Signed by Pierre Brissaud, the illustrator. Introduction by Louis Untermeyer $100.

241: Machiavelli, Niccolo THE PRINCE New York, 1954. Translated by Hill Thompson, preface by Irwin Edman, designed by George Macy $200.

242: Goethe, J(ohann) W(olfgang) von THE STORY OF REYNARD THE FOX New York, 1954. Signed by Fritz Eichenberg, the illustrator. Introduction by Edward Lazare. Translated by Thomas James Arnold $125.

243: Defoe, Daniel THE FORTUNES AND MISFORTUNES OF THE FAMOUS MOLL FLANDERS New York, 1954. Signed by Reginald Marsh, the illustrator. Introduction by John T. Winterich $200.

244: Proust, Marcel SWANN'S WAY New York, 1954. Signed by Bernard Lamotte, the illustrator. Translated by C .K. Scott Moncrieff. Introduction by Justin O'Brien $250.

245: Grammaticus, Saxo THE HISTORY OF AMLETH PRINCE OF DENMARK Copenhagen 1954. Signed by Sigurd Vasegaard, the illustrator. Translated by Oliver Elton. Introduction by Sir

Israel Gollancz. Prefatory note by Henrik de Kauffmann $100.

246: Milton, John L'ALLEGRO and IL PENSEROSO New York, 1954. 1,780 copies (280 went to Fellows of the Pierpont Morgan Library). Introductory essays by W. P. Trent and Chauncey B. Tinerk. Illustrations by William Blake $150.

247: Dreiser, Theodore AN AMERICAN TRAGEDY New York, 1954. Introduction by Harry Hansen. Illustrated by Reginald Marsh but not signed (his final work, issued posthumously) $125.

248: Riggs, Lynn GREEN GROW THE LILACS University of Oklahoma Press (Norman, OK) 1954. Signed by Thomas Hart Benton, the illustrator. Introduction by Brooks Atkinson $600.

249: Caesar, Julius THE GALLIC WARS Verona, 1954. Signed by Bruno Bramanti, the illustrator and Giovanni Mardersteig, the printer. Introduction by John Warrington. Preface by John Mason Brown $250.

250: Milton, John THE MASQUE OF COMUS Cambridge, 1954. Poem by John Milton, songs by Henry Lawes. Prefatory by Mark Van Doren and Hubert Foss. Illustrated by Edmund Dulac $175.

251: Popol Vuh THE BOOK OF THE PEOPLE ... Los Angeles, 1954. Signed by Everett Gee Jackson, the illustrator. Translated from the ancient Maya, with an introduction, by Delia Goetz and Sylvanus Griswold Morley $100.

252: Thackeray, William Makepeace THE NEWCOMBES *Memoirs of a Most Respectable* ... Cambridge, 1954. 2 vols. Signed by Edward Ardizzone, the illustrator. Introduction by Angela Thirkell $125.

253: Rousseau, Jean-Jacques THE CONFESSIONS OF JEAN-JACQUES ROUSEEAU New York,

1955. Signed by William Sharp, the illustrator. Introduction by A. S. B. Glover $100.

254: THE ARABIAN NIGHTS ENTERTAINMENTS Ipswich, 1954. 4 vols. Illustrated by Arthur Szyk. Translation and explanatory notes by Richard Burton. Unsigned as Szyk died before this work, his last, was printed $300.

255: Hugo, Victor NOTRE-DAME DE PARIS New York, 1955. Signed by Bernard Lamotte, the illustrator. Translated by Jessie Haynes, introduction by Justin O'Brien $100.

256: Sophocles OEDIPUS THE KING Haarlem, 1955. Signed by Demetrios Galanis, the illustrator. Translated by Francis Storr. Introduction by Thornton Wilder $150.

257: Holmes, Oliver Wendell THE AUTOCRAT OF THE BREAKFAST TABLE New York, 1955. Signed by Raymond J. Holden, the illustrator. Introduction by Van Wyck Brooks $75.

258: Dumas (Fils), Alexandre CAMILLE (LA DAME AUX CAMELIAS) New York, 1955. Signed by Bernard Lamotte, the illustrator. Translated by Edmund Gosse. Introduction by Andre Maurois $100.

259: Ibsen, Henrik PEER GYNT Oslo, 1955. Signed by Per Krohg, the illustrator. Translated, with an introduction by William and Charles Archer. $75.

260: Meredith, George THE SHAVING OF SHAGPAT New York, 1955. Signed by Honore Guilbeau, the illustrator. Introduction by Sir Francis Meredith Meynell $125.

261: Stendhal (Marie-Hendi Beyle) THE CHARTERHOUSE OF PARMA New York, 1955.

Signed by Rafaello Busoni, the illustrator. Translated by Lady Mary Loyd. Preface by Honore de Balzac $75.

262: Hardy, Thomas TESS OF THE D'URBERVILLES New York, 1956. Signed by Agnes Miller Parker, the illustrator. Introduction by Robert Cantwell $175.

263: Trollope, Anthony THE WARDEN New York (1955). Signed by Fritz Kredel, the illustrator. Introduction by Angela Thirkell $100.

264: Dostoevsky, Fyodor THE IDIOT New York, 1956. Signed by Fritz Eichenberg, the illustrator. Introduction by Avrahm Yarmolinski $150.

265: Carlyle, Thomas THE FRENCH REVOLUTION *A History* New York, 1956. Signed by Bernard Lamotte, the illustrator. Introduction by Cecil Brown $75.

266: Darwin, Charles THE JOURNAL OF RESEARCH … THE VOYAGE OF H.M.S. BEAGLE Cambridge 1956. Signed by Robert Gibbings, the illustrator. Introduction by Sir Gavin de Beer $350.

267: Thackeray, William Makepeace THE HISTORY OF HENRY ESMOND, ESQ. (New York), 1956. Signed by Edward Ardizzone, the illustrator. Introduction by Laura Benet $100.

268: Verne, Jules TWENTY THOUSAND LEAGUES UNDER THE SEA Los Angeles, 1956. Signed by Edward A. Wilson, the illustrator. Introduction by Fletcher Pratt $100.

269: Aurelius, Marcus MEDITIATIONS OF MARCUS AURELIUS New York, 1956. Signed by Hans Alexander Mueller, the illustrator. Translated by Meric Casaubon $75.

270: Bulwer-Lytton, Edward George THE LAST DAYS OF POMPEII Verona 1956. Signed by Kurt Craemer, the illustrator and Mardersteig, the printer. Introduction by Edgar Johnson $125.

271: Stevenson, Robert Louis THE BEACH OF FALESÁ Los Angeles, 1956. Signed by Millard Sheets, the illustrator. Introduction by J. C. Furnas $75.

272: Austen, Jane SENSE AND SENSIBILITY New York, 1957. Illustrated by Helen Sewell. Introduction by Stella Gibbons $125.

273: Heine, Heinrich POEMS OF HEINRICH HEINE New York, 1957. Signed by Fritz Kredel, the illustrator. Introduction by Louis Untermeyer $150.

274: Dickens, Charles DOMBEY AND SON Mt. Vernon, 1957. 2 vols. Signed by Henry C. Pitz, the illustrator. Introduction by John T. Winterich $125.

275: Prescott, Willian Hickling HISTORY OF THE CONQUEST OF PERU Mexico City, 1957. Signed by Everett Gee Jackson, the illustrator and Harry Block, the printer. Introduction by Samuel Eliot Morison $200.

276: Adams, Henry MONT-SAINT-MICHEL AND CHARTRES New York, 1957. Signed by Samuel Chamberlain, the photographer. Introduction by Francis Henry Taylor $150.

277: Stevenson, Robert Louis TRAVELS WITH A DONKEY (IN THE CEVENNES [on half title]) New York, 1957. Signed by Roger Duvoisin, the illustrator. Introduction by Andre Chamson $100.

278: Carus, Titus Lucretius OF THE NATURE OF THINGS Los Angeles, 1957. Signed by Paul Landacre, the illustrator. Translated by William Ellery Leonard, introduction by Charles E. Bennett $125.

279: Cook, Capt. James THE EXPLORATIONS OF CAPTAIN JAMES COOK IN THE PACIFIC ... New York, 1957. Signed by Geoffrey C. Ingleton, the illustrator and Douglas Dunstan, the designer. Taken from Cook's journals 1768-1779 $250.

280: Hersey, John THE WALL New York, 1957. Signed by William Sharp, the illustrator. Introduction by George N. Shuster $100.

281: Wilde, Oscar THE PICTURE OF DORIAN GRAY New York, 1957. Signed by Lucille Corcos, the illustrator. Introduction by Andre Maurois $200.

282: Harris, Joel Chandler UNCLE REMUS: HIS SONGS AND SAYINGS NY 1957. 1,500 cc. Introduction by Marc Connelly. Illustrated with woodcuts and signed by Seong Moy $150.

283: Dumas, Alexandre TWENTY YEARS AFTER New York, 1958. Signed by Edy Legrand, the illustrator. Introduction by Ben Ray Redman $100.

284: THE KORAN: SELECTED SURAS New York, 1958. Signed by Valenti Angelo, the decorator. Translated and introduction by Arthur Jeffrey $300.

285: Rhodius, Apollonius THE ARGONAUTICA Athens, 1957. Signed by A. Tassos, the illustrator. The text first in Greek and then the translation "Jason and The Golden Fleece" by Edward P. Coleridge with introduction by Moses Hadas $150.

286: Bulfinch, Thomas THE AGE OF FABLE New York, 1958. Signed by Joe Mugnaini, the illustrator. Introduction by Dudley Fitts $100.

287: Hardy, Thomas FAR FROM THE MADDING CROWD Cambridge 1958. Introduction by Robert Cantwell. Signed by Agnes Miller Parker, the illustrator. Also includes signed pull on handmade Japanese paper (in separate envelope matching slipcase) $200.

288: Alain-Fournier THE WANDERER: LE GRAND MEAULNES New York, 1958. Signed by Andre Dignimont, the illustrator. Translated by Francois Delisle, introduction by Henri Peyre $75.

289: CHRONICLE OF THE CID Haarlem, 1958. Signed by Rene Ben Sussan, the illustrator. Translated by Robert Southey, introduction by V. S. Pritchett $75.

290: Ovid METAMORPHOSES: IN FIFTEEN BOOKS Verona, 1958. Signed by Hans Erni, the illustrator and Hans Mardersteig, the printer. Introduction by Gilbert Highet $450.

291: Gilbert and Sullivan THE FIRST NIGHT GILBERT AND SULLIVAN (New York), 1958. Edited and introduced by Reginal Allen, foreword by Bridget D'Oyly Carte. Illustrated with contemporary drawings. Includes a carton of facsimiles of opening-night programs $200.

292: Trollope, Anthony BARCHESTER TOWERS New York, 1958. Signed by Fritz Kredel, the illustrator. Introduction by Angela Thirkell $100.

293: THE HISTORIES OF HERODOTUS OF HALICARNASSUS Haarlem, 1958. Signed by Edward Bawden, the illustrator. Introduction and translated by Harry Carter $250.

294: QUARTO-MILLENARY: THE FIRST 250 PUBLICATIONS AND THE FIRST 25 YEARS (1929 - 1954) OF THE LIMITED EDITIONS CLUB New York, 1959. 2,250 cc. Contains critiques by John T. Winterich and others $350.

295: Verne, Jules THE MYSTERIOUS ISLAND Baltimore, 1959. Signed by Edward A. Wilson, the illustrator. Translated by W.H.G. Kingston, introduction by Ray Bradbury $100.

296: Goethe, Johann Wolfgang von WILHELM MEISTER'S APPRENTICESHIP New York, 1959. Signed by William Sharp, the illustrator. Translated by Thomas Carlyle, introduction by Franz Schoenberner $150.

297: Saint-Simon, Duc de THE MEMOIRS OF LOUIS DE ROUVROY DUC DE SAINT-SIMON COVERING THE YEARS 1691-1723 (New York), 1959. 2 Vols. Signed by Pierre Brissaud, the illustrator. Introduction, etc. by Desmond Flower $75.

298: Jackson, Helen Hunt RAMONA Los Angeles, 1959. Signed by Everett Gee Jackson, the illustrator. Introduction by J. Frank Dobie $175.

299: Aristophanes THE BIRDS New York, 1959. Signed by Marian Parry, the illustrator. Introduction by Dudley Fitts $100.

300: Conrad, Joseph LORD JIM: A TALE New York, 1959. Signed by Lynd Ward, the illustrator. Introduction by Nicholas Monsarrat $150.

301: Congreve, William THE WAY OF THE WORLD New York, 1959. Signed by T.M. Cleland, the illustrator. Introduction by Louis Kronenberger $75.

302: Sienkiewicz, Henryk QUO VADIS? Verona, 1959. Signed by Salvatore Fiume, the illustrator and Giovanni Mardersteig, the printer. Issued in dustwrapper printed on spine only $175.

303: Collins, Wilkie THE MOONSTONE New York, 1959. Signed by Andre Dignimont, the illustrator. Introduction by Vincent Starrett $100.

304: Dostoevsky, Fyodor THE POSSESSED New York, 1959. 2 vols. Signed by Fritz Eichenberg, the illustrator. Translated by Constance Garnett, introduction by Marc Slonim $175.

305: Alarcon, Pedron Antonio de THE THREE-CORNERED HAT Los Angeles, 1959. Signed by Roger Duvoisin, the illustrator. Translated by Martin Armstrong, introduction by Gerald Brenan $75.

306: Froissard, Jean THE CHRONICLES OF ENGLAND... New York, 1959. Signed by Henry C. Pitz, the illustrator. Translated by Lord Berners, introduction by Sidney Painter $125.

307: Wells, H. G. TONO-BUNGAY New York, 1960. Signed by Lynton Lamb, the illustrator. Introduction by Norman Strouse $100.

308: London, Jack THE CALL OF THE WILD Los Angeles, 1960. Signed by Henry Varnum Poor, the illustrator. Introduction by Pierre Berton $150.

309: Flaubert, Gustave SALAMMBO Cambridge, 1960. Signed by Edward Bawden, the illustrator. Translated by J. S. Matthews, introduction by Justin O'Brien $125.

310: Maio, Puldius Virgilis THE ECLOGUES [OF VIRGIL] New York, 1960. Signed by Marcel Vertes, the illustrator. Translated by C. S. Calverley, introduction by Moses Hadas $125.

311: THE NIBELUNGENLIED New York, 1960. Signed by Edy Legrand, the illustrator. Translated by Margaret Armour, introduction by Franz Schoenberner $125.

312: Wallace, Lew BEN-HUR New York, 1960. Signed by Joe Mugnaini, the illustrator. Introduction by Ben Ray Redman $75.

313: Beerbohm, Max ZULEIKA DOBSON *Or an Oxford Love Story* Baltimore, 1960. Signed by

George Him, the illustrator. Introduction by Douglas Cleverdon $100.

314: Hugo, Victor THE TOILERS OF THE SEA Verona, 1960. Signed by Tranquillo Marangoni, the illustrator and Giovanni Mardersteig, the printer. Introduction by Matthew Josephson $150.

315: THE LIVING TALMUD *The Wisdom of the Fathers* ... New York, 1960. Signed by Ben-Zion, the illustrator. Introduction by Judah Goldin $250.

316: THE ROMANCE OF TRISTAN AND ISEULT New York, 1960. Signed by Serge Ivanoff, the illustrator. Retold by Joseph Bedier, introduction Padraic Colum, translated by Hilaire Belloc and Paul Rosenfield $100.

317: Balzac, Honore de EUGENIE GRANDET London, 1960. Signed by Rene Ben Sussan, the illustrator. Translated by Ellen Marriage, introduction by Richard Aldington $75.

318: THE BOOK OF PSALMS New York, 1960. Signed by Valenti Angelo, the illustrator. Intro-uction by Mark Van Doren $175.

319: Cooper, James Fenimore THE DEER-SLAYER (Hartford), 1961. Signed by Edward A. Wilson, the illustrator. Introduction by John T. Winterich $75.

320: Melville, Herman OMOO Oxford, 1961. Signed by Reynolds Stone, the illustrator. Introduction by Van Wyck Brooks $175.

321: Paine, Thomas RIGHTS OF MAN Lunen-burg, Vermont, 1961. Signed by Lynd Ward, the illustrator. Introduction by Howard Fast $200.

322: Schreiner, Olive THE STORY OF AN AFRI-CAN FARM (New York), 1961. Signed by Paul

Hogarth, the illustrator. Introduction by Isak Dinesen $200.

323: Conrad, Joseph NOSTROMO San Francisco, 1961. Signed by Lima de Freitas, the illustrator. Introduction by Rupert Croft-Cooke $125.

324: Howells, William Dean THE RISE OF SILAS LAPHAM Philadelphia, 1961. Signed by Mimi Korach, the illustrator. Introduction by Henry Steele Commager $75.

325: ODES AND EPODES OF HORACE New York, 1961. 2 vols. Translated and introduction by Louis Untermeyer. Second volume contains facsimile pages with bibliographic preface by John T. Winterich $150.

326: London, Jack THE SEA WOLF Hartford, 1961. Signed by Fletcher Martin, the illustrator. Introduction by Edmund Gilligan $125.

327: Thackeray, William Makepeace THE HISTORY OF PENDENNIS Ipswich, 1961. 2 vols. Signed by Charles Steward, the illustrator. Introduction by Robert Cantwell $75.

328: Aeschylus THE ORESTEIA New York, 1961. Signed by Michael Ayrton, the illustrator. Translated by E. D. A. Morstead, introduction by Rex Warner $125.

329: Tarkington, Booth MONSIEUR BEAUCAIRE New York, 1961. Signed by T.M. Cleland, the illustrator. Introduction by Donald Adams $75.

330: Scott, Sir Walter WAVERLEY (New York), 1961. Signed by Robert Ball, the illustrator. Introduction by Andrew Lang $100.

331: Wilder, Thornton THE BRIDGE OF SAN LUIS REY New York, 1962. Signed by Jean

Charlot, the illustrator. Introduction by Granville Hicks $150.

332: Twain, Mark THE INNOCENTS ABROAD *Or the New Pilgrims' Progress* New York, 1962. Signed by Fritz Kredel, the illustrator. Introduction by Edward Wagenknecht $125.

333: Mann, Thomas THE MAGIC MOUNTAIN New York, 1962. 2 vols. Signed by Felix Hoffman, the illustrator. Translated by H. T. Lowe-Porter $200.

334: Shaw, George Bernard MAN AND SUPER-MAN Mt. Vernon, 1962. Signed by Charles Mozley, the illustrator. Introduction by Sir Lewis Casson. Also includes *The Revolutionist's Handbook...* by John Tanner (Member of The Idle Rich Class) $150.

335: THE CONFESSIONS OF ST. AUGUSTINE Ipswich, 1962. Signed by Edy Legrand, the illustrator. Introduction by George N. Shuster $150.

336: Lewis and Clark THE JOURNALS OF THE EXPEDITION UNDER THE COMMANDE OF CAPTS. LEWIS AND CLARK Hartford, 1962. 2 vols. Introduction by John Bakeless. Edited by J. G. Pilkington $250.

337: Kipling, Rudyard KIM New York, 1962. Signed by Robin Jacques, the illustrator. Introduction by Charles Edmund Carrington $75.

338: Plato THE TRIAL AND DEATH OF SOCRATES Verona, 1962. Signed by Hans Erni, the illustrator and Giovanni Mardersteig, the printer. Translated, introduction, etc. by Benjamin Jowett $250.

339: Verne, Jules AROUND THE WORLD IN EIGHTY DAYS Los Angeles, 1962. Signed by Edward A. Wilson, the illustrator. Introduction by Ray Bradbury $125.

340: Grimm, J.L. and W. K. GRIMM'S FAIRY TALES New York, 1962-63. 4 vols. Signed by Lucille Corcos, the illustrator. Introduction by Louis Untermeyer, essay by Andrew Lang $175.

341: Cooper, James Fenimore THE SPY New York, 1963. Signed by Henry C. Pitz, the illustrator. Introduction by John T. Winterich $75.

342: Moliere TARTUFFE and THE WOULD-BE GENTLEMAN New York, 1963. Signed by Serge Ivanoff, the illustrator. Introduction by Henri Peyre $75.

343: Wyss, Johann David THE SWISS FAMILY ROBINSON Ipswich, 1963. Signed by David Gentleman, the illustrator. Introduction by Robert Cushman Murphy $150.

344: Darwin, Charles ON THE ORIGIN OF SPECIES Adelaide, Australia, 1963. Illustrated by Paul Landacre $300.

345: Eliot, George THE MILL ON THE FLOSS Mt. Vernon, 1963. Signed by Wray Manning, the illustrator. Introduction by David Daiches $100.

346: de Maupassant, Guy THE TALES OF GUY DE MAUPASSANT London, 1963. Signed by Gunther Boehmer, the illustrator. Translations by Lafcadio Hearn and others. Introduction by Justin O'Brien $100.

347: Suetonius Tranquillus, Gaius THE LIVES OF THE TWELVE CAESARS Verona, 1963. Signed by Salvatore Fiume, the illustrator and Giovanni Mardersteig, the printer. Introduction by Moses Hadas $200.

348: Tolstoy, Leo RESURRECTION New York, 1963. Signed by Fritz Eichenberg, the illustrator. Introduction by Ernest J. Simmons $150.

349: JOURNALS AND OTHER DOCUMENTS ON THE LIFE AND VOYAGES OF CHRISTOPHER COLUMBUS New York, 1963. Signed by Lima de Freitas, the illustrator. Translated and edited by Samuel Eliot Morison $150.

350: du Maurier, George PETER IBBETSON Hartford, 1963. 1,600 cc. Not signed. Introduction by Daphne du Maurier. Illustrated by the author $75.

351: James, Henry THE AMBASSADORS (New York), 1963. Signed by Leslie Saalburg, the illustrator $100.

352: THE BOOK OF PROVERBS New York, 1963. Signed by Valenti Angelo, the illustrator. Introduction by Dr. Robert Gordis $125.

353: Hardy, Thomas THE MAYOR OF CASTERBRIDGE New York, 1964. Signed by Agnes Miller Parker, the illustrator. Introduction by Frank Swinnerton $150.

354: Wells, H. G. THE WAR OF THE WORLDS and THE TIME MACHINE New York, 1964. 2 vols. Signed by Joe Mugnaini, the illustrator. Introduction by J. B. Priestley $125.

355: Aristotle THE POLITICS and THE POETICS Lunenburg, 1964. Signed by Leonard Baskin, the illustrator. Introduction by Horace M. Kallen $250.

356: Galsworthy, John THE MAN OF PROPERTY New York, 1964. Signed by Charles Mosley, the illustrator. Introduction by Evelyn Waugh $100.

357: Collins, Wilkie THE WOMAN IN WHITE Woodstock, Vermont, 1964. Signed by Leonard Rosoman, the illustrator. Introduction by Vincent Starrett $75.

358: Goldsmith, Oliver SHE STOOPS TO CONQUER New York, 1964. Signed by T. M.

Cleland, the illustrator. Introduction by Louis Kronenberger. (There were also 15 copies for presentation to Alfred Knopf) $75.

359: Austen, Jane EMMA New York, 1964. Signed by Fritz Kredel, the illustrator. Introduction by Stella Gibbons $125.

360: THE SATYRICON OF PETRONIUS New York, 1964. Signed by Antonio Sotomayer, the illustrator. Introduction by Gilbert Bagnani $75.

361: Twain, Mark THE PRINCE AND THE PAUPER Westerham, 1964. Signed by Clarke Hutton, the illustrator. Introduction by Edward Wagenknecht $100.

362: Franklin, Benjamin POOR RICHARD'S ALMANACKS FOR THE YEARS 1733-1758 Philadelphia, 1964. Signed by Norman Rockwell, the illustrator. Introduction by Van Wyck Brooks $600.

363: Nietzsche, Friedrich THUS SPAKE ZARA-THUSTRA New York, 1964. Translated by Thomas Common, introduction by Henry David Aiken $125.

364: Ibsen, Henrik THREE PLAYS OF HENRIK IBSEN *An Enemy of the People, The Wild Duck, and Hedda Gabler* Oslo, 1964. Signed by Fredrik Matheson, the illustrator. Introduction by John Gassner $75.

365: Dumas, Alexandre THE MAN IN THE IRON MASK New York, 1965. Signed by Edy Legrand, the illustrator. Introduction by Andre Maurois $125.

366: Stevenson, Robert Louis THE MASTER OF BALLANTRAE (New York), 1965. Signed by Lynd Ward, the illustrator. Introduction by G. B. Stern $125.

367: Melville, Herman BILLY BUDD and BENETO CERENO New York, 1965. Signed by Robert Shore, the illustrator. Introduction by Maxwell Geismar $100.

368: Burns, Robert THE POEMS OF ROBERT BURNS Glasgow, 1965. Signed by Joan Hassall, the illustrator. Introduction by DeLancey Ferguson $100.

369: BHAGAVAD GITA: THE SONG CELESTIAL Bombay, 1965. Signed by Y. G. Srimati, the illustrator. Translation by Edwin Arnold. Introduction by Shri Sri Prakasa $75.

370: Aeschylus PROMETHEUS BOUND and Percy Bysshe Shelley's PROMETHEUS UNBOUND New York, 1965. Introduction by Rex Warner, plates by John Farleigh $125.

371: Cooper, James Fenimore THE PATHFINDER Lunenberg, Vermont, 1965. Signed by Richard M. Powers, the illustrator. Introduction by Robert E. Spiller $75.

372: Conrad, Joseph THE NIGGER OF THE "NARCISSUS" Los Angeles, 1965. Signed by Millard Sheets, the illustrator. Introduction by Howard Mumford Jones $100.

373: Sinclair, Upton THE JUNGLE Baltimore, 1965. Signed by the author and Fletcher Martin, the illustrator $175.

374: Porter, William Sydney THE STORIES OF O. HENRY Burlington, 1965. Signed by John Groth, the illustrator. Introduction by Harry Hansen $200.

375: Petrarch THE SONNETS OF PETRARCH Verona, 1965. Signed by Aldo Salvadori, the illustrator and Giovanni Mardersteig, the printer. Introduction by Thomas G. Bergin $200.

376: Stoker, Bram DRACULA New York, 1965. Signed by Felix Hoffman, the illustrator. Introduction by Anthony Boucher $300.

377: Marlowe, Christopher FOUR PLAYS (*of Christopher Marlowe: Tamburlaine I, II, Dr. Faustus* and *Edward II*) New York, 1966. Signed by Albert Decaris, the illustrator. Introduction by Havelock Ellis $100.

378: Hope, Anthony THE PRISONER OF ZENDA Baltimore, 1966. Signed by Donald Spencer, the illustrator. Introduction by Sir Sydney Roberts $75.

379: Epictetus THE DISCOURSES AND MANUAL OF EPICTETUS Berne, 1966. Signed by Hans Erni, the illustrator. Introduction by P. E. Mattheson $125.

380: Dickens, Charles HARD TIMES New York, 1966. Introduction by John T. Winterich. Illustrated by Charles Raymond $100.

381: Shaw, George Bernard TWO PLAYS FOR PURITANS New York, 1966. Signed by George Him, the illustrator $75.

382: Keats, John THE POEMS OF JOHN KEATS Cambridge, 1966. Signed by David Gentleman, the illustrator. Introduction by Aileen Ward $125.

383: Scott, Sir Walter KENILWORTH Burlington, 1966. Signed by Clarke Hutton, the illustrator. Introduction by David Daiches $75.

384: Twain, Mark A TRAMP ABROAD (Hartford, 1966.) Signed by David Knight, the illustrator. With reproductions of drawings made by Mark Twain "without help" for the first edition. Introduction by Edward Wagenknecht $125.

385: Chekhov, Anton TWO PLAYS OF ANTON CHEKHOV: *The Cherry Orchard* and *Three Sisters*

New York, 1966. Signed by Lajos Szalay, the illustrator. Translated by Constance Garnett, introduction by Sir John Gielgud $75.

386: THE DEAD SEA SCROLLS Kent, England, 1966. Signed by Shraga Weil, the illustrator. Translated, introduction etc. by Geza Vermes $250.

387: Verne, Jules A JOURNEY TO THE CENTER OF THE EARTH New York, 1966. Signed by Edward A. Wilson, the illustrator. Introduction by Isaac Asimov $125.

388: Hawthorne, Nathaniel TWICE-TOLD TALES New York, 1966. Signed by Valenti Angelo, the illustrator. Introduction by Wallace Stegner $125.

389: Vasari, Giorgio LIVES OF THE MOST EMINENT PAINTERS Verona, 1966. 2 vols. Signed by Giovanni Mardersteig, the printer. Introduction by Marilyn Aronberg Lavin $350.

390: THE MONK AND THE HANGMAN'S DAUGHTER New York, 1967. Signed by Michel Ciry, the illustrator. (Written by Herr Richard Voss, although not mentioned in ref.a or b.) Adapted from the German by Ambrose Bierce, with introductions by Maurice Valency and Bierce $75.

391: James, Henry THE PORTRAIT OF A LADY (New York), 1967. Signed by Colleen Browning, the illustrator. Introduction by Robert W. Stallman $100.

392: Dostoevsky, Fyodor THE GAMBLER and NOTES FROM UNDER-GROUND Bloomfield, 1967. Signed by Alexandre Alexeieff, the illustrator. Translated by Constance Garnett, introduction by George Steiner $100.

393: Euripides THREE PLAYS OF EURIPIDES: MEDEA, HIPPOLYTUS, and THE BACCHAE London, 1967. Signed by Michael Ayrton, the illustrator. Introduction by Philip Vellacott $100.

394: THE BOOK OF BALLADS (New York), 1967. Signed by Fritz Kredel, the illustrator. Edited, with introduction, by MacEdward Leach $75.

395: Wells, H. G. THE INVISIBLE MAN New York, 1967. Signed by Charles Mozley, the illustrator. Introduction by Bernard Bergonzi $100.

396: Alcott, Louisa May LITTLE WOMEN New York, 1967. Signed by Henry C. Pitz, the illustrator. Introduction by Edward Weeks $150.

397: Jefferson, Thomas THE WRITINGS OF THOMAS JEFFERSON Lunenburg, Vermont, 1967. Signed by Lynd Ward, the illustrator. Selected and introduction by Saul K. Padover $175.

398: Shakespeare, William THE POEMS OF WILLIAM SHAKESPEARE Cambridge, 1967. Signed by Agnes Miller Parker, the illustrator. Introduction etc. by Peter Alexander $125.

399: Prescott, William H. THE HISTORY OF THE REIGN OF FERDINAND AND ISABELLA THE CATHOLIC New York, 1967. Signed by Lima de Freitas, the illustrator. Introduction by C. Harvey Gardiner $100.

400: Mitchell, Margaret GONE WITH THE WIND New York, 1968. 2 vols. Signed by John Groth, the illustrator. Introduction by Henry Steele Commager $350.

401: Defoe, Daniel A JOURNAL OF THE PLAGUE YEAR Bloomfield, 1968. Signed (or initialed) by Domenico Gnoli, the illustrator. Introduction by J. R. Sutherland $100.

402: Joyce, James A PORTRAIT OF THE ARTIST AS A YOUNG MAN New York, 1968. Signed by Brian Keogh, the illustrator. Introduction by Hugh Kenner $150.

403: Kipling, Rudyard THE JUNGLE BOOKS Lunenburg, Vermont, 1968. Signed by David Gentleman, the illustrator. Introduction by Bonamy Dobree $150.

404: THE BOOK ECCLESIASTES New York, 1968. Signed by Edgar Miller, the illustrator. Introduction by Kenneth Rexroth $150.

405: Maupassant, Guy de BEL-AMI New Yor, 1968. 2,000 cc. Signed by Bernard Lamotte, the illustrator. Introduction by Alec Waugh $60.

406: Wilde, Oscar THE SHORT STORIES OF OSCAR WILDE (New York), 1968. Signed by James Hill, the illustrator. Introduction by Robert Gorham Davis $125.

407: Donne, John THE POEMS OF JOHN DONNE Cambridge, 1968. Signed by Imre Reiner, the illustrator. Introduction by Frank Kermode $100.

408: Thoreau, Henry David CAPE COD Portland, 1968. Signed by Raymond J. Holden, the illustrator. Introduction by Joseph Wood Krutch $150.

409: Plato (THREE DIALOGUES OF PLATO) *Lysis, or Friendship*: *The Symposium*; and *Phaedrus* (New York), 1968. Signed by Eugene Karlin, the illustrator. Introduction by Whitney J. Oates $125.

410: Cooper, James Fenimore THE PILOT (Baltimore), 1968. Signed by Robert Quackenbush, the illustrator. Introduction by John T. Winterich $75.

411: AMERICAN INDIAN LEGENDS L. A. 1968. Signed by Everett Gee Jackson, the illustrator. Selected, edited and introduction by Allan A. Macfarland $125.

412: Remarque, Erich Maria ALL QUIET ON THE WESTERN FRONT (New York), 1969. Signed by

John Groth, the illustrator. Introduction by Harry Hansen $125.

413: Conrad, Joseph HEART OF DARKNESS New York, 1969. Signed by Robert Shore, the illustrator. Introduction by Leo Gurko $75.

414: Dumas, Alexandre MARGUERITE DE VALOIS New York, 1969. Signed by Edy Legrand, the illustrator. Introduction by Henri Peyre $75.

415: Scott, Sir Walter THE TALISMAN Ipswich, 1968. Signed by Federico Castellone, the illustrator. Introduction by Thomas Caldecot Chubb $75.

416: Browning, Robert THE POEMS OF ROBERT BROWNING Cambridge, 1969. Signed by Peter Reddick, the illustrator. Introduction by C. Day Lewis $100.

417: Creasey, Sir Edward S. THE FIFTEEN DECISIVE BATTLES OF THE WORLD (New York, 1969.) Signed by Joseph Domjan, the illustrator. Introduction by Hanson W. Baldwin $100.

418: Hardy, Thomas JUDE THE OBSCURE New York, 1969. Signed by Agnes Miller Parker, the illustrator. Introduction by John Bayley $150.

419: Aquinas, Thomas THE WRITINGS OF ST. THOMAS AQUINAS Chatham, England, 1969. Signed by Reynolds Stone, the illustrator. Selected and with introduction by George N. Shuster $150.

420: Xenophon THE ANABASIS Athens, 1969. Signed by A. Tassos, the illustrator. Translated by Henry G. Dakyns, introduction by Robert Payne $125.

421: James, Henry DAISY MILLER Cambridge, 1969. Signed by Gustave Nebel, the illustrator. Introduction by John Holloway $125.

422: Irving, Washington THE ALHAMBRA (New York), 1969. Signed by Lima de Freitas, the illustrator. Introduction by Angel Flores $75.

423: Steinbeck, John OF MICE AND MEN New York, 1970. Signed by Fletcher Martin, the illustrator. Introduction by John T. Winterich $200.

424: Frazer, Sir James George THE GOLDEN BOUGH New York, 1970. 2 vols. Signed by James Lewicki, the illustrator. Introduction by Stanley Edgar Hyman $125.

425: Yeats, W. B. THE POEMS OF W. B. YEATS New York, 1970. Signed by Robin Jacques, the illustrator. Introduction by William York Tindall $200.

426: Washington, Booker T. UP FROM SLAVERY New York, 1970. Signed by Denver Gillen, the illustrator. Introduction by Booker T. Washington III $100.

427: Livy THE HISTORY OF EARLY ROME Verona, 1970. Signed by Raffaele Scorzelli, the illustrator and Giovanni Mardersteig, the printer $150.

428: THE ANALECTS OF CONFUCIUS Los Angeles, 1970. Signed by Tseng Yu-Ho, the illustrator. Translated, annotated and introduction by Lionel Giles $175.

429: Verne, Jules FROM THE EARTH TO THE MOON and AROUND THE MOON New York, 1970. 2 vols. Signed by Robert Shore, the illustrator. Introduction by Jean Jules-Verne $150.

430: Addison, Joseph THE SPECTATOR London, 1970. Signed by Lynton Lamb, the illustrator. Introduction by Robert Halsband $100.

431: Twain, Mark THE NOTORIOUS JUMPING FROG AND OTHER STORIES New York, 1970. Signed by Joseph Low, the illustrator. Introduction by Edward Wagenknecht. Assume first of this selection $125.

432: RUSSIAN FOLK TALES New York, 1970. Signed by Teje Etchemendy, the illustrator. Selected, edited and introduction by Albert B. Lord $75.

433: Pushkin, Alexander THE CAPTAIN'S DAUGHTER AND OTHER STORIES (New York), 1971. Signed by Charles Mozley, the illustrator. Translated by Ivy and Tatiana Litvinov. Introduction by Kathryn Feuer $75.

434: Dickens, Charles THE SHORT STORIES OF CHARLES DICKENS New York, 1971. Signed by Edward Ardizzone, the illustrator and Joseph Blumenthal, the designer. Introduction by Walter Allen $150.

435: Darwin, Charles THE DESCENT OF MAN and SELECTION IN RELATION TO SEX Adelaide, So. Australia, 1971. Signed by Fritz Kredel, the illustrator. Introduction by Ashley Mantagu $200.

436: Austen, Jane NORTHANGER ABBEY (New York), 1971. Signed by Clark Hutton, the illustrator. Introduction by Sylvia Townsend Warner $125.

437: Baudelaire, Charles THE FLOWERS OF EVIL New York, 1971. 2 vols. Signed by Pierre-Yves Tremois, the illustrator. Introduction by James Laver $100.

438: Camus, Albert THE STRANGER (New York), 1971. Signed by Daniel Maffia, the illustrator. Translated by Stuart Gilbert, introduction by Wallace Fowlie $150.

439: James, Henry WASHINGTON SQUARE New York, 1971. Signed by Lawrence Beall Smith, the illustrator. Introduction by Louis S. Auchincloss $75.

440: Ovidius Naso, P. (Ovid.) THE ART OF LOVE (New York), 1971. Signed by Eric Fraser, the illustrator. Translated, with introduction and notes, by B. P. Moore $125.

441: Pascal, Blaise LES PENSEES Bloomfield, 1971. Signed by Ismar David, the illustrator. Translated and introduction by Martin Turnell $75.

442: SIR GAWAIN AND THE GREEN KNIGHT New York, 1971. Signed by Cyril Satorsky, the illustrator. Modern translation and introduction by James L. Rosenberg $200.

443: Shelley, Percy B. THE POEMS OF PERCY BYSSHE SHELLEY Cambridge, 1971. Signed by Richard Shirley Smith, the illustrator. Introduction by Stephen Spender $125.

444: Mann, Thomas DEATH IN VENICE New York, 1972. Signed by Felix Hoffmann, the illustrator. Translated by Kenneth Burke, introduction by Erich Heller $150.

445: O'Neill, Eugene AH, WILDERNESS! New York, 1972. Signed by Shannon Stirweiss, the illustrator. Introduction by Walter Kerr $100.

446: Conrad, Joseph YOUTH, TYPHOON, and THE END OF THE TETHER Los Angeles, 1972. Signed by Robert Shore, the illustrator and Ward Ritchie, the printer/designer $100.

447: Tolstoy, Leo CHILDHOOD, BOYHOOD, YOUTH New York, 1972. Signed by Fritz Eichenberg, the illustrator. Introduction by John Bayley $125.

448: Twain, Mark ROUGHING IT New York, 1972. Signed by Noel Sickles, the illustrator. Introduction by Edward Wagenknecht $125.

449: White, Gilbert THE NATURAL HISTORY OF SELBORNE Ipswich, 1972. Signed by John Nash, the illustrator. Introduction by the Earl of Cranbrook $250.

450: THE MEMOIRS OF CASANOVA Haarlem, 1972. Signed by Rene ben Sussan, the illustrator. Introduction by J. Rives Childs $100.

451: Bierce, Ambrose THE DEVIL'S DICTIONARY New York, 1972. Signed by Fritz Kredel, the illustrator. Introduction by Louis Kronenberger $125.

452: THE ORATIONS AND ESSAYS OF CICERO Verona, 1972. Signed by Salvatore Fiume, the illustrator. Introduction by Reginald H. Barrow. Printed by Hans Martersteig $150.

453: THE BOOK OF THE DEAD New York (1972). 2 vols. Translation and introduction by Raymond O. Faulkner. Accompanied by a volume of photographs by Peter Parkinson, mounted accordion-style to form strip 16' 5" long $200.

454: THE PANCHANTANTRA New York, 1972. Signed by Y.G. Srimati, the illustrator. Introduction by Arthur W. Ryder $75.

455: Blake, William THE POEMS OF WILLIAM BLAKE Cambridge, 1973. Introduction by Aileen Ward, illustrated with Blake's colored engravings $200.

456: Voltaire CANDIDE, or OPTIMISM New York, 1973. Signed by May Neama, the illustrator. Introduction by Anatole Broyard $75.

457: Wilde, Oscar LADY WINDERMERE'S FAN and THE IMPORTANCE OF BEING EARNEST London, 1973. Signed by Tony Walton, the illustrator. Introduction by Sir John Gielgud $125.

458: Dumas, Alexandre THE QUEEN'S NECKLACE New York, 1973. Signed by Edy Legrand and Cyril Arnstram, the illustrators. Introduction by Henri Peyre $75.

459-465: LEC skipped 7 numbers at this point "to conform with the number of the corresponding Monthly Letter"

466: Chekhov, Anton THE SHORT STORIES OF ANTON CHEKHOV Avon, Connecticut, 1973. 2,000 cc. Signed by Lajos Szalay, the illustrator. Introduction by Helen Muchnic $75.

467: IRISH FOLK TALES Avon, Connecticut, 1973. 2,000 cc. Signed by Ted Gensamer, the designer/decorator. Introduction by William Butler Yeats, illustrated by Rowel Fries $125.

468: London, Jack WHITE FANG Lunenburg, Vermont, 1973. 2,000 cc. Signed by Lydia Dabcovich, the illustrator. Introduction by Ray Gardner $100.

469: Wharton, Edith THE AGE OF INNOCENCE Avon, Connecticut, 1973. 2,000 cc. Signed by Lawrence Beall Smith, the illustrator. Introduction by W. B. Lewis $125.

470: Wordsworth, William THE POEMS OF WILLIAM WORDSWORTH Cambridge, 1973. 2,000 cc. Signed by John O'Connor, the illustrator $75.

471: Kipling, Rudyard TALES OF EAST AND WEST Avon, Connecticut, 1973. 2,000 cc. Signed by Charles Raymond, the illustrator. Introduction by Bernard Bergonzi $75.

472: Huxley, Aldous BRAVE NEW WORLD (Avon, Connecticut), 1974. 2,000 cc. Signed by Mary McAfee, the illustrator. Introduction by Ashley Montagu $125.

473: GILGAMESH Avon, Connecticut, 1974. 2,000 cc. Signed by Irving Amen, the illustrator.

Translated by William Ellery Leonard, introduction by Leonard Cottrell $75.

474: Boswell, James JOURNAL OF A TOUR TO THE HEBRIDES WITH SAMUEL JOHNSON, LL.D Bloomfield, 1974. 2,000 cc. Illustrated by Thomas Rowlandson, introduction by Robert Halsband $100.

475: Weems, Mason L. THE LIFE OF WASHINGTON (New York), 1974. 2,000 cc. Signed by Robert Quackenbush, the illustrator. Introduction by Henry Steele Commager $100.

476: Thucydides THE HISTORY OF THE PELOPONNESIAN WAR Avon, Connecticut, 1974. 2 vols. 2,000 sets. Signed by A. Tassos, the illustrator. Introduction by Peter Pouncey $125.

477: Twain, Mark PUDD'NHEAD WILSON Avon, Connecticut, 1974. 2,000 cc. Signed by John Groth, the illustrator. Introduction by Edward Wagenknecht. Also a separate small volume in wraps PUDD'NHEAD WILSON'S CALENDAR also illustrated by Garth $125.

478: Shaw, George Bernard PYGMALION and CANDIDA Avon, Connecticut, 1974. 2,000 cc. Signed by Clarke Hutton, the illustrator. Introduction by Alan Strachan $100.

479: Crane, Stephen MAGGIE *A Girl of the Streets* (New York), 1974. 2,000 cc. Signed by Sigmund Abeles, the illustrator. Introduction by Shirley Ann Grau $100.

480: Bradbury, Ray THE MARTIAN CHRONICLES Avon, Connecticut, 1974. 2,000 cc. Signed by the author and Joseph Mugnaini, the illustrator. Introduction by Martin Gardner $300.

481: Wilder, Thornton OUR TOWN Avon, Connecticut, 1974. 2,000 cc. Signed by the author and

Robert J. Lee, the illustrator. Introduction by Brooks Atkinson $200.

482: Dostoevsky, Fyodor A RAW YOUTH Verona, 1974. 2 vols. 2,000 cc. Signed by Fritz Eichenberg, the illustrator. Introduction by Konstantin Mochulsky $125.

483: Tennyson, Alfred Lord THE POEMS OF ALFRED, LORD TENNYSON Cambridge, 1974. 2,000 cc. Signed by Reynolds Stone, the illustrator. Introduction by John D. Rosenberg $200.

484: Dickens, Charles AMERICAN NOTES Avon, Connecticut, 1975. 2,000 cc. Signed by Raymond F. Houlihan, the illustrator. Introduction by Angus Wilson $100.

485: Wharton, Edith THE HOUSE OF MIRTH (New York), 1975. 2,000 cc. Signed by Lily Harmon, the illustrator. Introduction by Arthur Mizener $100.

486: Conrad, Joseph AN OUTCAST OF THE ISLANDS Avon, Connecticut, 1975. 2,000 cc. Signed by Robert Shore, the illustrator. Introduction by Clifton Fadiman $75.

487: Jerome, Jerome K. THREE MEN IN A BOAT Ipswich, 1975. 2,000 cc. Signed by John Griffiths, the illustrator. Introduction by Stella Gibbons $75.

488: Thoreau, Henry David A WEEK ON THE CONCORD AND MERRIMACK RIVERS Lunenburg, 1975. 2,000 cc. Signed by Raymond J. Holden, the illustrator. Introduction by Charles R. Anderson $100.

489: Sophocles ANTIGONE Haarlem, 1975. 2,000 cc. Signed by Harry Bennett, the illustrator. Introduction by D. S. Carne-Ross $100.

490: Walpole, Hugh THE CASTLE OF OTRANTO Westerham, 1975. 2,000 cc. Signed by W. S. Lewis, the editor/introduction. Contemporary illustrations $100.

491: Burke, Edmund ON CONCILIATION WITH AMERICA AND OTHER PAPERS ON THE AMERICAN REVOLUTION Lunenburg, Vermont, 1975. 2,000 cc. Signed by Lynd Ward, the illustrator. Introduction and prefaces by Peter J. Stanlis $125.

492: Fernandez de Oviedo y Valdes, Capt. Gonzalo THE CONQUEST AND SETTLEMENT OF THE ISLAND OF BORIQUEN or PUERTO RICO Lunenburg, 1975. 2,000 cc. Signed by Jack and Irene Delano, the illustrators. Introduction and notes by E. Raymond Turner $100.

493: Lawrence, D. H. SONS AND LOVERS Avon, Connecticut, 1975. 2,000 cc. Signed by Sheila Robinson, the illustrator. Introduction by Robert Gorham Davis $100.

494: Bligh, William A VOYAGE TO THE SOUTH SEAS Adelaide, So. Australia, 1975. 2,000 cc. Signed by Geoffrey C. Ingleton, the illustrator and Douglas Dunstan, the designer. Introduction by Alan Villiers $175.

495: Kafka, Franz THE TRIAL Avon, Connecticut, 1975. 2,000 cc. Signed by Alan E. Cober, the illustrator. Introduction by Erich Heller (full leather) $175.

496: Pater, Walter THE RENAISSANCE Verona, 1976. 2,000 cc. Signed by Martino Mardersteig, the designer. Introduction by Kenneth Clarke $150.

497: Arnold, Sir Edwin THE LIGHT OF ASIA Avon, Connecticut, 1976. 2,000 cc. Illustrated by Ayres Houghtelling. Introduction by Melford E. Spiro $75.

498: Defoe, Daniel ROXANA, THE FORTUNATE MISTRESS Avon, Connecticut, 1976. 2,000 cc. Illustrated and signed by Bernd Kroeber. Introduction by James R. Sutherland $75.

499: Stevenson, Robert Louis NEW ARABIAN NIGHTS Avon, Connecticut, 1976. 2,000 cc. Signed by Clarke Hutton, the illustrator. Introduction by Norman H. Strouse $75.

500: Gogol, Nikolai THE OVERCOAT and THE GOVERNMENT INSPECTOR Westport, Connecticut, 1976. 2,000 cc. Signed by Saul Field, the illustrator. Introduction by Alfred Kazin $75.

501: Cabell, James Branch JURGEN *A Comedy of Justice* Westport, Connecticut (1976). 2,000 cc. Signed and illustrated by Virgil Burnett. Introduction by Edward Wagenknecht $75.

502: Turgenev, Ivan THE TORRENTS OF SPRING Westport, Connecticut, 1976. 1,600 cc. Signed by Lajos, the illustrator. Introduction by Alec Waugh $75.

503: Austen, Jane PERSUASION Westport, Connecticut, 1977. 1,600 cc. Signed and illustrated by Tony Buonpastore. Introduction by Louis Auchincloss $125

504: Hesse, Herman STEPPENWOLF Westport, Connecticut, 1977. 1,600 cc. Signed by Helmut Ackermann, the illustrator $125.

505: Hugo, Victor THE BATTLE OF WATERLOO Westport, Connecticut, 1977. 1,600 cc. Illustrated by Edouard Detaille. Introduction by Drew Middleton. Epilogue by Reginald Colby $75.

506: Sassoon, Siegfried MEMOIRS OF A FOXHUNTING MAN (London), 1977. 1,600 cc. Signed by Paul Hogarth, the illustrator. Introduction by Geoffrey Keynes $100.

507: THE SERMON ON THE MOUNT New York, 1977. 1,600 cc. Commentaries and introduction by Roman A. Greer. Decorated by Leo Watt, designed by John Dreyfus $100.

508: THE BALLADS OF ROBIN HOOD Cambridge, 1977. 1,600 cc. Illustrated by David Gentleman. Introduction by Jim Lees. Designed by John Dreyfus $100.

509: This number was not used by LEC.

510: Anderson, Sherwood WINESBURG, OHIO Lunenburg, 1978. 1,600 cc. Signed by Ben F. Stahl, the illustrator. Introduction by Malcolm Cowley. Also noted a *hors commerce* issue, designated "H. C." (Waiting for Godot Books 2/97) $125.

511: Flaubert, Gustave THREE TALES New York, 1978. 1,600 cc. Signed by May Neama, the illustrator. Introduction by Guy de Maupassant $75.

512: THE BOOK OF THE PROPHET ISAIAH New York, 1979. 2,000 cc. Signed by Chaim Gross, the illustrator. Introduction by Franklin H. Littell $200.

513: Villon, Francois THE LYRICAL POEMS OF FRANCOIS VILLON New York, 1979. 2,000 cc. Signed by Stephen Harvard, the designer. Introduction by Robert Louis Stevenson. Poems in French and English, with the latter versions by A. C. Swinburne, Dante Gabriel Rossetti, W. E. Henley, John Payne and Leonie Adams (who selected the poems for inclusion) $100.

514: Singer, Isaac Bashevis THE GENTLEMAN FROM CRACOW and THE MIRROR New York, 1979. 2,000 cc. Signed by the author and Raphael Soyer, the illustrator $250.

515: Carson, Rachel THE SEA AROUND US New York, 1980. 2,000 cc. Signed by Alfred Eisenstaedt, the photographer $250.

516: Fitzgerald, F. Scott THE GREAT GATSBY (New York, 1980.) 2,000 cc. Signed by Fred Meyer, the illustrator. Introduction by Charles Scribner III $150.

517: Graves, Robert POEMS New York, 1980. 2,000 cc. Signed by Paul Hogarth, the illustrator $100.

518: Rilke, Rainer Maria SELECTED POEMS OF RAINER MARIA RILKE New York, 1981. 2,000 cc. Signed by Robert Kipniss, the illustrator. Translated by C. F. MacIntyre. Preface by Harry T. Moore $125.

519: Sassoon, Siegfried MEMOIRS OF AN INFANTRY OFFICER Portland, 1981. 2,000 cc. Signed by Paul Hogarth, the illustrator. Introduction by David Daiches $100.

520: Crane, Hart THE BRIDGE New York, 1981. 2,000 cc. Signed by Richard Mead Benson, the photographer. Introduction by Malcolm Cowley $150.

521: Homer THE ODYSSEY (New York), 1981. 2,000 cc. Signed by Barry Moser, the illustrator. Translated by T. E. Shaw (Lawrence). Preface by Jeremy M. Wilson $250.

522: Grimmelshausen, Johann von THE ADVENTURES OF SIMPLICUSSIMUS Charlotte, 1981. 2,000 cc. Signed by Fritz Eichenberg, the illustrator. Translation and introduction by John Spielman $100.

523: Cowley, Malcolm EXILE'S RETURN New York, 1981. 2,000 cc. Signed by the author and Bernice Abbott, the photographer. Includes photographs by Abbott, Man Ray and Andre Kertesz, et al. Introduction by Leon Edel $300.

524: Fitzgerald, F. Scott TENDER IS THE NIGHT Lunenburg (1982). 2,000 cc. Signed by Fred Meyer, the illustrator and Charles Scribner III (the publisher) $150.

525: O'Neill, Eugene THE ICEMAN COMETH Lunenburg, 1982. 2,000 cc. Signed by Leonard Baskin, the illustrator. Introduction by Irma Jaffe. Includes an original lithograph (signed in the stone) bound at rear $250.

526: Dostoevsky, Fyodor THE HOUSE OF THE DEAD Boston, 1982. 2,000 cc. Signed by Fritz Eichenberg, the illustrator. Foreword by Boris Shragin $125.

527: Bradbury, Ray FAHRENHEIT 451 New York, 1982. 2,000 cc. Signed by the author and Joe Mugnaini, the illustrator $300.

528: Finney, Charles G. THE CIRCUS OF DR. LAO Lunenburg, 1982. 2,000 cc. Signed by Claire Van Vliet, the illustrator. Introduction by Edward Hoagland $150.

529: Brecht, Bertolt THE THREEPENNY OPERA (New York, 1982.) 2,000 cc. Signed by Jack Levine (illustrator) and Eric Bentley (introduction) $150.

530: Heaney, Seamus POEMS AND A MEMOIR BY SEAMUS HEANEY (New York, 1982). 1,500 cc. Signed by the author (who also contributes a preface), Henry Pearson (illustrator) and Thomas Flanagan (introduction). A first edition of this selection including eight "early uncollected poems." $450.

531: Williams, Tennessee A STREETCAR NAMED DESIRE New York, 1982. 2,000 cc. Signed by Al Hirshfeld, the illustrator. Foreword by Jessica Tandy, introduction by the author (an essay that appeared in "The New York Times: drama section on November 30, 1947) $300.

532: Garcia Marquez, Gabriel ONE HUNDRED YEARS OF SOLITUDE (New York, 1982). 2,000 cc. Signed by Rafael Ferrer, (illustrator), Alastair Reid (introduction) and Gregory Rabassa (translator). An original graphic is laid-in $350.

533: Walcott, Derek POEMS OF THE CARIBBEAN New York (1982). 2,000 cc. Signed by the author and Romare Bearden, the illustrator. Introduction by Joseph Brodsky. A numbered (1/250 cc) lithograph by Bearden is laid-in some copies. Between The Covers notes the publisher sold copies of the lithograph separately $500.

534: Colette BREAK OF DAY New York, 1983. 2,000 cc. Signed by Francoise Gilot, the illustrator. Introduction by Robert Phelps. $150.

535: Hersey, John HIROSHIMA New York, 1983. 1,500 cc. Signed by the author, Robert Penn Warren (poem), and Jacob Lawrence (illustrator). $750.

536: Cather, Willa A LOST LADY New York, 1983. 1,500 cc. Signed by William Bailey, the illustrator. Introduction by John Hollander. $200.

537: Milosz, Czeslaw THE CAPTIVE MIND New York (1983). 1,500 cc. Signed by the author (who adds a new preface for this edition) and Janusz Kapusta, the illustrator $200.

538: Singer, Isaac Bashevis THE MAGICIAN OF LUBLIN New York, 1984. 1,200 cc. Signed by the author and Larry Rivers, the illustrator. $500.

539: Kafka, Franz METAMORPHOSIS New York (1984). 1,500 cc. Signed by Jose Luis Cuevas, the illustrator. Introduction by Robert Coles $350.

540: Miller, Arthur DEATH OF A SALESMAN New York (1984). 1,500 cc. Signed by the author, who adds a new foreword, and Leonard Baskin, the illustrator $600.

541: Borges, Jore Luis FICCIONES New York (1984). 1,500 cc. Signed by Sol LeWitt, the illustrator. Introduction by Alexander Coleman. Translated by Anthony Kerrigan and others. $500.

542: Poe, Edgar Allan THE FALL OF THE HOUSE OF USHER New York, 1985. 1,500 cc. Signed by Raphael Soyer, who did a tribute to Alice Neel, the illustrator died before the book was published; however, she did sign some sheets.

Signed by Neel: $1,000.
Not signed by Neel: $600.

543: Conrad, Joseph THE SECRET SHARER New York (1985). 1,500 cc. Signed by Bruce Chandler, the illustrator. Introduction by Ian Watt. In print at $200 $250.

544: Grass, Gunter THE FLOUNDER New York, 1985. 1,000 cc. 3 vols. Signed by the author, who also illustrated the book. Translated by Ralph Mannheim. $750.

545: Rimbaud, Arthur A SEASON IN HELL New York (1986). 1,000 cc. Signed Robert Mapplethorpe, the artist and Paul Schmidt, translation and introduction. There were also 40 signed numbered portfolios of the illustrations sold separately $2,000.

546: Joyce, James DUBLINERS (New York, 1986.) 1,000 cc. Signed by Robert Ballagh (photogravures) and Tom Flanagan (introduction). $600.

547: Bernanos, Georges THE DIARY OF A COUNTRY PRIEST (New York, 1986.) 1,000 cc. Signed by Fritz Eichenberg, the illustrator. Introduction by Robert Coles. $300.

548: Kafka, Franz IN THE PENAL COLONY New York (1987). 800 cc. Signed by Michael Hofftka, the illustrator. Translation by Willa and Edwin Muir. $400.

549: Ionesco, Eugene JOURNEYS AMONG THE DEAD Munich (1987). 1,000 cc. Signed by the author, who also illustrated the book. Translation by Barbara Wright. Also includes a new preface in the form of a "Conversation with Ionesco | Eugene Ionesco and Verena Heyden-Rynsch | Paris, March 14, 1987." $250.

550: Rilke, Rainer Maria THE NOTEBOOKS OF MALTE LAURIDS BRIGGE (New York, 1987.) 800 cc. Translated by Stephen Mitchell. Not signed. (This book was substituted by the club but never advertised) $250.

551: Faulkner, William HUNTING STORIES (New York, 1988.) 850 cc. Signed by Neil Welliver, the illustrator. Although announced to be signed by Cleanth Brooks (introduction), it was not. $500.

552: Carpentier, Alejo THE KINGDOM OF THIS WORLD (New York, 1987.) 750 cc. Signed Roberto Juarez (illustrations) and John Hersey (introduction). There was also twenty signed numbered sets of the illustrations sold separately $400.

553: Paz, Octavio THREE POEMS (New York, 1988.) 750 cc. Signed by the author and Robert Motherwell, the artist. There were also 20 signed numbered exhibition sets of the illustrations; and 50 signed numbered portfolios. Both in wooden boxes $3,000.

554: Lampedusa, Giuseppe di THE LEOPARD No place (1988). 750 cc. Signed by the artist Piero Guccione and Leonard Sciascia, introduction. Translated by Archibald Colquhoun. $250.

555: Durrenmatt, Friedrich OEDIPUS (New York, 1989.) 650 cc. 2 vols. Signed by the author and Marie Casindas (photogravures). Translated by Leila Vennewitz. Foreword by the author. $400.

556: Warren, Robert Penn ALL THE KING'S MEN (New York, 1989.) 550 cc. 2 vols. Signed by the author and the artist Hank O'Neal (photogravures). New introduction. There were also

30 signed numbered sets of the photogravures sold separately $850.

557: GENESIS (New York), 1989. 425 cc. Signed by the artist Jacob Lawrence. There were also 22 signed numbered exhibition sets; and 50 signed numbered portfolios of the illustrations sold separately $2,000.

558: Beckett, Samuel NOHOW ON (New York), 1989. 550 cc. Signed by Beckett and the illustrator Robert Ryman. $4,000.

559: Hemingway, Ernest THE OLD MAN AND THE SEA (New York, 1990.) 600 cc. Signed by Alfred Eisenstaedt (photogravures). Oblong size in clam shell box. There were also 30 signed numbered sets of the photogravures sold separately $1,500.

560: Whitman, Walt THE SONG OF THE OPEN ROAD (New York), 1990. 550 cc. Illustrated with photogravures by Aaron Sisking and signed by him. There were also 12 signed numbered exhibition sets; and 30 signed numbered sets of the photogravures sold separately $1,250.

561: O'Hara, Frank POEMS New York, 1990. 500 cc. Illustrated with 17 lithographs by Willem de Kooning. Introduction by Riva Castleman. There were also 12 numbered exhibition sets; and 60 numbered portfolios $3,000.

562: Kawabata, Yasunari SNOW COUNTRY New York, 1990. 375 cc. Signed by the illustrator, Tadakki Kuwayama, and translator, Edward Seidensticker. There were also 40 signed numbered sets of the illustrations $1,750.

563: Mann, Thomas THE BLACK SWAN New York, 1990. 375 cc. Signed by the illustrator, John Hejduk. Afterword by David Shapiro. $1,250.

564: Mitchell, Joseph THE BOTTOM OF THE HARBOR New York, 1991. 250 cc. With photographs by Berenice Abbott. Signed by Mitchell. $1,500.

565: Pasternak, Boris MY SISTER/LIFE New York, 1992. 250 cc. Illustrated and signed by Yuri Kuper. There were also 40 signed numbered sets of the etchings sold separately $750.

566: Mallarme, Stephane UN COUP DE DES No place (1992). 300 cc. Illustrated and signed by Ellsworth Kelly $1,500.

567: Walker, Margaret FOR MY PEOPLE New York, 1992. 400 cc. Illustrated by Elizabeth Catlett and signed by her and Walker $2,000.

568: Pound, Ezra CATHAY New York, 1992. 300 cc. Illustrated with etchings by Francesco Clements and signed by him. $2,000.

569: Conrad, Joseph HEART OF DARKNESS New York, 1992. 300 cc. Illustrated and signed by Sean Scully $1,500.

570: Harrer, Heinrich SEVEN YEARS IN TIBET New York, 1993. 300 cc Signed by the author. Unattributed photogravures. Wrapped in a red and yellow flag, held between two carved wooden boards $750.

571: Bronte, Emily WUTHERING HEIGHTS New York, 1993. 300 cc. Illustrated and signed by Balthus $2,000.

572: Angelou, Maya OUR GRANDMOTHERS New York, 1994. 400 cc. Illustrated by John Biggers. Signed by the author and the artist $1,250.

573: Aragon, Louis LE PAYSAN DE PARIS [New York, 1994.] 300 cc. Photogravure illustrations by Henri Cartier-Bresson. Signed by Cartier-Bresson $2,000.

574: Paz, Octavio SIGHT AND TOUCH [New York] (1994). 300 cc. Signed by the author and artist. Illustrated by Balthus (Count Balthazar Klossowski de Rola). Paintings made into multi-color woodcuts by Keiji Shinohara. Signed by author and artist $2,000.

575: THE REVELATION OF ST. JOHN THE DIVINE New York, 1995. 300 cc. Illustrated with fifteen relief engravings by Allan Rohan Crite $1,750.

576: Kyoka, Izumi THE TALE OF THE WANDERING MONK New York, 1995. 300 cc. Illustrated and signed by Setsuko Ideta $1,750.

577: Giono, Jean THE MAN WHO PLANTED TREES New York, 1995. 300 cc. Photographs by Martine Franck who also signed the book $1,750.

578: Rimbaud, Arthur VOWELS New York, 1996. 300 cc. Watercolors by Henri Cartier-Bresson who also signed the book $2,000.

579: Senghor, Léopold Sédar POEMS OF LÉOPOLD SÉDAR SENGHOR Volume 1 (New York, 1996.) 300 cc. Signed by the author and artist, Lois Mailou Jones $2,000.

580: Harrer, Heinrich THE WHITE SPIDER [New York], 1996. 300 cc. With photographs by the author and signed by him $2,000.

SPECIAL PUBLICATIONS:

S1: Dwiggins, W.A. TOWARDS A REFORM OF THE PAPER CURRENCY New York, 1932. 452 cc. Signed by Dwiggins $600.

S2: THE DOLPHIN *A Journal of the Making of Books* No. 1, 1933. 1,200 cc $175.

S3: THE DOLPHIN *A Journal of the Making of Books* No. 2, 1935. 2,000 cc $125.

S4: THE DOLPHIN *A History of the Printed Book* No. 3, 1938. 1,800 cc. Edited by Lawrence C. Wroth $150.

S5: THE DOLPHIN *A Periodical for All People Who Find Pleasure in Fine Books* No. 4. Designed by W.A. Dwiggins

Part I: Fall, 1940 500 cc in green buckram: $200.
11,500 cc. Wraps: $50.

Part II: Winter, 1941. 3,000 cc. Bound in green buckram: $75.

Part III: Winter, 1941. 3,000 cc. Bound in green buckram: $75.

S6: Boccaccio, Giovanni THE DECAMERON New York, 1940. 2 vols. 530 cc. Illustrated by Fritz Kredel, introduction by Edward Hutton $500.

S7: Grahame, Kenneth THE WIND IN THE WILLOWS New York, 1940. 2,020 cc. Signed by Bruce Rogers, the designer. Introduction by A. A. Milne, illustrated by Arthur Rackham $1,250.

S8: Steinbeck, John THE GRAPES OF WRATH New York, 1940. 2 vols. 1,146 cc. Signed by Thomas Hart Benton, the illustrator. Introduction by Joseph Henry Jackson and Thomas Craven $1,000.

OTHER PUBLICATIONS (Numbered for APG purposes)

OP1: Dill, Francis P. and Porter Garnett THE IDEAL BOOK Limited Editions Club (New York), 1931. 2,600 cc. Wraps. Two essays. Jointly awarded the prize offered by LEC for Best Essay on subject $50.

OP2: Dill, Francis P. and Porter Garnett THE IDEAL BOOK Limited Editions Club, New York, 1932. 500 cc. The second printing, the first in cloth (issued without dustwrapper). Prepared as a keepsake for The American Institute of Graphic Arts $75.

OP3: Jackson, Holbrook OF THE USES OF BOOKS (1937.) 1,500 cc. 30 pages in boards $60.

OP4: THE LIMITED EDITIONS CLUB, INC: YOUR FAVORITE BOOKS... The Tenth Anniversary Series. (No-date.) Paperwraps. Prospectus and history $40.

OP5: Jackson, Joseph Henry WHY STEINBECK WROTE *THE GRAPES OF WRATH* Booklets For Bookman, London/New York (1940). [0] Wraps. Also includes essays by Carter Meredith and A .A. Milne $50.

OP6: TEN YEARS AND WM. SHAKESPEARE *A Survey of The Publishing Activities of The Limited Editions Club From October 1929 to October 1940* (1940) $75.

OP7: A RECORD OF THE PROCEEDINGS AT THE LIMITED EDITIONS CLUB'S DINNER TO CELEBRATE THE TWENTY-FIRST BIRTHDAY OF THE CLUB & THE FIFTIETH BIRTHDAY OF IT'S FOUNDER 1950. 3,000 cc. Includes photographs of dinner $50.

OP8: Robert, Maurice and Frederic Warde A CODE FOR THE COLLECTOR OF BEAUTIFUL BOOKS 1936 $75.

OP9: TO EDWARD F. FOLLEY, THE LEC ON THE OCCASION OF IT'S 21ST BIRTHDAY PRESENTS THIS GREETING IN TOKEN OF IT'S APPRECIATION FOR AND ADMIRATION OF THE BIBLIOGRAPHICAL ACTIVITIES OF THIS HONORED CHARTER MEMBER DURING ALL OF THE CLUB'S 21 YEARS 1950. Laminated plastic broadside printed in two colors enclosed in a special marbled paper covered box $75.

OP10: BIBLIOGRAPHY OF THE FINE BOOKS PUBLISHED BY THE LIMITED EDITIONS CLUB 1929-1985 New York City (1985). 800 no. cc. $400.

Following is an index of the authors, illustrators, etc. for your convenience

INDEX

JACK LONDON
(1876-1916)

John Griffith London was born in San Francisco, the illegitimate son of an itinerant Irish astrologer (W.H. Chaney) whom London never met. His mother married John London when Jack was eight months old.

London grew up along the Oakland waterfront but was a heavy reader at an early age. He was guided to better literature by the librarian of the Oakland Public Library, Ina Coolbrith (Poet Laureate of California).

At fifteen he went on the road as a tramp. By sixteen he was an oyster-pirate and longshoreman near San Francisco Bay; and then a seaman on a sealing schooner in the north Pacific. He joined Coxey's Army at eighteen and went East by hopping freight trains. He spent 30 days in jail for vagrancy in Pennsylvania.

He returned to California and joined the Socialist Labor Party. When gold was discovered in the Klondike he was off to find it but only brought back material for later books.

In 1899 the "Atlantic Monthly" bought a long story "An Odyssey of the North" and Houghton Mifflin offered him a contract for a volume of short stories (*The Son of The Wolf*). He married Bessie Maddern in 1900 and divorced her in 1905 to marry Charmian Kittredge.

The Call of The Wild was the first book to bring him broad recognition, which was to lead to his being called the highest paid, best-known and most popular writer in the world by 1913. His 50 books made him over a million dollars which he managed to spend on lavish hospitality and building (or rebuilding after a fire destroyed) his Wolf House, among other extravagances.

On slow days he covered the Russo-Japanese War, ran for mayor of Oakland on the Socialist ticket, sailed the "Snark" to Hawaii; and pioneered in agriculture and livestock breeding at Wolf House.

He died of a morphine overdose in 1916 at the age of 40.

REFERENCES:

The primary reference for this guide was ref.a which carried through 1965 and contains detailed bibliographical descriptions including the first print run quantities.

(a) Blanck, Jacob. BIBLIOGRAPHY OF AMERICAN LITERATURE. Volume 5. New Haven: Yale University Press, 1969. Used through 1965 unless otherwise stated.

(b) Sisson, James E. III and Robert W. Martens. JACK LONDON FIRST EDITIONS. Oakland: Star Rover House, 1979.

(c) Inventory, dealer catalogs, etc.

Note: Estimated prices are for fine copies without dustwrapper until 1920. Dustwrappers would, of course, increase the values shown substantially.

001a: THE SON OF THE WOLF ... Houghton, Mifflin, Boston/New York, 1900. [0] Three trial bindings are known (No priority):

Binding A: Rough grass-green V cloth, stamped in silver $3,500.

Binding B: Greenish-black V cloth, stamped in silver $3,500.

Binding C: White buckram stamped in red only $3,500.

001b: THE SON OF THE WOLF ... Houghton, Mifflin, Boston/New York, 1900. [0] Wraps. 19 cc possibly for review $7,500.

001c: THE SON OF THE WOLF ... Houghton, Mifflin, Boston/New York, 1900. [0] 2,028 cc. First printing: Gray cloth stamped in silver. Pagination (i-viii); no blank leaf following p(252); collation: 1(4), 2-22(6) $1,500.

001d: THE SON OF THE WOLF ... Houghton, Mifflin, Boston/New York, 1900. [0] 1,010 cc. Second printing: Gray cloth stamped in silver. Pagination: (i-vi) blank leaf following p(252). Identifiable only by its collation (the first six gatherings have eight leaves, and then all but the last have six leaves). $600.

001e: THE SON OF THE WOLF ... Houghton, Mifflin, Boston/New York, 1900. [0] 763 cc of third printing. Same as second except collation differs: 1-21(6), 22(4) $350.

001f: THE SON OF THE WOLF ... Houghton, Mifflin, Boston/New York, 1900. [0] 241 cc of third printing. Cover in green V cloth stamped in white and red with illustration of man in arctic dress on front cover $350.

001g: THE SON OF THE WOLF ... A.P. Watt, London, 1900. [0] 6 cc. Cancel title page of first printing $1,500.

001h: THE SON OF THE WOLF ... Isbister & Co., London, 1902. [0] Copyright page blank. Red cloth stamped in gold on front and spine, spine imprint "Pitman," gold stamped design on spine, blind stamp design on front. Collation: (i-viii), (1)-251, (251-253) ads including *God of His Father* and Gorky's *Three Men*. (Ref.c) $600.

001i: AN ODYSSEY OF THE NORTH Mills & Boon, London, 1913. [0] $150.

001j: AN ODYSSEY OF THE NORTH Mills and Boon, London, no date. [] Published 1915 $100.

001k: AN ODYSSEY OF THE NORTH Haldemann Julius Co., Girard, Kansas (1920). [0] Wraps. "Little Blue Book No. 1022." Cover title "A Heroic Tale of The Far North" (ref.c) $35.

001l: THE SON OF THE WOLF ... Haldemann Julius Co., Girard, Kansas (1920). [0] Wraps. "Little Blue Book No. 152" $35.

002a: THE GOD OF HIS FATHERS … McClure, Phillips, New York, 1901. [0] $1,000.

002b: THE GOD OF HIS FATHERS Isbister, London, 1902. [] $750.

002c: THE GOD OF HIS FATHERS Mills and Boon, London, 1915. [] $100.

003a: CHILDREN OF THE FROST Macmillian, New York/London, 1902. [0] Wraps. Pagination: (i-iv), (1)-263. Printed for copyright purposes $2,500.

003b: CHILDREN OF THE FROST Macmillan, New York/London, 1902. [1] 3,466 cc. "Set Up And Electrotyped September, 1902" $1000.

003c: CHILDREN OF THE FROST Macmillan, London, 1902. [] $250.

003d: CHILDREN OF THE FROST Mills & Boon, London (1915). [] 1915 (ref.a). (Boston Book Annex catalogued a copy with a 1917 copyright?) $100.

004a: THE CRUISE OF THE DAZZLER Century Co., New York, 1902. [1] "Published October, 1902" $2,000.

004b: THE CRUISE OF THE DAZZLER Hodder & Stoughton, London (1906). [] $450.

004c: THE CRUISE OF THE DAZZLER Hodder & Stoughton, London (1906). [] First English edition, Colonial issue in red cloth lettered in black. Only the binding indicates this is a colonial edition (Macdonnell Rare Books 6/96) $450.

004d: THE CRUISE OF THE DAZZLER Mills & Boon, London, 1915. [] $125.

005a: A DAUGHTER OF THE SNOWS J.B. Lippincott, Philadelphia, 1902. [1] "Published October, 1902." Another copy noted exactly the same except the words "Second Edition" added on first half title (ref.c) $750.

005b: A DAUGHTER OF THE SNOWS Isbister, London, 1904. [] $150.

006a: THE KEMPTON - WACE LETTERS Macmillan, New York/London, 1903. [1] "Set Up And Electrotyped May 1903." Anonymous, neither London's nor co-author Anna Strunsky's name appears $1,000.

006b: THE KEMPTON - WACE LETTERS Macmillan, New York/London, 1903. [] Second printing had author's names on title page $250.

006c: THE KEMPTON - WACE LETTERS Isbister, London, 1903. [] $250.

006d: THE KEMPTON - WACE LETTERS Mills and Boon, London, 1921. [] $150.

007a: THE CALL OF THE WILD Macmillan, New York/London, 1903. [0] Wraps. 2 known copies. Presumably issued to secure copyright $5,000.

007b: THE CALL OF THE WILD Macmillan, New York/London, 1903. [1] 71,584 cc. "Set Up, Electrotyped and Published July 1903." Top edge gilt in all references, but we had one without gilt, no priority. (Catalogued at $2,000 to $8,500 in dustwrapper) $1,000.

007c: THE CALL OF THE WILD Heinemann, London, 1903. [0] $500.

007d: THE CALL OF THE WILD George N. Morang, Toronto, 1903. [0] Blue green cloth. Macmillan bought Morang in 1906 and reissued the Morang 1905 sheets in binding stamped "Macmillan" at foot of spine, which may have been the first book issued by Macmillan (David Mason 10/89) $350.

007e: THE CALL OF THE WILD Limited Editions Club, New York, 1960. [2] 1,500 sgd no. cc. Illustrated and signed by Henry Varnum Poor, issued without dustwrapper. In slipcase $75/150

007f: THE CALL OF THE WILD Franklin Library, Franklin Center, 1977. [2] "Limited Edition." In full leather. One of the 100 Greatest Masterpieces... series. Illustrated by David J. Passalacqua $60.

008a: THE PEOPLE OF THE ABYSS Macmillan, New York/London, 1903. [1] 3,982 cc. "Published October, 1903" Gray-blue cloth stamped in black and gold $850.

008b: THE PEOPLE OF THE ABYSS Macmillan, New York/London, 1903. [1] Later (remainder?) issue in plain binding of dark blue cloth lettered in black on front cover and in gilt on spine; sheets trimmed (Thomas Goldwasser 12/95). Also noted a copy in dark green vertically-ribbed cloth with both covers plain, and with the title, author, two bands and small decoration in gilt on spine; 3 pages undated ads (Sumner & Stillman 10/97) $400.

008c: THE PEOPLE OF THE ABYSS Macmillan?, Toronto, 1903. [] Canadian issue from the

American sheets. Blue cloth stamped in gilt (Country Lane Books 10/95) $250.

008d: THE PEOPLE OF THE ABYSS Isbister, London, 1903. [] $250.

009a: THE FAITH OF MEN ... Macmillan, New York/London, 1904. [1] 6,802 cc. "Set Up, Electrotyped, and Published April, 1904" $600.

009b: THE FAITH OF MEN ... Heinemann, London, 1904. [] $200.

010a: THE BANKS OF THE SACRAMENTO Daily Mail Publishing Office, London, 1904. [0] Wraps. 12 leaves prepared for copyright purposes $1,500.

011a: THE TRAMP Wilshire's Magazine, New York, no date. [0] Published in 1904. Earliest issue with publisher's addresses as 125 E. 2304 St, NY. Later issue gives publisher's address as 200 Williams St., NY (not before 1905) $450.

011b: THE TRAMP Charles Kerr, Chicago, no date [circa 1904]. [] Wraps. (Maurice F. Neville List K) $200.

012a: THE SEA-WOLF Macmillan, New York / London, 1904. [0] Title-page not a cancel; copyright notices dated 1904 only. Only one copy of this state $6,000.

012b: THE SEA-WOLF Macmillan, New York / London, 1904. [1] 63,339 cc. Title page is a cancel; copyright notices dated 1903 and 1904. "Published October, 1904." Some copies stamped in gold on spine - some in white. No known priority $650.

012c: THE SEA-WOLF Heinemann, London, 1904. [0] $200.

012d: THE SEA-WOLF Limited Editions Club, Hartford, 1961. [2] 1,500 sgd and no. cc. Illustrated and signed by Fletcher Martin. Issued without dustwrapper. In slipcase $75/150

013a: THE SCAB Charles H. Kerr, Chicago, no date. [0] Wraps. Published in 1905. Reprinted from the *Atlantic Monthly*. Reprinted several times; earliest issue has publisher's address as 56 5th Ave., Chicago. Later printings have other addresses or none on title page $300.

014a: WAR OF THE CLASSES Macmillan, New York/London, 1905. [1] 2,530 cc. "Published April, 1905" $750.

014b: WAR OF THE CLASSES Macmillan, New York/London, 1905. [0] Wraps. Presumes simultaneous issue $500.

014c: WAR OF THE CLASSES Heinemann, London, 1905. [] $250.

014d: WAR OF THE CLASSES Mills & Boon, London (1905). [] Actually published in 1920 $100.

015a: THE GAME Macmillan, New York/London, 1905. [1] 26,420 cc (a & b). "Published June 1905." First issue does not have *Metropolitan Magazine* rubber stamp on copyright page. $275.

015b: THE GAME Macmillan, New York/London, 1905. [0] "Published June 1905." Rubber stamped on copyright page "Copyright, 1905, by the *Metropolitan Magazine* Co." Two forms of stamp known, no priority: 1/16" tall and 3/32" tall $175.

015c: THE GAME Heinemann, London, 1905. [] $175.

015d: THE GAME Morang & Co., Toronto, 1905. [] $150.

016a: TALES OF THE FISH PATROL Macmillan, New York/London, 1905. [1] 8,392 cc. "Published

September, 1905" . Also noted in variant binding of red cloth , with leafy designs and boy and girl pictured reading (American Book Prices Current 1994) $500.

016b: TALES OF THE FISH PATROL Heinemann, London, 1906. [] "Published September, 1905. Reprinted December, 1905, February 1906" on copyright page. Printed in U.S.A. with an English title page and sold to us as the first English edition by Robert Temple Books. BAL 118877 states the English edition was listed as February 17, 1906 (no details). Woodbridge, London, & Tweney 41 simply report the date of 1906. $300.

017a: WHITE FANG Macmillan, New York / London, 1905. [0] Gray paper wraps. "Printed for copyright purposes only" $1,500.

017b: WHITE FANG Macmillan, New York / London, 1906. [1] 48,195 cc (b & c). "Published October, 1906." Presumed earliest state with title-leaf integral. (One copy in dustwrapper catalogued at $3,500.) $500.

017c: WHITE FANG Macmillan, New York / London, 1906. [1] "Published October, 1906." Presumed later state with title leaf tipped-in $400.

017d: WHITE FANG Methuen, London, 1907. [] $125.

017e: WHITE FANG Limited Editions Club, Lunenburg, Vermont, 1973. [2] 2,000 sgd no. cc. Illustrated and signed by Lydia Dabcovich. Issued without dustwrapper. In slipcase $40/75

018a: JACK LONDON *A Sketch of His Life and Work* Macmillan, New York, 1905. [] Red printed wraps. "Jack London is known to have personally written the majority of the text in this sketch of his life..." BAL V: 465: col. 1. (Macdonnell Rare Books 8/95) $150.

019a: WHAT COMMUNITIES LOSE BY THE COMPETITIVE SYSTEM Twentieth Century Press, London, no date. [] Wraps. Published 1906 $350.

020a: CIRCULATE "THE JUNGLE" DEAR COMRADES: HERE IT IS AT LAST! Jungle Publishing Co., New York (1906). [0] Open letter urging support for Sinclair's *The Jungle*. Single leaf, 6" x 3 ½", printed on verso only $150.

020b: THE BOOKS OF UPTON SINCLAIR... Jungle Publishing Co., New York, no date. [0] Wraps. Published in 1906. Single sheet folded to 8 pages. Pale yellow paper. 6 5/16" x 4 ½". Full text of an open letter $125.

020c: A TERRIBLE BOOK...APPEAL TO REASON Girard, Kansas, no date. [0] Wraps. Single sheet folded to 6 pages. 5 7/8" x 3 7/16". Contains full text of open letter $75.

020d: THE JUNGLE... (Jungle Publishing Co., New York), no date. [0] Wraps. 1906? single sheet folded to 4 pages. 6 ¼" x 3 ½" 1st printing: Price of *The Jungle* on p.(4) given as $1.35 Extract of open letter on p.(1) $100.

020e: THE JUNGLE... (Jungle Publishing Co., New York), no date. [0] Wraps. 1906? Single sheet folded to 4 pages. 6 ¼" x 3 ½" 2nd printing: Price of *The Jungle* on p.(4) given as $1.20. Extract of open letter on p.(1) $75.

020f: A NEW EDITION OF THE JUNGLE (Pasadena, California), no date. [0] Wraps. Circa 1920. Single sheet folded to 4 pages. Brown paper. 1st printing: London's open letter on p.(4); imprint on p.(3) $40.

020g: A NEW EDITION OF THE JUNGLE (Pasadena, California), no date. [0] Wraps. Circa 1920.

Single sheet folded to 4 pages. Brown paper. 2nd printing: London's open letter on pp.(3-4); imprint on p.(4) $30.

020h: A NEW EDITION OF THE JUNGLE (Pasadena, California), no date. [0] Wraps. A Single sheet folded to 4 pages. Brown paper. 6 ¾" x 4 7/16". Full text of open letter on pp.(2-3); imprint on p.(4) $25.

020i: "THE JUNGLE IS GOING SPLENDIDLY..." Jungle Publishing Co. Princeton, New Jersey, no date. [0] Single sheet. Printed on verso only. 5 13/16" x 3 7/16" Private letter. 1st printing $25.

020j: "THE JUNGLE IS GOING SPLENDIDLY..." Jungle Publishing Co., New York, no date. [0] Single sheet printed on verso only. 5 ¾" x 3 9/16". Private letter. 2nd printing $25.

021a: MOONFACE ... Macmillan, New York / London, 1906. [1] Wraps. "Published (blank), 1906." Printed for copyright purposes. Printed tan paperwraps $1,250.

021b: MOONFACE ... Macmillan, New York / London, 1906. [1] 8,400 cc. "Published September, 1906" $500.

021c: MOONFACE ... Heinemann, London, 1906. [] $150.

021d: MOONFACE ... Regent Press, New York (1906). Actually published 1915 Reprint/reissue $50.

022a: LOVE OF LIFE ... Macmillan, New York / London, 1906. [1] Wraps. Prepared for copyright purposes only. On copyright page: "Published (blank), 1906" $1,250.

022b: LOVE OF LIFE ... Macmillan, New York / London, 1907. [1] 7,973 cc. "Published September, 1907" $350.

022c: LOVE OF LIFE … Everett & Co., London, 1908. [] $125.

022d: LOVE OF LIFE … Mills & Boon, London, 1916. [] $60.

023a: BEFORE ADAM Macmillan, London / New York, 1906. [1] Wraps. Prepared for copyright purposes. Tan paperwraps. "Published (blank), 1906" on copyright page $1,000.

023b: BEFORE ADAM Macmillan, New York / London, 1907. [1] "Published February, 1907." (One copy in dustwrapper catalogued for $3,000.) $200.

023c: BEFORE ADAM Macmillan of Canada, Toronto, 1907. [] (The Book Treasury 7/96) $125.

023d: BEFORE ADAM Werner Laurie, London (1908). [] $75.

023e: BEFORE ADAM Macmillan, New York, 1962. [1] With a biographical introduction by Willy Ley, an epilogue by Loren Eiseley, and illustrations by Leonard Fisher $15/75

024a: THE APOSTATE ... APPEAL TO REASON Girard, Kansas, 1906. [0] Wraps. Salmon colored wraps $300.

024b: THE APOSTATE... Charles H. Kerr, Chicago, no date [1906 per Macdonnell Rare Books 8/95]. [0] $75.

024c: THE APOSTATE... Haldeman-Julius Co., Girard, Kansas, no date. [0] Wraps. Published 1924? Little Blue Book No. 640 $30.

024d: HE RENOUNCED THE FAITH Appeal Publishing, Girard, Kansas, no date. [0] Wraps. Published 1920. "Appeal Pocket Series No. 47" $30.

025a: SCORN OF WOMEN Macmillan, New York / London, 1906. [1] 920 cc. "Published November, 1906." Top edges gilt. "The Macmillan Company" on spine $2,200.

025b: SCORN OF WOMEN Macmillan, New York / London, 1906. [0] "Published November, 1906." Variant binding with top edges plain; "Macmillan" on spine. Remainder binding? $1,500.

025c: SCORN OF WOMEN Macmillan, London, 1907. [0] $450.

026a: JACK LONDON HIS LIFE & LITERARY WORK Macmillan, New York, 1906. [] Wraps. Text entirely written by London (Pepper & Stern List N) $200.

027a: WHAT LIFE MEANS TO ME (Intercollegiate Socialist Society Princeton, New Jersey), no date. [0] Wraps. Published 1906. On p.(4) is imprint of Appeal to Reason Press, Girard, Kansas $400.

027b: WHAT LIFE MEANS TO ME Charles Kerr, Chicago, no date. [0] Wraps. Not issued before 1912 $175.

027c: JACK LONDON'S WHAT LIFE MEANS TO ME No publisher, San Francisco, 1916. [0] Wraps. "Memorial Edition" $150.

026d: WHAT LIFE MEANS TO ME Haldeman & Julius Co., Girard, Kansas (1924). [0] Wraps. Little Blue Book No. 30 $25.

028a: THE IRON HEEL Macmillan, New York / London, 1907. [1] Wraps. Tan paper dustwrapper printed for copyright purposes only $1,000.

028b: THE IRON HEEL Macmillan, New York / London, 1908. [1] 12,472 cc. "Published February, 1908" $500.

028c: THE IRON HEEL Appeal to Reason, Girard, Kansas, 1908. [1] "Published February, 1908." Macmillan sheets with tipped in title page and spine without Macmillan although otherwise the same $250.

028d: THE IRON HEEL Wilshire Book Co., New York, 1908. [0] $60.

028e: THE IRON HEEL Everett, London, 1908. [] $100.

028f: THE IRON HEEL Mills & Boon, London, 1916. [] $50.

029a: THE ROAD Macmillan, New York, 1907. [1] 5,360 cc (a & b). "Published November, 1907." Gray cloth stamped in gold and black. Also noted in red cloth lettered in black (American Book Prices Current 1994) $600.

029b: THE ROAD Macmillan, New York, 1907. [0] "Published November 1907." Variant binding (possible remainder) in cream cloth stamped in black only, top edges plain (Macdonnell Rare Books 7/94) $400.

029c: THE ROAD Mills & Boon, London, 1914. [] $175.

030a: MARTIN EDEN Macmillan, New York, 1908. [1] Wraps. Printed for copyright purposes only. Tan paper dustwrapper. "Published (blank), 1908" on copyright page $1,000.

030b: MARTIN EDEN M.A. Donohue Co., Chicago, 1908. [] (Ref.c) $450.

030c: MARTIN EDEN Macmillan, New York, 1909. [1] 17,309 cc. "Published September 1909" $400.

030d: MARTIN EDEN Heinemann, London, 1910. [] $125.

031a: A BRIEF EXPLANATION No publisher (Hobart, Tasmania? 1909?). [0] Wraps. Mimeographed (press release?) statement $300.

032a: REVOLUTION Charles H. Kerr, Chicago (1909). [0] Wraps. Ads on p.(32) headed: "A Socialist Success" Publisher's address: 118 Kinzie Street. Terminal ads $350.

032b: REVOLUTION Charles H. Kerr, Chicago (1909). [0] Wraps. Ads on p.(32) headed: "Pocket Library of Socialism." Publishers address in terminal ads: 118 W. Kinzie Street $300.

032c: REVOLUTION Charles H. Kerr, Chicago (1909). [] P.32 headed "Socialist Periodicals" address is "118 West Kinsie" (Kevin MacDonnell #1) $250.

032d: REVOLUTION Charles H. Kerr, Chicago (1909). [0] Wraps. Ads on p.(32) Headed: "Study Socialism" $175.

032e: REVOLUTION Charles H. Kerr, Chicago (1909). [0] Wraps. Ads on p.32 headed: "Socialist Literature" $125.

033a: GLEN ELLEN, SONOMA CO., CA... (Prison Reform League, Los Angeles, 1910.) [0] Single leaf letter printed on letterhead of Prison Reform League 8 7/16" x 5 ½" $300.

034a: LOST FACE Macmillan, New York, 1910. [1] 6,954 cc. "Published March, 1910" $450.

034b: LOST FACE Mills & Boon, London, no date [1915]. [] $100.

035a: REVOLUTION … Macmillan, New York, 1910. [1] 2,130 cc (a & b). "Published March, 1910." Maroon cloth stamped in gold and blind stamped. "The Macmillan Company" on spine. Terminal ads (priority listed as probable in BAL) $600.

035b: REVOLUTION ... Macmillan, New York, 1910. [0] "Published March 1910." Variant: brown cloth, stamped in black, "Macmillan" on spine, no ads $350.

035c: REVOLUTION ... Mills & Boon, London, 1920. [] $125.

036a: BURNING DAYLIGHT Macmillan, New York, 1910. [1] 27,108 cc (a & b). "Published October 1910." First printing: One blank leaf follows P(374); At foot of spine "Macmillan" or "The | Macmillan | Company" - no clear priority. The latter reported by Merle Johnson but no copy seen by Blanck. Blanck felt this might have been an advance printing rather than the first. (Copy in dustwrapper brought $2,200 at auction) $350.

036b: BURNING DAYLIGHT Macmillan, New York, 1910. [1] "Published October 1910." Second printing: 3 blank leaves follow p.(374); at foot of spine "Macmillan" or "The | Macmillan Company" - No clear priority $150.

036c: BURNING DAYLIGHT Heinemann, London, 1911. [] $75.

036d: BURNING DAYLIGHT Land's End... (Chicago, 1911). [0] Wraps. A synopsis and reprint of portions of novel with letter from London granting permission to publish $100.

037a: THEFT Macmillan, New York / London, 1910. [1] 990 cc. "Published November 1910." Maroon cloth sides, white cloth shelfback, top edges gilt. Variant: Olive and red cloth, front cover plain, author's name and book title in rectangular box at top of spine. Also noted in plain gray cloth, lettered in black on spine (Calif. Book auction 2/89) and yellow-tan cloth (ref.c). Also in pale lavender cloth with plain top edges and front unstamped (Robert Dagg 3/91) and "pinkish T" cloth (Waiting For Godot 9/92) $2,500.

038a: BUNCHES OF KNUCKLES (The New York Herald, Paris, 1910.) [0] Wraps. Christmas Supplement. Sunday, December 18, 1910 $350.

039a: WHEN GOD LAUGHS ... Macmillan, New York, 1911. [1] 3,758 cc. "Published January 1911" $600.

039b: THE CHINAGO ... Leslie-Judge Co., New York (1911). [] Reprints seven stories from 38a under new title $200.

039c: WHEN GOD LAUGHS ... Mills & Boon, London, 1912. [] $150.

040a: ADVENTURE Thomas Nelson & Sons, London | Edinburgh | Dublin | Leeds | New York | Leipzig | Paris (1911). [1] "First published in 1911." (February) $750.

040b: ADVENTURE Macmillan, New York, 1911. [1] 14,600 cc. "Published March 1911." Blue cloth stamped in white and Blue. Variant: red cloth stamped in white $350.

040c: ADVENTURE Mills & Boon, London, 1916. [] $100.

041a: THE CRUISE OF THE SNARK Macmillan, New York, 1911. [1] Published June 1911." A variant review copy (note with publisher's with review slip laid in) without inserted plate between pp. 270-271. "As this plate is not called for in the list of illustrations we postulate that the decision to add it was made after the earliest copies had been sent out, and thus the absence of this plate would determine the first issue of the book (Thomas A. Goldwasser 12/95) $750.

041a: THE CRUISE OF THE SNARK Macmillan, New York, 1911. [1] 4,265 cc. "Published June 1911". $650.

041c: THE CRUISE OF THE SNARK Mills & Boon, London, 1913. [] $150.

042a: THE STRENGTH OF THE STRONG Charles H. Kerr & Co., Chicago (1911). [0] First book edition (also see 060). White paperwraps printed in blue. Publisher's address is 118 West Kinzie Street, Chicago. Note: Reprints can be identified by the following - 1912 date on title, or with publisher's address as 341-349 E. Ohio Street and/or text ending on p.29 (vs. 30 in first). Also noted in reddish brown pictorial wraps, larger than blue. Unrecorded. (Macdonnell Rare Books 12/92) $125.

042b: THE STRENGTH OF THE STRONG Haldeman-Julius, Girard, Kansas, no date. [0] Wraps. Little Blue Book 148. 64 pages without title page (Watermark West 11/90) $25.

043a: SOUTH SEA TALES Macmillan, New York, 1911. [1] 4,974 cc. "Published October, 1911" $600.

043b: SOUTH SEA STORIES Heinemann, London, 1911. [] Listed, but ever published? $NVA

043c: SOUTH SEA TALES Mills & Boon, London, 1912. [] $100.

043d: SOUTH SEA TALES World, Cleveland | New York (1946). [1] "First Printing March 1946" $15/60

044a: NORTH OF BAY COUNTIES CALIFORNIA... No publisher, place or date. [0] Wraps. Circa 1911. 9 3/8" x 6 ½". Illustrated $250.

045a: JACK LONDON GLEN ELLEN SONOMA CO., CALIF.. U.S.A.... No publisher, place or date. [0] Single cut sheet folded to make 4 pages. Printed in blue on blue-gray paper. Page size 6 5/16" x 3 ½". (Directions for getting to Glen Ellen etc.) $250.

046a: THE HOUSE OF PRIDE ... Macmillan, New York, 1912. [1] 4,340 cc. "Published March 1912." Fern green cloth. Variant: Dark green cloth $600.

046b: THE HOUSE OF PRIDE ... Mills & Boon, London, 1914. [] $125.

047a: A SON OF THE SUN Doubleday, Page, Garden City, New York, 1912. [0] (Goldwasser had Macmillan) $600.

047b: A SOUVENIR CHAPTER OF ... A SON OF THE SUN Mills & Boon, London (1913). [0] Wraps. First eight pages of text $100.

047c: A SON OF THE SUN Mills & Boon, London, 1913. [] $75.

047d: THE ADVENTURES OF CAPTAIN GRIEF (World, Cleveland | New York, 1954.) [0] A reprint under a different title $10/50

048a: WONDER OF A WOMAN *A "Smoke Bellew"* Story International Magazine Co., New York (1912). [0] Wraps. The text of the magazine appearance slightly altered in the book (next entry) $300.

048b: WONDER OF A WOMAN ... (Wolf House Books, Michigan, 1975.) [] 1,000 cc. In stapled wraps (Waiting For Godot L-1) $40.

049a: SMOKE BELLEW The Century Co., New York, 1912. [1] "Published, October 1912." Blue-green pictorial cloth. Variant: in plain gray-blue cloth $350.

049b: SMOKE BELLEW Mills & Boon, London, 1913. [] $100.

050a: THE SCARLET PLAGUE Paul R. Reynolds, New York, 1912. [0] Printed blue paperwraps. Presumably printed for copyright purposes $1,000.

050b: THE SCARLET PLAGUE Macmillan, New York, 1915. [1] 5,105 cc. "Published May 1915" $450.

050c: THE SCARLET PLAGUE Mills & Boon, London, 1915. [] First English edition with 17 Jack London titles on page facing the title page (Ferret Fantasy 5/95) $100.

051a: THE DREAM OF DEBS. *A Story of Industrial Revolt. By Jack London.* Charles H. Kerr, Chicago, no date [not before 1912]. [0] Wraps. 7 ¼" x 5" Presumed first issue. Back wrappers "History of the Supreme Court ..." Inner wrappers unprinted $250.

051b: THE DREAM OF DEBS *By Jack London* Charles H. Kerr, Chicago, no date [circa 1912]. [0] Wraps. 5 13/16" x 5 1/8" Presumed second issue. Back wrapper: "Books by Jack London..." Note: Later printing(s): p.(32) has publisher's ads; outer back wrapper headed: "Study Socialism" $175.

052a: THE NIGHT-BORN.... Century Co., New York, 1913. [1] "Published February, 1913." First printing: 1 blank leaf follows p.(292); bound in polished gray-blue cloth, gold stamped on front and spine except for black stamped totem poles $300.

052b: THE NIGHT-BORN... Century Co., New York, 1913. [1] "Published February 1913." Second printing: 2 blank leaves follow p.(292); bound in unpolished blue-gray cloth, stamped in blue, totem poles blind stamped on front and spine $125.

052c: THE NIGHT-BORN... Century Co., New York, 1913. [1] "Published February 1913." Third printing: 2 blank leaves follow p.(292); binding as in first printing. Variant: 2 blank leaves follow p.(292); bound in light gray cloth, blind stamped totem poles on front cover and with letters on front cover, spine printed in black (ref.c) $60.

052d: THE NIGHT-BORN... Mills & Boon, London, 1916. [] $75.

052e: THE NIGHT BORN Thomas Nelson and Sons, Paris, no date [but prior to 1920]. [] Wraps. Issued as publication No. 35 of "Nelson's Continental Library." Issued in lurid pictorial dustwrapper. Nelson's Colonial Library, set up to fill the vacuum left by Tauschnitz's alienation during World War I, had issued 82 titles in this series by 1919. (Wm. Reese 1/97) $75.

053a: HOW WILL YOUR VOTE EFFECT THIS BOY? No publisher (Fresno, California, 1913). [0] Wraps. Single sheet folded to make 4 pages, 8 ½" x 5 ½" $300.

054a: THE VALLEY OF THE MOON New York, 1913. [0] Reprinted from *Cosmopolitan Magazine* for April. Wraps. First installment of novel, not located by BAL $500.

054b: THE VALLEY OF THE MOON Macmillan, New York, 1913. [1] 23,779 cc. "Published October 1913" $250.

054c: THE VALLEY OF THE MOON Mills & Boon, London, 1914. [1] Primary binding is blue-green cloth lettered in gilt, with 32 pages of "Autumn Announcements" ads dated "13/1083." First edition states "Published 1914" (Glyn's Books 9/91). Later copies bound in blue cloth lettered in black, with later ads (Sumner & Stillman 10/97). Reprints read "Published in 1914" (Robert Temple 11/91) $100.

054d: THE VALLEY OF THE MOON (Publisher?), Santa Barbara, 1975. [] $35.

055a: THE ABYSMAL BRUTE The Century Co., New York, 1913. [1] "Published May 1913." Smooth olive-green cloth stamped in black (deep-green?) and yellow. (This title appears regularly in dustwrapper, from $600 at auction to $1,500 in catalogues) $250.

055b: THE ABYSMAL BRUTE The Century Co., New York, 1913. [0] Variant binding in rough green cloth stamped in black and green $200.

056a: JOHN BARLEYCORN The Century Co., New York, 1913. [1] "Published August, 1913." First printing: 1 blank leaf follows p.(343). Also noted with 2 blank leaves in front and 2 in back (Greg Brumfield) $200.

056b: JOHN BARLEYCORN The Century Co., New York, 1913. [0] "Published August, 1913." Second printing: 3 blank leaves follow p.(343) $100.

056c: JOHN BARLEYCORN Mills & Boon, London, 1914. [] Advance copy in dark brown wraps. "Will be published in July" (Ferret Fantasy 6/93) $400.

056d: JOHN BARLEYCORN Mills & Boon, London (1914). [] $75.

057a: JACK LONDON BY HIMSELF... Macmillan, New York, no date. [0] Printed self-wrapper. Published 1913. Cover title printed black and red 7 ¼" x 5 5/16" [Also noted: *Jack London as Seen by Himself* Macmillan, New York (1913). [] 6 leaves (Macdonnell Rare Books 7/94)] $200.

057b: JACK LONDON BY HIMSELF Mills & Boon, London, 1913. [] Wraps. Primarily promotes *The Valley of the Moon.* Later printing primarily promotes *The Mutiny of the Elsinore* $100.

057c: JACK LONDON: THE AUTHOR WITH SALES Mills & Boon, London no date [circa 1915]. [] 8 stapled pages recycling material from a & b above (Waiting for Godot 10/89) $75.

058a: JACK LONDON SAYS (Hellier Denslow Studio, London, 1913.) [0] Wraps. Single leaf folded to make 4 pages. Page size: 5 7/16" x 3 11/16". Issued as an advertisement. Includes comments on bookplate design $200.

059a: A LETTER FROM JACK LONDON Glen Ellen | Sonoma County, California | April 15, 1913. No publisher, place or date. [0] 1913? Single cut sheet. 8 3/16" x 7 1/8". Testimonial for an antiseptic $100.

060a: THE STRENGTH OF THE STRONG Macmillan, New York, 1914. [1] 3,948 cc. "Published May 1914." Also see 041 $600.

060b: THE STRENGTH OF THE STRONG Mills & Boon, London, no date [1917]. [0] $125.

061a: THE GOOD SOLDIER No publisher, place or date. [circa 1914?] [] Broadside urging young men not to enlist. London denied authorship (Waiting For Godot 4/89) $200.

062a: THE MUTINY OF THE ELSINORE Macmillan, New York, 1914. [1] 16,884 cc. "Published September, 1914." Also noted with front board unstamped (Katie Books 11/91) $450.

062b: THE MUTINY OF THE ELSINORE Mills & Boon, London (1915). [0] On verso of title page: "Published 1915." Noted with 4 pp. of integral advertisements, followed by publisher's 32-pages of inserted ads at end coded "14/2649" and including their summer 1914 announcements. Bound in dull dark green beaded linen-grain cloth, ruled in blind on front cover and lettered in gilt on spine; fore edges mainly trimmed; lower edges rough trimmed (Robert Temple 12/95). Also noted: First English edition, Colonial issue with "Colonial Library" ink stamped on title page under publisher's imprint, the only apparent indication the book was intended for the colonies. (Sumner & Stillman 1/95) $150.

062c: THE MUTINY OF THE ELSINORE Nelson, London, 1916. [] $50.

THE SCARLET PLAGUE see 1912 entry (item 050)

063a: THE JACKET (THE STAR ROVER) Mills & Boon, London (1915). [1] "Published 1915." First issue with color frontispiece (Pepper & Stern 9/94) Blue-green cloth, spine stamped in gilt $350.

063b: JACK LONDON : THE AUTHOR WITH THE SALES Mills & Boon Ltd., London, 1915. [] 8 pages. Illustrated with photographs $125.

063c: THE STAR ROVER Macmillan (New York, 1915). [] Wraps. Prospectus. 8 page booklet (Bert Babcock 6/89) $125.

063d: A NEW IDEA IN FICTION: THE STAR ROVER Macmillan, New York, no date [1915]. [] Pictorial wraps (London photo). 4 pages. Sketch of London's life with blurbs on 28 of his books (Joseph the Provider 3/89) $125.

063e: THE STAR ROVER Macmillan, New York, 1915. [1] 13,021 cc. "Published October, 1915." (Copy in dustwrapper catalogued for $3,000) $400.

063f: THE STAR ROVER AUTOBIOGRAPHICAL INTRO Macmillan/Collier: Macmillan, New York/London (1963). [] Same as *Jack London By Himself* (057) $40.

064a: THE ACORN-PLANTER Macmillan, New York, 1916. [1] 1,350 cc. "Published February, 1916." Three forms of binding, no known priority. $1,500.

Spine lettered: THE | ACORN | PLANTER | JACK | LONDON | The | Macmillan | Company. Top edges gilt

Spine lettered: THE | ACORN | PLANTER | JACK | LONDON Top edges gilt (publisher's spine imprint worn away?)

Spine lettered: THE | ACORN | PLANTER | (3 dots) | JACK | LONDON | The | Macmillan | Company. Top edges gilt

064b: THE ACORN-PLANTER Mills & Boon, London (1916). [] $500.

065a: THE RESIGNATION OF JACK LONDON DEAR COMRADES No publisher, place or date. [0] Single cut sheet. 1916. 11" x 8 ½" printed in imitation of typewritten letter. (Text of his resignation from Socialist Party) $200.

066a: THE LITTLE LADY OF THE BIG HOUSE Macmillan, New York, 1916. [1] 18,448 cc. "Published April 1916." Variant: Copyright notices read "Copyright 1915 | by Jack London | copyright, 1916 | by Jack London." BAL also notes a "variant" with 1915 on title page. This would seem to us to be an advance copy and would be worth considerably more than the 1916 $250.

066b: THE LITTLE LADY OF THE BIG HOUSE Mills & Boon, London (1916). [] $100.

066c: THE LITTLE LADY OF THE BIG HOUSE Nelson, London, 1916. [] $50.

066d: THE LITTLE LADY OF THE BIG HOUSE Thomas Nelson and Sons, Paris, no date [but prior to 1920]. [] Wraps. Issued as publication No. 29 of "Nelson's Continental Library." Issued in lurid pictorial dustwrapper. Nelson's Colonial Library, set up to fill the vacuum left by Tauschnitz's alienation during World War I, had issued 82 titles in this series by 1919. (Wm. Reese 1/97) $75.

067a: AN OLD LIE FINALLY NAILED No publisher, place or date. [0] Wraps. Published 1916. Single sheet folded to make 4 pages 7 1/16" x 4" $200.

068a: THE TURTLES OF TASMAN Macmillan, New York, 1916. [1] 5,914 cc. "Published September, 1916." Also noted in variant binding with palm tree in blue and spine background to the illustration in yellow (American Book Prices Current 1994) $500.

068b: THE TURTLES OF TASMAN Mills & Boon, London (1916). [] $150.

069a: THE HUMAN DRIFT Macmillan, New York, 1917. [1] 3,056 cc. "Published, February, 1917." Red-brown cloth stamped on spine and front. Eight pages of publisher's advertisements at end. Also in reddish-brown cloth stamped in gold on spine but with blank front cover (Robert Dagg 3/91). Ref.a notes a variant in smooth red linen stamped on spine only but in black. Also noted, a copy in the primary binding, with rubber-stamp signature of London on front flyleaf. London died on November 22, 1916, and *The Human Drift* was the first book published after London's death, perhaps accounting for the presence of the rubber-stamp signature which has been noted on at least one other copy. (Waiting For Godot Books 8/95) $650.

069b: THE HUMAN DRIFT Mills & Boon, London (1919). [] $200.

070a: JERRY *Jack London's Last Great Story* (*Cosmopolitan Magazine*, no place, Feb. 1917.) [] 8 pages in stapled wraps. First separate appearance of the first installment of *Jerry of The Islands*, which was serialized from January to April 1917 (Waiting For Godot 2/90) $200.

071a: JERRY OF THE ISLANDS Macmillan, New York, 1917. [1] 13,024 cc. "Published, April, 1917." (Two copies in dustwrapper catalogued 1990-92 at $600 and $970) $250.

071b: JERRY OF THE ISLANDS Mills & Boon, London (1917). [0] On verso of title page: "Published 1917." Copies bearing the legend "First published in 1917" are reprints, dating from a later year. Bound in light crimson, faint vertical-rib cloth lettered in black on front cover and spine; fore- and lower-edges rough trimmed; 4 pp. of integral ads at end (Robert Temple 12/95) $75.

071c: JERRY OF THE ISLANDS Thomas Nelson and Sons, Paris, no date [but prior to 1920]. [] Wraps. Issued as publication No. 53 of "Nelson's Continental Library." Issued in lurid pictorial dustwrapper. Nelson's Colonial Library, set up to fill the vacuum left by Tauschnitz's alienation during World War I, had issued 82 titles in this series by 1919. (Wm. Reese 1/97) $50.

072a: MICHAEL BROTHER OF JERRY Macmillan, New York, 1917. [1] 10,320 cc. "Published, November, 1917." $250.

073a: EIGHT GREAT FACTORS OF LITERARY SUCCESS No publisher, place or date. [0] Single cut sheet. 8 7/16" x 6". Printed on recto only. Published 1917. Includes a holograph facsimile signature of London $250.

074a: THE RED ONE Macmillan, New York, 1918. [1] 5,342 cc. "Published, October, 1918." [Four copies in dustwrapper catalogued (1993-1996) for $2,250, $3,500 (2), and $4,200 (auction)] $750.

074b: THE RED ONE Mills & Boon, London (1919). [] $250.

074c: THE RED ONE Thomas Nelson and Sons, Paris, no date [but prior to 1920]. [] Wraps. Issued as publication No. 80 of "Nelson's Continental Library." Issued in lurid pictorial dustwrapper. Nelson's Colonial Library, set up to fill the vacuum left by Tauschnitz's alienation during World War I, had issued 82 titles in this series by 1919. (Wm. Reese 1/97) $75.

075a: HEARTS OF THREE Mills & Boon, London, no date. [] Published 1918. Note: Later printing on p.(iv) under "Books by Jack London" lists *Island Tales* $750.

075b: HEARTS OF THREE Macmillan, New York, 1920. [0] 4,990 cc. "Published, September, 1920" $500.

075c: HEARTS OF THREE Macmillan, New York, 1928. [] ("The Sonoma Edition." Reprint) (Alphabet Bookshop, Cat. 18) $60.

076a: ON THE MAKALOA MAT Macmillan, New York, 1919. [1] 4,972 cc. "Published, September 1919" $400/2,000

076b: ISLAND TALES Mills & Boon, London (1920). [0] "Published 1920" $75/400

077a: SMOKE AND SHORTY Mills & Boon, London (1920). [1] "Published 1920" $200/750

078a: HE RENOUNCED THE FAITH Appeal to Reason, no date. [0] Wraps. "People's Pocket Series No. 47." Published 1920 $150.

079a: BROWN WOLF AND OTHER STORIES.. Macmillan, New York, 1920. [0] $250/1,000

080a: TALES OF THE FAR NORTH Haldeman-Julius, Girard, Kansas (1920). [0] Wraps. "Little Blue Book No. 288." There is a second? printing (issue?) without date on copyright page; in plain covers. There is a third? printing (issue?) without date on copyright page in illustrated wraps (Watermark West 11/96) $40.

081a: DUTCH COURAGE ... Macmillan, New York, 1922. [1] 4,348 cc. "Published September 1922" $500/2,500

081b: DUTCH COURAGE … Mills & Boon, London (1923). [] $200/1,000

082a: STORIES OF SHIPS AND THE SEA Haldeman & Julius Co., Girard, Kansas (1922). [0] Wraps. Little Blue Book No. 1169 (cover title *Tales of Ships and Seas* ref.c). Printed blue paperwraps. Earliest printing has date "1922" present in copyright notice. Date absent in later printing(s). All stories are also in *Dutch Courage* …, priority unknown $75.

083a: TALES OF THE WHITE SILENCE Haldeman-Julius, Girard, Kansas, no date. [0] Wraps. Little Blue Book No. 1024." Cover title is: *Tales of the Big Snows.* Published 1926? $40.

084a: THE WIFE OF A KING Haldeman-Julius, Girard, Kansas, no date. [0] Wraps. "Little Blue Book No. 233." Published 1926? $40.

085a: THE CALL OF THE WILD … Macmillan, New York, 1926. [0] Leather shelfback $25/125

085b: THE CALL OF THE WILD … Dodd, Mead, New York (1960). [] $10/50

085c: THE CALL OF THE WILD, THE CRUISE OF THE DAZZLER … Platt & Munk, New York (1960). [] $12/60

086a: LONDON'S ESSAYS OF REVOLT Vanguard, New York, 1926. [0] Edited and introduction by Leonard D. Abbott. First thus. Includes *Apostate*, *Dream of Debs*, *How I Became A Socialist, What Life Means To Me*, *The Scab* and *Revolution* $100/500

087a: STORIES OF ADVENTURE Haldeman-Julius, Girard, Kansas, no date. [0] Wraps. "Little Blue Book NO. 1168." Published 1927? $40.

088a: SELECTED STORIES OF JACK LONDON World Syndicate | Three Pay Sales | New York | Cleveland, 1930. [] Two volumes. Red cloth, in dustwrappers (Boston Book Company); BAL 12019-wraps $40/200

088b: SELECTED STORIES OF JACK LONDON World Publ | Leslie Publ | Cleveland | Boston, 1930. [] In tissue and printed dustwrapper. No publisher but has "NY | 1933" on spine (Joseph The Provider 3/88). Also noted in unprinted brown paper dustwrapper and printed dustwrapper with "1933" on spine (Beasley Books 2/90) $25/125

089a: THE SEA SPRITE AND THE SHOOTING STAR. (Privately Published, no place, 1932.) [0] 35 cc (per American Book Prices Current 1994). Single cut sheet folded to make 4 pages. 10 ¾" x 5 ¾" cream-white paper $200.

090a: THE LETTERS OF WESTERN AUTHORS NUMBER 12 December 1935. Jack London with comment by Charmian Kittredge London Book Club of California (San Francisco, 1935). [0] Wraps. Single cut sheet folded to 4 pages. 9 15/16" x 8 ¼". Pasted to p.(3) is envelope containing a facsimile Jack London letter printed on sleeves $75.

091a: CHAPTER V OF *THE IRON HEEL*... Socialist Labor Party of Australia, Sydney, 1936. [] Wraps. First separate edition $150.

092a: JACK LONDON'S STORIES FOR BOYS Cupples & Leon, New York (1936). [] Also noted a possible later issue in red cloth with seven titles listed on rear panel of dustwrapper (Alphabet Bookshop 3/97) $25/100

093a: BEST SHORT STORIES OF JACK LONDON Sun Dial Press, Garden City, New York (1945). [] $15/60

094a: LOVE OF LIFE ... Paul Gleck, London (1946). [0] Introduction by George Orwell. "1946 | Catalogue No. 159/9" on copyright page (ref.c) $35/175

095a: THE SCARLET PLAGUE, LOVE OF LIFE, THE UNEXPECTED Staples Press Ltd., London, 1946. [] First edition of this collection (Alphabet Bookshop 3/97) $25/75

096a: JACK LONDON AMERICAN REBEL Citadel Press, New York, 1947. [0] Contains first book appearance of some of the essays (ref.c) $25/100

097a: FOUR SHORT STORIES Longmans Green, London/New York/Toronto (1949). [] Wraps $40.

098a: THE SUN-DOG TRAIL ... World Cleveland / New York (1951). [1] $15/75

099a: JACK LONDON'S TALES OF ADVENTURE Hanover House, Garden City (1956). [] (Waiting For Godot Cat. 15) $15/75

100a: SHORT STORIES Hill & Wang, New York (1960). [] Wraps $25.

101a: THE BODLEY HEAD JACK LONDON The Bodley Head, London (1963). [] $15/75

102a: WHITE FANG ... Dodd, Mead, New York (1963). [] $12/60

103a: THE ASSASSINATION BUREAU, LTD. McGraw-Hill, New York/Toronto/London (1963). [] Galley in loose sheets, ring bound in plain boards (William Reese Co. 11/91) $400.

103b: THE ASSASSINATION BUREAU, LTD. McGraw-Hill, New York/Toronto/London (1963). [1] 2,500 cc $25/100

103c: THE ASSASSINATION BUREAU, LTD. McGraw-Hill, New York/Toronto/London (1963). [1] 10,000 cc. Wraps $35.

103d: THE ASSASSINATION BUREAU, LTD. Deutsch, London (1964). [] (Maurice Neville List Q) $15/75

104a: THE SEA-WOLF SELECTED STORIES New American Library (New York, 1964). [1] Wraps $25.

105a: STORIES OF HAWAII Appleton-Century, New York (1965). [1] $15/75

106a: LETTERS FROM JACK LONDON CONTAINING AN UNPUBLISHED CORRESPONDENCE BETWEEN LONDON AND SINCLAIR LEWIS... Odyssey Press, New York (1965). [0] $15/75

106b: LETTERS FROM JACK LONDON ... Macgibbon & Kee, London, 1966. [] Edited by Ring Hendricks and Irving Shepard (Peter Ellis 12/89) $15/75

107a: GREAT SHORT WORKS Harper & Row, New York (1965). [] $10/50

108a: TO BUILD A FIRE Evelyn Woods Reading Dynamics (no place, 1966). [] Wraps. (Waiting For Godot Cat L-1) $35.

108b: TO BUILD A FIRE (Tales For Travelers, Napa, California, 1986.) [] Single sheet folded map style (Boston Book Annex Cat. 31) $35.

109a: JACK LONDON REPORTS Doubleday, Garden City, New York, 1970. [1] 4,109 cc. Edited by Ring Hendricks and Irving Shepard (ref.b) $15/75

110a: DAUGHTERS OF THE RICH Holmes Book Co., Oakland, 1971. [1] 1,000 cc (Pepper & Stern) $35/100

110b: DAUGHTERS OF THE RICH Holmes Book Co., Oakland, 1971. [1] 2,900 cc. Wraps (ref.b) $50.

111a: JACK LONDON'S ARTICLES AND SHORT STORIES IN THE (OAKLAND) HIGH SCHOOL REGIS THE LONDON COLLECTOR Cedar Springs, 1971. [1] 300 cc. Wraps. Issued as "The London Collector No. 3." Errata slip attached to Front page of first printing (ref.b) $60.

112a: GOLD *A Play in Three Acts* Holmes Book Co., Oakland, 1972. [1] 1,000 cc. Written with Herbert Heron (ref.b) $20/50

112b: GOLD Holmes Book Co., Oakland, 1973. [2] 100 cc. "Illustrated Limited Issue" (ref.c) $225.

113a: JACK LONDON AT YALE (Wolf House Books, Michigan, 1972.) [] Facsimile of 1906 edition. 28 pages in stapled wraps (Waiting For Godot L-1) $40.

114a: GOLIAH *A Utopian Essay* Thorp Springs Press (Berkeley, California) no date [but 1974]. [] Pictorial wraps. First separate edition. First published in *Red Magazine* and later collected in London's *Revolution And Other Essays*. Edited by Dale L. Walker. Preface by Philip Jose Farmer (Watermark West Cat. 8 gave date of 1973) $40.

115a: CURIOUS FRAGMENTS... Kennkat Press, Port Washington, 1975. [] (Pepper & Stern List M) $40.

116a: THE SCIENCE FICTION OF JACK LONDON Gregg Press, Boston, 1975. [0] 400 cc. Issued without dustwrapper (L.W. Currey 8/92) $75.

117a: DEAR MATE (Holmes Book Co., Oakland, 1976.) [2] 300 cc. Wraps. London's inscriptions to Charmian in his books $75.

118a: SELECTED SCIENCE FICTION & FANTASY STORIES Fictioneer Books (Lakemont, Georgia, 1978). [0] about 1,500 cc (L.W. Currey 1/93). Annotated by Dick Weiderman, illustrated by Philip Craig Russell (ref.c) $15/50

119a: JACK LONDON ON THE ROAD: THE TRAMP DIARY … Utah State University Press, Logan, Utah (1979). [] (Waiting For Godot L-1) $10/50

120a: NO MENTOR BUT MYSELF A COLLECTION OF ARTICLES, ESSAYS, REVIEWS ... Kennikat Press, Port Washington, 1979. [] Edited by Dale L. Walker $15/75

121a: IF JAPAN WAKENS CHINA Modern Times, Takoma, 1979. [] Wraps (Maurice F. Neville List K) $40.

122a: SPORTING BLOOD Presidio Press (Novato, California, 1981). [0] Selections of London's sports writings edited by Howard Lachtman (ref.c) $10/40

123a: DEAREST GREEK Eureka Publ., Cupertino, California (1983). [] 500 cc. In stapled wraps. Jack and Charmian's presentation inscriptions to George Sterling. Edited and introduction by Stanley Wertheim and Sal Noto (Waiting For Godot L-1) $40.

124a: LEARNING HAWAIIAN SURFING Boom Enterprises, Hawaii, 1983. [] Wraps. "Hawaiian Memorial Edition" (Waiting For Godot L-1) $40.

125a: A KLONDIKE TRILOGY ... Neville, Santa Barbara, 1983. [2] 26 ltr cc. Bound in full leather with autographed check of Jack London tipped-in $750.

125b: A KLONDIKE TRILOGY ... Neville, Santa Barbara, 1983. [2] 300 cc. Issued without dustwrapper $75.

126a: TOLD IN THE DROOLING WARD Jack London Research Center, Glen Ellen, California,

1984. [2] 1,000 signed cc. Wraps. Signed by the editor (Waiting For Godot) $35.

127a: FIVE POEMS Quintessence Publications (Amador City), 1984. [2] 250 cc. Wraps. (Maurice Neville List Q) $60.

128a: YOUNG WOLF *The Early Adventure Stories of Jack London* Capra Press, Santa Barbara (1984). [] Uncorrected proof in blue printed wraps, thin folio, pages printed on one side only (Heritage Book Shop 9/95) $50.

129a: THE OCTOPUS (Roxburghe and Zamorono Clubs), Orinda, California (1986). [2] 150 cc. Wraps $50.

130a: WITH A HEART FULL OF LOVE... Two Windows Press, Berkeley, California (1986). [2] 351 sgd no. cc. Signed by the publisher. Issued without dustwrapper (Pepper & Stern List U) $85.

131a: JACK LONDON'S CALIFORNIA *The Golden Poppy …* Beaufort Books, New York (1986). [] (Beasley Books Cat. 36) $10/40

132a: IN FAR COUNTRY... Jameson Books, Ottawa, Illinois, 1986. [] (Beasley Books Cat. 36) $10/40

133a: THE LETTERS OF JACK LONDON Volume One: 1896-1905 [Volume Two: 1906-1912] [Volume Three: 1913-1916] Stanford University Press, Stanford, 1988. [] Advance proofs in three spiral bound volumes (James Dourgarian 5/90) $150.

133b: THE LETTERS OF JACK LONDON Volume One: 1896-1905 Stanford University Press, Stanford, 1988. [] Edited by E. Labor, R.C. Leitz and I.M. Shepard $6/30

133c: THE LETTERS OF JACK LONDON Volume Two: 1906-1912 Stanford University Press,

Stanford, 1988. [] Edited by E. Labor, R.C. Leitz and I.M. Shepard (Wessex Books 7/97) $6/30

133d: THE LETTERS OF JACK LONDON Volume Three: 1913-1916 Stanford University Press, Stanford, 1988. [] Edited by E. Labor, R.C. Leitz and I.M. Shepard (Wessex Books 7/97) $6/30

133e: THE LETTERS OF JACK LONDON Volume One: 1896-1905. Volume Two: 1906-1912. Volume Three: 1913-1916. Stanford University Press, Stanford, 1988. []"Deluxe Edition." Three volumes in slipcase. Published @ $199.50 (Wessex Books 7/97) $100.

134a: TO BUILD A FIRE and THE MEXICAN Engdahl Typography, Vineland, California, 1989. [2] 200 sgd cc. Signed by Lee Engdahl, printer $60.

135a: THE JACK LONDON CREDO Quintessence Press, Amador City, 1991. [2] 200 cc. Illustrated broadside (Chloe's Books 12/91) $30.

136a: STORIES OF BOXING William Brown, Iowa, 1992. [] Edited by James Bankes; Preface by Becky London; Forward by Russ Kingman $10/30

137a: THE COMPLETE STORIES OF JACK LONDON Stanford University Press, Stanford, 1993. [] 3 vols. (Eric Stevens 9/95) $165

ROBERT LUDLUM

Ludlum was born in New York City in 1927. He served in the Marine Corps from 1945 to 1947. In 1951 he graduated from Wesleyan University. Ludlum acted on the stage and television, as well as producing stage plays through 1969 when he took up writing full-time. He also writes as Jonathan Ryder and Michael Shepherd.

001a: THE SCARLATTI INHERITANCE World, New York (1971). [1] Printed acetate dustwrapper. (The Book-of-the-Month Club edition states "First..." It has a blind stamp on back cover right corner but it is easy to overlook.) First has "A3696" on back of dustwapper and Book Club has "0360" on back. Also text on first dustwrapper starts 1/4 inch from top of front flap while Book Club starts 3/4 inch from the top (Allan Asselstine) $50/250

001b: THE SCARLATTI INHERITANCE Hart Davis, London (1971). [] Also noted in trial dustwrapper announcing the approximate publication date of June 1971 (Nicholas Pounder 8/95). However, the only copy we've handled had the same dustwrapper $25/125

001c: THE SCARLATTI INHERITANCE Armchair Detective, New York, 1991. [2] 26 sgd ltr cc. Issued without dustwrapper. In slipcase $175.

001d: THE SCARLATTI INHERITANCE Armchair Detective, New York, 1991. [2] 100 sgd no. cc. Issued without dustwrapper. In slipcase $100.

001e: THE SCARLATTI INHERITANCE Armchair Detective, New York, 1991. [] Trade edition in dustwrapper. $5/25

002a: THE OSTERMAN WEEKEND World, New York (1972). [1] Printed acetate dustwrapper, priced $6.95 with "A 3918" on bottom right corner of back panel. Also noted "First Printing" copies with "7452" where price should be and same number (A 3918) on back; and "First Printing" copies with no price and "7452" at bottom right corner of back panel of dustwrapper. The latter two editions do not have Book-of-the-Month dots but the covers of the book are smoother and lighter blue than the true first. $40/200

002b: THE OSTERMAN WEEKEND Hart Davis, London, 1972. [] $20/100

002c: THE OSTERMAN WEEKEND Armchair Detective Library, New York, 1990. [2] 26 ltr cc. Issued without dustwrapper. In slipcase (Pepper & Stern 11/94) $150.

002d: THE OSTERMAN WEEKEND Armchair Detective, New York, 1991. [2] 100 sgd no. cc. Issued without dustwrapper. In slipcase $85.

002e: THE OSTERMAN WEEKEND Armchair Detective, New York, 1991. [] Trade edition. In dustwrapper $5/25

003a: THE MATLOCK PAPER Dial Press, New York, 1973. [1] $25/125

003b: THE MATLOCK PAPER Hart Davis MacGibbon, London (1973). [1] $15/75

004a: TREVAYNE Delacorte, New York (1973). [1] Written as Jonathan Ryder $35/175

004b: TREVAYNE Weidenfeld & Nicolson, London (1974). [1] Dark blue cloth with gold lettering on spine $25/125

004c: TREVAYNE Bantam, New York (1989). [0] Wraps. First under his name $25.

005a: THE CRY OF THE HALIDON Delacorte, New York (1974). [1] Written under the name Jonathan Ryder $25/125

005b: THE CRY OF THE HALIDON Weidenfeld & Nicolson, London, 1974. [] Written under the name Jonathan Ryder $15/75

006a: THE RHINEMANN EXCHANGE Dial Press, New York, 1974. [1] $20/100

006b: THE RHINEMANN EXCHANGE Hart Davis MacGibbon, London, 1975. [] $12/60

007a: THE ROAD TO GANDOLFO Dial Press, New York, 1975. [1] Written as Michael Shepherd. Generally seen with three dustwrappers designed by Tom Upshur (blue), Jack Ribik (dark blue), and David Holzman (purple-plum). The latter seems more common to us, but have no idea of priority.

One dustwrapper: $15/60
Two dustwrappers: $15/75
Three dustwrappers: $15/125

007b: THE ROAD TO GANDOLFO Hart Davis MacGibbon, London, 1976. [] $15/75

008a: THE GEMINI CONTENDERS Dial Press, New York, 1976. [1] $15/75

008b: THE GEMINI CONTENDERS Hart Davis MacGibbon, London, 1976. [] $12/60

009a: THE CHANCELLOR MANUSCRIPT Dial Press, New York, 1977. [] Uncorrected proof in brown printed wraps (Bev Chaney 2/89) $125.

009b: THE CHANCELLOR MANUSCRIPT Dial Press, New York, 1977. [1] $12/60

009c: THE CHANCELLOR MANUSCRIPT Hart Davis MacGibbon, London (1977) [] $10/50

010a: THE HOLCROFT COVENANT Marek, New York (1978). [] Uncorrected proof in green wraps $75.

010b: THE HOLCROFT COVENANT Marek, New York (1978). [1] $12/60

010c: THE HOLCROFT COVENANT Hart Davis, Granada / MacGibbon, London, 1978 [] $10/50

011a: THE MATARESE CIRCLE Marek, New York (1979). [1] $10/50

011b: THE MATARESE CIRCLE Granada, London, 1979 [] $8/40

012a: THE BOURNE IDENTITY Marek, New York (1980). [0] One of an undisclosed number of copies signed by the author on a tipped-in leaf (Loblolly Books 9/96) $75/125

012b: THE BOURNE IDENTITY Marek, New York (1980). [0] $10/50

012c: THE BOURNE IDENTITY Granada, London, 1980. [1] "Published by ... 1980" $8/40

013a: ROBERT LUDLUM (OMNIBUS) Heinemann / Octopus, New York, 1981. [1] includes *The Scarlatti Inheritance, The Osterman Weekend, The Matlock Paper* and *The Gemini Contenders* $25/75

014a: THE PARSIFAL MOSAIC Random House, New York (1982). [4] Signed tipped in sheet $75/125

014b: THE PARSIFAL MOSAIC Random House, New York (1982). [4] $10/50

014c: THE PARSIFAL MOSAIC Granada, London (1982). [1] "Published by Granada Publishing 1982" $8/40

015a: VIEWPOINT: UNRAVELING THE MYSTERIES OF TRAVELS American Express Member Only Newsletter For October 1982. [0] Wraps. Front page and part of last page (of 4 pages). For the completist $30.

016a: THE AQUITAINE PROGRESSION Random House, New York (1984). [4] $10/50

016b: THE AQUITAINE PROGRESSION Granada, London (1984). [1] "Published by Granada ... 1984" $10/40

017a: THE ROBERT LUDLUM SAMPLER (Bantam, New York, 1984.) [3] Wraps. No title page. Excerpts from nine novels. Short note to the reader from Ludlum on first page $15.

018a: THE BOURNE SUPREMACY Random House, New York (1986). [] Uncorrected proof in yellow wraps (Waverley Books 4/89) $75.

018b: THE BOURNE SUPREMACY Franklin Press, Franklin Center, 1986. [2] "Limited Signed Edition." Full leather with special message $75.

018c: THE BOURNE SUPREMACY Random House, New York (1986). [4] $10/45

018d: THE BOURNE SUPREMACY Grafton, London (1986). [1] "Published by Grafton ... 1986" $8/40

019a: THE ICARUS AGENDA Random House, New York (1988). [] Uncorrected proof in yellow wraps (Waverley Books 3/89) $60.

019b: THE ICARUS AGENDA Random House, New York (1988). [4] One of an undisclosed number of copies signed by the author on a tipped-in leaf (Loblolly Books 9/96) $75/100

019c: THE ICARUS AGENDA Random House, New York (1988). [4] 500,000 cc (PW). (Published 3/88 @ $19.95) $7/35

019d: THE ICARUS AGENDA Grafton, London, 1988. [] (Reading Matters 3/95) $7/35

020a: THE LUDLUM TRIAD Random House, New York (1989). [4] Includes *The Holcroft Covenant, The Matarese Circle* and *The Bourne Identity* $15/45

021a: THE BOURNE ULTIMATUM Random House, New York, 1990. [] Uncorrected proof in yellow wraps (Waverley Books 3/90) $60.

021b: THE BOURNE ULTIMATUM Random House, New York, 1990. [2] 350 sgd no. cc. Issued without dustwrapper. In slipcase $75/125

021c: THE BOURNE ULTIMATUM Random House, New York, 1990. [] $6/30

022a: THE ROAD TO OMAHA Harper Collins, London, 1991 [] (Cornstalk Bookshop 10/97) $8/40

022b: THE ROAD TO OMAHA Random House, New York (1992). [4] $5/25

023a: THE SCORPIO ILLUSION Bantam, New York (1993). [] (Published 6/93 @ $23.95) $5/25

023b: THE SCORPIO ILLUSION Harper Collins, London, 1993. [] (Cornstalk Bookshop 8/95) $6/30

024a: THE APOCALYPSE WATCH Bantam, New York, 1995. [] (Nouveau Rare Books 11/96) $5/25

024b: THE APOCALYPSE WATCH Harper Collins, London, 1995. [] (Christine Kovach 10/97) $7/35

025a: MATARESE COUNTDOWN Bantam Books, New York (1997). [3] Published @ $27.50

NORMAN MAILER

Norman Mailer was born in Long Branch, New Jersey on January 31, 1923. He obtained an engineering degree from Harvard University in 1943; and attended the Sorbonne in Paris in 1947. He served in the Army in W.W.II (1944 to 1946). As well as writing, he was the Co-Editor of *Dissent* magazine from 1952 to 1963 (and is still a contributing editor); and Co-Founding Editor of the *Village Voice*. Mailer ran for mayor of New York City in 1969. He won a Pulitzer Prize and National Book Award for non-fiction with *The Armies of The Night* in 1969; and a Pulitzer in fiction for *The Executioner's Song* in 1980.

There is much more that could be said about the man so many expected would write the "Great American Novel;" but most of this man's accomplishments and failures have been highlighted by either himself or the press; probably highlighted more than any other writer of the second half of this century.

The bulk of the bibliographical information furnished herein was provided by J. Michael Lennon, Director and Professor of English and Vice-President for Academic Affairs at Wilkes University, who edited *Conversations With Norman Mailer* (entry no. 048). The printing quantities are estimates furnished by Mailer. We would also like to thank Thomas Fiske and Charles Michaud for their assistance.

In addition to these items there are a number of publicity handouts, position papers and notes to workers that were generated during the NYC mayoral campaign. We have seen these catalogued in the $50 to $100 range. How many of these, if any, were actually written by Mailer is unclear but they would certainly reflect his thoughts and opinions and would presumably have been approved by him.

REFERENCES:

(a) Lennon, J. Michael. Collection.

(b) FIRST PRINTINGS OF AMERICAN AUTHORS. Volume 5. Matthew J. Bruccoli and E. E. Frazer Clark, Jr., editors. Detroit, Michigan: Gale Research Co. (1987).

(c) Inventory, dealer catalogs, etc.

001a: THE FOUNDATION Privately published, California, 1943-44. [] Wraps. Mimeographed. Also published as "A Calculus at Heaven" in *Cross-Section: A Collection of American Writing*, edited by Edwin Seaver. N.Y., L.B. Fisher, 1944. Later reprinted in *Advertisements for Myself* $750.

002a: THE NAKED AND THE DEAD Rinehart, New York, 1948. [5] Advance reading copy bound in red and black wraps with flaps as in final dust-wrapper $750.

002b: THE NAKED AND THE DEAD Rinehart, New York/Toronto (1948). [5] 25,000 cc. Black boards with white lettering, in red and black dust-wrapper priced $4.00 and with Mailer's picture on back panel $125/600

002c: THE NAKED AND THE DEAD Wingate, London, 1949. [2] Collector's Book Club issue, using sheets of first English edition and issued simultaneously with it. 253 copies with 240 numbered. In full leather, issued without dust-wrapper $750.

002d: THE NAKED AND THE DEAD Wingate, London (1949). [1] $40/200

002e: THE NAKED AND THE DEAD Franklin Library, Franklin Center, Pennsylvania, 1979. [2] 10,000 cc. Signed by Mailer, Includes "A special message to subscriber from Norman Mailer" $125.

003a: BARBARY SHORE Rinehart, New York, 1951. [5] Advance copy. Perfect bound in wraps used for trade edition dustwrapper. Copies with both variants of dustwrapper also noted (see below) $450.

003b: BARBARY SHORE Rinehart, New York / Toronto, no date. [5] 20,000 cc. Black boards with white lettering. Two dustwrappers on first edition apparently issued simultaneously: red and black; green and black $50/250

003c: BARBARY SHORE Cape, London (1952). [] (Ref.b) $20/100

003d: BARBARY SHORE Cape, London (1971). [] Adds "Note from the Author" by Mailer reprinted from *Advertisements for Myself* $10/40

004a: THE DEER PARK Putnam, New York (1955). [] Uncorrected galley proofs in narrow 4to wraps with printed label $400.

004b: THE DEER PARK Putnam, New York (1955). [0] 25,000 cc. Black cloth with green lettering. Two dustwrappers noted on first editions: author's name in orange, word "Park" in green; and reverse of this. Priority unknown $35/175

004c: THE DEER PARK Wingate, London (1957). [1] $15/75

004d: THE DEER PARK Shakespeare Head Press (Pty.) Ltd. (Sydney, 1957). [] First Australian edition from the English sheets. (Bertram Rota 5/98) $15/60

004e: THE DEER PARK (Berkley, New York, 1976.) [] Wraps. "Berkley Windhover Edition, NOVEMBER, 1976." A 3264. New preface and notes by Mailer. The "Notes" consist of "Fourth Advertisement for Myself: The Last Draft of *The Deer Park*" and "Postscript to the Fourth Advertisement for Myself", both reprinted from *Advertisements for Myself* $35.

005a: THE WHITE NEGRO City Lights Books (San Francisco, 1957). [0] Black and white wraps. 8 5/8" x 5 3/4". Front cover: 35¢ $500.

005b: THE WHITE NEGRO City Lights Books (San Francisco, 1957). Later printings (front cover): 50¢ $50.

006a: (Promotional Statement about Vance Bourjaily's *The Violated*) Dial, New York (1958). [0] single sheet $75.

007a: ADVERTISEMENTS FOR MYSELF Putnam, New York (1959). [0] Advance uncorrected proof (galleys). Perfect bound in tall dark green wraps with label on front $400.

007b: ADVERTISEMENTS FOR MYSELF Putnam, New York (1959). [0] 10,000 cc. Red and black cloth, red and gold lettering $25/125

007c: ADVERTISEMENTS FOR MYSELF Deutsch (London, 1961). [] New edition. Abridged (by about 40 pages). Black cloth with gold lettering, in red, black and orange dustwrapper $15/75

007d: ADVERTISEMENTS FOR MYSELF Berkley (New York, 1976). [] Wraps. Copyright page: "G.P. Putnam/Berkley Windhover Edition, DECEMBER 1976." B 3282. New edition with a new preface by Mailer $30.

008a: DEATHS FOR THE LADIES AND OTHER DISASTERS Putnam, New York (1962). [0] 5,000 cc. Black and white cloth with white lettering in black and white dustwrapper $60/300

008b: DEATHS FOR THE LADIES AND OTHER DISASTERS Putnam, New York (1962). [0] Simultaneously published in wraps $50.

008c: DEATHS FOR THE LADIES AND OTHER DISASTERS Deutsch (London, 1962). [] Wraps. No hardbound U.K. edition (David Rees 2/92) $50.

008d: DEATHS FOR THE LADIES AND OTHER DISASTERS New American Library (New York, 1971). [1] Wraps. Signet Book W4853. Adds an introduction by Mailer $25.

009a: THE PRESIDENTIAL PAPERS Putnam, New York (1963). [0] Advance edition dustwrapper is purple and white with orange and white lettering. No blurbs, text (except title, author) or photos $25/200

009b: THE PRESIDENTIAL PAPERS Putnam, New York (1963). [0] 10,000 cc. First and second impression dustwrappers have photo of Mailer in J.F.K. style rocker $25/100

009c: THE PRESIDENTIAL PAPERS Deutsch (London, 1964). [] New preface by Mailer, probably the special preface to Bantam edition $15/75

009d: THE PRESIDENTIAL PAPERS Bantam, New York (1964). [1] Wraps. Copyright page: "A Bantam Book | published May 1964." S2727. Contains "Special Preface to Bantam Edition" (noting J.F.K.'s death) $35.

009e: THE PRESIDENTIAL PAPERS "Berkley Windhover Edition, OCTOBER, 1976." [] Wraps. A 3243. New edition. Adds another new preface by Mailer $20.

010a: GARGOYLE, GUIGNOL, FALSE CLOSET (Dolmen Press, Dublin, 1964.) [2] 100 cc. 2 pages. Scarce. Reprinted from *Architectural Forum, 120* (April 1964), pp. 96-97 $400.

011a: AN AMERICAN DREAM Dial Press, New York, 1965. [0] 50,000 cc. Red, white and blue dustwrapper containing head shot of Mailer's fourth wife, Beverly Bentley. Blue cloth spine and gray boards, silver lettering; or full blue cloth. (Thomas Fiske believes that blue cloth is second. Charles Michaud has seen a blue cloth first that was inscribed in month of publication {3/65}) $15/75

011b: AN AMERICAN DREAM Deutsch (London, 1965). [] Advance uncorrected proof in blue printed wraps (Dalian 5/90) $150.

011c: AN AMERICAN DREAM Deutsch (London, 1965). [] (Ref.b) $12/60

011d: AN AMERICAN DREAM Warner Brothers (Los Angeles, 1966). [] Screenplay by Mann Rubin based on the novel by Mailer. Pinned self-wraps with printed label dated 3/1/66 (Serendipity Books) $400.

012a: CANNIBALS AND CHRISTIANS Dial Press, New York, 1966. [0] Review copy consisting of gathered signatures, ring bound, preceded publication. Also spiral bound 4to printed galleys with changes on slips pasted over original (Joseph The Provider 9/90. The same?) $400.

012b: CANNIBALS AND CHRISTIANS Dial Press, New York, 1966. [0] 10,000 cc. (b & c) First issue has color photograph of Vertical City (Lego Block architectural model built by Mailer), same as on dustwrapper, photo tipped-in on page opposite title page (frontis) $40/75

012c: CANNIBALS AND CHRISTIANS Dial Press, New York, 1966. [0] Photograph frontis is printed $10/40

012d: CANNIBALS AND CHRISTIANS Deutsch, (London, 1967). [] Maroon cloth, gold lettering (ref.b) $12/60

012e: CANNIBALS AND CHRISTIANS Granada, London / Toronto / Sydney / New York (1979). [] Wraps. Panther book. Abridged edition (ref.b) $20.

013a: THE DEER PARK A PLAY Dial, New York, 1967. [1] Black cloth with gold lettering. In red, white and black dustwrapper $25/125

013b: THE DEER PARK A PLAY Dell, New York (1967). [1] Wraps. $40.

013c: THE DEER PARK A PLAY Weidenfeld & Nicolson, London (1970). [1] (Ref.c) $12/60

014a: THE BULLFIGHT CBS Legacy Collection / MacMillan (New York, 1967). [0] 5,000 cc. Maroon boards with gold lettering. In white dustwrapper. Housed in a clear plastic box. Accompanied by 33 1/3 rpm record of Mailer reading from the text and a poem by Garcia Lorca. Text contains bull-fight photos. Very scarce with record. (Full leather (burgundy) binding in dustwrapper. (Fine Books 1/92).

Price with record but without box / and with box : $200/450

014b: THE BULLFIGHT CBS Legacy Collection / MacMillan (New York, 1967). [0] Issued without record or box $35/125

015a: THE SHORT FICTION OF NORMAN MAILER Dell (New York, 1967). [1] Wraps. 10,000 cc. "First Dell Printing - May 1967." #7850. (Also see 041a) $40.

016a: WHY ARE WE IN VIETNAM? Putnam, New York (1967). [1] 50,000 cc. Blue cloth, gold lettering, red, white and black dustwrapper. Includes a dedication to six of Mailer's friends. The name of one of these friends, Buzz Farbar, was misspelled as Buzz Farber. This edition was apparently recalled and the dedication page excised. The dedication was restored in three American paperback reprintings but does not appear in the hardback "first" editions per ref.a. However, corrected tipped-in dedications do show up in some copies (see below) $200/250

016b: WHY ARE WE IN VIETNAM? Putnam, New York (1967). [1] With tipped-in corrected dedication page (Thomas Fiske and Charles Michaud) $100/125

016c: WHY ARE WE IN VIETNAM? Putnam, New York (1967). [1] Without dedication page $10/40

016d: WHY ARE WE IN VIETNAM? Weidenfeld & Nicolson, London (1969). [] (Ref.b) $10/50

016e: WHY ARE WE IN VIETNAM? Putnam / Berkely (New York, 1977). [] Wraps. " G.P. Putnam's Sons | Berkley Windhover Edition, January, 1977." Adds a new preface by Mailer (ref.b) $25.

017a: TRIAL OF THE WARLOCK Playboy, Shueisha, Japan, 1977. [] Screenplay adaptation of J.K. Husyman's 1891 novel *La-Bas*. The Japanese volume was translated from the *Playboy* issue of December 1976. Gray-brown cloth, red and white dustwrapper. The only cloth bound edition $77/250

018a: THE ARMIES OF THE DEAD New American Library, New York (1968). [] Narrow galleys, ring bound, with original title $350.

018b: THE ARMIES OF THE NIGHT *History as a Novel, the Novel as History* New American Library (New York, 1968). [1] 35,000 cc. Published May 6, 20 years to the day after *The Naked and The Dead*. Black cloth, white lettering, in white, red and black dustwrapper. Pulitzer Prize and National Book Award for non-fiction in 1969. First published in a somewhat different form in *Harper's*, March 1968 (Part I), and *Commentary*, April 1968 (Part II) $15/75

018c: THE ARMIES OF THE NIGHT Weidenfeld & Nicolson, London (1968). [1] Light green cloth with black lettering, in white and black dustwrapper $15/75

019a: THE IDOL AND THE OCTOPUS POLITICAL WRITINGS...ON THE KENNEDY AND JOHNSON ADMINISTRATIONS Dell (New York, 1968). [1] Wraps. 10,000 cc. "First Printing - June, 1968." #3952. Most these selections appeared previously in *The Presidential Papers* (item 009) and *Cannibals and Christians* (item 012) $40.

020a: MIAMI AND THE SIEGE OF CHICAGO AN INFORMAL HISTORY OF THE REPUBLICAN AND DEMOCRATIC CONVENTIONS OF 1968 New American Library (New York, 1968). [1] Wraps. "First Printing, October 1968." Signet Special Q3785 $40.

020b: MIAMI AND THE SIEGE OF CHICAGO *An Informal History of the Republican and Democratic Conventions of 1968* World, New York/Cleveland (1968). [1] 15,000 cc. "First printing, October 1968." Black cloth with red lettering, in red, white and blue dustwrapper. Assume issued simultaneously $15/75

020c: MIAMI AND THE SIEGE OF CHICAGO *An Informal History of the American Political Conventions of 1968* Weidenfeld & Nicolson, London (1968). [] New title (ref.b) $15/60

021a: NATIONAL BOOK AWARD IN ARTS & LETTERS 1969 ACCEPTANCE SPEECH (National Book Awards, New York, 1969.) [0] Two sheets, stapled $125.

022a: RUNNING AGAINST THE MACHINE Doubleday, Garden City, New York, 1969. [] Edited by Peter Manso. Compilation of papers and articles from the Norman Mailer-Jimmy Breslin New York Democratic mayoral primary. Several speeches and articles by Mailer not published elsewhere. Also one paragraph dedication by Mailer to campaign staff. Simultaneously published in cloth and wrappers. Red cloth with black lettering, in black dustwrapper with red and white lettering $50/150

022b: RUNNING AGAINST THE MACHINE Doubleday, Garden City, New York, 1969 [] Wraps $50.

023a: A FIRE ON THE MOON Weidenfeld & Nicolson, London (1970). [0] (Ref.b) $12/60

023b: OF A FIRE ON THE MOON Little, Brown, Boston (1971). [1] 25,000 cc. Green cloth with gold lettering. Copyright 1970, published January 1971. Lennon believes this preceded the English edition $10/50

023c: OF A FIRE ON THE MOON Little, Brown, Boston (1971). [1] 500 cc (Gemini Fine Books 2/94). With signed tipped-in leaf (Waiting For Godot 4/90) $75/125

024a: KING OF THE HILL New American Library (New York, 1971). [1] Wraps. "First Printing, April 1971." Signet Special N 4787 $40.

025a: MAIDSTONE *A Mystery* New American Library (New York, 1971). [1] Wraps. "FIRST PRINTING, OCTOBER 1971." Signet Film Series W4782 $50.

026a: THE PRISONER OF SEX Little, Brown, Boston / Toronto (1971). [] Uncorrected proof in orange printed wraps. Preceded publication (Waiting for Godot Books 9/93) $200.

026b: THE PRISONER OF SEX Little, Brown, Boston/Toronto (1971). [1] 10,000 cc. Green boards with gold lettering. In gold and white dustwrapper. Note: inside front flap of dustwrapper contains price ($5.95 on first edition only) $10/40

026c: THE PRISONER OF SEX Weidenfeld & Nicolson, London (1971). [] (Ref.b) $10/40

027a: THE LONG PATROL, 25 YEARS OF WRITING ... World/Times Mirror, New York (1971). [1] Edited by Robert F. Lucid. Selections from 13 of Mailer's works $15/60

028a: EXISTENTIAL ERRANDS Little, Brown, Boston/Toronto, 1972. [] Uncorrected proof in yellow-orange wraps (Boston Book Co. & Book Annex 10/92) $150.

028b: EXISTENTIAL ERRANDS Little, Brown, Boston/Toronto (1972). [1] 10,000 cc. Yellow and black boards with gold lettering. In white dustwrapper $10/50

029a: ST. GEORGE AND THE GODFATHER New American Library (New York, 1972). [1] Wraps. "First printing, September, 1972." Signet special W5122 $40.

029b: ST. GEORGE AND THE GODFATHER Arbor House, New York (1983). [3] First hardback edition. Copyright 1972 but rear flap of dustwrapper has "9-83" so, assume 1983 publication $10/50

030a: MARILYN, A PREVIEW Grosset & Dunlap, New York (1972). [] 12 page promotional pamphlet (Astoria Books 4/90) $50.

030b: MARILYN, A BIOGRAPHY Grosset & Dunlap, New York, 1973. [2] Limited signed edition in white cloth and publisher's black clam shell case. Signed by Lawrence Shiller (the book's "producer") as well as Mailer. No limitation quantity stated $200/300

030c: MARILYN, A BIOGRAPHY (Grosset & Dunlap, New York, 1973.) [1] 100,000 cc. Tan cloth with gold lettering. (There were also 125,000 Book Club copies) $25/75

030d: MARILYN, A BIOGRAPHY (Grosset & Dunlap, New York, 1973.) [] Second printing in white plastic(?). Signed by Mailer but no limitation (Charles Michaud) $50/75

030e: MARILYN, A BIOGRAPHY (Hodder & Stoughton, London, 1973.) [] (Ref.b) $25/75

030f: MARILYN, A BIOGRAPHY Grosset & Dunlap, New York, 1974. [] "First printing paperback edition, 1974" stated. Bound in the embossed cloth of first edition and has the first edition dustwrapper loosely fitted (Tall Stories 6/95) $25/50

030g: MARILYN, A BIOGRAPHY Warner, New York, 1975. [1] Wraps. Includes new final chapter "The Murder File" $40.

031a: THE 1974 MARILYN MONROE DATE-BOOK Alskog (Los Angeles, 1973). [0] Spiral bound wraps $40

032a: THE FAITH OF GRAFFITI Praeger, New York, 1974. [2] Limited to 350 copies. Signed by all three contributors (Mailer, Mervyn Kurlansky and Jon Naar, photographers). 14-inch folio in cloth slipcase $75/150

032b: THE FAITH OF GRAFFITI Alskog/Praeger, New York (1974). [1] Brown cloth in green dustwrapper. The title and copyright page are the same and appear twice, on the verso of the front free endpaper and the recto of the rear free endpaper $20/75

032c: THE FAITH OF GRAFFITI Alskog/Praeger, New York (1974). [1] Wraps $25.

032d: WATCHING MY NAME GO BY (Mathews Miller Dunbar, London, 1974.) [1] $25/100

032e: WATCHING MY NAME GO BY (Mathews Miller Dunbar, London, 1974.) [1] Wraps $30.

033a: THE FIGHT Little, Brown, Boston/Toronto (1975). [1] 20,000 cc. Black cloth, silver lettering $10/50

033b: THE FIGHT Hart-Davis, MacGibbon, London (1976). [0] $10/40

034a: GENIUS AND LUST *A Journey Through the Major Writings of Henry Miller* Grove, New York (1976). [1] Tan cloth, blue lettering. 80 pages of commentary by Mailer, 500 pages of Miller excerpts. Dustwrapper drawing of Miller by Norris Church Mailer (his sixth wife) $20/60

035a: SOME HONORABLE MEN POLITICAL CONVENTIONS 1960-1972 Little, Brown Boston/Toronto (1976). [1] 10,000 cc. Original preface, rest of book reprinted for *Presidential Papers*, *Cannibals*, *Miami* and *St. George*. Blue cloth with silver lettering. In black and white dustwrapper $10/50

036a: A TRANSIT TO NARCISSUS Howard Fertig, New York, 1978. [1] Uncorrected proof in cream colored wraps $200.

036b: A TRANSIT TO NARCISSUS Howard Fertig, New York, 1978. [1] 1,000 cc. Tan cloth with black lettering $50/150

037a: THE EXECUTIONER'S SONG Little, Brown, Boston / Toronto (1979). [1] Uncorrected Advance Proof in blue wraps. Also seen in two volumes (Gemini Fine Books 2/94) $200.

037b: THE EXECUTIONER'S SONG Little, Brown Boston/Toronto (1979). [1] 100,000 copies. Blue cloth, silver and gold lettering. In blue, black and gold dustwrapper. Pulitzer Prize in Fiction for 1980 $12/60

037c: THE EXECUTIONER'S SONG Hutchison (London, 1979). [] (Ref.b) $12/60

037d: THE EXECUTIONER'S SONG The Execution's Song Production Co., Los Angeles, 1981. [0] 197 pages (only recto numbered). Green wraps, pin bound. Shooting draft of screenplay, September 25 $300.

037e: THE EXECUTIONER'S SONG Lawrence Schiller Productions, Holly-wood, 1981. [] 4to punch bound sheets in printed covers (Antic Hay 5/91)

i. 150 pages. Feature draft $250.
ii. 196 pages. Corrected second draft $250.
iii. 197 pages. Shooting draft $250.

038a: OF A SMALL AND MODEST MALIGNANCY WICKED AND BRISTLING WITH DOTS Lord John Press, Northridge, 1980. [2] 100 sgd no. cc. Deluxe edition on Curtis Rag and bound in leather. Issued without dustwrapper in slipcase. First appeared in *Esquire* Nov. 1977 $150/250

038b: OF A SMALL AND MODEST MALIGNANCY WICKED AND BRISTLING WITH DOTS Lord John Press, Northridge, 1980. [2] 300 sgd no. cc on Mohawk Superfine and bound in cloth. Issued without dustwrapper. In slipcase $50/100

039a: OF WOMEN AND THEIR ELEGANCE Simon & Schuster, New York (1980). [] Loose pages with sample photograph laid in publisher's box with differences from published book (George Robert Minkoff 6/90) $300.

039b: OF WOMEN AND THEIR ELEGANCE Simon & Schuster, New York (1980). [3] Photographs by Milton H. Greene $25/75

039c: OF WOMEN AND THEIR ELEGANCE Hodder & Stoughton, London / Sydney / Auckland / Toronto (1980). [] Sheets of the American edition (ref.b) $25/75

040a: PIECES AND PONTIFICATIONS Little, Brown, Boston/Toronto (1982). [1] Uncorrected proof in blue wraps with "Pontification" misspelled on title page $200

040b: PIECES AND PONTIFICATIONS Little, Brown, Boston / Toronto (1982). [1] Bound uncorrected proof in tan wraps with price ($22.95) and 448 pages. Also noted in creme wraps (Lame Duck Books 9/91) $100.

040c: PIECES AND PONTIFICATIONS Little, Brown, Boston / Toronto (1982). [1] Purple cloth with silver lettering in white, green and purple dustwrapper $10/50

040d: PIECES Little, Brown, Boston / Toronto (1982). [1] Blue wraps. Republished in two volumes $30.

040e: PONTIFICATIONS Little, Brown, Boston / Toronto (1982). [1] White wraps. Edited by Michael Lennon $30.

040f: PIECES AND PONTIFICATIONS New English Library (London, 1983). [1] Black cloth with gold lettering. In red, tan, white and black dustwrapper (ref.b) $10/40

041a: THE ESSENTIAL MAILER New English Library (Kent, 1982). [1] "This collection first published in Great Britain by ... in 1982." First British edition of *The Short Fiction of Norman Mailer* and *Existential Errands*, which are combined in this edition. Green-blue cloth with silver lettering. In red, white, blue and black dustwrapper $15/60

041b: THE ESSENTIAL MAILER New English Library (Kent, 1982). [] Wraps. Assume simultaneous. $30.

042a: ANCIENT EVENINGS Little, Brown, Boston / Toronto (1983). [] Uncorrected proof. Two volumes. Offset from typescript. 1,746 pages (Christopher Stephen's 11/91) with many differences from final book $250.

042b: ANCIENT EVENINGS Little, Brown, Boston / Toronto (1983). [] Uncorrected proof in yellow wraps with $19.95 price and 704 pages noted on cover $100.

042c: ANCIENT EVENINGS Little, Brown, Boston / Toronto (1983). [2] 350 sgd no. cc. Issued without dustwrapper. In slipcase $75/150

042d: ANCIENT EVENINGS Little, Brown, Boston / Toronto (1983). [1] 100,000 cc. Black cloth with gold and red lettering. In red, black and gold dustwrapper $10/40

042e: ANCIENT EVENINGS Macmillan, London, 1983. [] Advance uncorrected proof in yellow wraps (Dalian 5/90) $75.

042f: ANCIENT EVENINGS Macmillan, London, 1983. [] $10/50

043a: THE LAST NIGHT Targ Editions, New York, 1984. [2] 250 sgd no. cc. Black and white boards. Iin plain white dustwrapper $125/150

044a: TOUGH GUYS DON'T DANCE Random House, New York (1984). [4] Uncorrected proof in yellow wraps $100.

044b: TOUGH GUYS DON'T DANCE Franklin Library, Franklin Center, 1984. [2] Signed "limited" first edition. In full brown leather with "Special Message from the Author" not in Random House edition $75.

044c: TOUGH GUYS DON'T DANCE Random House, New York (1984). [2] 350 sgd no. cc. Issued without dustwrapper. In slipcase $60/125

044d: TOUGH GUYS DON'T DANCE Random House, New York (1984). [4] 100,000 cc. Black cloth with gold lettering. In black, yellow and gold dustwrapper $6/30

044e: TOUGH GUYS DON'T DANCE Joseph, London (1984). [] (Ref.b) $10/40

044f: TOUGH GUYS DON'T DANCE *A Screenplay* Cannon Films, no place, 1986. [] 116 pp (only recto numbered). Blue wraps, pin bound. Draft 4.2 by Mailer, October 11, 1986 $250.

045a: FRAGMENT FROM VIETNAM *A Play in One Act* Eurographica, Helsinki (1985). [2] 12 author's copies. Edited by Rolando Pieraccini. Blue-gray wraps. Also contains Mailer's self-interview from the *New York Times Book Review* (17 September 1967, 4-5, 40) $400.

045b: FRAGMENT FROM VIETNAM *A Play in One Act* Eurographica, Helsinki (1985). [2] 350 no. copies as above. Card wraps. In dustwrapper (Richard Budd Books 2/95) $200.

046a: HUCKLEBERRY FINN, ALIVE AT 100 Caliban Press (Montclair), 1985. [2] 50 no. cc. Casebound in boards $200.

046b: HUCKLEBERRY FINN, ALIVE AT 100 Caliban Press (Montclair), 1985. [2] 200 no. cc. Sewn in red crimson wraps $100.

047a: 48TH INTERNATIONAL PEN CONGRESS PRESS KIT New York, 1986. January 12-18. [] Includes 11 page speech by Mailer. Loose sheets stapled in gray folder $50.

048a: CONVERSATIONS WITH NORMAN MAILER University Press of Mississippi, Jackson / London (1988). [3] 1,500 cc. Edited by J. Michael Lennon $20/60

048b: CONVERSATIONS WITH NORMAN MAILER University Press of Miss. Jackson / London (1988). [3] 3,500 cc. Wraps. Issued simultaneously $25.

049a: HARLOT'S GHOST Random House, New York (1991). [4] Advance uncorrected proof. In glossy wraps using publisher's device as pattern. Gives tentative publication date of October 15, 1991 $200.

049b: HARLOT'S GHOST Random House, New York (1991). [2] 300 sgd no. cc. Issued without dustwrapper. In slipcase. Published at $200 $150/200

049c: HARLOT'S GHOST Random House, New York (1991). [4] 186,000 cc (PW). Issued in two dustwrappers (gray and red). Reportedly there were only 250 of the red dustwrapper (Bev Chaney 2/92). James Pepper Rare Books, 1/97 calls the "brilliant pinkish-red" dustwrapper a trial dustwrapper and indicates there were only approximately 30 copies. However, an article in PW states Mailer "had approved the original gray dustwrapper. It continued to outsell the strawberry four to one..." (Lennon believes Mailer meant in one or two stores. He was told by Mailer's agent that there were 150 of the red.) Published August 1991 at $30.

In red dustwrapper: $7/75
In gray dustwrapper: $7/35

049d: HARLOT'S GHOST Michael Joseph, London (1991). [] Advance partial proof in glossy wraps. 345 pp. (Nicholas Burrows Books 2/93) $60.

049e: HARLOT'S GHOST Michael Joseph, London, 1991. [1] $8/40

050a: HOW THE WIMP WON THE WAR Lord John Press, Northridge, 1992. [2] 26 sgd ltr cc. Issued without dustwrapper $250.

050b: HOW THE WIMP WON THE WAR Lord John Press, Northridge, 1992. [2] 275 sgd no. cc. Issued without dustwrapper $75.

051a: OSWALD'S TALE Franklin Library, Franklin Center, 1996. [2] Signed ltd. edition in full leather (Waverley Books 10/96) $100.

051b: OSWALD'S TALE Random House, New York, 1995. [] Uncorrected proof. In blue patterned wraps (Waverley Books 6/95) $100.

051c: OSWALD'S TALE Random House, New York (1995). [] (Published May 1995 @ $30.00.) Note: the Book-of-the-Month Club in unpriced dustwrapper does not have ISBN number above bar code on back of dustwrapper and the book itself is in a Little Brown binding, although the sheets and title page are Random House and also state first. $6/30

051d: OSWALD'S TALE Little, Brown, London, 1995. [4] (Nicholas Pounder 11/95) $6/30

052a: PICASSO *Portrait of Picasso as a Young Man* Atlantic, New York, 1996. [] $6/30

053a: THE GOSPEL ACCORDING TO THE SON Random House, New York (1997). [1] Published @ $22.00

054a: THE TIME OF OUR TIME Random House, New York (1998). [] Uncorrected proof. Wraps (Ken Lopez 5/98) $150.

054b: THE TIME OF OUR TIME Random House, New York (1998). [4] Published at $39.50

INTRODUCTIONS & SELECTED APPEARANCES

055a: THE WESTERN DEFENCES Allan Wingate, London, 1951. [] Edited by Brigadier J. G. Smyth. Contain's Mailer's "The Defense of the Compass," pp.134-44, an early and almost completely different version of "The Meaning of Western Defense" in *Advertisements for Myself* (1959). $50/250

056a: VIEWS OF A NEARSIGHTED CANNONEER Excelsior Press, New York (1961). [] Wraps. Foreword by Mailer, written by Seymour Krim. Krim's first book $10/40

057a: THE BEARD Coyote (San Francisco), 1967. [2] 40 specially bound copies. Signed by the author, Michael McClure. Foreword by Mailer $175.

057b: THE BEARD Coyote (San Francisco), 1967. [1] 5,000 cc. Wraps $30.

058a: THE END OF OBSCENITY | THE TRIALS OF LADY CHATTERLEY, TROPIC OF CANCER and FANNY HILL Deutsch (London, 1969). [0] Foreword by Mailer. Written by Charles Rembar $10/50

058b: THE END OF OBSCENITY | THE TRIALS OF LADY CHATTERLEY, TROPIC OF CANCER and FANNY HILL Bantam, Toronto / New York / London (1969). [1] Wraps. Copyright page: "Bantam edition published September 1969." Q5236. New edition $20.

059a: THIS IS MY BEST *In the Third Quarter of the Century* Doubleday, New York, 1970. Edited by Whit Burnett. Contains 2-page letter (pp.99-100) from Mailer prefacing Mailer's choice "Deborah" from *An American Dream*, pp.100-110. Never reprinted $15/60

060a: STING LIKE A BEE *The Muhammad Ali Story* Abelard-Schuman, London / New York / Toronto, 1971. [0] Preface by Mailer written by Jose Torres $15/40

060b: STING LIKE A BEE *The Muhammad Ali Story* Curtis Books, New York, 1971. [] Wraps $20.

061a: THE JOKER Warner (New York, 1974). [1] Wraps. Introduction by Mailer. Written by Jean Malaquais. Translated by Herma Briffault $25.

062a: FICTION WRITER'S HANDBOOK Harper & Row, New York/Evanston/San Francisco/London (1975). [1] Preface by Mailer. Written by Hallie and Whit Burnett $10/35

063a: ST. PATRICK'S DAY WITH MAYOR DALEY AND OTHER THINGS TOO GOOD TO MISS Seabury, New York (1976). [0] Foreword by Mailer. Written by Eugene Kennedy $10/40

063a: PAPA A PERSONAL MEMOIR Houghton Mifflin, Boston, 1976. [3] Preface by Mailer. Written by Gregory H. Hemingway $10/40

064a: FIRST FLOWERING *The Best of the Harvard Advocate* Addison-Wesley, Massachusetts / California / London / Amsterdam / Ontario / Sydney (1977). [3] Preface by Mailer. Edited by Richard M. Smoley. From “Our Man at Harvard” in *Esquire*, April 1977 $10/40

065a: SOON TO BE A MAJOR MOTION PICTURE Putnam, New York (1980). [0] Introduction by Mailer. Written by Abbie Hoffman. Reprinted with changes as foreword to *The Best of Abbie Hoffman* $15/60

065b: SOON TO BE A MAJOR MOTION PICTURE Putnam, New York (1980). [0] Wraps. Issued simultaneously $25.

066a: THE LAW OF THE LAND *The Evolution of Our Legal System* Simon & Schuster, New York, 1980. By Charles Pembar (Mailer’s first cousin). Contains a court deposition by Mailer defending his father from charges of being disloyal and a leftist, pp.370-75. Never reprinted $25/75

067a: IN THE BELLY OF THE BEAST *Letters from Prison* Random House, New York (1981). [3] (Also states "First Edition.") Introduction by Mailer. Written by Jack Henry Abbott $10/35

067b: IN THE BELLY OF THE BEAST *Letters from Prison* Hutchison, London, 1982. [] Introduction by Mailer. Written by Jack Henry Abbott (ref.b) $10/40

068a: DEAR MUFFO *35 Years in the Fast Lane* Stein and Day, New York (1982). [1] Foreword by Mailer. Written by Harold Conrad $10/40

069a: AFTER THE LAST GENERATION *A Critical Study of the Writers of Two Wars* Arbor House, New York (1985). [3] Wraps. Written by John W. Aldridge. With an introduction by Mailer $20.

070a: DISCRIMINATIONS *Essays & Afterthoughts* DaCapo Press (New York, 1985). [] Wraps. Introduction by Norman Mailer. Written by Dwight MacDonald (originally by Grossman in 1974. This the first with Mailer introduction) $25.

Bernard Malamud

BERNARD MALAMUD

Malamud was born in Brooklyn in 1914. He graduated from the City College of New York and then received a M.A. from Columbia. He taught at various New York high schools in the 1940's and at Oregon State from 1949 to 1961. He received a National Book Award for *The Magic Barrel* and a Pulitzer Prize for *The Fixer*.

Thanks to Joan Norris Boothe for her assistance in the preparation of this guide.

REFERENCES:

(a) Lepper, Gary M. A BIBLIOGRAPHICAL REFERENCE TO SEVENTY-FIVE MODERN AMERICAN AUTHORS. Berkeley: Serendipity Books, 1976.

(b) Kosofsky, Rita N. BERNARD MALAMUD *An Annotated Check-list*. Kent State (1969).

(c) Vinson, James (editor). CONTEMPORARY NOVELISTS, Second Edition. New York: St. Martin's Press (1976).

(d) Eppard, Philip B. (editor). FIRST PRINTINGS OF AMERICAN AUTHORS, Volume 5. Detroit: Gale Research (1987).

(e) Inventory.

001a: THE NATURAL Harcourt, New York (1952). [1] The latest thinking seems to be that there is no priority among red, blue and gray bindings. Two recent review copies offered for sale were in the gray binding (Robert Wendler 2/96). Malamud's widow told us his copy was in blue. $350/2,000

001b: THE NATURAL Eyre & Spottiswode, London, 1963. [1] Uncorrected proof. In printed tan wraps. "To Be Published March 1963 at 21s Net." Includes 10 pages of notes on baseball not in U.S. edition $600.

001c: THE NATURAL Eyre & Spottiswode, London, 1963. [1] Contains 10 pages of notes on baseball not included in U.S. edition $100/500

002a: KIM OF KOREA Julian Messner, Inc., New York (1955). [0] Written under the name Peter Lumn with Faith Norris $100/500

002b: KIM OF KOREA The Copp Clark Company, Ltd., Toronto, 1955. [] Published simultaneously with the American edition $75/400

003a: THE ASSISTANT Farrar Straus, New York, 1957. [1] Reviews of *The Natural* on back panel $50/350

003b: THE ASSISTANT Farrar Straus, New York, 1957. [1] Reviews of this title on back panel $50/250

003c: THE ASSISTANT Eyre & Spottiswode, London, 1959. [1] First book published in England (ref.b) $40/200

004a: MAGIC BARREL ... Farrar Straus, New York (1958). [] Uncorrected galley. In narrow sheets, punched at top and string tied into plain wraps with typed label and front panel of dustwrapper art mount thereon (William Reese Co. 5/89) $1,000.

004b: MAGIC BARREL ... Farrar Straus, New York (1958). [1] Winner of the National Book Award for 1959 $30/150

004c: MAGIC BARREL ... Jewish Publ. Society, Philadelphia, 1958. [1] No priority (ref.a) but this issue is noted as the first issue (Sylvester & Orphanos #41) $30/150

004d: MAGIC BARREL ... Eyre & Spottiswode, London, 1960. [1] $25/100

004e: MAGIC BARREL and IDIOT'S FIRST Franklin Library, Franklin Center, 1978. [2] "Limited Edition." In full leather (ref.c) $60.

004f: MAGIC BARREL ... Tales for Travellers (Napa, California, 1985). [0] 15,000 cc. Wraps. Map folded. First separate edition. (Later printing over-stamped on back with either "Parke-Davis" or "Dermik") $35.

005a: NATIONAL BOOK AWARD ACCEPTANCE SPEECH (Privately Printed, New York) 1959. [0] Wraps. Two mimeographed sheets $100.

006a: A NEW LIFE Farrar, Straus and Cudahy, New York (1961). [] Unbound sewn signatures in dustwrapper. Apparently issued as an advance reading copy (Antic Hay Rare Books 6/96) $250.

006b: A NEW LIFE Farrar Straus, New York (1961). [1] $25/100

006c: A NEW LIFE Eyre & Spottiswode, London (1962). [] Uncorrected proof in printed green wraps (Dalian Books 5/90) $125.

006d: A NEW LIFE Eyre & Spottiswode, London (1962). [1] (Ref.b) $12/60

007a: IDIOT'S FIRST Farrar Straus, New York (1963). [] Uncorrected galley proofs. In plain wraps with typed label (William Reese Co. 5/89) $500.

007b: IDIOT'S FIRST Farrar Straus, New York (1963). [1] $15/75

007c: IDIOT'S FIRST Eyre & Spottiswode, London, 1964. [] $12/60

Also see 004e

008a: TWO NOVELS BY BERNARD MALAMUD... Random House, New York, 1964. [] First two books (ref.b) $10/40

009a: THE FIXER Farrar Straus, New York (1966). [1] Winner of Pulitzer Prize for 1967 $25/100

009b: THE FIXER Eyre & Spottiswode, London (1967). [] (Ref.b) $15/75

009c: THE FIXER Franklin Library, Franklin Center, 1978. [2] "Limited Edition." In full leather $60.

010a: A MALAMUD READER Farrar Straus, New York (1967). [] Uncorrected galley proofs punched at left and string tied in plain wraps with typed label (William Reese Co. 5/89) $200.

010b: A MALAMUD READER Farrar Straus, New York (1967). [0] Edited by Philip Rahv $15/75

011a: PICTURES OF FIDELMAN Farrar Straus, New York (1969). [] Uncorrected proof. In tall, thin, spiral bound, pale blue wraps (James Jaffe 5/92) $200.

011b: PICTURES OF FIDELMAN Farrar Straus, New York (1969). [1] $12/60

011c: PICTURES OF FIDELMAN Eyre & Spottiswode, London, 1970. [] (Ref.c) $10/50

012a: THE TENANTS Farrar Straus, New York (1971). [1] Approximately 250 copies with signed tipped in sheet. In orange cloth $150/200

012b: THE TENANTS Farrar Straus, New York (1971). [1] First binding in orange cloth (Caney Booksellers 5/88) $15/60

012c: THE TENANTS Farrar Straus, New York (1971). [1] Second binding in dark red $15/50

012d: THE TENANTS Metheun, London (1972). [1] (Ref.e) (Published February 23, 1972 at £1.95) $10/50

013a: REMBRANDT'S HAT Farrar Straus, New York (1973). [] Uncorrected proof. In green wraps (William Reese 5/89) $150.

013b: REMBRANDT'S HAT Farrar Straus, New York (1973). [1] $10/50

013c: REMBRANDT'S HAT Eyre & Methuen, London, 1973. [] (Ref.c) $8/40

014a: TWO FABLES Bennington / Banyon, Benn. / Pawlet (1978). [2] 320 sgd no. cc. Issued without dustwrapper. Excerpt from *The Magic Barrel* $175.

015a: DUBIN'S LIVES Farrar Straus, New York (1979). [1] Wraps. Uncorrected page proof. In peach colored printed wraps which differs from published version, but with the 5 words (see below) (ref.d) $200.

015b: DUBIN'S LIVES Farrar Straus, New York (1979). [1] Missing the last five words on bottom of p.231 "When he asked her why," (ref.c) $175/200

015c: DUBIN'S LIVES Farrar Straus, New York (1979). [1] Approximately 70 copies sent out for review with 5 words in last line p.231 written in (Jos. the Provider Cat. 24) (ref.d calls this second state) $150/175

015d: DUBIN'S LIVES Franklin Press, Franklin Center, 1979. [2] "Limited Edition." In full leather. Contains special message $50.

015e: DUBIN'S LIVES Farrar Straus, New York (1979). [2] 750 cc. "For friends of..." Issued in plain glassine dustwrapper (with p.231 tipped in) (ref.d - third state) $35/40

015f: DUBIN'S LIVES Farrar Straus, New York (1979). [1] With p.231 tipped in (ref.d) $10/50

015g: DUBIN'S LIVES Chatto & Windus, London, 1979. [] (Ref.d) $8/40

016a: GOD'S GRACE Farrar Straus, New York (1982). [2] 300 sgd no. cc. Issued without dustwrapper. In slipcase $75/175

016b: GOD'S GRACE Farrar Straus, New York (1982). [1] $8/40

016c: GOD'S GRACE Chatto & Windus, London, 1982. [] $8/40

017a: THE STORIES Farrar Straus, New York (1983). [] Uncorrected proof. In pale blue wraps $100.

017b: THE STORIES Farrar Straus, New York (1983). [2] 300 sgd no. cc. Issued without dustwrapper. In slipcase $100/150

017c: THE STORIES Farrar Straus, New York (1983). [1] $10/40

017d: THE STORIES Chatto & Windus / Hogarth, London, 1984. [] Advance proof in plain wraps. Bound in proof dustwrapper (Ian McKelvie 2/90) $75.

017e: THE STORIES Chatto & Windus / Hogarth, London, 1984. [1] "Published in 1984 by ..." $8/40

018a: ON BEING ACQUAINTED WITH EUDORA WELTY Stuart Wright, no place, 1984. [2] Wraps. 5 sgd no. cc (Black Sun Books #71) $300.

019a: LONG WORK, SHORT LIFE (Bennington College, Bennington, Vermont), 1984. [2] Wraps. 1,000 no. cc (Glenn Horowitz #13) $75.

020a: THE PEOPLE AND OTHER UNCOLLECTED FICTION Farrar Straus, New York, 1989. [] Uncorrected proof. In green wraps $75.

020b: THE PEOPLE AND OTHER UNCOLLECTED FICTION Farrar Straus, New York (1989). [1] Edited by Robert Giroux. Published November 1989 at $18.95 $7/35

020c: THE PEOPLE AND OTHER UNCOLLECTED FICTION Chatto & Windus, London (1990) $7/35

021a: THE MAGIC BARREL Tales for Travellers (Napa, California, 1985). [0] Wraps. Single sheet map folded. First separate edition $30.

022a: CONVERSATIONS WITH BERNARD MALAMUD University Press of Mississippi, Jackson (1991). [] Interviews from 1958-1986. Edited by Lawrence Lasher $20/40

022b: CONVERSATIONS WITH BERNARD MALAMUD University Press of Mississippi, Jackson (1991). [] Wraps $25.

DAVID MARKSON

Markson was born in Albany, New York, in 1927 and educated at Union College and Columbia; his master's thesis was the first extended critical treatment of Malcolm Lowry's *Under The Volcano*. The "spiritual son" of Lowry and Conrad Aiken, Markson also associated with the Beats in the late '50s and early '60s. He has spent long periods in England, Spain, and Mexico, but considers Greenwich Village home.

We would like to thank Steven Moore for the preparation of the bibliographical information herein.

001a: THE LOVE-MAKERS Pyramid Books, New York (1956). [] Pictorial wraps. Pyramid Giant G227. Edited by "Mark Merrill," pseudonym of David Markson. Contains short stories by various authors $75.

002a: WOMEN AND VODKA Pyramid, New York (1956). [] Wraps. Edited by "Mark Merrill." (Reissued as *Great Tales of Old Russia* under Markson's real name in 1963) $50.

003a: EPITAPH FOR A TRAMP Dell (New York, 1959). [1] Wraps. (Reissued as *Fannin* in 1971) $75.

004a: EPITAPH FOR A DEAD BEAT Dell (New York, 1961). [1] Wraps $60.

005a: MISS DOLL, GO HOME Dell (New York, 1965). [1] Wraps $50.

006a: THE BALLAD OF DINGUS MAGEE (Bobbs-Merrill, Indianapolis / Kansas City / New York, 1965). [1] Wraps. Advance copy in stiff white wraps printed in black $100.

006b: THE BALLAD OF DINGUS MAGEE (Bobbs-Merrill, Indianapolis / Kansas City / New York, 1965.) [1] [Actually purblished spring of 1966] $10/50

007a: GOING DOWN (Holt, Rinehart and Winston, New York / Chicago / San Francisco, 1970) [1] $7/35

008a: SPRINGER'S PROGRESS Holt, Rinehart and Winston, New York (1977). [3] Also states "FIRST EDITION." Uncorrected proofs in blue wraps printed in black $75.

008b: SPRINGER'S PROGRESS Holt, Rinehart and Winston, New York (1977). [3] Also states "FIRST EDITION." "Advance Complimentary Reading Copy" in yellow wraps printed in black $60.

008c: SPRINGER'S PROGRESS Holt, Rinehart and Winston, New York (1977) [3] Also states "FIRST EDITION" $7/35

009a: MALCOLM LOWRY'S *VOLCANO* Times Books (New York, 1978). [0] "Unrevised Proofs" in yellow wraps printed in black $100.

009b: MALCOLM LOWRY'S *VOLCANO* Times Books (New York, 1978). $10/50

010a: WITTGENSTEIN'S MISTRESS Dalkey Archive Press (Elmwood Park, Illinois, 1988). [1] "Advance Uncorrected Galleys" in blue wraps printed in black $60.

010b: WITTGENSTEIN'S MISTRESS Dalkey Archive Press, Elmwood Park (1988) [1] $8/40

010c: WITTGENSTEIN'S MISTRESS Jonathan Cape (London, 1989). [1] Uncorrected proof. In orange-red wraps printed in black $50.

010d: WITTGENSTEIN'S MISTRESS Jonathan Cape, London, 1989. [1] $8/40

011a: COLLECTED POEMS Dalkey Archive, Elmwood Park, 1993. [] Wraps. (Published September 1993) $25.

012a: READER'S BLOCK Dalkey Archive Press (Normal, Illinois, 1996). [1] "Advance Uncorrected Galley" in yellow wraps printed in black $50.

012b: READER'S BLOCK Dalkey Archive Press, Normal, Illinois, 1996. [1] Wraps. Published at $12.95.

Paule Marshall

PAULE MARSHALL

Marshall was born in 1929 in Brooklyn, the setting for her first book about a West Indian girl transplanted to Brooklyn. She graduated from Brooklyn College in 1953 and has been writing full-time since her first book.

We appreciate the assistance of Charles Dickison for bibliographical information on a number of these books.

001a: BROWN GIRL, BROWNSTONES Random House, New York (1959). [1] $150/850

001b: BROWN GIRL, BROWNSTONES W.H. Allen, London, 1960. [] $60/350

001c: BROWN GIRL, BROWNSTONES Black Oak Books, Berkeley, 1991. [] "They danced near the edge of the circle ..." 6 1/2" x 11" broadside (Ken Lopez 1/92) $40.

002a: SOUL CLAP HANDS AND SING Atheneum, New York, 1961. [1] $60/300

002b: SOUL CLAP HANDS AND SING W.H. Allen, London, 1962. [1] $25/125

003a: THE CHOSEN PLACE, THE TIMELESS PEOPLE Harcourt Brace, New York (1969). [1] $50/250

003b: THE CHOSEN PLACE, THE TIMELESS PEOPLE Longmans, London, 1970. [1] $20/100

004a: REENA Feminist Press, Old Westbury, New York (1983). [3] Wraps $75.

004b: MERLE Virago (London, 1985). [0] Advance proof in blue printed wraps with publication date of 2/21/85 at £9.95. No place or date in book except copyright 1983 by Feminist Press. New title $100.

004c: MERLE Virago (London, 1985). [] $25/125

004d: MERLE Virago (London, 1985). [] Wraps $30.

005a: PRAISESONG FOR THE WIDOW Putnam, New York (1983). [0] Uncorrected proof. In orange wraps (Lame Duck Books 9/91) $150.

005b: PRAISESONG FOR THE WIDOW Putnam, New York (1983). [0] $12/60

005c: PRAISESONG FOR THE WIDOW Virago (London, 1983). [] (Keane-Egan Books 12/95) $10/50

006a: DAUGHTERS Atheneum, New York, 1991. [] Advance excerpt. 25 pages, pictorial wraps Also noted as 32 pp. (Magnum Opus 3/95) $40.

006b: DAUGHTERS Atheneum, New York, 1991. [] (Published October 1991 @ $19.95) $7/35

William Maxwell

WILLIAM MAXWELL

William Maxwell was born in Lincoln, Illinois in 1908. He received his undergraduate degree from the University of Illinois and his masters from Harvard. He taught for a short period and then spent his entire working career as a member of the staff of *The New Yorker* magazine.

001a: BRIGHT CENTER OF HEAVEN Harper, New York, 1934. [1] $200/1,000

001b: BRIGHT CENTER OF HEAVEN Musson, Toronto, 1934. [] $60/350

002a: THEY CAME LIKE SWALLOWS Harper, New York, 1937. [1] "First Edition" stated and with the numbers "1186" at bottom of back panel of dustwrapper which is headed "New Harper Fiction." (The dustwrapper with "1213" headed "Fiction of outstanding merit..." is, in our opinion, the second printing $100/600

002b: THEY CAME LIKE SWALLOWS Musson, Toronto, 1937. [] $60/300

002c: THEY CAME LIKE SWALLOWS M. Joseph, London, 1937. [] $60/300

002d: THEY CAME LIKE SWALLOWS Vintage, New York, 1960. [1] Wraps. Slightly revised by author $35.

003a: THE FOLDED LEAF Harper, New York, 1945. [1] $60/300

003b: THE FOLDED LEAF Faber, London (1946). [] 5,579 cc $30/150

003c: THE FOLDED LEAF Vintage, New York, 1959. [1] Slightly revised by author $35.

004a: HEAVENLY TENANTS Harper, New York (1946). [0] Pictures by Ilonka Karasz. Dark blue cloth, dustwrapper priced at $2.00 with "6317" at bottom of front flap $75/250

004b: HEAVENLY TENANTS Musson, Toronto, 1946. [] $50/150

005a: TIME WILL DARKEN IT Harper, New York, 1948. [1] $40/200

005b: TIME WILL DARKEN IT Musson, Toronto, 1948. [] $20/100

005c: TIME WILL DARKEN IT Faber, London, 1949. [] 3,500 cc $25/125

005d: TIME WILL DARKEN IT Vintage (New York, 1962). [1] Wraps. Revised edition $35.

006a: THE WRITER AS ILLUSIONIST Smith College (Northampton, 1955). (Unitelum Press, New York, 1955 [Ken Lopez 1/93].)[0] Wraps (in dustwrapper [Waiting For Godot #13]) $100/150

007a: STORIES Farrar Straus, New York (1956). [1] With Cheever, Stafford, and Daniel Fuchs $15/75

008a: THE ANXIOUS MAN PAX, New York, 1957. [] Large folio sheet folded twice (Waiting For Godot #L-One) $125.

009a: THE CHATEAU Knopf, New York, 1961. [1] $25/125

009b: THE CHATEAU McClelland, Toronto, 1961. [] $15/75

010a: THE OLD MAN AT THE RAILROAD CROSSING Knopf, New York, 1966. [] Galley proofs. In spiral bound printed wraps (William Reese Co. 11/90) $200.

010b: THE OLD MAN AT THE RAILROAD CROSSING Knopf, New York, 1966. [] Uncorrected proof. In blue printed wraps (Bev Chaney, Jr. 5/96) 125.

010c: THE OLD MAN AT THE RAILROAD CROSSING Knopf, New York, 1966. [1] $20/100

011a: ANCESTORS Knopf, New York, 1971. [] Uncorrected proof. In tall, pad-bound wraps (Ken Lopez 1/93) $150.

011b: ANCESTORS Knopf, New York, 1971. [1] $15/75

012a: OVER BY THE RIVER ... Knopf, New York, 1977. [] Uncorrected proof. In tall brick red wraps $100.

012b: OVER BY THE RIVER ... Knopf, New York, 1977. [1] $15/75

013a: SO LONG, SEE YOU TOMORROW Knopf, New York, 1980. [1] $10/50

013b: SO LONG, SEE YOU TOMORROW Secker, London (1989). [1] (Ken Lopez 1/95) $10/40

014a: LETTERS / SYLVIA TOWNSEND WARNER Viking, New York (1983). [1] "Published in 1983 by ..." Edited by Maxwell $10/40

014b: LETTERS / SYLVIA TOWNSEND WARNER Chatto & Windus, London, 1982. [] $10/40

015a: FIVE TALES Cummington Press, Omaha, 1988. [2] 60 no. cc $125.

015b: FIVE TALES Cummington Press, Omaha, 1988. [2] 160 no. cc. Hors Commerce $100.

016a: THE OUTERMOST DREAM Knopf, New York, 1989. [] Uncorrected proof. In orange wraps (Bev Chaney 2/89) $60.

016b: THE OUTERMOST DREAM Knopf, New York, 1989. [1] Essays and reviews. (Published April 1989 @ $19.95) $8/40

017a: BILLY DYER ... Knopf, New York, 1992. [] Uncorrected proof. In yellow wraps (Bev Chaney 11/91) $60.

017b: BILLY DYER ... Knopf, New York, 1992. [1] 7/35

018a: ALL THE DAYS AND NIGHTS *The Collected Stories* Knopf, New York, 1995. [] Uncorrected proof. First issue in printed cream (white) colored wraps (Bev Chaney, Jr. 1/95) $50.

018b: ALL THE DAYS AND NIGHTS *The Collected Stories* Knopf, New York, 1995. [1] Advance reading copy. In 4-color decorated wraps. Issued for promotional purposes with a leaf bound in that is signed by the author. Issued in publisher's decorated card-stock slipcase (Ken Lopez 5/95) $75/100

018c: ALL THE DAYS AND NIGHTS *The Collected Stories* Knopf, New York, 1995. [] (Published 1/95 @ $25.00) $5/25

019a: MRS. DONALD'S DOG BUN AND HIS HOME AWAY FROM HOME Knopf, New York, 1995. [] Folded and gathered sheets laid into dust wrapper (Bookfinders 9/96) $40/75

019b: MRS. DONALD'S DOG BUN AND HIS HOME AWAY FROM HOME Knopf, New York (1995) [3] $5/25

020a: THE HAPPINESS OF GETTING IT DOWN RIGHT *Letters of Frank O'Connor and William Maxwell* Knopf, New York, 1996. [] Uncorrected proof. In blue printed wraps (Bev Chaney, Jr. 12/96) $40.

020b: THE HAPPINESS OF GETTING IT DOWN RIGHT *Letters of Frank O'Connor and William Maxwell* Knopf, New York, 1996. [1] $5/25

Joe McElroy

JOSEPH McELROY

McElroy was born in Brooklyn in 1930. He graduated from William and Mary and received a masters from Columbia University. He has taught English at various universities.

001a: A SMUGGLER'S BIBLE Harcourt Brace & World, New York (1966). [] Uncorrected proof. In yellow printed wraps. May have been as many as 200 copies (Glenn Horowitz #7). $400.

001b: A SMUGGLER'S BIBLE Harcourt Brace & World, New York (1966). [] Advance Reading Copy. In tan printed wraps (Pettler & Lieberman 6/95) $300.

001c: A SMUGGLER'S BIBLE Harcourt Brace & World, New York (1966). [1] (Published September 28, 1966) $50/250

001d: A SMUGGLER'S BIBLE Longmans, Toronto, 1966. [] $25/125

001e: A SMUGGLER'S BIBLE Deutsch (London, 1968). [1] $30/150

002a: HIND'S KIDNAP Harper, New York (1969). [1] $20/100

002b: HIND'S KIDNAP Anthony Blond, (London, 1970). [1] $15/75

003a: ANCIENT HISTORY Knopf, New York, 1971. [1] (Published May 21, 1971) $15/60

004a: LOOKOUT CARTRIDGE Knopf, New York, 1974. [] Uncorrected proof. In light blue wraps (Serendipity 2/89) $150.

004b: LOOKOUT CARTRIDGE Knopf, New York, 1974. [1] First issue: cloth spine and paper covered boards (Christopher Stevens) $15/75

004c: LOOKOUT CARTRIDGE Knopf, New York, 1974. [1] Full cloth binding $10/50

005a: PLUS Knopf, New York, 1977. [1] $15/60

005b: PLUS Knopf, New York, 1977. [1] Wraps. Simultaneous issue $25.

006a: SHIPROCK *A Place* Wm. Ewert, Concord, New Hampshire (1980). [2] 13 cc. Specially bound for presentation in quarter leather and boards (James Jaffe #12) $300.

006b: SHIPROCK *A Place* Wm. Ewert, Concord, New Hampshire (1980). [2] 26 sgd ltr cc $175.

006c: SHIPROCK *A Place* Wm. Ewert, Concord, New Hampshire (1980). [2] 200 (of 220) sgd no. cc $75.

007a: WOMEN AND MEN Knopf, New York, 1987. [] Uncorrected proof. Two volumes. In yellow wraps (Lame Duck Books 4/90) $100.

007b: WOMEN AND MEN Ultramarine, Hastings-on-Hudson, 1987. [2] 99 sgd no. cc. Issued in half-leather $175.

007c: WOMEN AND MEN Knopf, New York, 1987. [1] 7,000 cc. (Published February 27, 1987.) Incorrect copyright on first state (J & J Hanrahan 2/89). (Bev Chaney states "reportedly 2,500 cc" 2/92) $10/40

008a: THE LETTER LEFT TO ME Knopf, New York, 1988. [] Uncorrected proof. In red wraps (Bev Chaney List C) $75.

008b: THE LETTER LEFT TO ME Knopf, New York, 1988. [] 8,500 cc. (Published October 1988 @ $16.95) $7/35

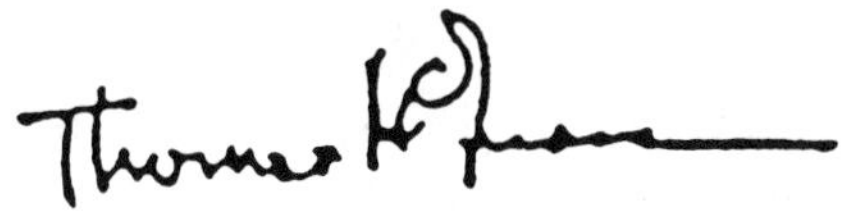

THOMAS McGUANE

McGuane was born in Michigan in 1939. He received a B.A. at Michigan State University and a Masters in Drama from Yale. He has been writing full-time since the success of his first book.

We wish to thank both Jack Mullenax and Michael Raskin for the bibliographic information supplied for the preparation of this guide.

001a: THE SPORTING CLUB Simon & Schuster, New York (1968). [1] Advance uncorrected proof. In tall yellow wraps $1,000.

001b: THE SPORTING CLUB Simon & Schuster, New York (1968). [1] Red cloth, gilt lettering $50/250

001c: THE SPORTING CLUB Andre Deutsch (London, 1969). [1] Green boards, gilt lettering $30/150

001d: THE SPORTING CLUB Doubleday, Toronto (1969) [] $25/125

002a: THE BUSHWHACKED PIANO Simon & Schuster, New York (1971). [] Uncorrected proof. In tall pad bound yellow wraps $450.

002b: THE BUSHWHACKED PIANO Simon & Schuster, New York (1971). [1] Brown cloth, black title letters $25/125

002c: THE BUSHWHACKED PIANO Minerva, London, 1989. [] Wraps. (Nicholas and Helen Burrows 1/95) $40.

003a: NINETY-TWO IN THE SHADE Farrar, Straus & Giroux, New York (1973). Uncorrected page proof. In yellow wraps $300.

003b: NINETY-TWO IN THE SHADE Farrar, Straus & Giroux, New York (1973). [1] Cloth in two shades of blue with silver lettering $20/100

003c: NINETY-TWO IN THE SHADE Collins, London (1974). [] Advance copy. In red wraps $150.

003d: NINETY-TWO IN THE SHADE Collins, London (1974). [1] Red boards, silver title letters $15/75

004a: THE MISSOURI BREAKS Ballantine, New York (1976). [1] Paperback original "First Edition: June 1976." No. 25218-7 with $1.75 price $60.

005a: THE ANGLER'S COAST Doubleday, New York, 1976. [1] Introduction by McGuane to Russell Chatham's book $12/60

006a: PANAMA Farrar, Straus & Giroux, New York (1978). [] Tall narrow gray-green wraps (Ken Lopez 10/91) $250.

006b: PANAMA Farrar, Straus & Giroux, New York (1978). [1] Green cloth spine, green boards, silver title letters $8/40

006c: PANAMA McGraw-Hill Ryerson, Toronto (1978). [] $8/40

006d: PANAMA Penguin Books, Harmondsworth, 1979. [1] Wraps $30.

007a: AN OUTSIDE CHANCE ... Farrar, Straus & Giroux, New York (1980). [1] Uncorrected proof. In green wraps $125.

007b: AN OUTSIDE CHANCE ... Farrar, Straus & Giroux, New York (1980). [1] Cream cloth spine and brown boards with bronze title letters $12/60

007c: AN OUTSIDE CHANCE ... McGraw-Hill Ryerson, Toronto (1980). [] $10/50

007d: AN OUTSIDE CHANCE ... Penguin Books, Harmondsworth (1982). [1] Wraps $30.

007e: AN OUTSIDE CHANCE ... Houghton Mifflin, Boston, 1990. [3] 4,200 cc. 4 new essays and introduction by Geoffrey Wolff. (Published October 1990 @ $19.95) $10/35

007f: AN OUTSIDE CHANCE ... Houghton Mifflin, Boston, 1990. [] 7,000 cc. Wraps $25.

008a: NOBODY'S ANGEL Random House, New York, 1982. [] Uncorrected proof. In red wraps $125.

008b: NOBODY'S ANGEL Random House, New York (1982). [4] 5,000 cc. Brown cloth spine and tan boards with gilt letters $10/50

008c: NOBODY'S ANGEL Random House, New York (1982). [4] Wraps. Issued simultaneously $25.

008d: NOBODY'S ANGEL Random House of Canada Ltd., Toronto (1981). [] $8/40

009a: THE VANISHING BREED New York Graphic Society / Little Brown, Boston (1982). [2] 750 sgd no. cc. Leather spine. Issued in slipcase. Short introduction by McGuane. Signed by McGuane and William Albert Allard, a photographer $350/450

009b: THE VANISHING BREED New York Graphic Society / Little Brown, Boston (1982). [1] 17,500 cc $35/100

009c: THE VANISHING BREED New York Graphic Society / Little Brown, Boston (1982). [1] 10,000 cc. Wraps $40.

010a: DEEP CREEK Winn, Seattle, 1984. [2] 150 sgd cc. Paintings by Russell Chatham and signed by him (not by others), text by McGuane, Hunter Thompson and Jim Harrison. Includes 2 of Chatham's signed plates in rear pocket. There is no limitation page. Plates are numbered and signed. Issued without dustwrapper or slipcase. (Published October 1984 @ $175) $750.

010b: RUSSELL CHATHAM Clark City Press, Livingston, Montana, 1987. [3] Wraps. Adds 4 full page photographs in front (pages 6 through 9 unnumbered) and changed two in back; otherwise, exactly the same as 010a but no acknowledgment that it was ever published before $40.

011a: IN THE CRAZIES Winn, Seattle, 1985. [2] 185 sgd no. cc (190 copies in total). With large portfolio of 10 various sized plates signed and numbered by artist Russell Chatham. Book signed by both McGuane and Chatham. Book has leather spine and cloth covered boards in gray cloth slipcase. Portfolio is in matching gray cloth. Published at $1,500. $2,250/2,500

012a: SOMETHING TO BE DESIRED Random House, New York (1984). [4] Uncorrected proof. In yellow wraps (Bert Babcock 2/92) $100.

012b: SOMETHING TO BE DESIRED Random House, New York (1984). [4] Blue cloth spine and white boards with silver title letters. (Published October 29, 1984 @ $14.95) $8/40

012c: SOMETHING TO BE DESIRED Random House of Canada, Toronto (1984). [] $8/40

012d: SOMETHING TO BE DESIRED Secker & Warburg, London (1985). [1] Red boards and gilt letters $8/40

013a: TO SKIN A CAT Dutton, New York (1986). [] Advance uncorrected proof. In mint green wraps. Also noted hand numbered (#134) and sgd (Else Fine Books 8/93) $75.

013b: TO SKIN A CAT Dutton, New York (1986). [2] 250 sgd no. cc. Advance excerpt. Wraps (Beasley Books #34) $75.

013c: TO SKIN A CAT Dutton, New York, 1986. [3] Also states "First Edition." (Published October 1986 @ $16.95) $7/35

013d: TO SKIN A CAT Dutton, New York (1987). [3] Wraps. Also states "First Edition" $20.

013e: TO SKIN A CAT Secker & Warburg, London (1987). [1] Red boards, gilt letters $8/40

014a: KEEP THE CHANGE Houghton Mifflin, Boston, 1989. [3] Advance reading copy. In decorated wraps $60.

014b: KEEP THE CHANGE Houghton Mifflin, Boston, 1989. [2] 150 sgd no. cc. Issued without dustwrapper. In slipcase $150/200

014c: KEEP THE CHANGE Houghton Mifflin, Boston, 1989. [3] 30,000 cc. Tan cloth spine and green boards with green title letters and gilt signature on front cover. (Published September 1989 @ $18.95) $10/40

014d: KEEP THE CHANGE McClelland & Stewart (Toronto, 1989). [] (Annex Books 4/96) $10/40

014e: KEEP THE CHANGE Secker & Warburg, London, 1990. [0] $10/40

015a: NOTHING BUT BLUE SKIES Houghton Mifflin, Boston, 1992. [3] Advance uncorrected proof. In pictorial wraps $75.

015b: NOTHING BUT BLUE SKIES Houghton Mifflin, Boston, 1992. [2] 300 sgd no. cc $100/150

015c: NOTHING BUT BLUE SKIES Houghton Mifflin, Boston, 1992. [3] 50,000 cc (PW) $5/25

015d: NOTHING BUT BLUE SKIES McClelland & Stewart, Toronto, 1992. [] Wraps. Printed card covers with flaps. A paperback original (Annex Books 2/96) $35.

016a: SONS Lord John Press, Northridge, 1993. [2] 26 sgd ltr cc $ 200/250

016b SONS Lord John Press, Northridge, 1993. [2] 300 sgd no. cc. Blue cloth. In blue cloth slipcase $50/75

017a: LIVE WATER Meadow Run Press (Stone Harbor, New Jersey, 1996). [2] 1,500 cc. In slipcase. Twelve fly fishing essays. Issued without dustwrapper. In slipcase (Bev Chaney, Jr. 2/96) $100/125

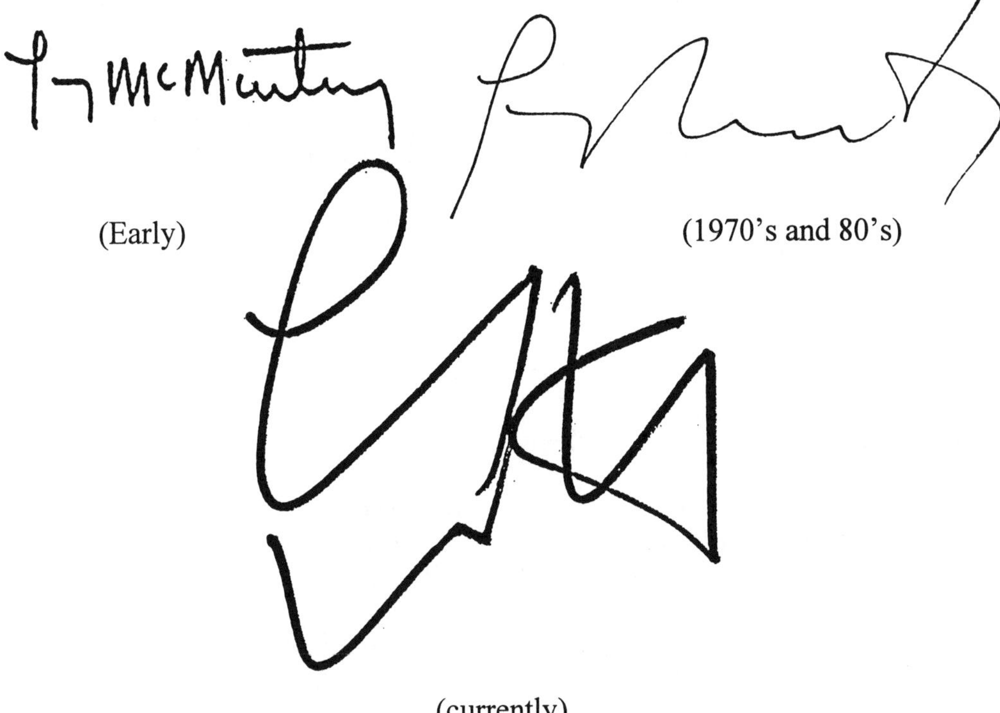

(Early) (1970's and 80's)

(currently)

LARRY McMURTRY

Larry McMurtry was born in Wichita Falls, Texas in 1936. He spent most of his early years in the ranching country of north-central Texas. He holds a master's degree from Rice University. He received a Wallace Stegner Fellowship at Stanford and was awarded a Guggenheim Fellowship for creative writing in fiction. *Horseman Pass By* (Hud), *The Last Picture Show*, and *Terms of Endearment* were made into successful movies with the latter receiving the Academy Award for the Best Picture of 1983.

McMurtry is also a prolific essayist and screen writer and operates antiquarian bookstores in Tucson, Arizona, Archer City, Texas and in the Georgetown section of Washington, D.C. with his partner, Marcia Carter. His book, *Lonesome Dove*, won the Pulitzer Prize for Fiction for 1986.

REFERENCES:

(a) Lepper, Gary M. A BIBLIOGRAPHICAL INTRODUCTION TO SEVENTY-FIVE MODERN AMERICAN AUTHORS. Berkeley: Serendipity Books, 1976.

(b) Bruccoli, Matthew J. (Series Editor.) FIRST PRINTINGS OF AMERICAN AUTHORS. Volume 4. Detroit: Gale Research Company (1979).

(c) Inventory, catalogs, publishers' records. Used for all entries after 011.

001a: HORSEMAN, PASS BY Harper, New York (1961). [1] Approximately 5,000 cc. One of A.C. Greene's *50 Best Books on Texas* $300/1,500

001b: HUD Popular Library, New York (1961). [1] Wraps. Movie title of *Horseman Pass By*. No. 60-2130. States "First Printing February, 1961." $60.

001c: HORSEMAN, PASS BY Sphere, London, 1971. [1] Wraps. (Ref.c) $100.

002a: TEXAS INSTITUTE...AWARDS...SPEECH (Texas Institute, Dallas, 1962.) [0] Wraps. Ditto sheets of text of speech $350.

003a: LEAVING CHEYENNE Harper & Row, New York (1963). [1] Approximately 3,500 cc. One of A.C. Greene's *50 Best Books on Texas*. Dustwrapper priced at $4.50, reportedly changed to $4.95 after publication. We've been told there is a dustwrapper with a printed price of $4.95 but have never seen one. We've only seen with gummed sticker over old price or with dustwrapper price-clipped with " $4.95" sticker or stamped in red at bottom of front flap.

003b: LEAVING CHEYENNE Sphere, London (1972). [1] $100.

004a: DAUGHTER OF THE TEJAS New York Graphic, Greenwich, Connecticut (1965). [1] Ghostwritten for Orphelia Ray. In gray dustwrapper. Although this was ghosted by McMurtry, he believes it's possible it may have been rewritten by someone else before publication $50/250

004b: DAUGHTER OF THE TEJAS New York Graphic, Greenwich, Connecticut (1965). [1] White dustwrapper. We assume this is a remainder dustwrapper $50/200

005a: THE LAST PICTURE SHOW Dial, New York, 1966. [] Uncorrected galley proof (7 1/2" x 12"). Punched at top and string tied with printed cover sheet (William Reese 5/89) $4,000.

005b: THE LAST PICTURE SHOW Dial, New York, 1966. [1] Wraps. Spiral-bound reading copies in plain stiff olive covers (Joseph The Provider 9/89). (Green card covers -Ken Lopez 4/92) $2,000.

005c: THE LAST PICTURE SHOW Dial, New York, 1966. [1] $150/600

005d: THE LAST PICTURE SHOW Dial, New York (1966?). [0] "Book Club Edition" stated on bottom corner of front dustwrapper flap, no price on top of front dustwrapper flap. Does not state "First Edition" on copyright page $6/30

005e: THE LAST PICTURE SHOW Sphere, London, 1972. [] Wraps. $75.

005f: THE LAST PICTURE SHOW Simon & Schuster, New York, no date [1989]. [3] Hardback reprint published at $18.95 but could be confusing because it has the number "1" in series and is not clearly marked as a reprint $5/25

006a: IN A NARROW GRAVE Encino, no place or date. [] Galley proof. 5½" x 24". "Pulled

5/17/68." With the "skycrapers" misprint (Detering Book Gallery 12/92) $3,500.

006b: IN A NARROW GRAVE Encino, no place or date. [] Galley proof. 5½" x 24". "Revised 6/12/68." With the "skycrapers" misprint (Detering Book Gallery 12/92) $3,000.

006c: IN A NARROW GRAVE Encino, Austin, 1968. [0] 845 cc. With "skycrapers" vs. "skyscrapers" on p.105:12 and many other errors. All but 15 were reportedly destroyed but seems more common $1,500/2,000

006d: IN A NARROW GRAVE Encino, Austin, 1968. [2] 250 sgd no. cc. Issued in slipcase $1,500/,2000

006e: IN A NARROW GRAVE Encino, Austin, 1968. [0] $150/750

006f: IN A NARROW GRAVE Encino, Austin, 1968. [0] Has "B" on copyright page (second printing) $40/200

006g: IN A NARROW GRAVE Simon & Schuster, New York (1989). [3] Wraps. Also states "First Touchstone Edition." Includes new preface $25.

007a: MOVING ON Simon & Schuster, New York, 1970. [] Uncorrected proof. In tall yellow wraps (Detering Book Gallery 7/95) $1,500.

007b: MOVING ON Simon & Schuster, New York, 1970. [] Advance reading copy. Folded sheets stapled into dustwrapper (Joseph the Provider) $1,000.

007c: MOVING ON Simon & Schuster, New York (1970). [1] 22,500 cc $40/200

007d: MOVING ON Weidenfeld, London (1971). [1] (Ref.c) $30/150

007e: MOVING ON Simon & Schuster, New York (1987). [3] Wraps. Also states "First Touchstone Edition." Includes new preface $25.

008a: "TEXAS IS RICH IN UNREDEEMED DREAMS" Texas Library Association, Austin (1971). [0] Broadside. First issue is printed on white paper stock. Text is from *In A Narrow Grave...* $750.

008b: "TEXAS IS RICH IN UNREDEEMED DREAMS" Texas Library Association, Austin (1971). [0] Broadside. Second issue is on tan paper stock. The majority are on tan stock, but there are a few on white which were (reportedly) done initially and rejected in favor of the tan. $500.

009a: ALL MY FRIENDS ARE GOING TO BE STRANGERS Simon & Schuster, New York (1972). [] Uncorrected proof. Pad bound. In tall yellow wraps (Ken Lopez 12/90) $1,000.

009b: ALL MY FRIENDS ARE GOING TO BE STRANGERS Simon & Schuster, New York (1972). [1] 10,000 cc $40/200

009c: ALL MY FRIENDS ARE GOING TO BE STRANGERS Secker & Warburg, London (1972). [1] (Ref.c) $20/100

009d: ALL MY FRIENDS ARE GOING TO BE STRANGERS Simon & Schuster, New York (1989). [3] Wraps. Also states "First Touchstone Edition." Includes new preface $25.

009e: ALL MY FRIENDS ARE GOING TO BE STRANGERS Book of Month Club, New York (1989). [1] "This edition was specially created in 1989 for BOMC." Also includes *Terms of Endearment* and new prefaces for each which are the only hardback appearances of the prefaces $10/35

010a: IT'S ALWAYS WE RAMBLED... Hallman, New York, 1974. [2] 300 sgd no. cc. Issued without dustwrapper or slipcase $500.

011a: TERMS OF ENDEARMENT Simon & Schuster, New York (1975). [3] Advance uncorrected proof. In tall yellow printed wraps (ref.c) $750.

011b: TERMS OF ENDEARMENT Simon & Schuster, New York (1975). [3] 16,500 cc. One of those Simon & Schuster "aged page" editions, printed before they used acid-free paper. Price would be for better than usual copies $35/175

011c: TERMS OF ENDEARMENT Allen, London, 1977. [1] 2,000 cc $15/75

011d: TERMS OF ENDEARMENT Allen, London, 1977. [1] 100,000 cc. Wraps $25.

011e: TERMS OF ENDEARMENT Simon & Schuster, New York (1989). [3] Wraps. Also states "First Touchstone Edition." Includes new preface (ref.c) $20.

012a: SOMEBODY'S DARLING Simon & Schuster, New York (1987). [3] Advance uncorrected proof. In yellow wraps (ref.c) $500.

012b: SOMEBODY'S DARLING Simon & Schuster, New York (1987). [3] $12/100

012c: SOMEBODY'S DARLING Simon & Schuster, New York (1987). [3] Wraps (ref.c). Also states "First Touchstone Edition." New preface $15.

013a: CADILLAC JACK Simon & Schuster, New York (1982). [3] Advance uncorrected proof. In yellow wraps (ref.c) $300.

013b: CADILLAC JACK Simon & Schuster, New York (1982). [2] 250 sgd no. cc. Issued without dustwrapper. In slipcase (ref.c) $275/350

013c: CADILLAC JACK Simon & Schuster, New York (1982). [3] 22,500 cc (ref.c) $15/75

013d: CADILLAC JACK Simon & Schuster, New York (1985). [3] Wraps. Also states "First Touchstone Edition." ISBN numbers would indicate a hardback edition, but none published. Includes new preface $15.

013e: CADILLAC JACK W.H. Allen, London, 1986. [0] $15/75

014a: THE DESERT ROSE Simon & Schuster, New York (1983). [3] Wraps. Advance uncorrected proof. In yellow wraps (ref.c) $250.

014b: THE DESERT ROSE Simon & Schuster, New York (1983). [2] 250 sgd no. cc. Issued without dustwrapper. In slipcase (ref.c) $275/350

014c: THE DESERT ROSE Simon & Schuster, New York (1983). [3] 19,800 cc (ref.c) $12/60

014d: THE DESERT ROSE W.H. Allen, London, 1985. [1] $12/60

014e: THE DESERT ROSE Simon & Schuster, New York (1985). [3] Wraps. Also states "First Touchstone Edition." Includes new preface. ISBN numbers would indicate there was a hardback edition, but none published $15.

015a: LONESOME DOVE Simon & Schuster, New York (1985). [3] Approximately 500 cc. Advance uncorrected proof. In yellow printed wraps $600.

015b: "PIGS ON THE PORCH" Simon & Schuster (New York, 1985). [0] 500 cc. Promotional broadside for book, which starts "When Augustus came out on the porch..." 500 copies were printed for bookstore promotion, but not too many seemed to have survived $350.

015c: LONESOME DOVE Simon & Schuster, New York (1985). [3] 41,000 cc. P.621.16 "none" vs. "done" (presume all copies - Jenkins #187). Pulitzer Prize in 1986. Also noted with "Pulitzer Prize Winner / Fiction" in circle on front of dustwrapper, otherwise no differences from first edition dustwrapper $50/250

015d: LONESOME DOVE Pan Books London / Sydney (1986). [3] Also states "This edition published 1986 by Pan Books Ltd." Pictorial wraps. Noted with white circular sticker on front cover indicating the book won the Pulitzer Prize for fiction. No hardcover edition $75.

016a: TENT LIFE IN SIBERIA Peregrine Smith, Salt Lake City (1986). [3] Wraps. 3,000 cc. McMurtry introduction to this reprint of George Kennan's book $40.

017a: A WALK IN PASADENA WITH DIANNIE AND MARY ALICE No publisher, place or date [1985]. [0] 50 cc (or perhaps more). Some copies have picture of Grammy Hall, Diane Keaton's grandmother. Oversize heavy paper wraps. Author retained 8 copies and the others were given to Dianne Keaton. $1,500.

018a: TEXASVILLE Simon & Schuster, New York (1987). [0] Xerox copy of manuscript. Cheaply bound in two volumes with black cloth spine. 10 no. copies (Monroe Stahr Books 9/95) $300.

018b: TEXASVILLE Simon & Schuster, New York (1987). [] Uncorrected proof. In yellow wraps. Housed in publisher's slipcase and sleeve with label on spine and reduced photocopy of yellow wrapper on front of case. (Priscilla Juvelis 4/95) $200/300

018c: TEXASVILLE Simon & Schuster, New York (1987). [3] 367 cc. Uncorrected proof. In yellow wraps. Assume same as above but without slipcase $200.

018d: TEXASVILLE Simon & Schuster, New York (1987). [3] 100,000 cc. (Published April 1987 @ $18.95) $7/35

018e: TEXASVILLE Sidgewick & Jackson, London (1987). [1] $8/40

019a: FILM FLAM Simon & Schuster, New York (1987). [0] Xerox copy of manuscript with "The Hired Man" as "The Hired Pen" and without "A Walk In Pasadena With ..." (Bev Chaney #47) $350.

019b: FILM FLAM Simon & Schuster, New York (1987). [3] Xerox copy of proof. With *The Hired Men* changed in ink to *The Hired Pen* on contents page and " A Walk..." added at end of contents and added at back, using sheets xeroxed from the limited edition (17a above) $300.

019c: FILM FLAM Simon & Schuster, New York (1987). [] Uncorrected proof. In yellow wraps $200.

019d: FILM FLAM Simon & Schuster, New York (1987). [3] 15,000 cc. (Published June 5, 1987 @ $16.95) $15/75

020a: COWBOYS Wind River Press for the Book Club of Texas (Austin, 1988). [0] 14" x 20" poster with one drawing by Barbara Holman (ref.c) $200.

021a: ANYTHING FOR BILLY Simon & Schuster, New York (1988). [3] Uncorrected proof. In yellow wraps $150.

021b: ANYTHING FOR BILLY Simon & Schuster, New York (1988). [3] 201,000 cc. (Published October 1988 @ $18.95.) Also, we have one copy (in our personal collection) of a proof dustwrapper that is very similar to the *Lonesome Dove* dustwrapper. Reportedly there were a number sent to sales force but have never seen it offered for sale $7/35

021c: ANYTHING FOR BILLY Collins, London, 1989. [1] $8/40

022a: SOME CAN WHISTLE Simon & Schuster, New York (1989). [] Uncorrected proof. In yellow wraps $150.

022b: SOME CAN WHISTLE Simon & Schuster, New York (1989). [3] (Published October 1989 @ $19.95) $7/35

022c: SOME CAN WHISTLE Century, London (1990). [1] $8/40

023a: BUFFALO GIRLS Simon & Schuster, New York, 1990. [] Unbound sheets with holographic changes reproduced $150.

023b: BUFFALO GIRLS Simon & Schuster, New York (1990). [3] Uncorrected proof. In yellow wraps $150.

023c: BUFFALO GIRLS Simon & Schuster, New York (1990). [3] $5/25

023d: BUFFALO GIRLS Century, London (1991). [2] 500 no. cc. Uncorrected proof. Wraps $75.

023e: BUFFALO GIRLS Century, London (1991). [] $7/35

024a: THE EVENING STAR Simon & Schuster, New York (1992). [] 8 1/2" x 11". Reproduced manuscript sheets $150.

024b: THE EVENING STAR Simon & Schuster, New York (1992). [3] Uncorrected proof. In yellow wraps $125.

024c: THE EVENING STAR Simon & Schuster, New York (1992). [3] (Published June 1992 @ $23) $5/25

024d: THE EVENING STAR Orion, London (1992). [1] $7/35

025a: STREETS OF LAREDO Simon & Schuster, New York, 1993. [3] Uncorrected proof. In yellow wraps $125.

025b: STREETS OF LAREDO Simon & Schuster, New York, 1993. [3] 250,000 cc (350,000 cc [PW] 5/31/93). (Published 6/93 @ $25.00) $5/25

026a: PRETTY BOY FLOYD Simon & Schuster, New York (1994). [3] Uncorrected proof. In yellow wraps (Waiting For Godot Books 2/95) $100.

026b: PRETTY BOY FLOYD Simon & Schuster, New York (1994). [] "A Limited Edition Special Advance Reader's Excerpt. Not For Resale. Uncorrected proof." Pictorial wraps. Written with Diana Ossana $50.

026c: PRETTY BOY FLOYD Simon & Schuster, New York (1994). [3] 275,000 cc (PW). (Published 9/94 @ $ 23.00.) Written with Diana Ossana 5/25

026d: PRETTY BOY FLOYD Orion (London, 1996). [1] $7/35

027a: THE LATE CHILD Simon & Schuster, New York (1995). [3] Uncorrected proof. In yellow printed wraps (Ken Lopez 4/95) $100.

027b: THE LATE CHILD Simon & Schuster, New York (1995). [3] $5/25

027c: THE LATE CHILD Orion (London, 1996). [1] $8/40

028a: DEAD MAN'S WALK Simon & Schuster, New York, 1995. [] Tape bound manuscript. 3 vols. Author's typescript with corrections. Photocopied. (Estimated at only about 12 copies [Waverley Books 1/96]) $200.

028b: DEAD MAN'S WALK Simon & Schuster, New York / London / Toronto / Sydney / Singapore (1995) [3] Uncorrected proof. In yellow wraps $75.

028c: DEAD MAN'S WALK Simon & Schuster, New York / London / Toronto / Sydney / Singapore (1995). [3] Advance copy of trade edition. Orange and black sticker on front panel of dustwrapper reading: "Advance Copy - September Publication Compliments of Simon & Schuster (Vagabond Books 2/96) $7/35

028d: DEAD MAN'S WALK Simon & Schuster, New York / London / Toronto / Sydney / Singapore (1995). [3] $5/25

028e: DEAD MAN'S WALK Orion (London, 1995). [1] $8/40

029a: SPLENDORS & MISERIES OF BEING AN AUTHOR-BOOKSELLER Antiquarian Booksellers' Association of America, no place (1995). [2] 750 cc. In Stapled wraps. The text of McMurtry's address to the ABAA in Chicago on May 20, 1995 $50.

030a: ZEKE AND NED Simon & Schuster (New York, 1997). [3] Written with Diana Ossana. Published @ $25.

031a: COMANCHE MOON Simon & Schuster (New York, 1997). [3] Uncorrected proof in yellow printed wraps (Bev Chaney, Jr. 10/97) $75.

031b: COMANCHE MOON Simon & Schuster (New York, 1997). [3]

VLADIMIR NABOKOV
1899-1977

Nabokov was born in St. Petersburg, Russia, of aristocratic parents in 1899. After the Russian Revolution, he emigrated to England where he graduated from Cambridge in 1922. He came to the United States in 1940 and became a naturalized citizen in 1945. He was a professor of Russian literature at Cornell University from 1948 to 1959.

We have concerned ourselves with only those books of the author published in English. There are 22 other Nabokov items (in Russian) not included here, but which are included in Ref.a.. We have listed them chronologically as they appeared in translation before 1941. Nabokov's first book *Stikhi* was a collection of 68 poems published in Russia in 1916 but never translated into English. His first book to be translated was *Camera Obscura* and was published in England in 1936. We have included some of the scientific off-prints; there were 18 in total. We left out those that had little or no bibliographical information in the primary reference or were single sheets.

We wish to thank Michael Juliar for permission to use his bibliography, and for the updates and editing that he was kind enough to provide.

REFERENCES:

(a) Juliar, Michael. VALADIMIR NABOKOV *A Descriptive Bibliography*. New York: Garland, 1986. (An excellent reference.)

(b) Eppard, Philip B., Editor. FIRST PRINTINGS OF AMERICAN AUTHORS. Volume 5. Detroit: Gale Research (1987).

(c) Inventory or dealer catalogs.

001a: CAMERA OBSCURA John Long, London (1936). [0] Author's last name listed on book as "Nabokoff-Sirin." Translated by Winifred Roy. Ref.a notes only seven copies located. $2,000/20,000

001b: LAUGHTER IN THE DARK Bobbs-Merrill, Indianapolis/New York (1938). [1] New title. Author's last name listed as "Nabokoff." Translated into English by Nabokov. The presumed first issue binding is green (based on the two copyright deposit copies at the Library of Congress) $300/1,500

001c: LAUGHTER IN THE DARK Bobbs-Merrill, Indianapolis/New York (1938). [1] Variant bindings: orange, brown or red $250/1,250

001d: LAUGHTER IN THE DARK New Directions (New York, 1960). [1] "New Edition 1960." Two variants, one has two extra lines at bottom of copyright page "New Directions... New York 14," the other does not. Ref.a gives no priority, but states about 1,490 copies in variant without address and 1,468 copies in the other. Publisher records show 1,492 copies bound November 10, 1960; and 1,409 copies bound later $15/75

001e: LAUGHTER IN THE DARK Weidenfeld & Nicolson, London (1961). [0] $30/150

002a: DESPAIR John Long, London (1937). [1] Author's last name listed as "Nabokoff-Sirin." Black cloth stamped in gilt (ref.a). Also noted in orange cloth lettered in black (Joseph The Provider 9/90) $2,000/20,000

002b: DESPAIR Putnam, New York (1966). [0] Author's last name listed as "Nabokov." Revised with new material and new foreword. The first issue dustwrapper has the title in reddish-pink on front dustwrapper flap $35/175

002c: DESPAIR Putnam, New York (1966). [0] Title on front flap in black $25/125

002d: DESPAIR Weidenfeld & Nicolson, London (1966). [1] $15/75

003a: THE REAL LIFE OF SEBASTIAN KNIGHT New Directions, Norfolk, Connecticut (1941). [0] 1,500 cc (total a & b, approximately 750 in each binding). First issue binding: woven red burlap $250/750

003b: THE REAL LIFE OF SEBASTIAN KNIGHT New Directions, Norfolk, Connecticut (1941). [0] Bound in smooth red cloth with two dustwrapper variants, author's name spelled "Nabokov" and Nabokoff." No priority although 003a is shown with "Nabokov" spelling, which would seem to indicate it was first. There is also the feeling that the "Nabokoff" was printed first but set aside and only used on the later second issue copies when they ran out of the other dustwrappers $100/500

003c: THE REAL LIFE OF SEBASTIAN KNIGHT Editions Poetry, London (1945). [1] First issue dustwrapper in red with gold and black lettering $75/400

003d: THE REAL LIFE OF SEBASTIAN KNIGHT Editions Poetry, London (1945). [1] Dustwrapper in yellow with red and black lettering. Note: both c&d priced 8s.6d $75/350

004a: THE NEARCTIC FORMS OF LYCAEIDES HUB... Museum of Comparative Zoology (Cambridge, 1943). [0] 100 cc. Off-print from *Psyche* in stapled wraps $1,250.

005a: NOTES ON THE MORPHOLOGY OF THE GENUS LYCAEIDES Psyche (Cambridge, 1944). [0] 100 cc. Off-print in stapled wraps $1,250.

006a: NIKOLAI GOGOL New Directions, Norfolk, Connecticut (1944). [0] Tan cloth with brown lettering. 5 titles listed on verso of half-title. Dustwrapper has illustration of hand holding a pen and is priced $1.50 $75/350

006b: NIKOLAI GOGOL New Directions, Norfolk, Connecticut (1944). [0] Tan cloth with blue stamping and 14 titles listed on verso of half-title. Dustwrapper priced $2.00, and 14 titles listed on back flap $50/250

006c: NIKOLAI GOGOL Editions Poetry, London (1947). [1] Noted in tan or green cloth, priority unknown $50/250

007a: THREE RUSSIAN POETS *Selections from Pushkin, Lermontov and Tyutchev* New Directions, Norfolk, Connecticut (1944). [0] Translation by Nabokov. Part of the Poets of the Year series. Plain gray paper boards. Dustwrapper gray with brown lettering and $1.00 upper corner of front flap $125/350

007b: THREE RUSSIAN POETS *Selections from Pushkin, Lermontov and Tyutchev* Norfolk, Connecticut (1944). [0] Variant with dustwrapper glued to boards and in dustwrapper $100/300

007c: THREE RUSSIAN POETS *Selections from Pushkin, Lermontov and Tyutchev* New Directions, Norfolk, Connecticut (1944). [0] Tan stapled pamphlet. Dustwrapper bluish-gray with brown lettering and $0.50 in lower right corner of front flap $50/200

007d: PUSHKIN LERMONTOV TYUTCHEV Lindsay Drummond Ltd., London, 1947. [1] This edition includes 11 poems not in the American edition (007a) $50/250

008a: NOTES ON NEOTROPICAL PLEBEJINAE (Museum of Comparative Zoology, Cambridge, 1945.) [0] 100 cc. Off-print from *Psyche* in stapled wraps $1,000.

009a: A THIRD SPECIES OF ECHINARGUS NABOKOV Museum of Comparative Zoology (Cambridge, 1945). [0] 100 cc. Single leaf. Note on an article that appeared in *Psyche* $1,000.

010a: BEND SINISTER Henry Holt, New York (1947). [1] $60/300

010b: BEND SINISTER Weidenfeld & Nicolson, London (1960). [1] $40/200

010c: BEND SINISTER Time, New York (1964). [0] Wraps. 75,000 cc. First edition has one "X" in colophon on last page. Adds new foreword by Nabokov $40.

011a: NINE STORIES (New Directions, New York, 1947.) [0] Wraps. Published as *Direction Two*. This issue was devoted entirely to Nabokov. (Probably a few copies in cloth, perhaps black, would be worth quite a bit more) $300.

012a: A NEW SPECIES OF CYCLARGUS NABOKOV Cornell University, Ithaca (1948). [0] Wraps. Cover has "Reprinted From *The Entomologist...*" $750.

013a: THE NEARCTIC MEMBERS OF THE GENUS LYCAEIDES HUBNER (LYCAENIDAE LEPIDOPTERA) Museum of Comparative Zoology, Cambridge, 1949. [] Wraps. The article occupies the entire issue of this bulletin (Vol. 101, No. 4) $750.

014a: CONCLUSIVE EVIDENCE *A Memoir* Harper, New York (1951). [1] Also has "A-A" on copyright page $75/350

014b: SPEAK, MEMORY *A Memoir* Gollancz, London, 1951. [] Uncorrected Proof. In reddish-brown wraps. New Title $450.

014c: SPEAK, MEMORY *A Memoir* Gollancz, London, 1951. [0] First issue in blue-green cloth with black stamping. In dustwrapper without *Daily Mail* device on spine and at bottom of front flap. New Title $75/350

014d: SPEAK, MEMORY *A Memoir* Gollancz, London, 1951. [0] Second issue in blue cloth and gilt stamping. In dustwrapper with *Daily Mail* device on spine and at bottom of front flap ("Daily Mail Book of the Month" wrap-around band on some copies) $60/300

014e: SPEAK, MEMORY *An Autobiography Revised* Putnam, New York (1966). [0] 5,000 cc. States "Revised Edition" on copyright. Revised and adds new foreword $30/150

014f: SPEAK, MEMORY *An Autobiography Revised* Weidenfeld & Nicolson, London (1967). [1] $25/125

015a: LOLITA Olympia Press, Paris (1955). [0] Approximately 5,000 cc. Wraps. Two volumes. Printed price "Francs : 900" on back cover. Somewhat less if new price sticker added over original price $3,000.

015b: LOLITA Putnam, New York (1958). [0] One volume. Adds afterword by Nabokov $60/300

Note: book club copies have "Book Club Edition" on the corner of front flap (Cannot be distinguished from the trade edition without dustwrapper)

015c: LOLITA Weidenfeld & Nicolson, London (1959). [1] Black cloth stamped in silver. Foreword by the author under the name John Ray, Jr., Ph.D. (Ulysses 6/97) $40/200

015d: THE ANNOTATED LOLITA McGraw-Hill, New York/Toronto (1970). [1] Edited by Alfred Appel. Putnam text with many corrections $15/75

015e: THE ANNOTATED LOLITA Weidenfeld & Nicolson, London (1971). [1] $15/75

015f: LOLITA Franklin Library, Franklin Center, 1979. [2] "Limited edition" in full leather. Illustrated by Herbert Tauss $100.

015g: LOLITA Franklin Library, Franklin Center, 1981. [2] "Limited Edition." Illustrated by Jerry Pinkney $75.

016a: PNIN Doubleday, Garden City, 1957. [1] Noted with "46946" above or below price on dustwrapper flap (priority unknown) $50/250

016b: PNIN Heinemann, Melbourne / London / Toronto (1957). [] Uncorrected proof in orange wraps. Author, title and month of publication typed on front cover (Nicholas Pounder 5/90). Ref.a has white label on front $400.

016c: PNIN Heinemann, Melbourne / London / Toronto (1957). [1] $30/150

017a: A HERO OF OUR TIME Doubleday Anchor, Garden City, 1958. [1] Wraps. Written by Mihail Lermontov and translated by Vladimir Nabokov with Dmitri Nabokov. Cover illustration and topography by Edward Gorey $75.

017b: A HERO OF OUR TIME Oxford University Press, Oxford, 1984. [1] (Ref.c) $35/175

017c: A HERO OF OUR TIME Oxford University Press, Oxford, 1984. [1] Wraps $40.

018a: NABOKOV'S DOZEN Doubleday, Garden City, 1958. [1] A collection of 13 stories $50/250

018b: NABOKOV'S DOZEN Heinemann, London / Melbourne / Toronto (1959). [1] $30/150

018c: SPRING IN FIALTA Popular Library, New York (1959). [] Wraps. First paperback edition of the book published originally as *Nabokov's Dozen* (Between The Covers 12/94) $35.

018d: NABOKOV'S DOZEN Franklin Library, Franklin Center, 1977. [2] "Limited Edition." In full brown leather (Antic Hay Rare Books 6/93) $75.

019a: INVITATION TO A BEHEADING Putnam, New York (1959). [0] Translated with Dimitri Nabokov $30/150

019b: INVITATION TO A BEHEADING Weidenfeld & Nicolson, London (1960). [1] $25/125

020a: POEMS Doubleday, Garden City, 1959. [1] The Library of Congress deposit copy has "A25" on lower right corner of p.44. Ref.a calls this and the following "variants". $50/250

020b: POEMS Doubleday, Garden City, 1959. [1] "A26" on lower right corner of p.44 (priority unknown, we assume this is a later issue). Also noted an advance review copy with publisher's slip laid in of this state of p. 44, adding confusion to the question of priority (Robert Dagg 9/95) $40/200

020c: POEMS Weidenfeld & Nicolson, London (1961). [1] $30/150

021a: THE SONG OF IGOR'S CAMPAIGN Rándom House, New York (1960). [1] Wraps. Translated by Nabokov $75.

021b: THE SONG OF IGOR'S CAMPAIGN Weidenfeld & Nicolson, London (1961). [1] $40/200

022a: PALE FIRE Putnam, New York (1962). [1] "First Impression" also on front dustwrapper flap. Red endpapers $50/250

022b: PALE FIRE Weidenfeld & Nicolson, London (1962). [] Uncorrected proof. In brown wraps (Thomas Goldwasser 6/92) $300.

022c: PALE FIRE Weidenfeld & Nicolson, London (1962). [1] $30/150

023a: NOTES ON PROSODY Bollingen Series LXXII (Bollingen, New York, 1963). [0] 200 cc 30 copies of which went to Nabokov to give as Christmas gifts. This is an off-print taken from his translation of Pushkin's *Eugene Onegin* to be published later that same year. Wraps and dustwrapper $300/400

023b: NOTES ON PROSODY Pantheon (New York, 1964). [0] 3,500 cc. Wraps and dustwrapper (which is glued at spine to the wrappers). Appendix II to 025a below $100.

023c: NOTES ON PROSODY Routledge & Kegan Paul, London (1965). [1] 500 cc $50/200

024a: THE GIFT Putnam, New York (1963). [0] Book bulks 3.3 cm. Dustwrapper priced $5.95 (priority assumed) $40/200

024b: THE GIFT Putnam, New York (1963). [0] Book 3.8 cm wide. Dustwrapper priced $6.95. Assume a second issue $30/150

024c: THE GIFT Weidenfeld & Nicolson, London (1963). [] Uncorrected proof. In gray wraps (Waiting For Godot 7/90) $300.

024d: THE GIFT Weidenfeld & Nicolson, London (1963). [0] $25/125

025a: EUGENE ONEGIN *A Novel in Verse* By Aleksandr Pushkin. Pantheon (New York, 1964). [0] 4 volumes. Translation, introduction and commentary by Nabokov. In dustwrappers and slipcase. Earliest sets have ribbon place markers $200/400

025b: EUGENE ONEGIN *A Novel in Verse* Pantheon (New York, 1964). [0] Without ribbons $175/350

025c: EUGENE ONEGIN *A Novel in Verse* Routledge & Kegan Paul, London (1964). [1] 4 volumes $175/350

025d: EUGENE ONEGIN *A Novel in Verse* Revised Edition. Princeton University Press (1975). [0] 2,856 cc. 4 volumes. Bollingen Series LXXII $100/200

025e: EUGENE ONEGIN *A Novel in Verse* Revised Edition. Routledge & Kegan Paul, London (1975). [1] 1,000 cc. 4 volumes. (Sheets imported) $100/200

026a: THE RETURN OF PUSHKIN Edition N.P. Belaieff, London, 1964? [] Wraps? Translated by Nabokov $125.

027a: THE DEFENSE Putnam, New York (1964). [0] $35/175

027b: THE DEFENSE Weidenfeld & Nicolson, London (1964). [0] $25/125

028a: THE EYE Phaedra, New York (1965). [1] Advance review copy. In plain white wraps and cloth spine. Publisher's address on copyright page. Dustwrapper printed on white laid uncoated paper with Trident Press mentioned at bottom of back flap. Also noted in a dustwrapper described as being identical to the trade issue dustwrapper except being slightly larger. Also noted with cream paper spine sewn in published dustwrapper (Steven Temple). Also noted as an uncorrected proof in plain white card covers in slightly oversized dustwrapper (no mention of cloth spine [Nigel Williams 6/98]) $75/125

028b: THE EYE Phaedra, New York (1965). [1] Publisher's address on copyright page. Dustwrapper printed on white laid uncoated paper with Trident Press mentioned at bottom of back flap. Although Ref.a does not assign a priority to this issue, we believe it would be first as it matches the advance copy $15/75

028c: THE EYE Phaedra, New York (1965). [1] Assume second issue without publisher's address on copyright page. Dustwrapper printed on white smooth coated paper without Trident mentioned $10/50

028d: THE EYE Weidenfeld & Nicolson, London (1966). [] Advance uncorrected proof. In orange printed wraps $100.

028e: THE EYE Weidenfeld & Nicolson, London (1966). [1] $15/75

029a: THE WALTZ INVENTION Phaedra (New York), 1966. [1] A play in three acts

Variant a: Blue cloth. Bound in 4 signatures, 1st is on an non-acidic paper, the other 3 are on acidic bulky paper (such as newsprint). White endpapers. Dustwrapper has "New York 17, N.Y." on back flap. Bulks about 10 mm $17/75

Variant b: As variant a except all 4 signatures are on a non-acidic paper $15/75

Variant c: As variant b except with red endpapers. Bulks 8.5 mm $15/75

Variant d: As variant c except back flap of dustwrapper lacks "New York 17, N.Y." Bulks 8.5 mm $15/75

Variant e: As variant a except dark blue cloth, 8 extra blank pages after text, and has a dustwrapper totally different from other variants (most notable difference if you do not have two dustwrappers to compare is that this variant has a blue background). Back flap has publisher at 27 Washington Square (in lieu of 220 East 22nd St.). We assume this is not a variant but a later issue, as 22nd Street was an earlier address $10/40

029b: THE WALTZ INVENTION Weidenfeld & Nicolson (London, 1967). [1] $15/75

030a: NABOKOV'S QUARTET Phaedra (New York), 1966. [1]

Variant a: Green endpapers. Pages bulk about 10.5 mm $20/100

Variant b: White endpapers. Pages bulk about 8.5 mm $15/75

Variant c: White endpapers. Pages bulk about 8.5 mm. Two different kinds of paper used (one for the first signature and another for the second and third signatures) $12/60

030b: NABOKOV'S QUARTET Weidenfeld & Nicolson, London (1967). [1] $15/75

031a: KING, QUEEN, KNAVE McGraw-Hill, New York/Toronto (1968). [1] "First Edition 45715." Bottom edge rough-trimmed. Many of this state were destroyed by the publisher $100/150

031b: KING, QUEEN, KNAVE McGraw-Hill, New York/Toronto (1968). [1] "First Edition 45715." Bottom edge smoothly trimmed $15/75

032a: KING, QUEEN, KNAVE Weidenfeld & Nicolson, London (1968). [1] $15/75

033a: NABOKOV'S CONGERIES Viking, New York (1968). [1] Selected with a critical introduction by Page Stegner, an extensive bibliographical essay by Stegner; and an essay by

Nabokov "Reply To My Critics" not published before $25/100

034a: NOTES ON PROSODY AND ABRAM GANNIBAL Princeton University Press (Princeton, New Jersey, 1969). [0] 5015 cc. Wraps. Bollingen Series. Extract from *Eugene Onegin* $125.

035a: ADA *or Ardor: A Family Chronicle* McGraw-Hill, New York / Toronto (1969). [] Uncorrected proof. In olive printed wraps with mimeographed title page (Thomas Goldwasser 2/91) $300.

035b: ADA *or Ardor: A Family Chronicle* McGraw-Hill, New York / Toronto (1969). [1] "First Edition 45720" $15/75

035c: ADA *or Ardor: A Family Chronicle* Weidenfeld & Nicolson, London (1969) [1] $12/60

035d: ADA *or Ardor: A Family Chronicle* Penguin (Harmondsworth, 1970). [0] Wraps. Adds "Notes to Ada by Vivian Darkbloom" by Nabokov $50.

036a: MARY McGraw-Hill, New York / Toronto (1970). [1] Translated by Michael Glenny, in collaboration with Nabokov (original in Russian in 1926) $15/75

036b: MARY Weidenfeld & Nicolson, London (1971). [1] $12/60

037a: ANNIVERSARY NOTES Northwestern University Press (Evanston, Illinois), 1970. [0] Wraps. "Supplement to Triquarterly 17." 16-page stapled pamphlet with Nabokov's response to the Triquarterly tribute for his 70th birthday. Written in March 1970 but published winter 1970 $100.

038a: POEMS AND PROBLEMS McGraw-Hill, New York / Toronto (1971). [1] Copyright 1970, published March 1971 $20/100

038b: POEMS AND PROBLEMS Weidenfeld & Nicolson, London (1972). [1] $15/75

039a: GLORY McGraw-Hill, New York / Toronto (1971). [1] Translated by Dmitri Nabokov in collaboration with the author (original in Russian in 1932) $12/60

039b: GLORY McGraw-Hill Weidenfeld & Nicolson, London (1972). [1] $12/60

040a: TRANSPARENT THINGS McGraw-Hill, New York/St.Louis/San Francisco/Toronto (1972). [3] $12/60

040b: TRANSPARENT THINGS Weidenfeld & Nicolson, London (1973). [1] $10/50

041a: A RUSSIAN BEAUTY *and Other Stories* McGraw-Hill, New York/Toronto (1973). [3] Also states "First Edition" $12/60

041b: A RUSSIAN BEAUTY *and Other Stories* Weidenfeld & Nicolson, London (1973). [1] $10/50

042a: STRONG OPINIONS McGraw-Hill, New York/St. Louis/San Francisco/Toronto (1973). [3] $12/60

042b: STRONG OPINIONS Weidenfeld & Nicolson, London (1974). [1] $10/50

043a: LOLITA *A Screenplay* McGraw-Hill, New York/St. Louis/San Francisco/Toronto (1974). [3] (The original screenplay by Seven Arts Productions {1961}, punch-bound mimeographed sheets, was catalogued by Jos. the Provider 2/90 for $650.) Nabokov was nominated for an Academy Award for his screenplay $20/100

044a: LOOK AT THE HARLEQUINS! McGraw-Hill, New York/St. Louis/San Francisco/Toronto (1974). [3] $12/60

044b: LOOK AT THE HARLEQUINS! Weidenfeld & Nicolson, London (1975). [1] $10/50

045a: TYRANTS DESTROYED *and Other Stories* McGraw-Hill, New York/Toronto (1975). [ ] Uncorrected proof. In red printed wraps (Chloe's Books 4/96) $250.

045b: TYRANTS DESTROYED *and Other Stories* McGraw-Hill, New York/Toronto (1975). [3] $15/60

045c: TYRANTS DESTROYED *and Other Stories* Weidenfeld & Nicolson, London (1975). [1] $10/50

046a: DETAILS OF A SUNSET *and Other Stories* McGraw-Hill, New York/St. Louis / San Francisco / Toronto (1976). [3] $15/60

046b: DETAILS OF A SUNSET *and Other Stories* Weidenfeld & Nicolson, London (1976). [1] $15/60

047a: FIVE NOVELS Collins, London, 1979. [] An omnibus which collects *Lolita; The Gift; Invitation to a Beheading; King, Queen Knave;* and *Glory* $15/60

048a: THE NABOKOV- WILSON LETTERS Harper & Row, New York / Hagerstown / San Francisco / London, 1979. [] Uncorrected proof. In green wraps $200.

048b: THE NABOKOV - WILSON LETTERS Harper & Row, New York / Hagerstown / San Francisco / London (1979). [3] Also states "First Edition." 15,000 cc. Edited by Simon Karlinsky. Errata slip (Between The Covers 12/94) $12/60

048c: THE NABOKOV-WILSON LETTERS Weidenfeld & Nicolson, London (1979). [1] $10/50

048d: THE NABOKOV-WILSON LETTERS Harper Colophon, New York (1980). [3] Wraps.

Also states "First Harper ... published 1980." Corrected edition $15.

049a: LECTURES ON LITERATURE Harcourt Brace Janovich/Bruccoli Clark, New York/London, 1980. [] Uncorrected proof. In blue wraps (Wm. Reese Co. 12/92) $200.

049a: LECTURES ON LITERATURE Harcourt Brace Janovich / Bruccoli Clark, New York / London (1980). [4] Edited by Fredson Bowers $15/75

049b: LECTURES ON LITERATURE Weidenfeld & Nicolson, London (1980). [1] $12/60

050a: LECTURES ON ULYSSES *A Facsimile of the Manuscript* Bruccoli Clark, Bloomfield Hills/Columbia, 1980. [2] 20 cc numbered I-XX (reserved for the publisher). (Also 20 copies of letter "A" reserved for the publisher? -Fine Books 5/92) $300.

050b: LECTURES ON ULYSSES *A Facsimile of the Manuscript* Bruccoli Clark, Bloomfield Hills / Columbia, 1980. [2] 480 no. cc. Bound in natural buckram, in glassine dustwrapper (ref.c). Note: publisher offered copies in custom bindings $150.

051a: LECTURES ON RUSSIAN LITERATURE Harcourt Brace Jovanovich / Bruccoli Clark, New York / London (1981). [4] Edited by Fredson Bowers $15/75

051b: LECTURES ON RUSSIAN LITERATURE Weidenfeld & Nicolson, London (1982). [1] $12/60

052a: LECTURES ON DON QUIXOTE Harcourt Brace / Bruccoli Clark, San Diego / New York / London, 1983. [] Uncorrected proof (calling for "foreword to come" by Reynolds Price) $200.

052b: LECTURES ON DON QUIXOTE Harcourt Brace / Bruccoli Clark, San Diego / New York / London, 1983. [4] Foreword by Guy Davenport (the dustwrapper lists it as a preface, the title page as an introduction) $12/60

052c: LECTURES ON DON QUIXOTE Weidenfeld & Nicolson, London (1983). [1] $10/50

053a: THE MAN FROM THE U.S.S.R. *and Other Plays* Harcourt Brace / Bruccoli Clark, San Diego (1984). [3] "First Edition ABCDE." (Published December 14, 1984 @ $24.95.) Introduction and translation by Dmitri Nabokov) $15/60

053b: THE MAN FROM THE U.S.S.R. *and Other Plays* Harcourt Brace / Bruccoli Clark, San Diego (1985). [3] Wraps. "First Harvest ... 1985/ABC..." $20.

053c: THE MAN FROM THE U.S.S.R. *and Other Plays* Weidenfeld & Nicolson, London (1985). [] (Ref.b) $10/50

054a: THE ENCHANTER Putnam, New York (1986). [3] Wraps. Uncorrected proof. In orange printed wraps (ref.c) $150.

054b: THE ENCHANTER Putnam, New York (1986). [3] (Published October 1986 @ $16.95) (ref.b) $10/50

054c: THE ENCHANTER Picador (London, 1987). [] (I.D. Edrich 6/91) Also noted in promotional wrap-around band (Andrew Hayes 6/95) $10/40

055a: CARROUSEL | THREE TEXTS BY VLADIMIR NABOKOV Spectatorpers Aartswoud, The Netherlands, 1987. [2] 40 no. cc (1 to 40). Natural white boards. Issued without dustwrapper. Not for sale $350.

055b: CARROUSEL | THREE TEXTS BY VLADIMIR NABOKOV Spectatorpers Aartswoud, The Netherlands, 1987. [2] 60 no. cc (41 to 100). Plain rust wraps. In white dustwrapper $200/300

055c: CARROUSEL | LAUGHTER AND DREAMS | PAINTED WOOD | THE RUSSIAN SONG Spectatorpers Aartswoud, The Netherlands, 1987. [2] 40 no. cc in Roman numerals. Includes introduction by Dmitri Nabokov not in first two issues. Natural white boards. Issued without dustwrapper $250.

055d: CARROUSEL | LAUGHTER AND DREAMS | PAINTED WOOD | THE RUSSIAN SONG Spectatorpers Aartswoud, The Netherlands, 1987. [2] 110 no. cc. In plain rust colored wraps and white dustwrapper $200/250

055e: CARROUSEL | LAUGHTER AND DREAMS | PAINTED WOOD | THE RUSSIAN SONG Spectatorpers Aartswoud, The Netherlands, 1987. [] Unspecified number of copies marked "H.C." (hors commerce) $175.

056a: VLADIMIR NABOKOV *Selected Letters 1940-1977* Harcourt Brace, San Diego, 1989. [1] Also states "First Edition." Edited by Dmitri Nabokov and Matthew Bruccoli. (Published September 1, 1989 @ $29.95) (Ref.c) $15/50

056b: VLADIMIR NABOKOV *Selected Letters 1940-1977* Weidenfeld & Nicolson, London (1990) [1] $10/40

057a: THE STORIES OF VLADIMIR NABOKOV Alfred A. Knopf, New York, 1995. [] Uncorrected proof. In printed light tan wraps. Apparently, a later issue proof with 12 additional pages of material not in the first proof (Bev Chaney, Jr. 2/96). Also noted in cream colored printed wraps. Same? (Waverley Books 5/96) $100.

057b: THE STORIES OF VLADIMIR NABOKOV
Alfred A. Knopf, New York, 1995. [] (Bev Chaney, Jr. 10/95) (Published October 1995 @ $35.00) $10/35

FLANNERY O'CONNOR
(1925-1964)

Flannery O'Connor was born in Georgia in 1925. She graduated from Georgia State College for Women and studied writing for two years at the State University of Iowa. Sixteen years after her death, her first book, *Wise Blood*, was made into a movie directed by John Huston. That same year, she was given a special award from the National Book Award Committee for the significant body of writing she produced in her short writing career. She is considered one of the best short story writers of the post war generation. She is probably one of the best, certainly one of the strongest, of the century.

REFERENCES:

(a) Bruccoli & Clarke. FIRST PRINTINGS OF AMERICAN AUTHORS. Volume 1. Detroit: Gale Research (1977). Used through 1971 for U.S. editions.

(b) Farmer, David. FLANNERY O'CONNOR A DESCRIPTIVE BIBLIOGRAPHY. New York: Garland Publishing, 1981. Used through 1980 for U.K. editions and quantities for both U.S. and U.K. editions.

(c) Inventory, dealer catalogs, etc.

001a: WISE BLOOD Harcourt Brace, New York (1952). [1] 3,000 cc $350/2,500

001b: WISE BLOOD Neville Spearman, London (1955). [1] 3,000 cc $75/400

001c: WISE BLOOD Farrar, Straus & Cudahy, New York (1962). [0] Includes "Author's Note to the Second Edition" $50/250

001d: WISE BLOOD Faber & Faber, London (1968). [1] 3,000 cc. "First published in Great Britain in mcmlxviii." Also includes author's note (ref.b) $25/125

002a: A GOOD MAN IS HARD TO FIND Harcourt Brace, New York (1955). [1] 2,500 cc (a & b). First issue dustwrapper has *Wise Blood* on rear panel. Dustwrapper spine usually faded, the estimated price would be for unfaded one $250/1,500

002b: A GOOD MAN IS HARD TO FIND Harcourt Brace, New York (1955). [1] In second issue dustwrapper with this title on back panel (ref.c) $150/600

002c: THE ARTIFICIAL NIGGER AND OTHER TALES Neville Spearman, London (1957). [1] 2,000 cc. New title $150/600

002d: A GOOD MAN IS HARD TO FIND Faber & Faber, London (1968). [1] (Joseph Dermont 1/92.) "First Published in England mcmlxviii" (Nicholas and Helen Burrows 1/95) $25/125

003a: THE VIOLENT BEAR IT AWAY Farrar, Straus & Cudahy, New York (1960). [0] $100/500

003b: THE VIOLENT BEAR IT AWAY Longmans, Green & Co. (London, 1960). [] Advance review copy. In blue cloth with label. (Apparently another binding, not simply a variant cloth color?) (George Robert Minkoff 11/95) $500.

003c: THE VIOLENT BEAR IT AWAY Longmans, Green & Co. (London, 1960). [1] 3,500 cc. "This edition first published 1960." Red cloth reportedly scarcer than orange $50/250

004a: SOME ASPECTS OF THE GROTESQUE IN SOUTHERN FICTION (Wesleyan College, Macon, Georgia, 1960.) [0] Ref.a lists this item as being published in 1960 in an edition of 20 copies. In 1985 we tried to find out who put this entry in ref.a, but we were never successful. We did find out, indirectly, from Ms Ann Munck, Chairman of the English Department at Wesleyan, that O'Connor's speech on October 27, 1960 (during the Eugenia Dorothy Blount Lamar Lecture Series) was taped. She also believes that Mercer University borrowed the tape to transcribe the speech for their literary magazine, where it did appear. A copy was catalogued by Henry Turlington with the following comments:

"Five single-spaced mimeographed pages from typescript. Copy of the speech as O'Connor presented it at Wesleyan College, October 27, 1960. It seems pretty clear that this is what FPAA refers to in its bibliographical entry on O'Connor, although many have regarded it as a ghost. The mimeograph was made by O'Connor's friend, Thomas Gossett from a manuscript which she sent him for review. In a letter to this cataloguer, Dr. Gossett wrote that O'Connor 'did send me a copy of her article ... I am fairly sure she sent it in 1961 or 1962. At the time she was using the article ... for lectures she gave at various colleges over the country. She explained that if she published the article at that time she would not have been able to use it for her lectures.' Dr. Gossett goes on to say that he typed a copy of the article, returned the original to O'Connor, and gave copies to his students in San Antonio. It should be noted that there are a number of differences between this version of O'Connor's most famous essay and the published version." $1,500.

005a: A MEMOIR OF MARY ANN Farrar, Straus & Cudahy, New York (1961). [1] Written by the Domincan Nuns of Our Lady of Perpetual Help Home. Introduction by O'Connor. Noted with top edge stained blue and unstained. Priority unknown (Chapel Hill Rare Books 1/90) $25/125

005b: DEATH OF A CHILD Burns & Oates, London (1961). [0] New title. Edited and introduction by Flannery O'Connor. (Also issued by Catholic Book Club in 1961, but ref.b would seem to indicate that this was later) $25/125

006a: THREE BY FLANNERY O'CONNOR New American Library / Signet (New York, 1964). [1] Wraps. 109,000 cc. First thus. First three books $45.

007a: EVERYTHING THAT RISES MUST CONVERGE Farrar, Straus & Giroux, New York (1965). [1] $60/300

007b: EVERYTHING THAT RISES MUST CONVERGE Faber & Faber, London (1966). [] Uncorrected proof. In unprinted blue wraps (Waiting For Godot 10/90) $350.

007c: EVERYTHING THAT RISES MUST CONVERGE Faber & Faber, London (1966). [1] 2,470 cc $50/250

007d: EVERYTHING THAT RISES MUST CONVERGE (Tales For Travelers, Napa, California, 1985.) [0] 15,000 cc. Wraps. Single sheet folded to make 24 pages (map style). First separate edition (later printings were over-stamped on the back with either "Parke-Davis" or "Dermik" $50.

008a: THE ADDED DIMENSION *The Art and The Mind of Flannery O'Connor* Fordham University Press, New York (1966). [] Contains the first publication of a selection of letters and first book appearances of some of the essays. Edited by Melvin J. Friedman and Lewis A. Lawson $35/175

009a: MYSTERY AND MANNERS Farrar, Straus & Giroux, New York (1969). [1] $50/250

009b: MYSTERY AND MANNERS Faber & Faber, London (1972). [1] 1,000 cc. First state without author's name on spine of book $100/200

009c: MYSTERY AND MANNERS Faber & Faber, London (1972). [1] 1,000 cc. Second state with author's name on spine of book $75/150

010a: THE COMPLETE STORIES Farrar, Straus & Giroux, New York (1971). [] Advance uncorrected set of galleys in red printed wraps (George Robert Minkoff 1/95) $350.

010b: THE COMPLETE STORIES Farrar, Straus & Giroux, New York (1971). [1] $40/200

010c: THE COMPLETE STORIES Franklin Library, Franklin Center, 1980. [] Full leather (Pharos 1/91) $100.

010d: THE COMPLETE STORIES Franklin Library, Franklin Center, 1983. [] Full leather (Pharos 11/89) $100.

011a: THREE SHORT STORIES (World Today Press, Hong Kong, 1975.) [] Wraps. First thus. In English and Chinese (Henry Turlington 1/90) $150.

012a: THE HABIT OF BEING Farrar, Straus & Giroux, New York (1979). [] Uncorrected proof. In mauve wraps (Nouveau Books 2/91) $250.

012b: THE HABIT OF BEING Farrar, Straus & Giroux, New York (1979). [1] Letters edited by Sally Fitzgerald $25/100

012c: THE HABIT OF BEING Faber & Faber, London, 1980. [] $15/75

013a: HIGHER EDUCATION Palaemon Press (Winston-Salem, North Carolina, 1980). [2] 26 ltr cc. 8" x 10" broadside $200.

013b: HIGHER EDUCATION Palaemon Press (Winston-Salem, North Carolina, 1980). [2] 100 no. cc. 8" x 10" broadside $125.

014a: HOME OF THE BRAVE Albondocani, New York, 1981. [2] 26 ltr cc. Wraps $350.

014b: HOME OF THE BRAVE Albondocani, New York, 1981. [2] 200 no. cc $175.

015a: THE PRESENCE OF GRACE AND OTHER BOOK REVIEWS University of Georgia Press, Athens (1983). [3] Compiled by Leo J. Zuber. Introduction by Carter W. Martin $15/75

016a: THE CORRESPONDENCE OF FLANNERY O'CONNOR AND THE BRAINARD CHANEYS University Press of Mississippi, Jackson (1986). [] Proof in spiral bound plain wraps with printed label (William Reese Co. 2/92) $200.

016b: THE CORRESPONDENCE OF FLANNERY O'CONNOR AND THE BRAINARD CHANEYS University Press of Mississippi, Jackson (1986). [3] 188 previously unpublished letters (117 by O'Connor), edited by C. Ralph Stephens $25/75

016c: THE CORRESPONDENCE OF FLANNERY O'CONNOR AND THE BRAINARD CHANEYS University Press of Mississippi, Jackson (1986). [3] Wraps $35.

017a: CONVERSATIONS WITH FLANNERY O'CONNOR University Press of Mississippi, Jackson / London (1987). [] Uncorrected proof. In spiral bound printed wraps (William Reese Co. 2/92) $150.

017b: CONVERSATIONS WITH FLANNERY O'CONNOR University Press of Mississippi, Jackson / London (1987) [3] $25/75

017c: CONVERSATIONS WITH FLANNERY O'CONNOR University Press of Mississippi, Jackson / London (1987) [3] Wraps $35.

018a: REVELATION Tales For Travellers (Napa, California, 1987). [0] 15,000 cc. Wraps (map folded). First separate edition. (Later printings were overstamped on back with either "Parke-Davis" or "Dermik" $40.

019a: COMPLETE WORKS Library of America (New York, 1988). [] Includes a few stories not in book form before and 21 unpublished letters (Ampersand 7/92) $25/50

020a: THE COMPLETE STORIES Faber & Faber, London, 1990. [] Wraps. Only issued in paperback in the U.K. (Nicholas & Helen Burrows 4/95) $35.

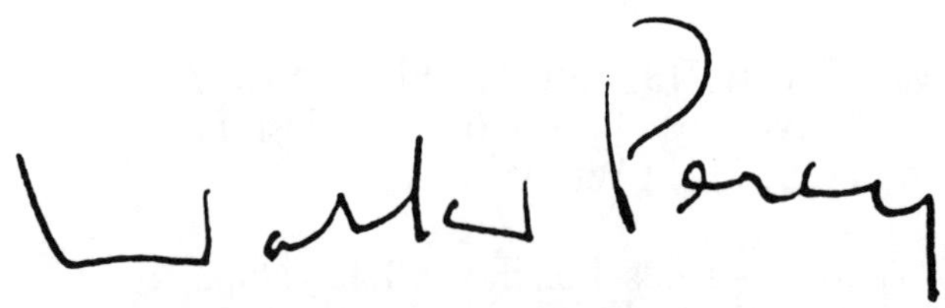

WALKER PERCY
1916-1990

Percy was born in Birmingham, Alabama in 1916. He received his B.A. from the University of North Carolina in Chapel Hill and a M.D. from Columbia University. Percy interned at Bellevue in 1942. He contracted tuberculosis and after recovering he decided to give up medicine and become a full-time writer.

> "Percy finds the modern world in a state of moral confusion, the values of the past no longer work and the majority of the men are spiritually dead, abstracted and if sensitive, ingrown and cut off from life outside themselves... (in spite of this) his rendering of characters and scenes is strikingly fresh, vivid and bitingly satirical. He is a moral and, ultimately, a religious writer, but he is also a novelist of manners who can delineate with remarkable skill the contrasts between certain kinds of Northerners, Southerners and Middle Westerners..."

-W. S. Stuckey in *Contemporary Novelists*,
St. Martins Press (1976)

REFERENCES:

(a) Wright, Stuart. WALKER PERCY A BIBLIOGRAPHY: 1930-1984 (Connecticut): Meckler Publishing (1986).

(b) Hobson, Linda Whitney. WALKER PERCY *A Comprehensive Descriptive Bibliography.* New Orleans: Faust publishing Company, 1988.

(c) Inventory or dealer / publisher catalogs.

001a: SYMBOL AS NEED Fordham University (New York), 1954. [0] 25-50 cc (Priscilla Juvelis 4/95) Offprint from *Thought*. Stapled printed cream colored wraps with title page as cover $1,000.

002a: SYMBOL AS HERMENEUTIC IN EXISTENTIALISM *Philosophy and Phenomenological Research* (cover title). No place, 1956. [0] Wraps. An offprint, apparently without the title on cover $750.

003a: SEMIOTIC AND A THEORY OF KNOWLEDGE (Modern Schoolman, no place, 1957.) [0] Wraps. An offprint, assume without a cover $750.

004a: SYMBOL, CONSCIOUSNESS AND INTERSUBJECTIVITY The Journal of Philosophy (Lancaster), 1958. [0] Wraps. An offprint $650.

005a: CULTURE *The Antimony of the Scientific Method* New Scholasticism, no place, 1958. [0] Wraps. An offprint $650.

006a: THE MESSAGE IN THE BOTTLE Thought Magazine, no place, 1959. [0] Wraps. An offprint from the *Fordham University Quarterly* (for published book of same title see item 016 below) $450.

007a: NAMING AND BEING (The Personalist, Bruges, 1960.) [0] Wraps. An offprint. Assume in plain wraps $450.

008a: THE SYMBOLIC STRUCTURE OF THE INTERPERSONAL PROCESS Psychiatry Journal..., Washington, D.C., 1961. [0] Wraps. An offprint $450.

009a: THE MOVIEGOER Knopf, New York, 1961. [1] 3,000 cc. National Book Award for 1962. (Ref.b stated 1,500 copies; but the Knopf records at Humanities Research Center indicate 3,000.) There is a Book Club edition (we assume) exactly like the first but states "Published..." vs. "First Edition: on copyright page and lacks price and "0561" on front dustwrapper corners $400/2,000

009b: THE MOVIE-GOER Eyre & Spottiswoode, London, 1963. [1] $100/400

009c: THE MOVIEGOER Franklin Library, Franklin Center, 1980. [2] Signed limited edition. Issued in full leather. Includes special message by the author $200.

010a: THE LAST GENTLEMAN Farrar Straus & Giroux, New York, no date [circa 1966]. [] Uncorrected proof. In spiral-bound printed wraps (William Reese Co. 5/96) $1,000.

010b: THE LAST GENTLEMAN Farrar Straus, New York (1966). [1] $60/300

010c: THE LAST GENTLEMAN Eyre & Spottiswoode, London (1967). [1] $30/150

011a: LOVE IN THE RUINS Farrar Straus, New York (1971). [1] $25/125

011b: LOVE IN THE RUINS Eyre & Spottiswoode, London (1971). [1] $20/100

012a: WHY DON'T YOU LINGUISTS HAVE AN EXPLANATORY THEORY OF LANGUAGE? No publisher or place, 1972. [2] 7 cc. "Original edition... consists of an original and six (6) copies of which this is no..." Xerox pages in 3-ring binder (Library of Congress) $NVA

013a: TOWARD A TRIADIC THEORY OF MEANING Psychiatry Journal..., no place, 1972. [0] No cover. 10 leaves with "Reprinted from..." top of first page $400.

014a: REVIEWS No publisher, place or date. [0] Tear sheets from *Tulane Law Review* 1972. Reportedly 10 copies $NVA

015a: LANTERNS ON THE LEVEE Louisiana State University, Baton Rouge (1973). [0] Wraps. Introduction to William Alexander Percy's book $35.

016a: THE MESSAGE IN THE BOTTLE Farrar Straus, New York (1975). [1] 8,000 cc. Top edge stained orange (Nouveau Rare Books, Steve Silberman talked to publisher and obtained quantity) $25/125

016b: THE MESSAGE IN THE BOTTLE Farrar Straus, New York (1975). [1] 2,000 cc. Top edge unstained (Nouveau Rare Books) $15/75

017a: LANCELOT Farrar Straus, New York (1977). [1] $10/50

017b: LANCELOT Secker & Warburg, London (1977). [1] $15/75

018a: GOING BACK TO GEORGIA University of Georgia, no place, 1978. [0] Wraps. The Ferdinand Phinizy Lecture $250.

019a: BOURBON Palaemon Press, Winston-Salem (1979). [2] 5 sgd ltr (A to E) copies. In full green leather $750.

019b: BOURBON Palaemon Press, Winston-Salem (1979). [2] 50 sgd no. cc (Roman numerals) for use of author and publisher. Marbled wraps. In dustwrapper $300/350

019c: BOURBON Palaemon Press, Winston-Salem (1979). [2] 200 sgd no. cc. Marbled wraps. In dustwrapper $200/250

019d: BOURBON Palaemon Press (Winston-Salem, 1981). [2] 26 sgd ltr cc. Cloth spine and boards. Issued without dustwrapper or slipcase. Second edition adding Percy's favorite drink $350.

019e: BOURBON Palaemon Press (Winston-Salem, 1981). [2] 50 sgd no. cc (Roman numerals). Cloth spine and boards. Issued without dustwrapper or slipcase. Limitation states one of 150 copies but ref.a indicates that less than 100 copies, including 019d, were actually bound $175.

020a: QUESTIONS THEY NEVER ASKED ME Lord John Press, Northridge, 1979. [2] 50 sgd no. cc. Bound in full blue leather $300.

020b: QUESTIONS THEY NEVER ASKED ME Lord John Press, Northridge, 1979. [2] 300 sgd no. cc. Patterned paper covered boards with blue cloth spine. A few copies had an "O" for "Q" on title page, and a few of these were bound in error; these copies are not numbered (Sylvester & Orphanos 11/92) $175.

021a: A CONFEDERACY OF DUNCES Louisiana State University, Baton Rouge, 1980. [0] 2,500 cc. Percy's foreword to John Kennedy Toole's book $150/750

021b: A CONFEDERACY OF DUNCES Allen Lane (London, 1981). [1] Reportedly 1,500 copies $75/350

022a: THE SECOND COMING Franklin Library, Franklin Center, 1980. [2] Limited signed first edition. In full leather. With special message from Percy. (Facsimile signature? [C. Dickens Books 6/95]) $150.

022b: THE SECOND COMING Farrar Straus, New York (1980). [2] 450 sgd no. cc. Issued without dustwrapper. In slipcase $200/250

022c: THE SECOND COMING Farrar Straus, New York (1980). [1] $10/50

022d: THE SECOND COMING Secker & Warburg, London (1981). [] (Ref.b) $10/50

023a: SEWANEE Frederic C. Beil, New York, 1982. [0] 3,000 cc. First separate appearance of this chapter from *Lanterns On The Levee*. Percy introduction the same as in 015a. Issued without dustwrapper $40.

024a: LOST IN THE COSMOS Farrar Straus, New York (1983). [] Uncorrected proof. In printed blue wraps (Bev Chaney #7) $300.

024b: LOST IN THE COSMOS Farrar Straus, New York (1983). [2] 350 sgd no. cc. Issued without dustwrapper. In slipcase $200/250

024c: LOST IN THE COSMOS Farrar Straus, New York (1983). [1] Top edge unstained (Books by Lee 12/93) $8/40

024d: LOST IN THE COSMOS Arrow Books, London, 1984. [] Wraps. No U.K. hardback (Ian McKelvie 6/91) $35.

025a: THE CITY OF THE DEAD Lord John Press, Northridge, 1984. [2] 26 sgd ltr cc. Broadside. Illustrated by Lyn Hill $300.

025b: THE CITY OF THE DEAD Lord John Press, Northridge, 1984. [2] 100 sgd cc. Broadside illustrated by Lyn Hill. Signed but not numbered (R. Anthony Polzin 3/94) $150.

026a: DIAGNOSING THE MODERN MALAISE Faust Publ., New Orleans, 1985. [2] 50 sgd no. cc. Specially bound (ref.c) $250.

026b: DIAGNOSING THE MODERN MALAISE Faust Publ., New Orleans, 1985. [2] 250 sgd no. cc. Issued without dustwrapper or slipcase $150.

027a: CONVERSATIONS WITH WALKER PERCY University Press of Mississippi, Jackson (1985). [3] Edited by Lewis A. Lawson and Victor A. Krammer (ref.c) $20/60

027b: CONVERSATIONS WITH WALKER PERCY University Press of Mississippi, Jackson (1985). [3] Wraps $25.

028a: NOVEL WRITING IN AN APOCALYPTIC TIME Faust Publ., New Orleans, 1986. [2] 100 sgd no. cc. Afterword by Eudora Welty. Signed by both. Deluxe edition (Published July 1986 @ $150.) (ref.c) $300.

028b: NOVEL WRITING IN AN APOCALYPTIC TIME Faust Publ. New Orleans 1986 [2] 300 sgd no. cc. (Published July 1986 @ $75.) (ref.c) $175.

Note: There were also 60 unnumbered copies reserved for presentation (Lemuria List J)

029a: THE THANATOS SYNDROME Franklin Library, Franklin Center, 1987. [2] Limited signed edition. In full leather. With a special message from the author. The true first edition (Bev Chaney Jr. 1/95) $150.

029b: THE THANATOS SYNDROME Farrar Straus, New York (1987). [] Uncorrected proof. In printed red wraps (Bev Chaney) $150.

029c: THE THANATOS SYNDROME Farrar Straus, New York (1987). [2] 250 sgd no. cc. In slipcase. (Published April 1987 @ $75.) (Ref.c) $200/250

029d: THE THANATOS SYNDROME Farrar Straus, New York (1987). [0] 75,000 cc (PW). (Published April 1987 @ $17.95) $7/35

029e: THE THANATOS SYNDROME Deutsch, London (1987). [] $8/40

030a: THE STATE OF THE NOVEL *Dying Art or New Science* Faust Publ., New Orleans, 1988. [2] 75 sgd no. cc. Deluxe edition $250.

030b: THE STATE OF THE NOVEL *Dying Art or New Science* Faust Publ., New Orleans, 1988. [2] 250 sgd cc (not numbered per K. Anthony Polzin 3/94) $175.

031a: SIGNPOSTS IN A STRANGE LAND Farrar Straus, New York (1991). [] Uncorrected proof. In blue wraps (Bev Chaney 9/91) $125.

031b: SIGNPOSTS IN A STRANGE LAND Farrar Straus, New York (1991). [] 12,500 cc. Essays (some first appearances) edited by Patrick Samway, S.J. $7/35

032a: MORE CONVERSATIONS WITH WALKER PERCY University Press of Mississippi, Jackson, 1993. [] (Published 6/93 @ $32.50) (Bev Chaney, Jr. 1/95) $20/40

032b: MORE CONVERSATIONS WITH WALKER PERCY University Press of Mississippi, Jackson, 1993. [] Wraps. (Published 6/93 @$14.95) $20.

033a: THE CORRESPONDENCE OF SHELBY FOOT AND WALKER PERCY W. W. Norton, New York (1996). [] Uncorrected proof. In beige (tan) printed wraps (Ken Lopez 12/96) $75.

033b: THE CORRESPONDENCE OF SHELBY FOOT AND WALKER PERCY W. W. Norton, New York (1996). [] $5/25

REYNOLDS PRICE

Reynolds Price was born in Macon, North Carolina in 1933. He graduated from Duke in 1955, then studied for three years as a Rhodes Scholar at Merton College, Oxford. In 1958 he returned to Duke, where he is now James B. Duke Professor of English. *A Long and Happy Life* received the William Faulkner Foundation Award for the most notable first novel of the year (1962). Price's books have received numerous other awards and have been translated into fourteen languages.

REFERENCES:

(a) Wright, Stuart and James L.W. West. REYNOLDS PRICE *A Bibliography 1949-1984.* Charlottesville: University Press of Virginia (1986).

(b) Ray A. Roberts. "Reynolds Price: A Bibliographical Checklist" in AMERICAN BOOK COLLECTOR. July/August 1981. Pages 15-23.

(c) Gary M. Lepper. A BIBLIOGRAPHICAL INTRODUCTION TO SEVENTY-FIVE MODERN AMERICAN AUTHORS. Berkeley: Serendipity Books, 1976. Pages 349-352.

(d) FIRST PRINTINGS OF AMERICAN AUTHORS. Volume 1. Detroit: Gale Research / Bruccoli Clark (1977). Pages 301-303. (Compiled by Clayton S. Owens.)

We wish to express our appreciation to D. Edmond Miller who prepared the original bibliographic portion of this guide with the generous assistance of Reynolds Price, Lawrence McIntyre of Atheneum Publishers, and the staff of the Rare Book Room of Perkins Library, Duke University.

001a: ONE SUNDAY IN LATE JULY (Encounter Magazine, London, 1960.) [0] 50 cc. Wraps. Offprint, cream colored wraps state "Reprinted from Encounter, March, 1960" $2,500.

002a: A LONG AND HAPPY LIFE Atheneum, New York, 1961. [1] Uncorrected proof. Plastic ring-bound, light blue wraps. Paper label on cover gives tentative publication date of September 13, 1961 and tentative price of $3.50 $600.

002b: A LONG AND HAPPY LIFE Atheneum, New York, 1962. [1] 500 cc. Advance reading copy. In yellow wraps. Cover states "This is an advance copy..." and gives tentative publication date of January 5, 1962 and price of $3.95. (Ref.c notes a later issue bound in the dustwrapper for the finished book) $250.

002c: A LONG AND HAPPY LIFE Atheneum, New York, 1962. [1] 5,500 cc (c & d). First state dustwrapper: rear panel prints names of those providing blurbs in pale yellowish-green. (Published March 19, 1962) $35/175

002d: A LONG AND HAPPY LIFE Atheneum, New York, 1962. [1] Second state dustwrapper: rear panel prints names of those providing blurbs in darker bluish-green. (Published March 19, 1962) $35/125

002e: A LONG AND HAPPY LIFE Chatto & Windus, London, 1962. [0] 4,900 cc. (Published March 22, 1962) $25/125

Note: A LONG AND HAPPY LIFE was published in its entirety in a special section of *Harper's Magazine*, April 1962.

003a: THE NAMES AND FACES OF HEROES Atheneum, New York, 1963. [1] 6,000 cc. (Published June 25, 1963) $30/150

003b: THE NAMES AND FACES OF HEROES Chatto & Windus, London, 1963. [0] 2,750 cc. (Published September 29, 1963) $25/125

004a: A GENEROUS MAN Atheneum, New York, 1966. [1] Uncorrected proof. Plastic ring-bound, light blue wraps. Cover has paper label. Text printed on rectos only $500.

004b: A GENEROUS MAN Atheneum, New York, 1966. [1] 500 cc. Wraps. Advance reading copy. Bound in the dustwrapper for the finished book $150.

004c: A GENEROUS MAN Atheneum, New York, 1966. [1] 9,500 cc. (Published March 25, 1966) $15/75

004d: A GENEROUS MAN Chatto & Windus, London, 1967. [0] 4,000 cc. (Published January 12, 1967) $12/60

Note: A LONG AND HAPPY LIFE and A GENEROUS MAN were issued in a combined edition by the Quality Paperback Book Club in 1976. The text was offset from the second printing of each book.

005a: THE THING ITSELF (Duke University Library, Durham, North Carolina, 1966.) [0] 750 cc (estimated). White wraps. (Ref.c states 500 copies.) (Probably published June 1966) $200.

006a: LOVE AND WORK Atheneum, New York, 1968. [1] Uncorrected proof. In plastic ring-bound wraps. Light-blue cover has paper label $350.

006b: LOVE AND WORK Atheneum, New York, 1968. [1] 10,000 cc. (Published May 29, 1968) $12/60

006c: LOVE AND WORK Chatto & Windus, London, 1968. [0] 1,250 cc. (Published October 24, 1968) $15/75

007a: LATE WARNING Albondocani Press, New York, 1968. [2] 26 sgd ltr cc. Wraps. (Published December 26, 1968) $350.

007b: LATE WARNING Albondocani Press, New York, 1968. [2] 150 sgd no. cc. Wraps. (Published December 26, 1968) $175.

008a: TORSO OF AN ARCHAIC APOLLO (Albondocani Press & Ampersand Books, New York, 1969.) [2] Wraps. States "three hundred copies," but 110 copies with Albondocani Press and Ampersand Books mentioned on first page and 210 cc with the greeting only on first page (no priority). Price's Christmas greeting for 1969. (Published December 12, 1969) $150.

009a: PERMANENT ERRORS Atheneum, New York, 1970. [1] 5,000 cc. (Published September 23, 1970) $15/75

009b: PERMANENT ERRORS Chatto & Windus, London, 1971. [0] 1,500 cc. (Published March 25, 1971) $15/75

010a: TWO THEOPHANIES (Privately printed, Durham, North Carolina, 1971.) [2] 200 cc (a & b). Wraps. First state wrapper: purple printed in silver. Most copies are first state. Price's Christmas greeting for 1971 $200.

010b: TWO THEOPHANIES (Privately printed, Durham, North Carolina, 1971.) [2] Second state wrapper: gray printed in black $150.

011a: FOR ERNEST HEMINGWAY New American Review (New York, 1972). [0] Wraps. Offprint. Gray-blue wrappers state "Reprinted From New American Review 14." (Probably published April 1972) $125.

012a: THINGS THEMSELVES Atheneum, New York, 1972. [1] 3,500 cc. (Published May 22, 1972) $20/100

013a: THE FOURTH ECLOGUE OF VIRGIL (Privately printed, Durham, North Carolina, 1972.)

[2] 225 cc. Tan wraps printed in brown, Price's Christmas greeting for 1972. (Published December 15, 1972) $125.

014a: AN APOCRYPHAL HYMN OF JESUS (Privately printed, Durham, North Carolina, 1973.) [2] 215 cc. Cream wraps printed in purple. Price's Christmas greeting for 1973. (Published December 15, 1973) $125.

015a: PRESENCE AND ABSENCE Bruccoli Clark, Bloomfield Hills, Michigan & Columbia, South Carolina, 1973. [2] 300 sgd no. cc. Three unsewn signatures laid into a brown cloth clam-shell box stamped in gold. There was a substantial overrun of this publication. Although the title page states 1973, the copyright notice contains the dates 1970, and 1974, and the book was actually issued in June, 1974 $100.

016a: A NATIVITY FROM THE APOCRYPHAL BOOK OF JAMES (Privately printed, Durham, North Carolina, 1974.) [2] 225 cc. Brown wraps printed in black. Price's Christmas greeting for 1974. (Published December 15, 1974) $125.

017a: THE SURFACE OF EARTH Atheneum, New York, 1975. [1] Wraps. Uncorrected proof. In dark blue wraps. Paper label on cover gives tentative publication date of May 23, 1975 $250.

017b: THE SURFACE OF EARTH Atheneum, New York, 1975. [1] 15,000 cc. (Published 14, 1975) $12/60

017c: THE SURFACE OF EARTH Arlington Books, London (1977). [1] 10,000 cc. (Published February 27, 1978) $10/50

018a: ANNUNCIATION (Privately printed, Durham, North Carolina, 1975.) [2] 225 cc. Tan wraps printed in black. Price's Christmas greeting for 1975. (Published December 15, 1975) $100.

019a: "A GREAT DEAL MORE" *Une Interview de Reynolds Price Recherches Anglaises et Americaines* Strasbourg, France, 1976. [0] Wraps. Offprint of a 1974 interview conducted by Georges Gary. Blue and white wrappers state "Extrait" $125.

020a: CONVERSATIONS: REYNOLDS PRICE & WILLIAM RAY Memphis State University, 1976. [0] 500 cc. Light green wraps. Bulletin #9 (Fall, 1976) of the Mississippi Valley Collection at Memphis State's John Willard Brister Library, comprising interviews from 1973-75 $75.

021a: THE GOOD NEWS ACCORDING TO MARK (Privately printed, Durham, North Carolina, 1976.) [2] 250 cc. Pictorial cream colored wraps printed in black and rust. First state with dark orange end-papers. Price's Christmas greeting for 1976. Distributed by Price. (Published November 15, 1976) $100.

021b: THE GOOD NEWS ACCORDING TO MARK (Privately printed, Durham, North Carolina, 1976.) [2] 250 cc. Pictorial cream colored wraps printed in black and rust with second state endpapers $75.

021c: THE GOOD NEWS ACCORDING TO MARK (Privately printed, Durham, North Carolina, 1976.) 50 sgd no. cc. Wraps. For sale in 1977 $200.

022a: EARLY DARK Atheneum, New York, 1977. [1] Uncorrected proof. In mustard colored wraps $250.

022b: EARLY DARK Atheneum, New York, 1977. [1] 3,000 cc (b & c). First state dustwrapper omits the author's name on the spine. (Published July 25, 1977) $15/75

022c: EARLY DARK Atheneum, New York, 1977. [1] Second state dustwrapper includes the author's name on the spine $15/50

023a: ORACLES Friends of Duke University Library, Durham, North Carolina, 1977. [2] 300 sgd no. cc. Signed by Price and the illustrator, Jacob Roquet. (Published October 1977) $100.

023b: ORACLES Friends of Duke University Library, Durham, North Carolina, 1977. [2] 6 sgd no. cc. These 6 overrun copies lack Roquet's etchings, containing instead original drawings by Price $400.

024a: LESSONS LEARNED Albondocani Press, New York, 1977. [2] 26 sgd ltr cc. Wraps. (Published December 21, 1977) $200.

024b: LESSONS LEARNED Albondocani Press, New York, 1977. [2] 200 sgd no. cc. Wraps $125.

025a: THE DREAM OF A HOUSE (Palaemon Press, Winston-Salem, North Carolina, 1977.) [0] Broadside. Uncorrected proof, lacking the poem's title and printed on heavier stock than the published broadside $150.

025b: THE DREAM OF A HOUSE (Palaemon Press, Winston-Salem, North Carolina, 1977.) [2] 26 sgd ltr cc. Broadside. (Published December 22, 1977) $250.

025c: THE DREAM OF A HOUSE (Palaemon Press, Winston-Salem, North Carolina, 1977.) [2] 100 sgd no. cc. Broadside. (Published December 22, 1977) $125.

026a: A PALPABLE GOD Atheneum, New York, 1978. [1] 15 cc. Uncorrected proof. In mustard colored wraps $300.

026b: A PALPABLE GOD Atheneum, New York, 1978. [1] 4,000 cc. (Published February 17, 1978) $12/60

027a: DEAD MAN, DYING GIRL Phosphenes (Walnut Creek, California), 1978. [2] 30 cc. Broadside. Imprinted "Presentation Copy" (not for sale) $100.

027b: DEAD MAN, DYING GIRL Phosphenes (Walnut Creek, California), 1978. [2] 26 sgd ltr cc. Broadside. Signed by Price and the illustrator, Chuck Miller. (Published April 15, 1978) $200.

027c: DEAD MAN, DYING GIRL Phosphenes (Walnut Creek, California), 1978. [2] 200 sgd no. cc. Broadside. Signed by Price and the illustrator, Chuck Miller. (Published April 15, 1978) $100.

028a: PURE BOYS AND GIRLS (Palaemon Press, Winston-Salem, North Carolina, 1978.) [2] 28 sgd Roman numeral copies. Broadside. Issued as part of a folio entitled "For Aaron Copland." (Published November 14, 1978.) Price for entire portfolio $500.

028b: PURE BOYS AND GIRLS (Palaemon Press, Winston-Salem, North Carolina, 1978.) [2] 50 sgd no. cc. Broadside. Issued as part of a folio entitled "For Aaron Copland." (Published November 14, 1978.) Price for entire folio $350.

029a: CHRIST CHILD'S SONG AT THE END OF THE NIGHT (Albondocani Press & Ampersand Books, New York, 1978.) [2] Wraps. States "four hundred copies," but 155 copies with Albondocani Press and Ampersand Books mentioned on first page, and 255 copies with the greeting only on first page (no priority). Price's Christmas greeting for 1978 (Published December 19, 1978) $75.

030a: FOR LEONTYNE AFTER ARIADNE (Privately printed, Durham, North Carolina, 1979.) [2] 100 sgd no. cc. Broadside. (Published April 5, 1979) $175.

031a: THE LINES OF LIFE (Stuart Wright, Winston-Salem, North Carolina, 1979.) [2] 2 sgd

Roman numeral copies. Broadside. (Published June 8, 1979) $350.

031b: THE LINES OF LIFE (Stuart Wright, Winston-Salem, North Carolina, 1979.) [2] 6 sgd ltr cc. Broadside. (Published June 1979) $300.

032a: QUESTION AND ANSWER The Baylor School, Chattanooga, 1979. [0] 500 cc. Wraps. The Second Archibald Yell Smith IV Lecture, given April 26, 1979 (this date appears on the cover) and published December 1, 1979. In white wraps $100.

033a: NINE MYSTERIES Palaemon Press (Winston-Salem, North Carolina, 1979.) [2] 9 sgd ltr cc. Deluxe issue binding: dark gray cloth with a black leather spine. Each copy contains on the title page an original color drawing by Price. (Published December 15, 1979) $600.

033b: NINE MYSTERIES Palaemon Press (Winston-Salem, North Carolina, 1979.) [2] 300 sgd cc. Regular issue binding: black cloth. (Published February 1, 1980) $75.

034a: SOCRATES AND ALCIBIADES (Palaemon Press, Winston-Salem, North Carolina, 1980.) [2] 75 sgd no. cc. Broadside. Issued as part of a folio entitled "For Robert Penn Warren." (Published April 24, 1980.) Price for entire folio $350.

035a: THE ANNUAL HERON Albondocani Press, New York, 1980. [2] 300 sgd no. cc. Wraps. (Published December 17, 1980) $100.

036a: A FINAL LETTER Sylvester & Orphanos, Los Angeles, 1980. [2] 4 sgd "Special Presentation" copies, each bearing the printed name of the recipient. (Also 30-35 overrun copies imprinted "Presentation Copy.") (Published February 6, 1981) $400.

036b: A FINAL LETTER Sylvester & Orphanos, Los Angeles, 1980. [2] 26 sgd ltr cc. In black cloth slipcase $350.

036c: A FINAL LETTER Sylvester & Orphanos L.A. 1980 [2] 300 sgd no. cc in glassine wraps. (Published February 6, 1981) $100.

037a: THE SOURCE OF LIGHT Atheneum, New York, 1981. [1] 50 cc. Uncorrected proof. In yellow wraps $250.

037b: THE SOURCE OF LIGHT Atheneum, New York, 1981. [1] 10,000 cc. (Published April 23, 1981) $10/50

038a: COUNTRY MOUSE, CITY MOUSE (Friends of the Library, North Carolina Wesleyan College, 1981.) [2] 50 sgd no. cc. Pictorial wraps. (Published October 11, 1981) $150.

038b: COUNTRY MOUSE, CITY MOUSE (Friends of the Library, North Carolina Wesleyan College, 1981.) [2] 450 cc. Pictorial wraps. (Published October 11, 1981) $50.

039a: A START Palaemon Press (Winston-Salem, North Carolina, 1981). [2] 8 cc. Left unbound $200.

039b: A START Palaemon Press (Winston-Salem, North Carolina, 1981). [2] 75 sgd no. cc. Bound in marbled boards with a brown leather spine. (Published December 30 1981) $175.

040a: LOVE ACROSS THE LINES South Atlantic Modern Language Association University, Alabama, 1982. [0] Cream colored wraps. Off-print from the *South Atlantic Review*, May 1982 $125.

041a: VITAL PROVISIONS Atheneum, New York, 1982. [1] Wraps. Uncorrected proof $200.

041b: VITAL PROVISIONS Atheneum, New York, 1982. [1] 1,000 cc in cloth. (Published November 30, 1982) $25/100

041c: VITAL PROVISIONS Atheneum, New York, 1982. [1] 2,000 cc in wraps. (Published November 30, 1982) $35.

042a: MUSTIAN Atheneum, New York, 1983. [1] Uncorrected proof. In light blue wraps $175.

042b: MUSTIAN Atheneum, New York, 1983. [1] 4,000 cc. (Published April 25, 1983) $12/60

043a: A FAIRLY CRUCIAL CHOICE (Office of the President of Duke University, Durham, North Carolina) 1983. [0] 6,000 cc. Blue wraps printed in gray. Number 11 in the *How to Think Straight Series*. (Published November 1983) $75.

044a: A CHAIN OF LOVE Nan'un-do, Tokyo (1984). [0] Wraps. Prints in English the text of 2 Price stories, along with commentary in Japanese. (Published February 2, 1984) $75.

045a: PRIVATE CONTENTMENT Atheneum, New York, 1984. [1] 3,000 cc. (Published March 26, 1984) $10/50

046a: KATE VAIDEN Atheneum, New York, 1986. [1] 144 cc. Wraps. Uncorrected proof. In buff colored wraps (made in December 1985) $200.

046b: KATE VAIDEN Atheneum, New York, 1986. [1] 15,000 cc. National Book Critics Circle Award for 1986. (Published June 23, 1986) $12/60

046c: KATE VAIDEN Chatto & Windus, London (1987). [1] "Published in 1987 by ..." $10/50

047a: NOON REST, BEST DAY Albondocani Press, New York, 1986. [] Wraps. Holiday greeting (Bev Chaney, Jr. 10/92) $50.

048a: THE LAWS OF ICE Atheneum, New York, 1986. [] (Published October 1986 @ $17.95) $8/40

049a: HOUSE SNAKE Lord John Press, Northridge, 1986. [2] 26 sgd ltr cc $300.

049b: HOUSE SNAKE Lord John Press, Northridge, 1986. [2] 150 sgd no. cc $50.

050a: A COMMON ROOM *Essays 1954-1987* Atheneum, New York, 1987. [] $10/50

051a: UNBEATEN PLAY FOR ROSE QUAINTANCE Hawk Hill, no place (1987). [2] 10 sgd no. cc. Wraps $250.

051b: UNBEATEN PLAY FOR ROSE QUAINTANCE Hawk Hill, no place (1987). [2] 65 cc $75.

052a: GOOD HEARTS Atheneum, New York, 1988. [] Uncorrected proof. In red wraps $100.

052b: GOOD HEARTS Atheneum, New York, 1988. [] $8/40

053a: REAL COPIES North Carolina Wesleyan College (Rocky Mount, 1988). [2] 26 sgd ltr cc (Alice Robbins) $200.

053b: REAL COPIES North Carolina Wesleyan College (Rocky Mount, 1988). [2] 50 sgd no. cc in wraps $75.

053c: REAL COPIES North Carolina Wesleyan College (Rocky Mount, 1988). [2] 500 no. cc Pictorial wraps. Trade issue (Waiting For Godot Books 2/95) $35.

054a: CLEAR PICTURES Atheneum, New York, 1989. [] Uncorrected advance proof. Blue wraps. Approximately 12 cc. As this proof was prepared from cut long galleys rather than actual page-proofs, there are some awkward spaces in the text, sometimes even in the middle of a sentence. Price was displeased with the slipshod production , so Atheneum reset and reprinted the proof. The version actually issued is a larger format in gray printed wraps; it includes the photographs ultimately used in the published book (this early issue does not include the photos). All of the blue proofs were destroyed save for a dozen or so rescued by an Atheneum employee. (Chapel Hill Rare Books 12/94) $200.

054b: CLEAR PICTURES Atheneum, New York, 1989. [] Uncorrected proof. In gray wraps. Includes photos used in published book (Chapel Hill Rare Books 12/94) $75.

054a: CLEAR PICTURES Atheneum, New York, 1989. [3] (Published June 1989 @ $19.95) $8/40

055a: BACK BEFORE DAY North Carolina Wesleyan College Press (Rocky Mount, 1989) [2] 100 specially bound copies. Issued without dustwrapper or slipcase. With signed poem "Spring Takes The Home Place" laid in (Alice Robbins) $100.

055b: BACK BEFORE DAY North Carolina Wesleyan College Press (Rocky Mount 1989) [2] 400 copies. In cloth. Issued without dustwrapper or slipcase $50.

056a: SPRING TAKES THE HOMEPLACE [North Carolina Wesleyan College, Rocky Mount, 1989.] [] 4 pp. promotional leaflet (H.E. Turlington Books 9/94) $20.

056b: SPRING TAKES THE HOMEPLACE [North Carolina Wesleyan College, Rocky Mount, 1989.] [2] 100 sgd no. cc (of a total edition of 500 cc) Folded leaflet (William Reese Company 2/96) $75.

056c: SPRING TAKES THE HOMEPLACE [North Carolina Wesleyan College, Rocky Mount, 1989.] [2] 400 cc. Folded leaflet $30.

057a: THE TONGUES OF ANGELS Atheneum, New York, 1990. [] Uncorrected proof. In red wraps $60.

057b: THE TONGUES OF ANGELS Atheneum, New York / Ultramarine, Hastings-on-Hudson, 1990. [2] 26 sgd ltr cc. Bound in leather $350.

057c: THE TONGUES OF ANGELS Atheneum, New York / Ultramarine, Hastings-on-Hudson, 1990. [2] 100 sgd no. cc $175.

057d: THE TONGUES OF ANGELS Atheneum, New York, 1990. [] With signed tipped-in sheet (Bert Babcock 5/91) $40/60

057e: THE TONGUES OF ANGELS Atheneum, New York, 1990. [] (Published May 16, 1990 @ $18.95) $7/35

058a: HOME MADE North Carolina Wesleyan College, Rocky Mount, 1990. [2] 26 sgd ltr cc. Illustrated with photographs by Roger Manley and signed by both. Issued in cloth without dustwrapper $200.

058b: HOME MADE North Carolina Wesleyan College, Rocky Mount, 1990. [2] 200 sgd no. cc. Issued in cloth without dustwrapper $75.

058c: HOME MADE North Carolina Wesleyan College, Rocky Mount, 1990. [] 300 cc. Wraps $35.

059a: THE USE OF FIRE Atheneum, New York, 1990. [] Uncorrected proof. In orange printed wraps $60.

059b: THE USE OF FIRE Atheneum, New York, 1990. [] (Published December 1990 @ $19.95) $6/30

060a: LOST HOMES Mud Puppy Press, Chapel Hill (1990). [2] 26 sgd ltr cc. $200.

060b: LOST HOMES Mud Puppy Press, Chapel Hill (1990). [2] 100 sgd no. cc. Issued in oblong wraps in dustwrapper $75.

061a: CONSOLATION (North Carolina Wesleyan College, Rocky Mount, 1990.) [] 4 pp. leaflet (H.E. Turlington Books 9/94) $30.

062a: NEW MUSIC *A Trilogy* Theatre Communications Group (New York, 1990). [] $15/60

062b: NEW MUSIC *A Trilogy* Theatre Communications Group (New York, 1990). [] Wraps. $25.

063: THE FORESEEABLE FUTURE *Three Long Stories* Atheneum, New York, 1991. [] Uncorrected advance proof. In white wraps $60.

063b: THE FORESEEABLE FUTURE *Three Long Stories* Atheneum, New York, 1991. [3] (Published May 1991 @ $19.95) $8/40

064a: CONVERSATIONS WITH REYNOLDS PRICE University of Mississippi, Jackson (1991). [] $20/40

064b: CONVERSATIONS WITH REYNOLDS PRICE University of Mississippi, Jackson (1991) [] Wraps $25.

065a: BLUE CALHOUN Atheneum, New York, 1992. [] Advance reading copy. In pictorial wraps $50.

065b: BLUE CALHOUN Atheneum, New York, 1992. [2] 350 sgd no. cc. Issued without dustwrapper. In slipcase $100/150

065c: BLUE CALHOUN Atheneum, New York, 1992. [] (Published May 1992 @ $22.95) $6/30

066a: "AND WAY IN THE NIGHT" Black Oak Books, Berkeley, 1992. [] 13 1/4" x 6 1/2" broadside $35.

067a: AN EARLY CHRISTMAS North Carolina Wesleyan College Press (Rocky Mount, 1992). [2] 100 sgd cc. Bound in cloth and marbled boards $100.

067b: AN EARLY CHRISTMAS North Carolina Wesleyan College Press (Rocky Mount, 1992). [2] 400 no. cc. In dark brown boards stamped in gold. Issued without dustwrapper (Bev Chaney, Jr. 1/95) $40.

068a: OUT ON THE PORCH Algonquin Books, Chapel Hill, 1992. [] (Published @ $16.95) $6/30

069a: THE COLLECTED STORIES Atheneum, New York, 1993. [] Uncorrected proof. In orange wraps $50.

069a: THE COLLECTED STORIES Atheneum, New York, 1993. [] (Published 6/93 @ $25.00) $10/40

070a: FULL MOON *And Other Plays* Theatre Communications Group (New York), 1993. [] (Published @ $24.95) $6/30

071a: THE HONEST ACCOUNT OF A MEMORABLE LIFE *An Apocryphal Gospel* North Carolina Wesleyan College Press (Rocky Mount, 1994). [2] 100 sgd no. cc. In marbled boards with purple cloth spine. Issued without dustwrapper (Chapel Hill Rare Books 11/94) $100.

071b: THE HONEST ACCOUNT OF A MEMORABLE LIFE *An Apocryphal Gospel* North Carolina Wesleyan College Press (Rocky Mount, 1994). [2] 400 no. cc. Waiting For Godot Books states total printing was 700 copies: 500 and first 100 specially bound, numbered and signed. Trade issue $35.

072a: A WHOLE NEW LIFE Atheneum, New York, 1994. [] Uncorrected proof. In printed white wraps (Bev Chaney, Jr. 5/95) $50.

072b: A WHOLE NEW LIFE Atheneum, New York, 1994. [] (Published 5/94 @ $20.00) (Bev Chaney, Jr. 1/95) $6/30

073a: THE PROMISE OF REST Scribner, New York (1995). [] Uncorrected proof. In blue wraps (Tom Davidson 6/98) $50.

073b: THE PROMISE OF REST Scribner, New York (1995). [] Advance Reading Copy. In pictorial wraps (Yesterday's Books 6/96) $40.

073c: THE PROMISE OF REST Scribner, New York (1995). [] $5/25

074a: THREE GOSPELS Scribner, New York (1996). [] Uncorrected Proof. In pictorial wraps (Bev Chaney, Jr. 12/96) $50.

074b: THREE GOSPELS Scribner, New York (1996). [] $5/25

075a: ROXANNA SLADE Scribner (New York, 1998). [3] Published at $25

NOTES:

Price's Christmas greetings were generally mailed in white envelopes, some with cardboard stiffeners. *A Fairly Crucial Choice* was also issued in a white envelope, by the Office of the President of Duke University.

Price has written or collaborated on several screenplays of *A Long and Happy Life*; he completed one version in 1965. In 1970, a screenplay he wrote with Richard Neubert was done up in conventional binders by Rubin Productions in Beverly Hills to be distributed among potential producers in Hollywood. Aside from the scenes included in *Things Themselves* (1972), none of these dramatic versions has been published.

Acting scripts were done up for the various productions of Price's play *Early Dark* and for the television production of his play *Private Contentment*, which preceded book publication by two years.

In 1985-86, Price circulated copies of three new plays among friends and potential producers. Approximately 50 copies each of *August Snow*, *New Music*, and *Better Days* were done up in conventional binders for this purpose. There were two issues of *August Snow*: a first draft, and a revised version following the premiere production of the play in Arkansas in 1985.

Mustian (1983) collects the novels *A Long and Happy LIFE* and *A Generous Man* and the story "A Chain of Love." A new introduction is added, called "A Place to Stand."

The following books by Price have been reprinted in one or more paperback editions:

A Long and Happy Life
The Names and Faces of Heroes
A Generous Man
Love and Work
Permanent Errors
The Surface of Earth
A Palpable God
Vital Provisions
Mustain

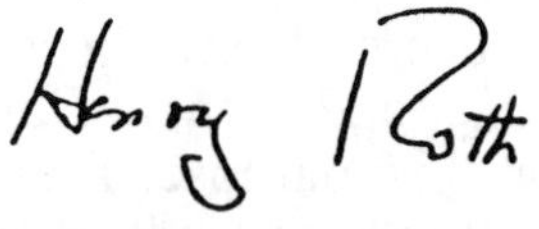

HENRY ROTH

Roth was born in Austria-Hungary in 1906. He graduated from the City College of New York in 1928. His first book *Call it Sleep* was well received by the critics and sold reasonably well, but it was not until it was reissued in 1960 that the book was recognized as one of the finest novels of the century and one of the best novels about childhood ever written by an American.

Roth worked for the WPA and as a teacher, metal-grinder, a hospital attendant, and waterfowl farmer. He wrote a second novel and started a third but was not satisfied with either and only published seven stories from 1938 to 1969. New books finally began to appear in 1979.

001a: CALL IT SLEEP Ballou, New York (1934). [0] Uncorrected proof. In unprinted heavy paper blue wraps. First page is the half-title (Quill & Brush 6/95) $6,000.

001b: CALL IT SLEEP Ballou, New York (1934). [0] $600/6,000

001c: CALL IT SLEEP Pageant Book, Paterson, New Jersey, 1960. [1] "Published 1960 by..." Introduction by Maxwell Geismar. Appreciation by Meyer Levin $50/250

001d: CALL IT SLEEP Michael Joseph, London (1963). [] Uncorrected proof. In brown wraps (Words Etcetera) $300.

001e: CALL IT SLEEP Michael Joseph, London (1963). [1] $50/250

001f: CALL IT SLEEP The Arion Press, San Francisco, 1995. [2] 300 sgd no. cc. Bound in leather backed pictorial boards. In pictorial cloth slipcase (Argosy Book Shop 10/95) $750.

002a: NATURE'S FIRST GREEN Targ Editions, New York, 1979. [2] 300 sgd no. cc. Issued in plain unprinted yellow dustwrapper $100/125

003a: SHIFTING LANDSCAPE *A Composite 1925-1987* Jewish Publ. Society, Philadelphia, 1987. [1] Uncorrected proof. In printed yellow-mustard wraps $200.

003b: SHIFTING LANDSCAPE *A Composite 1925-1987* Jewish Publ. Society, Philadelphia, 1987. [1] Edited and with introduction by Mario Materassi. (Published November 1987 @ $19.95) $8/40

004a: A STAR SHINES OVER MT. MORRIS PARK St. Martin's Press, New York (1994). [] Uncorrected proof. In blue wraps. *Mercy of a Rude Stream, Volume I* (Bev Chaney, Jr. 93) $150.

004b: A STAR SHINES OVER MT. MORRIS PARK St. Martin's Press, New York (1994). [2] 150 sgd no. cc. Bound in full leather. In slipcase. *Mercy of a Rude Stream, Volume I* (Bev Chaney, Jr. 93) $300/350

004c: A STAR SHINES OVER MT. MORRIS PARK St. Martin's Press, New York (1994). [] *Mercy of a Rude Stream, Volume I* $6/30

004d: A STAR SHINES OVER MT. MORRIS PARK Weidenfeld & Nicolson, London, 1994. [] Uncorrected Proof. Wraps. *Mercy of a Rude Stream, Volume I* (Nicholas Pounder 5/95) $75.

004e: A STAR SHINES OVER Mt. MORRIS PARK Weidenfeld & Nicolson, London (1994). [] *Mercy of a Rude Stream, Volume I* (Wessex Books 2/97) $7/35

005a: A DIVING ROCK ON THE HUDSON St. Martin's Press, New York, 1995. [] Uncorrected proof. In pictorial printed wraps. *Mercy of a Rude Stream, Volume II* (Waverley Books 6/95) $75.

005b: A DIVING ROCK ON THE HUDSON St. Martin's Press, New York (1995). [] *Mercy of a Rude Stream, Volume II* (Robin Wright Books 3/96) $6/30

005c: A DIVING ROCK ON THE HUDSON Weidenfeld & Nicolson, London, 1995. [] *Mercy of a Rude Stream, Volume II* $75.

006a: FROM BONDAGE St. Martin's Press, New York (1996). [3] Also states "First Edition." *Mercy of a Rude Stream, Volume III* $5/25

Evelyn Scott

EVELYN SCOTT
(1893-1963)

Scott was born in Tennessee and educated by tutors in New Orleans and at Newcomb College and Newcomb School of Art. She states:

> "I educated myself ... which inspired me with simultaneous ambitions to become a writer, a painter, an actress and a disciple of Pavlowa, Tolstoy, Schopenhauer, Nietzsche, Bergson and Karl Marx, all at once ... I rejected the idea of being a Southern belle ... and ran away from home..."

-*Twentieth Century Authors*,
Kunitz & Haycroft, Wilson, NY 1942

She was married to Cyril Kay Scott (original name - Frederick Creighton Wellman) in 1913 and to John Metcalfe in 1928.

Although at the time of her death she had not published a book in over twenty years and was, by most people, entirely forgotten, during her active career between the wars she participated in the major American literary movements, first in Greenwich Village and then as an expatriate in North Africa and Europe. She experimented with every form of literature, but her primary contributions were as the author of the first book of criticism of William Faulkner *On William Faulkner's The Sound and The Fury* (1929) and as the author of *The Wave*, which some consider to be the best Civil War novel ever written and the first book published by the firm of Jonathan Cape & Harrison Smith in 1929.

REFERENCES:

We wish to thank Henry Turlington (ref.a) whose collection was used for the majority of the bibliographical information herein.

(b) Eppard, Philip B. (Editor). FIRST PRINTINGS OF AMERICAN AUTHORS. Volume 5. Detroit: Bruccoli Clark Layman, Gale Research (1987).

001a: PRECIPITATIONS Nicholas L. Brown, New York, 1920. [0] Blue-green cloth with labels. Scott stated in an inscribed copy that blue-green cloth is the first issue. (Main Street Books 12/93) $50/250

001b: PRECIPITATIONS Nicholas L. Brown, New York, 1920. [0] Red cloth, second issue $40/200

002a: THE NARROW HOUSE Boni & Liveright, New York (1921). [0] Black cloth with blue lettering $60/300

002b: THE NARROW HOUSE Duckworth (London, 1921). [1] Orange paper boards (dustwrapper not seen). (Published October 6, 1921) $30/150

002c: THE NARROW HOUSE Harcourt Brace, New York, 1922. [0] Assume Boni & Liveright sheets were used for this printing $30/150

003a: NARCISSUS Harcourt Brace, New York (1922). [0] Black cloth with gray lettering $60/300

003b: BEWILDERMENT Duckworth, London (1922). [1] New title, dark gray cloth with yellow/gold lettering $60/300

004a: ESCAPADE Seltzer, New York, 1923. [0] Black cloth $50/500

004b: ESCAPADE *A Fragment of Autobiography* Cape, London, 1930. [] (Ref.b) $50/250

005a: THE GOLDEN DOOR Seltzer, New York, 1925. [0] Tan cloth spine and purple paper covered boards $40/200

006a: IN THE ENDLESS SANDS *A Christmas Book for Boys and Girls* Holt, New York (1925). [0] Written with C. Kay Scott. Pictorial cloth with lettering printed in red. Tipped-in frontis (ref.b) $60/300

007a: MIGRATIONS *An Arabesque in Histories* Albert & Charles Boni, New York, 1927. [0] Green cloth with black stamping $30/150

007b: MIGRATIONS *An Arabesque in Histories* Duckworth, London, 1927. [] (Ref.b) $25/125

008a: IDEALS *A Book of Farce & Comedy* Albert & Charles Boni, New York, 1927. [0] Gray binding $25/125

008b: IDEALS *A Book of Farce & Comedy* Albert & Charles Boni, New York, 1927. [0] Green (remainder) binding $15/100

009a: ON LOLA RIDGE Payson & Clarke, New York (1929). [] 2-page mimeographed news release. (Distributed with review copies of Ridge's *Firehead.* Ref.b) $75.

010a: ON WILLIAM FAULKNER'S "THE SOUND AND THE FURY" (Cape & Smith, New York, 1929.) [2] 1,000 cc. In wraps resembling *The Sound and The Fury* endpapers $250.

011a: THE WAVE Cape & Smith, New York (1929). [1] Blue cloth with gray lettering. (Also noted in Grosset & Dunlap dustwrapper which would constitute another issue) $30/150

011b: THE WAVE Cape, London, 1929. [] Ref.b $25/125

012a: WITCH PERKINS *A Story of the Kentucky Hills* Holt, New York (1929) [0] Green cloth printed with red $30/150

013a: BLUE RUM Cape & Smith, New York (1930). [1] Written as Ernest Souza. Proof dustwrapper has no printing on flaps or back panel $75/400

013b: BLUE RUM Cape, London, 1930. [] (Ref.b) $30/150

014a: THE WINTER ALONE Cape & Smith, New York (1930). [1] Black cloth spine with Lynd Ward pictorial boards (and endpapers). Cellophane dust-wrapper with flaps $75/200

015a: A CALENDAR OF SIN *American Melodramas* Cape & Smith, New York (1931). 2 volumes. In dustwrappers and unmarked cardboard slipcase $35/200

Without slipcase: $35/150

016a: EVA GAY *A Romantic Novel* Smith & Haas, New York (1933). [0] Brown cloth with gold lettering $40/200

016b: EVA GAY *A Romantic Novel* Lovat Dickson, London (1934). [1] Blue cloth spine printed in red $25/125

017a: BILLY THE MAVERICK Holt, New York (1934). [0] $35/175

018a: BREATHE UPON THESE SLAIN Smith & Haas, New York, 1934. [0] Blue cloth with silver, blue and black decorated spine $50/250

018b: BREATHE UPON THESE SLAIN Lovat Dickson, London, 1934. [] (Ref.b) $30/150

019a: BACKGROUND IN TENNESSEE McBride, New York (1937). [1] Rust colored cloth with blue lettering. Also see next entry. (Priority assumed.) (Published October 13, 1937) $20/100

019b: BACKGROUND IN TENNESSEE McBride, New York (1937). [1] Also noted in dark blue cloth with black lettering, and in green cloth with black lettering $15/75

020a: BREAD AND A SWORD Scribners, New York, 1937. [5] Orange cloth with black lettering $30/150

021a: THE SHADOW OF THE HAWK Scribners, New York, 1941. [5] Gray cloth with blue lettering $20/100

Sincerely
Thorne Smith

THORNE SMITH
(1892-1934)

James Thorne Smith, Jr. was born in Annapolis, Maryland in 1892. He attended Dartmouth and then served in the Navy for two years, until 1919. For the next ten years he wrote copy for advertising agencies. He became a full-time writer in 1928. In 1930, Ogden Nash signed Smith to a contract with Doubleday, Doran for which he produced a number of books before his untimely death in 1934.

The bibliographical information herein is based on an article on Smith by George H. Scheetz and Rodney N. Henshaw in the *Bulletin of Bibliography* (41/1-March 1984). Reference has also been made to E.F. Bleiler's *Checklist of Science Fiction & Supernatural Fiction*, Glen Rock, New Jersey: Firebell Books (1978); and Allen J. Hubin's *Crime Fiction 1749-1980, A Comprehensive Bibliography*, New York / London: Garland Publishing, 1984. The estimates are certainly no more than that for, with the exception of the first book, *The Stray Lamb* and *The Passionate Witch*, very few of the titles have been catalogued.

The signature of Thorne Smith is published with the permission of the Houghton Library, Harvard University, Cambridge, Mass.

001a: BILTMORE OSWALD *The Diary of a Hapless Recruit* Stokes, New York (1918). [0] Pictorial boards. In dustwrapper $50/250

002a: HAUNTS AND BY PATHS AND OTHER POEMS Stokes, New York (1919). [] Advance dummy in pictorial paper covered boards. 87 pages with 60 blank (Waiting For Godot 7/90) $750.

002b: HAUNTS AND BY PATHS AND OTHER POEMS Stokes, New York (1919). [0] $100/500

003a: OUT O'LUCK *Biltmore Oswald Very Much at Sea* Stokes, New York (1919). [0] $60/300

004a: TOPPER *An Improbable Adventure* McBride, New York, 1926. [1] "First Published February 1926." Bleiler (Ghosts) p.182 $300/1,500

004b: TOPPER *An Improbable Adventure* Robert Holden, London, 1926. [] $100/400

004c: THE JOVIAL GHOSTS *The Misadventure of Topper* Arthur Barker, London, 1933. [] $50/250

005a: DREAM'S END McBride, New York, 1927. [1] "First Published March 1927." Bleiler (Ghosts) p.182 $200/1,000

005b: DREAM'S END Jarrolds, London (1928). [] $125/500

006a: THE STRAY LAMB Cosmopolitan, New York, 1929. [0] Bleiler (Fantasy, Theriomorphy) p.182 $125/500

006b: THE STRAY LAMB Heinemann, London, 1930. [] $60/300

007a: DID SHE FALL? Cosmopolitan, New York, 1930. [0] Hubin (Crime Fiction) p.373 $125/500

007b: DID SHE FALL? Doubleday Doran, Garden City, 1932. [0] $30/150

007c: DID SHE FALL? Arthur Barker, London (1936). [1] $25/125

008a: LAZY BEAR LANE Doubleday Doran, Garden City, 1931. [1] $150/600

009a: THE NIGHT LIFE OF THE GODS Doubleday Doran, Garden City, 1931. [1] Bleiler (Pagan Gods, Fantasy) p.182 $100/450

009b: THE NIGHT LIFE OF THE GODS Arthur Barker, London, 1934. [0] $50/250

010a: TURNABOUT Doubleday Doran, Garden City, 1931. [1] Bleiler (Personality Change) p.182 $125/500

010b: TURNABOUT Arthur Barker, London, 1933. [0] $50/250

011a: TOPPER TAKES A TRIP Doubleday Doran, Garden City, 1932. [1] Bleiler (Ghosts) p.182 $100/450

011b: TOPPER TAKES A TRIP Arthur Barker, London, 1935. [0] $50/250

012a: THE BISHOP'S JAEGERS Doubleday Doran, Garden City, 1932. [1] $60/300

012b: THE BISHOP'S JAEGERS Arthur Barker, London, 1934. [0] $40/200

012c: THE BISHOP'S JAEGERS Pocket Books, New York, 1945. [1] Wraps. Includes afterword by author "What Thorne Smith..." $60.

013a: RAIN IN THE DOORWAY Doubleday Doran, Garden City, 1933. [1] Bleiler (Fantasy) p.182. Also noted with special Thorne Smith bookplate issued by the publisher on one half of which is printed: "KLEPTOMANIAC'S EDITION. What happens when you sit down in the evening to enjoy a new Thorne Smith? Like Topper's ghost, it's disappeared! Some friend has- *borrowed-* your copy... Now as a first-aid to the harassed book owner, we have devised a bookplate. Detach, sign, and paste in your copy of Thorne Smith...and if the book is ever caught on anyone else, *will his face be red!"* $75/350

013b: RAIN IN THE DOORWAY Arthur Barker, London, 1933. [0] $40/200

014a: SKIN AND BONES Doubleday Doran, Garden City, 1933. [1] Bleiler (Fantasy) p.182 $100/400

014b: SKIN AND BONES Arthur Barker, London (1936). [1] $50/200

015a: THE GLORIOUS POOL Doubleday Doran, Garden City, 1934. [1] Bleiler (Fantasy) p.182 $50/200

015b: THE GLORIOUS POOL Arthur Barker, London, 1935. [0] $30/150

015c: THE GLORIOUS POOL Pocket Books, New York, 1946. [1] Wraps. Includes afterword as in 12c, but retitled $50.

016a: THORNE SMITH, HIS LIFE AND TIMES Doubleday (Garden City, 1934). [] Wraps. Written by Roland Young, with some portions by Smith (listed as co-author). (Beasley Books 3/89) $75.

017a: THE THORNE SMITH 3-DECKER Doubleday Doran, Garden City, 1936. [1] Bleiler (Fantasy) p.182 $20/100

018a: THE THORNE SMITH TRIPLETS Doubleday Doran, Garden City, 1938. [0] Bleiler (Fantasy) p.182 $20/100

019a: THE PASSIONATE WITCH Doubleday Doran, Garden City, 1941. [1] Completed by Norman Matson $40/200

019b: THE PASSIONATE WITCH Methuen, London (1942). [1] Gray cloth with red lettering on spine. Dustwrapper price "7s 6d net" $20/100

019c: THE PASSIONATE WITCH Pocket Books, New York, 1946. [1] Wraps. Includes an afterword "About Thorne Smith" $40.

020a: THE THORNE SMITH THREE-BAGGER Doubleday Doran, Garden City, 1943. [1] Bleiler (Supernatural) p.182 $20/100

021a: BATS IN THE BELFRY Doubleday Doran, Garden City, 1943. [1] Written by Norman Batson. A sequel to *The Passionate Witch*, which Matson completed $30/150

W.M. SPACKMAN
1905-1990

William Mode Spackman was born May 20, 1905 in Coatesville, Pennsylvania and was a graduate of Princeton University and a Rhodes Scholar at Balliol College, Oxford. He was a radio writer, public-relations executive, and literary critic. He taught at both New York University and the University of Colorado. He was awarded the Harold D. Vursell Memorial Award by the American Academy and Institute of Arts and Letters in 1984; and the University Medal by the University of Colorado in 1985.

The bibliographical portion of this guide was prepared by Maurice B. Cloud and he wishes to thank Mr. Spackman for both his patience and assistance.

001a: HEYDAY Ballantine Books, New York (1953). [0] $25/75

001b: HEYDAY Ballantine Books, New York, 1953. [0] Wraps $30.

001c: HEYDAY Frederick Muller, Ltd., London, 1954. [0] Red cloth boards. Contains numerous changes and omissions from the Ballantine edition $25/75

002a: TWENTY-FIVE YEARS OF IT Perros-Guirec (Paris), 1967. [0] 6 cc (total edition 250 copies). Bound in cloth $200.

002b: TWENTY-FIVE YEARS OF IT Perros-Guirec (Paris), 1967. [0] 250 cc. Wraps $75.

003a: ON THE DECAY OF HUMANISM Rutgers University Press, New Brunswick, New Jersey, 1968. [0] 2,500 cc. Contains misprint: "dis-like" for "dis-taste" p.101:5/6 $15/75

004a: AN ARMFUL OF WARM GIRL Realforms Co. (Canto Review of The Arts), Andover, Massachusetts, 1977. [0] 3,000 cc. Wraps. Contains line: "What, dear?" p.77:39 $40.

004b: AN ARMFUL OF WARM GIRL Alfred A. Knopf, New York, 1978. [1] 14,616 cc. Dropped line "What, dear?" p.79:39 $8/40

004c: DIE UNSCHULD DER FUNFZIGER (The Innocence of the Fifties. German language edition of *An Armful of Warm Girl.*) Claassen, Dusseldorf, 1981. [1] 5,000 cc. Brown beveled boards and dustwrapper. Contains line "Aber wieso denn, Liebste?" ("What, dear?") dropped in Knopf edition p.125:10 $12/60

004d: AN ARMFUL OF WARM GIRL Van Vactor & Goodheart, Cambridge, Massachusetts, 1981. [0] 4,500 cc (combined printings). Both printings contain line "What, Dear?" p.79:39. (Note: reprinted in 1982 [0]) $25.

005a: A PRESENCE WITH SECRETS Alfred A. Knopf, New York, 1980. [] Uncorrected proof. In tall salmon colored wraps $50.

005b: A PRESENCE WITH SECRETS Alfred A. Knopf, New York, 1980. [1] 6,000 cc. Contains misprints "this" for "his" p.75:13 and "steaks" for "streaks" p.137:24 $10/40

005c: A PRESENCE WITH SECRETS Dutton Obelisk, New York, 1982. [1] 6,000 cc. Wraps. Contains introduction by Edmund White. Knopf misprints corrected $20.

006a: A DIFFERENCE OF DESIGN Alfred A. Knopf, New York, 1983. [] Uncorrected proof. In yellow printed wraps (Bert Babcock #48) $40.

006b: A DIFFERENCE OF DESIGN Alfred A. Knopf, New York, 1983. [1] 6,500 cc $7/35

007a: A LITTLE DECORUM, FOR ONCE Alfred A. Knopf, New York, 1985. [] Uncorrected proof. In cream colored wraps $35.

007b: A LITTLE DECORUM, FOR ONCE Alfred A. Knopf, New York, 1985. [1] 5,000 cc $6/30

008a: THE COMPLETE FICTION OF W. M. SPACKMAN Dalkey Archive, Normal, 1997. [] With afterword by Steven Moore. (*Heyday* [001a] is revised for this edition.) Published at $44.95 $10/40

008b: THE COMPLETE FICTION OF W. M. SPACKMAN Dalkey Archive, Normal, 1997. [] Wraps. Published at $16.95 $15.

WILLIAM STYRON

William Styron was born in Virginia in 1925. He served in the Marine Corps from 1943 to 1945, and attended Duke University, graduating in 1947. After being fired from the only job he ever held, a manuscript reader at McGraw-Hill Publishing Company, he began writing. Styron received a Pulitzer Prize in 1968 for his book *The Confessions of Nat Turner*.

REFERENCES:

(a) West, James L. III. WILLIAM STYRON *A Descriptive Bibliography*. Boston, Massachusetts: G. K. Hall & Co. (1977).

(b) Lepper, Garry M. A BIBLIOGRAPHICAL INTRODUCTION TO SEVENTY-FIVE MODERN AMERICAN AUTHORS. Berkeley: Serendipity Books, 1976.

(c) Bruccoli, Matthew (Series Editor). FIRST PRINTINGS OF AMERICAN AUTHORS. Volume 4. Detroit: Bruccoli Clark / Gale Research (1979).

(d) Dermont, Joseph A. PALAEMON PRESS Catalog 40. March, 1989.

We would also like to thank D. Edmond Miller for providing some of the detailed information herein.

001a: LIE DOWN IN DARKNESS Bobbs-Merrill, Indianapolis (1951). [1] Uncorrected proof. In paperwraps (ref.b) $1,000.

001b: LIE DOWN IN DARKNESS Bobbs-Merrill, Indianapolis (1951). [1] Some copies have unlettered bindings, no priority. (Published September 10, 1951) $75/350

001c: LIE DOWN IN DARKNESS Hamilton, London (1952). [1] $50/250

001d: LIE DOWN IN DARKNESS Franklin Library, Franklin Center, 1982. [2] In full leather. "Limited Edition" signed by Styron $75.

002a: THE LONG MARCH Modern Library, New York (1956). [0] Wraps. Number p22 - 95 cents. (Published October 29, 1956.) ("Vintage Book" edition was published in 1960.) First appeared as "Long March" in *Discovery*, No. 1, New York (1953) $200.

002b: THE LONG MARCH Hamish Hamilton, London (1962). [] Uncorrected proof. In yellows wraps $250.

002c: THE LONG MARCH Hamish Hamilton, London (1962). [1] (Remainder of this edition reissued in 1970 in Jonathan Cape dustwrapper) $50/250

002d: THE LONG MARCH Random House, New York (1968). [0] First U.S. hardbound edition. Three printings, no differences noted in ref.b but the dustwrappers may provide definite clues on the later printings: the first has "$3.95" and "3/68" at the top and bottom, respectively, of the front flap and mentions "*Confessions...*" on back panel $20/100

003a: SET THIS HOUSE ON FIRE Random House, New York (1960). [1] Light green dustwrapper lettered in red, title and publisher's information on flaps, but no text. West believes there were fewer than 12 copies in this dustwrapper, although this seems low. Ken Lopez catalogued (4/92) a copy in pale blue dustwrapper printed in red (same?) $20/850

003b: SET THIS HOUSE ON FIRE Random House, New York (1960). [1] Dark green dustwrapper lettered in white, with additional text on flaps. Published May 4, 1960 $20/100

003c: SET THIS HOUSE ON FIRE Hamilton, London (1961). [1] $25/125

004a: THE FOUR SEASONS Pennsvania State University Press, 1965. [2] 75 sgd no. cc. Boxed set of four etchings signed by the artist Harold Altman. Styron introduction $3,000.

005a: THIS QUIET DUST (Harper's Magazine, Inc.), no place (1965). [] Offprint. In blue-gray wraps (Captain's Bookshelf 10/93) $300.

005b: THIS QUIET DUST (Random House, New York, 1967.) [0] 500 cc. In printed blue wraps. Promotional pamphlet for "Nat Turner" (quantity per Chapel Hill Rare Books 5/88) $250.

006a: THE CONFESSIONS OF NAT TURNER Random House, New York (1967). [2] 500 sgd no. cc. Issued in slipcase $350/400

006b: THE CONFESSIONS OF NAT TURNER Random House, New York (1967). [1] Trade edition with extra leaf signed $150/200

006c: THE CONFESSIONS OF NAT TURNER Random House, New York (1967). [1] (Published October 9, 1967) $20/100

006d: THE CONFESSIONS OF NAT TURNER Cape, London (1968). [1] Review copies. "Proof Only" in red printed wraps in proof dustwrapper giving provisional publication date of May 2, 1968 on rear flap $250.

006e: THE CONFESSIONS OF NAT TURNER Cape, London (1968). [1] (Also noted with Pulitzer Prize wrap-around band) $15/75

006f: THE CONFESSIONS OF NAT TURNER Franklin Press, Franklin Center, 1976. [2] "Limited" edition. In full leather (not signed - part of Pulitzer series) $75.

006g: THE CONFESSIONS OF NAT TURNER Franklin Library, Franklin Center, 1979. [2] Signed limited edition. In full leather $75.

006h: THE CONFESSIONS OF NAT TURNER Vintage, New York (1993). [] Wraps. 25th anniversary edition with a new afterword by Styron $20.

007a: IN THE CLAP SHACK Random House, New York (1973). [0] Uncorrected proof. In printed red wraps $200.

007b: IN THE CLAP SHACK Random House, New York (1973). [0] (Published June 15, 1973) $15/75

008a: CHRISTCHURCH, AN ADDRESS... Briar-patch Press, Davidson (1977). [2] 26 sgd ltr cc. Wraps $250.

008b: CHRISTCHURCH, AN ADDRESS... Briar-patch Press, Davidson (1977). [2] 350 no. cc $100.

009a: ADMIRAL ROBERT PENN WARREN... Palaemon Press, Winston-Salem (1978). [2] 26 sgd ltr cc. Wraps (ref.c) $300.

009b: ADMIRAL ROBERT PENN WARREN... Palaemon Press, Winston-Salem (1978). [2] 200 sgd no. cc (ref.c) $100.

009c: ADMIRAL ROBERT PENN WARREN... Palaemon Press, Winston-Salem (1981). [2] 50 sgd no. (Roman) cc. In cloth and decorated paper covered boards. New edition signed by both Styron and Warren (ref.d) $250.

009d: ADMIRAL ROBERT PENN WARREN... Palaemon Press, Winston-Salem (1981). [2] 26 sgd ltr cc (signed by both). Bound in decorated paperwraps (ref.d). Noted in variant blue wraps (Jsoeph A. Dermont 5/98) $250.

009e: ADMIRAL ROBERT PENN WARREN... Palaemon Press, Winston-Salem (1981). [2] 74 sgd no. cc (signed by both). Wraps (ref.d). Noted in variant red wraps (Joseph A. Dermont 5/98) $175.

010a: SOPHIE'S CHOICE Random House, New York (1979). [1] Uncorrected proof. In red wraps (Issued February 15, 1979) $200.

010b: SOPHIE'S CHOICE Random House, New York (1979). [2] 500 sgd no. cc. Issued without dustwrapper. In slipcase $175/250

010c: SOPHIE'S CHOICE Random House, New York, 1979. [1] The trade edition with extra leaf "Advance Presentation Edition" bound in. Light blue cloth. In tissue dustwrapper. (Issued April 27, 1979) $75.

010d: SOPHIE'S CHOICE Franklin Library, Franklin Center, 1979. [2] "Limited Edition." Bound in full leather $75.

010e: SOPHIE'S CHOICE Random House, New York (1979). [1] 125,000 cc. Maroon cloth. (Published June 11, 1979) $12/60

010f: SOPHIE'S CHOICE Jonathan Cape, London, 1979. [] Uncorrected proof. In red wraps $175.

010g: SOPHIE'S CHOICE Jonathan Cape, London (1979). [1] Two variants noted: light brown endpapers and dustwrapper not priced; and white endpapers and priced dustwrapper. Priority unknown. (Robert Temple #37). (Our experience indicates that unpriced copies usually are meant for export to Canada, Australia, etc.) $10/50

011a: SHADRACH Sylvester & Orphanos, Los Angeles, 1979. [2] 4 sgd copies with name of recipient on each $500.

011b: SHADRACH Sylvester & Orphanos, Los Angeles, 1979. [2] 26 sgd ltr cc. Issued without dustwrapper $350.

011c: SHADRACH Sylvester & Orphanos, Los Angeles, 1979. [2] 300 sgd no. cc. Issued without dustwrapper $100.

012a: THE MESSAGE OF AUSCHWITZ Press de la Warr (Blacksburg), 1979. [2] 26 sgd ltr cc. Wraps $300.

012b: THE MESSAGE OF AUSCHWITZ Press de la Warr (Blacksburg), 1979. [2] 200 sgd no. cc. Wraps $100.

013a: AN ADDRESS AT THE 204th COMMENCEMENT OF HAMPTON- SYDNEY COLLEGE (Hampton-Sydney, 1980.) [2] 50 sgd no. cc. Wraps $300.

013b: AN ADDRESS AT THE 204th COMMENCEMENT OF HAMPTON- SYDNEY COLLEGE (Hampton-Sydney, 1980.) [2] 950 no. cc. Wraps. $75.

014a: AGAINST FEAR Palaemon Press, Winston-Salem (1981). [2] 50 sgd no. cc. In blue wraps. For private distribution (ref.d) $200.

014b: AGAINST FEAR Palaemon Press, Winston-Salem (1981). [2] 250 sgd no. cc. In gray wraps (ref.d) $75.

015a: AS HE LAY DEAD, A BITTER GRIEF Albondocani, New York, 1981. [2] 26 sgd ltr cc $300.

015b: AS HE LAY DEAD, A BITTER GRIEF Albondocani, New York, 1981. [2] 300 sgd no. cc. Wraps $100.

016a: THIS QUIET DUST *and Other Writings* Random House, New York (1982). [4] Advance uncorrected proof. In red printed wraps $150.

016b: THIS QUIET DUST *and Other Writings* Random House, New York (1982). [2] 250 sgd no. cc. Issued without dustwrapper. In slipcase $150/200

016c: THIS QUIET DUST *and Other Writings* Random House, New York (1982). [4] (Published November 30, 1982) $8/40

016d: THIS QUIET DUST *and other Writings* Jonathan Cape, London (1983). [] $10/50

016e: THIS QUIET DUST *and Other Writings* Vintage, New York (1993). [] Contains six previously uncollected essays $20.

017a: MR. JEFFERSON AND OUR TIMES Stuart Wright (Winston-Salem, 1984). [2] 14 sgd no. cc. In Japanese decorated paperwraps (ref.d) $350.

017b: MR. JEFFERSON AND OUR TIMES Stuart Wright (Winston-Salem, 1984). [2] 61 sgd cc. In marbled wraps (ref.d) $200.

018a: CONVERSATIONS WITH WILLIAM STYRON University Press of Mississippi, Jackson (1985). [] Uncorrected proof. Oblong folio. Spiral bound wraps with paper label $150.

018b: CONVERSATIONS WITH WILLIAM STYRON University Press of Mississippi, Jackson / London (1985). [3] Edited by James West III $25/50

018c: CONVERSATIONS WITH WILLIAM STYRON University Press of Mississippi, Jackson / London (1985). [3] Wraps $30.

019a: LETTER TO THE EDITOR OF THE PARIS REVIEW Press de la Warr, (Cambridge), 1986. [2] 6 specially bound sgd ltr cc. Wraps (Edmond Miller) $250.

019b: LETTER TO THE EDITOR OF THE PARIS REVIEW Press de la Warr, (Cambridge), 1986. [2] 20 sgd ltr cc. Wraps $200.

019c: LETTER TO THE EDITOR OF THE PARIS REVIEW Press de la Warr, (Cambridge), 1986. [2] 100 sgd no. cc. Wraps (Bert Babcock 5/91) $125.

020a: BLANKENSHIP Press de la Warr, State College, 1988. [2] 26 sgd ltr cc. Wraps. $200.

020b: BLANKENSHIP Press de la Warr, State College, 1988. [2] 100 sgd no. cc. Wraps. $100.

021a: DARKNESS VISIBLE Random House, New York (1990). [] Unrevised proofs. 83 pages. In yellow wraps (Edmond Miller) $125.

021b: DARKNESS VISIBLE Random House, New York (1990). [] Unrevised proofs. 84 pages. In yellow wraps. Issued June 1990 (Edmond Miller) $75.

021c: DARKNESS VISIBLE Random House, New York (1990). [4] Some copies signed on half title for sales force (Waverley Books 1/92) $50/75

021d: DARKNESS VISIBLE Random House, New York (1990). [4] 75,000 cc (PW). (Published September 4, 1990 @ $15.95) $6/30

021e: DARKNESS VISIBLE Jonathan Cape, London, 1991. [] $7/35

022a: INHERITANCE OF NIGHT: EARLY DRAFTS OF *LAY DOWN IN DARKNESS* Duke University Press, Durham / London, 1993. [2] 26 sgd ltr cc. In red cloth. Issued without dustwrapper. In slipcase (James S. Jaffe 11/94) $250.

022b: INHERITANCE OF NIGHT: EARLY DRAFTS OF *LAY DOWN IN DARKNESS* Duke University Press, Durham / London, 1993. [2] 250 sgd no. cc. In red cloth. Issued without dustwrapper. In slipcase. Published @ $125.00 $125.

022c: INHERITANCE OF NIGHT: EARLY DRAFTS OF *LAY DOWN IN DARKNESS* Duke University Press, Durham / London, 1993. [] 1,500 cc. Trade. Issued without dustwrapper $35.

023a: A TIDEWATER MORNING Eurographica, Helsinki, 1991. [2] 350 sgd no. cc. In heavy wraps (Bert Babcock 2/93) $200.

023b: A TIDEWATER MORNING *Three Tales From Youth* Random House, New York (1993). [4] Uncorrected proof. In blue, decorated, glossy printed wraps. (James S. Jaffe 11/94) $100.

023c: A TIDEWATER MORNING *Three Tales From Youth* Random House, New York (1993). [2] 200 sgd no. cc. Issued without dustwrapper. In slipcase $150/200

023d: A TIDEWATER MORNING *Three Tales From Youth* Random House, New York (1993). [] Published September 1993 @ $17.00 $7/35

023e: A TIDEWATER MORNING Jonathan Cape, London (1993). [] (Nicholas and Helen Burrows 9/95) $8/40

024a: A CHANCE IN A MILLION Press de la Warr, Pennsylvania, 1994. [2] 26 sgd ltr cc. In red sewn wraps with printed label on front cover (Waiting For Godot Books 2/95) $200.

024b: A CHANCE IN A MILLION Press de la Warr, Pennsylvania, 1994. [2] 200 sgd no. cc. In blue sewn wraps with printed label on front cover (Waiting For Godot Books 2/95) $60.

025a: GRATEFUL WORDS ABOUT F. SCOTT FITZGERALD F. Scott Fitzgerald Society (Hofstra

University), 1997. [2] 26 sgd ltr cc. In light blue stapled wraps $100.

025b: GRATEFUL WORDS ABOUT F. SCOTT FITZGERALD F. Scott Fitzgerald Society (Hofstra University), 1997. [2] 250 sgd no. cc. In cream colored wraps $45.

PETER TAYLOR
1917 - 1994

Taylor was born in Trenton, Tennessee in 1917. He was educated at Vanderbilt University (1936-37), Southwestern College (1937-38), and graduated from Kenyon College in 1940 before serving in the Army during W.W.II. He married Eleanor Lilly Ross in 1943. In addition to his writing career, Taylor was a Professor of English at the University of Virginia and had been a visiting lecturer at Indiana, University of Chicago, Oxford, Ohio State and Harvard among others. Peter Taylor died on November 2, 1994.

001a: A LONG FOURTH *and Other Stories* Harcourt, Brace, New York (1948). [1] 1,500 cc (quantity per Thomas A. Goldwasser 2/97) $100/500

001b: A LONG FOURTH *and Other Stories* Routledge, London, 1949. [] Erratum slip bound in $50/250

002a: A WOMAN OF MEANS Harcourt, Brace, New York (1950). [] Uncorrected proof. In bound signatures laid in proof dustwrapper (Joseph The Provider 9/92) $750/1,000

002b: A WOMAN OF MEANS Harcourt, Brace, New York (1950). [1] $100/500

002c: A WOMAN OF MEANS Routledge, London, 1950. [] $40/200

003a: THE WIDOWS OF THORNTON Harcourt, New York (1954). [1] $60/300

004a: TENNESSEE DAY IN ST. LOUIS Random House, New York (1957). [0] Also noted without dustwrapper price (Pharos Books) $50/250

005a: HAPPY FAMILIES ARE ALL ALIKE McDowell-Obolensky, New York (1959). [1] $50/250

005b: HAPPY FAMILIES ARE ALL ALIKE Macmillan, London, 1960. [] Yellow cloth with brown lettering (Henry Turlington) $30/150

005c: HAPPY FAMILIES ARE ALL ALIKE Macmillan, London, 1960. [] Variant bindings $25/100

006a: MISS LENORA WHEN LAST SEEN *and Fifteen Other Stories* Obolensky, New York (1963). [1] $50/250

007a: THE COLLECTED STORIES OF PETER TAYLOR Farrar, Straus & Giroux, New York (1969). [1] $25/100

008a: LITERATURE, SEWANEE AND THE WORLD (University of the South, Sewanee, 1972.) [] Wraps. About 100 cc. Eight pages plus cover title (H. E. Turlington 7/95) $300.

009a: PRESENCES *Seven Dramatic Pieces* Houghton Mifflin, Boston, 1973. [1] 1,750 cc $60/300

009b: PRESENCES *Seven Dramatic Pieces* Houghton Mifflin, Boston, 1973. [1] 2,500 cc. Wraps $75.

010a: IN THE MIRO DISTRICT *and Other Stories* Knopf, New York, 1977. [1] Uncorrected proof. In printed yellow wraps $200.

010b: IN THE MIRO DISTRICT *and Other Stories* Knopf, New York, 1977. [1] $15/75

010c: IN THE MIRO DISTRICT *and Other Stories* Knopf, New York, 1977. [1] Wraps $25.

010d: IN THE MIRO DISTRICT *and Other Stories* Chatto & Windus, London, 1977. [0] "Published by

Chatto & Windus Ltd." 1,750 cc (Chapel Hill Rare Books 1/91). First issue dustwrapper priced in pounds (Bert Babcock 12/90) $15/75

011a: THE ROAD *and Other Modern Stories* Cambridge University Press, Cambridge, 1979. [] Wraps. Edited by Taylor $40.

012a: THE EARLY GUEST Palaemon, Winston-Salem (1982). [2] 26 sgd ltr cc. Wraps. In dustwrapper $300.

012b: THE EARLY GUEST Palaemon, Winston-Salem (1982). [2] 140 sgd ltr cc $150.

013a: EUDORA WELTY Stuart Wright, no place, 1984. [2] 5 cc. Stiff white printed wraps. An off-print from *Eudora Welty: A Tribute* $250.

014a: THE OLD FOREST *and Other Stories* Dial, New York, 1985. [] Uncorrected proof. In printed, decorated tan wraps $200.

014b: THE OLD FOREST *and Other Stories* Dial, New York, 1985. [1] (Published February 8, 1985 @ $16.95) $15/75

014c: THE OLD FOREST *and Other Stories* Chatto & Windus / Hogarth, London (1985). [1] "Published in 1985 by ..." (Published August 15, 1985 @ $9.95) $15/75

015a: A STAND IN THE MOUNTAINS Beil, New York, 1985. [0] 1,000 cc. Issued without dust-wrapper. In plain cardboard mailing box/slipcase which was not used on all copies. Colophon states "Verona. March 1986" $50/75

016a: A SUMMONS TO MEMPHIS Knopf, New York, 1986. [1] Uncorrected proof. In blue wraps $250.

016b: A SUMMONS TO MEMPHIS Knopf, New York, 1986. [1] Presumed first issue dustwrapper with no mention of 1987 Pulitizer Prize on front flap, and with text on rear flap beginning, "now he gives us this..." (Published October 6, 1986 @ $15.95.) $20/100

016c: A SUMMONS TO MEMPHIS Knopf, New York, 1986. [1] Presumed second issue dustwrapper with "Winner of the 1987 Pulitzer Prize for Fiction" on front flap, and with text on rear flap beginning, "His highly acclaimed collection..." (Later printing?) $20/40

016c: A SUMMONS TO MEMPHIS Chatto & Windus, London, 1987. [] $10/50

017a: "A WALLED GARDEN" Tales For Travellers, Napa, California, 1987. [0] Map folded wraps. With a story by John Galsworthy $25.

018a: CONVERSATIONS WITH PETER TAYLOR University Press of Mississippi, Jackson / London (1987). [] Uncorrected proof. In spiral bound plain wraps with printed label (William Reese Co. 2/92) $100.

018b: CONVERSATIONS WITH PETER TAYLOR University Press of Mississippi, Jackson / London (1987). [3] $25/50

018c: CONVERSATIONS WITH PETER TAYLOR University Press of Mississippi, Jackson / London (1987). [3] Wraps $30.

019a: THE ORACLE AT STONLEIGH COURT Knopf, New York, 1993. [] Uncorrected proof. In gray printed wraps (Lame Duck Books 12/94) $100.

019b: THE ORACLE OF STONLEIGH COURT Knopf, New York, 1993. [2] 650 cc. Advance reading copy. From bound galleys. In glossy pictorial wraps and in pictorial cardboard slipcase. Not issued signed. (John Hudak 12/94) $50/75

019c: THE ORACLE OF STONLEIGH COURT Knopf, New York, 1993. [1] $7/35

019d: THE ORACLE OF STONLEIGH COURT Chatto & Windus, London (1993). [] (Nicholas Burrows 1/95) $10/50

020a: IN THE TENNESSEE COUNTRY Knopf, New York, 1994. [] Uncorrected proof. In light gray wraps (Waiting For Godot Books 2/95). Printed white wraps (Bev Chaney, Jr. 12/96) $60.

020b: IN THE TENNESSEE COUNTRY Knopf, New York, 1994. [1] (Published 8/94 @ $21.00) $6/30

020c: IN THE TENNESSEE COUNTRY Chatto and Windus, London (1994). [] (Bev Chaney, Jr. 2/96) $8/40

Dylan Thomas

DYLAN THOMAS
(1914 - 1953)

Thomas was born in Swansea, Glamorganshire, South Wales and educated at Swansea Grammar School, where he contributed to (and for a good while edited) the *Swansea Grammar School Magazine* (1925-1934). He appeared in 15 issues in all including his first published poem, "The Song of A Mischievous Dog," in the December 1925 issue (value about $500). He was a reporter for the Swansea evening newspaper for about a year. In 1934 the *Sunday Referee* chose him as its prize poet for the year and published, along with the Parton Bookshop, his first collection of verse *(18 Poems)*. His first book appearance was in *The Years Poetry*, John Lane, London (1934), which preceded *18 Poems* by just a few days.

In 1936, Edith Sitwell favorably reviewed his second book, *Twenty-five Poems* for the *Sunday Times* and his reputation started to expand. In the late 1940's he started working for B.B.C. and subsequently his radio and poetry readings in England and the U.S. brought him wide recognition. But financial problems and drinking plagued him most of his life and the drinking finally caught up with him in New York at the age of only 39.

We would like to thank Jeff Towns (Dylan's Book Shop, Swansea) for his review and assistance on this update.

REFERENCES

(a) Rolph, J. Alexander. DYLAN THOMAS *A Bibliography*. London / New York: J.M. Dent, New Directions (1956).

(b) Maud, Ralph. DYLAN THOMAS IN PRINT *A Bibliographical History*. London: J.M. Dent, (1970).

(c) Provided by New Directions.

(d) Inventory, dealer catalogs, Library of Congress.

Ref.a was used for items up to 020, unless otherwise noted. It is an excellent bibliography. Ref.b was used for items 021 through 031, unless otherwise noted. Ref.b is basically a check-list with no title page, copyright page or quantity information; and did not even include (except for printing quantities) the basic bibliographical information so well presented in ref.a. Therefore any information included on title page content or first edition identification after item 020 came from other sources.

001a: 18 POEMS Sunday Referee & Parton Bookshop, London (1934). [1] 250 cc. Black cloth, flat spine. No leaf between half-title and title pages which was inserted in the second issue. Front edge roughly trimmed. Pale gray dustwrapper lettered in darker gray $600/3,000

001b: 18 POEMS Sunday Referee & Parton Bookshop, London, no date [1936]. [1] 250 cc. Black cloth, rounded spine. Has leaf between half-title and title pages advertising this book and titles by George Barker and David Gascoyne. Front edge cut evenly. Same sheets as 001a. 500 copies in total (a&b). Still states "First Published 1934" $200/1,000

001c: 18 POEMS The Fortune Press, London, no date [circa 1942]. [1] Verso of title page still states "First Published in 1934..." Red buckram, lettered in gold (many later printings in various bindings). Yellow dustwrapper lettered in red. D'Arch Smith in his bibliography of the Fortune Press breaks down this title as follows:

-First issue [1942]: Printer's imprint is Knole Park Press $60/300

-Second issue [1946?]: Printers imprint is Poole J. Looker $25/125

-Third issue [1954?: Also Knole Park Press but with 5 misprints (which would suggest it was reset).

P.12:8 "no" for "nor", p.20:7 "fist" for "Fists", p.23:7 "word" for "world", p.23:27 "may" for "my" and p.30:12 "guns" for "guns." $20/100

002a: TWENTY-FIVE POEMS J.M. Dent, London (1936). [1] 730 cc. There were reprints in 1936, in same dustwrapper, and 1929 in beige / off-white dustwrapper (Jeff Towns) $200/1,000

003a: THE HAND Frederic Prokosch, Venice, 1939. [2] Wraps. Colored frontis by Prokosch. (Van Allen Bradley 1982-83 lists this "One of 3 (of 10) on Arches paper. $1,500.

004a: THE MAP OF LOVE J.M. Dent, London (1939). [] Uncorrected proof. In drab wraps. (The trade edition was entirely corrected and reset prior to publication [R.A. Gekoski]) $1,500.

004b: THE MAP OF LOVE J.M. Dent, London (1939). [1] 1,000 cc. First issue in fine grained mauve cloth, an almost silky texture; title blocked in gold on front cover; title and author's name in gold on spine; "Dent" blind-stamped at foot of spine; top edge stained dark-purple. 2,000 sets of sheets printed, balance used on other issues $125/600

004c: THE MAP OF LOVE J.M. Dent, London (1939). [1] 250 cc. Second issue bound in coarser, plum-colored, cloth. Else same as 004a $75/350

004d: THE MAP OF LOVE J.M. Dent, London (1939). [1] 250 cc. Third issue in purple cloth intermediate between fine and coarse grained; blocked in blue including "Dent" at foot of spine; top edge stained purple. Issued in February 1948 $40/200

004e: THE MAP OF LOVE J.M. Dent, London (1939). [1] 500 cc. Fourth issue bound as 003c but top edge unstained. Issued between December 1948 and February 1949 $25/125

005a: THE WORLD I BREATHE New Directions, Norfolk, Connecticut (1939). [0] 700 cc (a & b). With one star on either side of author's name on title page and spine (Van Allen Bradley 1982-83, not in ref.a or b). Also noted with one star on either side of name on title page and five stars on either side on spine (Jeff Towns) $200/850

005b: THE WORLD I BREATHE New Directions, Norfolk, Connecticut (1939). [0] With five stars on either side of author's name on title page and spine $150/750

006a: THE RULERS Koppel (London, 1940?). [] Wraps. 22 pages. Music with words by Thomas (Waiting For Godot #10) $350.

007a: PORTRAIT OF THE ARTIST AS A YOUNG DOG Dent, London (1940) [1] Proof in drab printed wraps (Jeff Towns) $2,000.

007b: PORTRAIT OF THE ARTIST AS A YOUNG DOG Dent, London (1940). [1] 1,500 cc. Green cloth stamped in silver and in blind. Top edges stained rust red. Also noted a variant in light green cloth lettered in red-brown with top edges unstained (I. D. Edrich 5/97) $150/600

007c: PORTRAIT OF THE ARTIST AS A YOUNG DOG New Directions, Norfolk, Connecticut (1940). [0] 1,000 cc. "Printed for New Directions ... September 1940" $100/400

007d: PORTRAIT OF THE ARTIST AS A YOUNG DOG Guild Books / Dent, London (1948). [1] 40,250 cc. Wraps. Actually published in March 1949, total quantity 50,250 cc, see next entry $50.

007e: PORTRAIT OF THE ARTIST AS A YOUNG DOG Guild Books / Dent, London (1948). [1] 10,000 cc. During 1952 a four-color dustwrapper was added to the book until they ran out $50/100

008a: FROM IN MEMORY OF ANN JONES Caseg Press, Llanllechid, Caernarvonshire (1942). [0] 500 cc. Caseg Broadsheet No. 5 $350.

009a: NEW POEMS New Directions, Norfolk, Connecticut (1943). [0] 1,000 cc. Issued in paper boards. Ref.a notes that the true first printing of this title was completely destroyed as the size differed from the other volumes in the "Poet of The Month" series, so there may be some unbound sheets somewhere $75/300

009b: NEW POEMS New Directions, Norfolk, Connecticut (1943). [0] 1,500 cc. Wraps. (Issued simultaneously.) Also in dustwrapper. (Have a note that dustwrapper with reviews would be later. But not sure of source of this) $50/150

010a: DEATHS AND ENTRANCES J.M. Dent & Sons Ltd., London (1946). [1] 3,000 cc. One of Cyril Connolly's 100 key books in *The Modern Movement* $75/350

010b: DEATHS AND ENTRANCES Gregynog (Newtown), 1984. [2] 28 no. (Roman) cc. Bound in a special designer binding by James Brockman (also 2 unnumbered copies) $2,000.

010c: DEATHS AND ENTRANCES Gregynog (Newtown), 1984. [2] 250 no. cc. Illustrated by John Piper. Dark green leather spine and blue-gray cloth. Issued in slipcase. (Also 20 unnumbered copies) $400/500

011a: SELECTED WRITINGS New Directions (New York, 1946). [0] 4,000 cc. "Reprints are identifiable only by the dustwrapper which has printing number stated on front flap" and in mauve cloth (ref.a). However, we believe Jeff Towns is correct in believing Rolph was looking at a later printing. Towns' copy is a file copy with "Publication Date November 20, 1946." The first is in green cloth, with the title on a double page spread and copyright pages starting "Copyright 1946..." Later printings have a single page title page and "Copyright 1939 / By New Directions / Copyright 1946." Dustwrapper has "Other New Directions Books..." on back panel. Address "500 Fifth Avenue." Later dustwrappers have "The New Classics Series..." on back, address "333 Sixth Avenue" $50/250

012a: TWENTY-SIX POEMS (New Directions, Norfolk, Connecticut, 1950.) [2] 8 sgd no. cc on Japanese vellum. Copies numbered III-X. Issued in slipcase. (American issue preceded English by 3 months.) (Brought $6,500. at auction in 1986 and has been catalogued at $9,500 and $13,000) $12,500.

012b: TWENTY-SIX POEMS (New Directions, Norfolk, Connecticut, 1950.) [2] 87 sgd no. cc on handmade paper. Copies numbered 61-147. Issued in slipcase $3,500.

012c: TWENTY-SIX POEMS J.M. Dent & Sons Ltd, London (1950). [2] 2 sgd no. cc on Japanese vellum. Copies numbered I-II. Issued in slipcase $12,500.

012d: TWENTY-SIX POEMS J.M. Dent & Sons Ltd, London (1950). [2] 50 sgd no. cc. Numbered 11-60 (copies 148-150 for author & publisher). Issued in slipcase $4,000.

013a: IN COUNTRY SLEEP New Directions (New York, 1952). [2] 100 sgd no. cc. Issued in dark brown slipcase $1,500/1,750

013b: IN COUNTRY SLEEP New Directions (New York, 1952). [0] 5,000 cc. Reportedly the first issue has Thomas photograph tipped to title, but all copies we've seen have the photograph $125/400

014a: COLLECTED POEMS 1934-1952 J.M. Dent & Sons Ltd, London (1952). [1] 68 copies of the proof in pale green wraps printed in black omitting author's prologue and introduction thereto $1,500.

014b: COLLECTED POEMS 1934-1952 J.M. Dent & Sons Ltd, London (1952). [] Later proof including prologue and introduction, but the prologue is changed for the trade edition (Jeff Towns). Not clear whether this proof would be part of the 68 copies noted by Rolph but assume it may have been as the outward appearance is the same $1,000.

014c: COLLECTED POEMS 1934-1952 J.M. Dent & Sons Ltd, London (1952). [2] 65 sgd no. cc. Full dark blue morocco. In plain cellophane dustwrapper. $4,000.

014d: COLLECTED POEMS 1934-1952 J.M. Dent & Sons Ltd, London (1952). [1] 4,760 cc $50/250

014e: THE COLLECTED POEMS OF DYLAN THOMAS New Directions (New York, 1953). [0] 4 page prospectus with 2 poems and reviews $60.

014f: THE COLLECTED POEMS OF DYLAN THOMAS New Directions (New York, 1953). [0] 6,000 cc (a & b). The word "daughter" misspelled on p.199 (corrected in later printings). (Note: the 1956, 11th printing had the first printing of the poem "Elegy" completed by Vernon Watkins and with a note by him) $50/250

014g: COLLECTED POEMS 1934-1952 Readers Union / Dent, London, 1954. [] First edition to include the expanded “Contents” table (Jeff Towns) $25/100

015a: THE DOCTOR AND THE DEVILS J.M. Dent & Sons Ltd, London (1947). [0] 35 cc. In stiff cork colored wraps. Proofs with the character "Salter" which was changed to "Rock" in final version. "1947" on verso of title page (The book was not produced until 1953) $1,500.

015b: THE DOCTOR AND THE DEVILS J.M. Dent & Sons Ltd, London (1953). 97 cc. Proof. In pale green wraps $750.

015c: THE DOCTOR AND THE DEVILS J.M. Dent & Sons Ltd, London (1953). [1] 4,000 cc $40/200

015d: THE DOCTOR AND THE DEVILS New Directions (Norfolk, 1953). [0] 1,500 cc. English sheets measuring 7 1/4" x 4 3/4" (second printing was 8" x 5 1/4"). (Published October 8, 1953 @ $2.50) $30/150

016a: UNDER MILK WOOD J.M. Dent & Sons Ltd, London (1954). [] Uncorrected Proof. Bound in dustwrapper. Noted with and without "Advance Proofs Only" stamped on front cover. While no clear priority has been established, Daniel Jones' (who wrote the preface and did the musical settings) copy has the statement, thus this state is likely the earliest (Robert Dagg 3/96) $850.

016b: UNDER MILK WOOD J.M. Dent & Sons Ltd, London (1954). [1] 6,400 cc. (Note: first separate appearance of this BBC commissioned work preceded the book by a month. This script was offered by Beasley Books for $1,000 in 1991) $50/250

016c: UNDER MILK WOOD New Directions (New York, 1954). [0] 6,000 cc. (Ref.c shows only 2,149 copies bound) 40/200

016d: UNDER MILK WOOD (Acting Edition.) J.M. Dent & Sons Ltd, London (1958). [1] Wraps (ref.b). Preface and musical settings by Daniel Jones $75.

016e: UNDER MILK WOOD (Acting Edition.) (New Directions, New York, 1958.) [0] (Ref.b.) Wraps. English sheets $60.

016f: UNDER MILK WOOD Timon Film, London, no date [circa 1970]. [] First draft screenplay by Andrew Sinclair. In black wraps (Jeff Towns) $600.

016g: UNDER MILK WOOD Timon Film, London, no date [circa 1970]. [] Release script by Andrew Sinclair. In red wraps (Jeff Towns) $500.

016h: UNDER MILK WOOD Folio Society, London, 1972. [] Lithographs by Ceri Richards. First illustrated edition. Issued without dustwrapper. In slipcase (ref.d) $50/75

016i: UNDER MILK WOOD J.M. Dent, London, 1995. "Definitive Edition." Edited by Walford Davies and Ralph Maud (Jeff Towns) $10/30

017a: QUITE EARLY ONE MORNING... J.M. Dent & Sons Ltd, London, 1954. [] Proof copy in plain gray wraps. Laid in dustwrapper of published edition (ref.d) $450/650.

017b: QUITE EARLY ONE MORNING... J.M. Dent & Sons Ltd, London, 1954. [1] 10,000 cc. First issue has full stop after "sailors" at end of verse 5 on pages 3 and 11 (comma added in subsequent printings) $25/125

017c: QUITE EARLY ONE MORNING New Directions (New York, 1954). [0] 3,200 cc. Wraparound band (Boston Book Annex #23). Later printings only identifiable by note on front dustwrapper flap. Contents differ from English edition $20/100

018a: CONVERSATION ABOUT CHRISTMAS New Directions, no place, 1954. [0] 2,000 cc. Wraps. Christmas greeting, 8 stapled pages plus covers in mailing envelope for "The Friends of J. Laughlin..." $150.

019a: MEMORIES OF CHRISTMAS J.M. Dent Don Mills, Ontario (1954). [] Christmas keepsake issued in Canada only. Priority of this and previous entry unknown (Letters 5/91) $200.

020a: TWO EPIGRAMS OF FEALTY No publisher or place (1953). [2] 30 no. cc. Wraps. "Printed for members of the Court of the Realm of Redonda" (John Gawsworth). Each a single printed sheet folded into quarters. 1953 appears at bottom of poems, but ref. b & d give 1954 as date. $500.

020b: GALSWORTHY AND GAWSWORTH No publisher or place (1953). [2] 30 no. cc. Wraps. "Printed for members of the Court of the Realm of Redonda" (John Gawsworth). Each a single printed sheet folded into quarters. 1953 appears at bottom of poems, but ref. b & d gives 1954 as date. $500.

021a: ADVENTURES IN THE SKIN TRADE *and Other Stories* New Directions (New York, 1955). [0] 5,000 cc $30/150

021b: ADVENTURES IN THE SKIN TRADE Putnam, London (1955). [] Proof copy. In manila wraps (Jeff Towns) $500.

021c: ADVENTURES IN THE SKIN TRADE Putnam, London (1955). [1] 6,900 cc. Title story (unfinished novel) only $25/125

021d: ADVENTURES IN THE SKIN TRADE Studio Services, New York (1966). [] Film script by Andrew Sinclair (Jeff Towns) $400.

021e: ADVENTURES IN THE SKIN TRADE J.M. Dent, London, 1967. [] A dramatization by Andrew Sinclair $15/60

021f: ADVENTURES IN THE SKIN TRADE *and Other Stories* New Directions, New York, 1968. [] A dramatization by Andrew Sinclair $15/60

022a: A PROSPECT OF THE SEA *and Other Stories and Prose Writings* J.M. Dent & Sons Ltd, London (1955). [] Uncorrected proof. In drab wraps. Noted with dustwrapper (I. D. Edrich 5/97) $$75/150

022b: A PROSPECT OF THE SEA *and other Stories and Prose Writings* J.M. Dent & Sons Ltd, London (1955). [1] 8,000 cc $20/100

023a: A CHILD'S CHRISTMAS IN WALES New Directions, Norfolk, Connecticut (1955). [0] 10,000 cc. Published in 1955, although copyright page states 1954. 7 1/4" x 5" in pale gray boards with title in red and author's name in black. First Separate edition $25/75

023b: A CHILD'S CHRISTMAS IN WALES J.M. Dent & Sons Ltd, London (1968). [1] Wraps. Noted in yellow with red lettering and red with black lettering (priority unknown) $50.

023c: A CHILD'S CHRISTMAS IN WALES New Directions, (New York, 1959). [1] This edition first published 1959. Woodcuts by Ellen Raskin $15/50

023d: A CHILD'S CHRISTMAS IN WALES New Directions, New York, 1969. [2] 100 sgd (artist) no. cc with 5 original prints by Fritz Eichenberg. Book is in leather backed boards. With the five prints signed by the artist enclosed in stiff black portfolio with printed labels. (Published October 15, 1969 @ $200.) (Ref.c.) Price is for book with portfolio $500/1,500

023e: A CHILD'S CHRISTMAS IN WALES New Directions, New York, 1969. [] 15,197 cc. (Published October 15, 1969 @ $4.) (Ref.c) $10/50

024a: LETTERS TO VERNON WATKINS J.M. Dent / Faber & Faber, London (1957). [1] Edited with introduction by Watkins $15/75

024b: LETTERS TO VERNON WATKINS New Directions (New York, 1957). [0] 5,051 cc. (Published December 11, 1957 @ $3.) (Ref.c) $12/60

025a: FOUR POEMS London County Council, Central School of Arts & Crafts, London, no date [circa 1959]. [] Green cloth stamped in gold. Issued without dustwrapper. Binding and illustrations by Fiona Campbell. Typographical design and typesetting by Christo van Niekerk. Printed with the permission of J. M. Dent (Ian McKelvie 10/95) $400.

026a: THE BEACH OF FALESA Stein & Day, New York (1963). [0] Proof in green wraps (Jeff Towns) $100.

026b: THE BEACH OF FALESA Stein & Day, New York (1963). [0] (Ref. b & d) $12/60

026c: THE BEACH OF FALESA Jonathan Cape, London (1964). [1] (Ref.d) $12/60

027a: MISCELLANY *Poems Stories Broadcasts* J.M. Dent & Sons, Ltd, London (1963). [] Aldine Paperback #13 (ref.d) $50.

028a: TWENTY YEARS A-GROWING J.M. Dent & Sons, Ltd., London (1964). [1] Proof in pink wraps (Jeff Towns) $125.

028b: TWENTY YEARS A-GROWING J.M. Dent & Sons Ltd., London (1964). [1] Film script based on Maurice O'Sullivan's story (ref.d) $12/60

029a: REBECCA'S DAUGHTERS Triton (London, 1965). [1] (Ref.d). In paper and cellophane dustwrapper (Am Here Books 4/93) $15/100

029b: REBECCA'S DAUGHTERS Little, Brown, Boston (1965). [1] (Ref.b & d) $12/60

030a: ME AND MY BIKE MacDonald, London (1964). [] Uncorrected proof in brown wraps with label on front (Ken Lopez 1/89). The half title contains the limitation statement altered in pencil from 1,000 to 500 copies. The proof does not contain the introductory Dylan Thomas letter which appears in the published version but contains a final illustration which does not appear in that book (I. D. Edrich 5/97) $200.

030b: ME AND MY BIKE Triton (London, 1965). [2] 500 no. cc. Issued in dustwrapper. In slipcase (ref.d) $25/100

030c: ME AND MY BIKE Triton (London, 1965). [1] (Ref.d) $15/75

030d: ME AND MY BIKE McGraw-Hill, New York (1965). [] Illustrated by Leonora Box (ref.d). English sheets $12/60

031a: THE DOCTOR AND THE DEVILS *and Other Scripts* New Directions (New York, 1966). [1] 3,485 cc. First printing dustwrapper has ad for *Collected Poems* on back. Second printing dustwrapper has ads for 9 other books by Thomas (ref. c & d) $10/50

032a: MISCELLANY TWO J.M. Dent, London (1966). [] Wraps. Aldine Paperback No. 49 (ref.d) $50.

033a: SELECTED LETTERS OF DYLAN THOMAS J.M. Dent, London (1966). [1] Proof in gray printed wraps (Jeff Towns) $125.

033b: SELECTED LETTERS OF DYLAN THOMAS J.M. Dent, London (1966). [1] $15/75

033c: SELECTED LETTERS OF DYLAN THOMAS New Directions (New York, 1967). [0] 3,915 cc. (Published May 15, 1967 @ $8.50.) (Ref. b & c) $12/60

034a: IN COUNTRY HEAVEN, AN UNFINISHED POEM-TO-BE BBC Third Programme, London, 1966. [] Mimeograph radio script. December 18, 1966. *In Country Heaven* had just appeared in the *Daily Telegraph* a few days before this broadcast but it did not contain the text of the five mimeograph worksheets that appear here for the first time. This is the first separate appearance, as well. (Beasley Books 12/94) $150.

035a: THE NOTEBOOKS OF DYLAN THOMAS New Directions (New York, 1967). [] 5,057 cc. (Published October 31, 1967 @ $8.50.) (Ref. b & c) $12/60

035b: POET IN THE MAKING J.M. Dent, London (1968). [] (Ref.d). New title $10/50

036a: TWO TALES... Sphere, New York, 1968. [] Contains *Me and My Bike* and *Rebecca's Daughters*. Illustrated by Leonora Box (ref.d) $12/60

037a: TWELVE MORE LETTERS (Turret Books, London, 1969.) [2] 26 ltr cc. Dark brown cloth. Issued in glassine dustwrapper $250.

037b: TWELVE MORE LETTERS (Turret Books, London, 1969.) [2] 175 no. cc. Yellow cloth. Issued in glassine dustwrapper (Argosy Bookstore Cat. 745) $100.

038a: EARLY PROSE WRITINGS J.M. Dent, London (1971). [] Proof in orange printed wraps with publicate date of September 23, 1971 $150.

038b: EARLY PROSE WRITINGS J.M. Dent, London (1971). [] (Ian McKelvie Cat. 57) $12/60

038c: EARLY PROSE WRITINGS New Directions, New York, 1972. [1] (Published March 22 or April 20, 1972 @ $8.75.) (Ref.c indicates 488 copies for New Directions and 100 for Dent and that later New Directions imported copies from Dent as follows: 3/27/74 - 500 copies of which 252 damaged, 4/25/76 - 406 copies) $25/100

039a: THE OUTING J. M. Dent, London (1971). [1] Wraps. Illustrated by Meg Stevens $60.

039b: THE OUTING J. M. Dent, London (1985). [1] Illustrated by Paul Cox $12/60

040a: THE POEMS OF DYLAN THOMAS J.M. Dent, London (1971) [] Proof in orange printed wraps. $150.

Note: The proof and the first edition contain a poem on p.221 which was actually written by Lillian Gard and published in *The Boys Own Paper* in November 1923. Thomas had plagiarized it. The poem is removed in later editions and replaced by "The Song of the Mischievous Dog." Later issues of the U.K. first and the U.S. first contain a printed errata slip which explains this incident. (Jeff Towns)

040b: THE POEMS OF DYLAN THOMAS J.M. Dent, London (1971). [] (Ian McKelvie Cat. 57). See note above $25/75

040c: THE POEMS OF DYLAN THOMAS New Directions (New York, 1971). [1] 8,118 cc. (Published September 22, 1971 @ $6.) (Ref.c.) See note above $25/75

041a: HOLIDAY MEMORY J.M. Dent, London (1972). [1] Wraps. Originally published in *Quite Early One Morning*. First separate publication (ref.d) $40.

041b: HOLIDAY MEMORY Lime Rock Press, Salisbury, Connecticut (1979). [2] 25 numbered (Roman) copies signed by the publishers. With four miniature mounted black and white photographs of Dylan Thomas's home $250.

041c: HOLIDAY MEMORY Lime Rock Press, Salisbury, Connecticut (1979). [2] 100 no. cc signed by the publishers. Miniature measuring 2" x 2" x 1/4" $150.

042a: SEVEN POEMS Art School Press, Camberwell, 1974. [2] 75 sgd no. cc. Folio cut in linoleum, signed by Keith Holmes who designed and printed the book $200.

043a: THE DEATH OF THE KING'S CANARY Hutchinson, London (1976). [] Uncorrected proof. In salmon pink wraps $150.

043b: THE DEATH OF THE KING'S CANARY Hutchinson, London (1976). [1] Written with John Davenport. Introduction by Constantine FizGibbon $12/60

043c: THE DEATH OF THE KING'S CANARY Viking, New York (1977). [1] "Published in 1977 by..." Written with John Davenport. Errata slip laid in $10/50

044a: THE FOLLOWERS J.M. Dent, London (1976). [2] First separate edition. Text cuts by Keith Holmes and signed by him. Vellum. In hinged box (Bromer #25) $350.

044b: THE FOLLOWERS London (1976). [1] Wraps. (Ref.d) $40.

044c: THE FOLLOWERS Raamin-Presse (Hamburg), 1977. [2] 30 sgd no. cc. 1 to 20 in German and 1 to 10 in English. With a numbered and signed etching by Roswitha Quadelieg $350.

044d: THE FOLLOWERS Raamin-Presse (Hamburg), 1977. [2] 90 sgd no. cc. 21 to 80 in German and 11 to 40 in English $200.

045a: FERN HILL Four Winds Press, (Locust Valley), 1978. [2] 30 cc. Large 4to sheets folded and laid in stiff green wraps folder (Wilder Books #28) $200.

046a: DRAWINGS TO POEMS BY DYLAN THOMAS Enitharmon Press (London), 1980. [] Drawings by Ceri Richards $25/75

047a: LAUGHARNE Lime Rock Press, Salisbury, Connecticut, 1980. [2] 25 sgd ltr cc. Text by Thomas. Photographs by Tryntje Van Ness Seymour $750.

047b: LAUGHARNE Lime Rock Press, Salisbury, Connecticut, 1980. [2] 75 cc (numbered? signed?). Published at $395 $450.

048a: THE COLLECTED STORIES Franklin Library, Franklin Center, 1980. [2] "Limited Edition." 25 stories illustrated by Paul Hogarth. Blue leather (ref.d) $100.

048b: THE COLLECTED STORIES J.M. Dent, London (1983). [1] 44 stories $12/60

048c: THE COLLECTED STORIES New Directions (New York, 1984). [1] "First published clothbound ... 1984." 44 stories $10/50

049a: THE PEACHES (Tales For Travellers, San Francisco, 1982.) [0] Wraps (map fold). Last copyright 1982 but probably published in 1985 or later $35.

050a: The following were illustrated and signed by Frederic Prokosch using Prometheus Press, Grasse (France), 1982. [2] 5 sgd no. cc. 6 1/4" x 4 1/2" (Howard Woolmer 10/90):

a. THE AIR YOU BREATHE	$125.
b. CONCEIVE THESE IMAGES	$125.
c. DO NOT GO GENTLE	$125.
d. THE ROD	$125.
e. SONG	$125.
The set:	$750.

051a: The following were illustrated and signed by Frederic Prokosch using Prometheus Press, Grasse (France), 1983. [2] 5 sgd no. cc. (Eric & Joan Stevens #131):

a. HIGH ON A HILL	$125.
b. HERE LIE THE BEASTS	$125.
c. POEM	$125.
d. LAST NIGHT	$125.
e. WAS THERE A TIME	$125.
The set:	$750.

052a: POEM ON HIS BIRTHDAY *In the Mustard-seed Sun* Tern Press (Marret Drayton, 1983). [2] 85 sgd no. cc. Illustrated and signed by Nicholas Parry. Issued without dustwrapper (George Houle #39) $250.

053a: THE COLLECTED LETTERS J.M. Dent, London (1985). [] Edited by Paul Ferris $12/60

053b: THE COLLECTED LETTERS Macmillan, New York, 1985. [] Uncorrected proof. In blue wraps $125.

053c: THE COLLECTED LETTERS Macmillan, New York, 1985. [] $10/50

053d: THE COLLECTED LETTERS Fitzhenry & Whiteside, Toronto ... (1985). [] (Blue Mountain Books 7/96) $10/50

054a: THE OUTING J.M. Dent, London (1985). [1] First separate and first illustrated edition $15/50

055a: THE MOUSE AND THE WOMAN Brighton Press, San Diego, 1988. [2] 20 sgd no. cc. Signed by the illustrator James Renner. First separate edition of a section of *The Adventures in the Skin Trade*. Pictorial cloth. Issued without dustwrapper. In slipcase. (Auction records 1993) $350.

055b: THE MOUSE AND THE WOMAN Brighton Press, San Diego, 1988. [2] 180 sgd no. cc. Signed by the illustrator James Renner. First separate edition of a section of *The Adventures in the Skin Trade*. Issued without dustwrapper. In slipcase. (Published @ $250.) $250.

056a: IN MY CRAFT OR SULLEN ART London, 1989. [] Broadside posted in London Subway (Bayside Books 12/89) $60.

057a: THE NOTEBOOK POEMS 1930-1934 J.M. Dent, London, 1989. [] $10/50

058a: THE BROADCASTS J.M. Dent, London, 1991. [] (I. D. Edrich 5/97) $10/40

058b: ON THE AIR WITH DYLAN THOMAS *The Broadcasts* New Directions (New York, 1992). [0] Edited by Ralph Maud. (Published @ $22.95) $7/35

059a: EIGHT STORIES New Directions, New York, 1993. [] 5,000 cc. Wraps. New series (PW 3/8/93) $25.

060a: LETTER TO LOREN Salubrious Press (Swansea), 1993. [2] 26 sgd ltr cc (Loren Maciver). Bound in quarter leather. In slipcase. Introduction and note by Jeff Towns $350.

060b: LETTER TO LOREN Salubrious Press (Swansea), 1993. [2] 200 no. cc. Bound in full cloth; issued without dustwrapper (Words Etcetera 10/95) $175.

061a: THE FILM SCRIPTS J.M. Dent, London, 1995. [] Edited by John Ackerman $10/40

061b: THE COMPLETE SCREENPLAYS Applause, New York (1995). [] $6/30

062a: THE DYLAN THOMAS OMNIBUS Phoenix Giants, London, 1995. [] (I. D. Edrich 5/97) $10/35

MARK TWAIN
Samuel Langhorne Clemens
1835-1910

Clemens was born in 1835 in Florida, Missouri. He spent his boyhood in Hannibal, Missouri and it was his boyhood recollections that produced his most famous stories, *The Adventures of Tom Sawyer* and *The Adventures of Huckleberry Finn*. In 1857 he became a Mississippi river pilot, an experience that gave him his pseudonym ("mark twain" was called out when the depth of water of two fathoms was reached).

He worked as a wandering printer and newspaperman ending up in San Francisco where Bret Harte encouraged him in his writing of "tall tales." Clemens won his first fame for his short story *The Celebrated Jumping Frog of Calaveras County*.

Clemens married and moved to Hartford, Connecticut in 1872, where his investments in printing and publishing ventures left him penniless by 1894. He began lecturing around the world to pay off these debts.

His bad investments, the death of two of his daughters and the long illness and death of his wife combined to change his writing from the humorous to the pessimistic.

Mark Twain is considered to be one of the finest writers America has produced.

The retail prices herein are our best estimates based on dealer catalog prices and auction records where available. The price(s) estimated are for fine copies **without dustwrappers before 1920** although we know the books were issued in dustwrappers from at least the 1890's on and estimated prices with dustwrapper before 1920 would be at least three times more than unjacketed copies. Starting in 1920 the two prices indicate estimates without/with dustwrappers. Truly fine or better copies of the early books are not common and should command the prices shown and conversely worn copies or those with defects would sell for considerably less. Copies bound in original publisher's leather are consistently catalogued or sold at auction for more than the cloth bound copies. We tried to mention this on each title where we knew it applied but if we missed some titles, the general rule still applies. It also should be noted that issues with gilt edges seem to consistently bring more than their plain edge counterparts.

We would like to thank Carl Hahn for his assistance in the preparation of this guide; and Ken Sanderson of the Mark Twain Project at the Bancroft Library in Berkeley.

REFERENCES:

Unless otherwise noted, information is for ref.a through 1956 and ref.b thereafter.

(a) Blanck, Jacob. BIBLIOGRAPHY OF AMERICAN LITERATURE. Volume II. New Haven / London: Yale University Press (1957).

(b) McBride, William M. MARK TWAIN *A Bibliography of the Collections of the Mark Twain Memorial and the Stowe-Day Foundation.* Hartford: McBride Publications (1984).

(c) Fox, Alan C. CATALOGUE ONE. (Sherman Oaks, 1980).

(d) Holmes, David J. THE JULES L. MERRON COLLECTION OF MARK TWAIN. Catalogue 38. Philadelphia (1992).

001a: THE CELEBRATED JUMPING FROG OF CALAVERAS COUNTY *and Other Sketches* C.H. Webb, New York, 1867. [0] Possibly 1,000 cc (Macdonnell Rare Books 8/95). First issue has single leaf of ads on cream-yellow paper before title-page. P.66: last line "life" unbroken. P.198: last line "this" unbroken. In various cloth colors. Usually with frog in left corner of front cover, variant has frog in middle. One copy reported with p.198 unprinted, which may be earliest state $20,000.

001b: THE CELEBRATED JUMPING FROG OF CALAVERAS COUNTY *and Other Sketches* C.H. Webb, New York, 1867. [0] Second printing lacks ads before title-page. Type noted above either broken or worn. There were two other printings in the same format. These sell for $500 to $750 $3,000.

Note: Intermediate states of above exist

001c: THE CELEBRATED JUMPING FROG OF CALAVERAS COUNTY *and Other Sketches* George Routledge & Sons, London, 1867. [0] Wraps $6,000.

001d: THE JUMPING FROG ++ John Camden Hotten, London, no date. [0] Wraps (pictorial?). (Published 1867?) $1,500.

001e: THE CELEBRATED JUMPING FROG ++ George Routledge & Sons, London, 1868. [0] Wraps $1,250.

001f: THE CELEBRATED JUMPING FROG OF CALAVARAS COUNTY ++ A. S. Irving, Toronto, 1870. [] Pictorial light brown wraps printed in green (Heritage Book Shop 2/97) $2,000.

001g: THE JUMPING FROG IN ENGLISH... Harper & Bros., New York / London, 1903. [0] First separate edition (thus - considerably revised from the 1867 original; however, except for the final three-page note this had appeared in this form in *Sketches* (1875)). Issued in dustwrapper. $150.

001h: THE NOTORIOUS JUMPING FROG... Duschnes, New York, 1932. [2] 200 cc. In green boards. Issued without dustwrapper $125.

001i: JIM SMILEY & HIS JUMPING FROG Pocahontas Press (Chicago), 1940. [] $75.

001j: THE NOTORIOUS JUMPING FROG *& Other Stories* Limited Editions Club, New York, 1970. [2] 1,500 cc. Signed by Joseph Low, the illustrator. Selected and introduced by Edward Wagenknecht. Issued without dustwrapper. In slipcase $75/125

001k: THE CELEBRATED JUMPING FROG OF CALAVARAS COUNTY *and Other Sketches* West Virginia Pulp & Paper Co., no place, 1959. [] Leather spine. Issued without dustwrapper. In slipcase $40/60

001l: THE JUMPING FROG Cheloniidae Press, Easthampton, Massachusetts (1985). [2] 15 sgd no. cc. (Additionally, there were 5 copies of the State Proof Edition in this binding [Lame Duck Books 9/95]) Illustrated and signed by James Alan Robinson. Bound in full leather and in tray case with an additional suite of prints with state proofs of etchings and working proofs of wood engravings $2,500.

001m: THE JUMPING FROG Cheloniidae Press, Easthampton, Massachusetts (1985). [2] 50 sgd no. cc. Illustrated and signed by James Alan Robinson. Bound in quarter leather. In tray case with an additional suite of engravings $1,000.

001n: THE JUMPING FROG Cheloniidae Press, Easthampton, Massachusetts (1985). [2] 250 sgd no. cc. Wraps. Illustrated and signed by James Alan Robinson $175.

001o: THE JUMPING FROG Chronicle Books, San Francisco (1987). Woodcuts by Alan James Robinson. Cream cloth. Issued without dustwrapper? $35.

002a: ADDRESS TO HIS IMPERIAL MAJESTY: -ALEXANDER II. EMPEROR OF RUSSIA... No publisher, place, or date? [0] Broadside printed on gray paper measuring 11 1/2" x 10 3/4" $NVA

003a: THE PUBLIC TO MARK TWAIN *Correspondence...* New Mercantile Library (San Francisco, 1868). [0] Single sheet, 15" x 5 7/8" $NVA

004a: THE INNOCENTS ABROAD... American Publishing Company, Hartford; Bliss & Co., Newark; R.W. Bliss & Co., Toledo; F.G. Gilman, Chicago; Nettleton & Co., Cincinnati; F.A. Hutchinson & Co., St. Louis; H.H. Bancroft, San Francisco, 1869. [0] Publisher's prospectus consisting of prelims, selections from text, representation illustrations, publisher advertisements and spaces for subscriber's names. Two binding backstrips (ref.d) $7,500.

004b: THE INNOCENTS ABROAD... American Publ. Co. Hartford; Bliss & Co. Newark; R.W. Bliss & Co. Toledo; F.G. Gilman Chicago; Nettleton & Co. Cincinnati; F.A. Hutchinson & Co. St. Louis; H.H. Bancroft San Francisco. 1869 [0] First issue: pp. xvii-xviii table of contents lacks page reference numbers; p. xviii the last entry reads "Thankless Devotion-A Newspaper Valedictory" <leaders>; p.129 no illustration; p.(643) Chapter "XLI"; p.(654) "Personal History ..." Bound variously in black cloth, sheep, morocco and half calf. Binding, other than cloth, would probably be worth more than the cloth prices shown $2,000.

Variant in purple cloth binding, all edges gilt, beveled covers with gilt decoration on spine and both covers. In addition, the cloth is in a different and more ornate pattern than the standard cloth (BAL “RH” cloth , as opposed to BAL “C” cloth (Pepper & Stern 2/95)

Note: "Although the print run of the first edition is unknown, sales in the first six months totaled 31,500 copies, of which 16,910 were bound in cloth. The print run of the first edition may have been as high as 10,000 copies. The first batch delivered from the bindery consisted of 128 cloth copies, 250 in full sheep, and 25 in 3/4 leather. Although cloth copies later comprised the majority of copies sold (88,000 of the first 125,000), the lop-sided ratio of sheep to 3/4 leather copies probably persisted, judging from surviving copies." (Macdonnell Rare Books 11/94)

004c: THE INNOCENTS ABROAD... Publishers and places as 004b, 1869. [0] Second issue: pp. xvii-xviii page reference numbers present in table of contents; p. xviii the last entry reads "Thank-less devotion-A Newspaper Valedictory-Conclusion <leaders> 638"; p.129 portrait of Napoleon III; p.<643> Chapter LXI; p.<654> Personal History ... $1,000.

004d: THE INNOCENTS ABROAD ... Publishers and places as 004b, 1869. [0] Third issue: same as for second issue except p.<654> has ad "History of the Bible ... Album Family Bible" $750.

Note: Intermediate issues are known. Also seen, an issue with imprint: "San Francisco, California: H.H. Bancroft and Company, Hartford, Connecticut: American Publishing Company, 1869"

004e: THE INNOCENTS ABROAD ... American Publishing Co., Hartford, 1870. [] Prospectus. 8vo, 55 leaves of text and illustrations, 3 leaves of subscriptions. Issued in black cloth with cloth and leather samples on pastedowns (Heritage Book Shop Catalog 162). Also noted THE INNOCENTS ABROAD American Publishing Company, Hartford, 1870. [] Salesman's Dummy, consisting of several chapters of text, title page, a printed prospectus, press reviews, illustrations, advertisements, and a section of blank ruled pages at the rear for subscriber's names. Two binding samples bound in, being those of the issues in cloth and publisher's sheep. Brown cloth stamped in gilt on front cover (James Cummins 2/97) $2,000.

004f: INNOCENTS ABROAD ... John Camden Hotten, London, no date [1870]. [0] Cloth. First English edition. Unauthorized by Twain. (First half of *Innocents Abroad*) $750.

004g: INNOCENTS ABROAD ... John Camden Hotten, London, no date [1870]. [0] Simultaneous issue in wraps $600.

004h: THE NEW PILGRIM'S PROGRESS ... John Camden Hotten, London, no date [1870]. [0] Cloth. Second half of *Innocents Abroad* $750.

004i: THE NEW PILGRIM'S PROGRESS ... John Camden Hotten, London, no date [1870]. [0] Simultaneous issue in wraps $600.

004j: THE INNOCENTS ABROAD A.S. Irving, Toronto, 1870. [] Cloth. Redated preface 1870, but same as original preface $500.

004k: THE INNOCENTS ABROAD A.S. Irving, Toronto, 1870. [] Wraps $500.

004l: MARK TWAIN'S PLEASURE TRIP ON THE CONTINENT... John Camden Hotten, London, no date [1871]. [0] Printed boards, also issued in cloth. Also noted in stiff pictorial boards. 6 1/4" x 4", with 22 pages of ads dated 1871 (Ergo Books #801). New title. Reprints complete text. Also noted as "Yellow Back." Includes *Innocents Abroad* and *The New Pilgrim's Progress* (Ergo Books 12/90) $750.

004m: THE INNOCENTS ABROAD American Publishing Company, Hartford, 1871. [] Prospectus. First edition, later issue. This prospectus has the American publishing Company imprint preceding the H. H. Bancroft and Company imprint on the title page. Black cloth stamped in gilt. Contains cloth backstrip design affixed to the front pastedown, and the "library (i. e. sheep) binding" affixed to the rear pastedown, some sample text and illustrations, plus order sheets. (Heritage Book Shop 8/97) $1,000.

004n: THE INNOCENTS ABROAD American Publishing Company, Hartford, 1872. [] Prospectus. First edition, later issue. Black cloth stamped in gilt. Contains spine samples, order blanks. "It is commonly asserted that sample books precede the first edition, but copies of the sample book for this title are found dated 1869, 1870, 1871, and 1872. Those of later date, like this one, contain numerous extracts of reviews of the book, not present in the first sample books. This copy contains 39 reviews of the book (many more than located by Tenney) and six reviews of Twain's 1871 lecture season which was based on material in this book. In 1869 just 1,231 sample books were printed, and by 1872 a total of only 2,016 had been printed..." (Macdonnell Rare Books 4/96) $1,750.

004o: THE INNOCENTS ABROAD George Routledge & Sons, London (1872). [0] Pictorial wraps. First half $500.

004p: THE NEW PILGRIM'S PROGRESS... Author's English Edition. George Routledge, London, no date [1872]. [0] Wraps. Second half of *The Innocents Abroad.* Title page mentions Routledge is Twain's only authorized publisher. First issue has imprint of Bradbury, Evans & Company on p.255 $500.

004q: THE NEW PILGRIM'S PROGRESS... Author's English Edition. George Routledge, London, no date [1872]. [0] Wraps. Second issue with imprint of Bradbury, Agnew & Co. on p.255 $400.

004r: THE NEW PILGRIMS PROGRESS... Author's English Edition. George Routledge, London, no date [1872]. [0] Wraps. Third issue with imprint of Woodfall & Kinder on p.255 $300.

004s: THE NEW PILGRIMS PROGRESS Joseph Knight Co., Boston, 1895. [] 2 volumes. Issued with linen dustwrappers. Illustrations include 30 full page photogravures (Kenneth Karmiole 6/92) $200/300

004t: ROUGHING IT and THE INNOCENTS AT HOME Chatto & Windus, London, 1898. [] First complete English edition. Pictorial blue cloth stamped in gilt (Second Life Books 8/93) $150.

004t: THE INNOCENTS ABROAD OR THE NEW PILGRIM'S PROGRESS Limited Editions Club, New York, 1962. [2] 1,500 sgd cc. Issued in slipcase. Illustrated and signed by Fritz Kredel $75/125

005a: MARK TWAIN'S (BURLESQUE) AUTO-BIOGRAPHY AND FIRST ROMANCE Sheldon & Co., New York (1871). [0] Wraps. First issue lacks ads for Ball, Black & Co. on copyright page; no priority between 005a & b (i.e. cloth vs. Wraps) $750.

005b: MARK TWAIN'S (BURLESQUE) AUTO-BIOGRAPHY AND FIRST ROMANCE Sheldon & Co., New York (1871). [0] In green, terra-cotta or purple cloth. First issue lacks ads for Ball, Black & Co. on copyright page $750.

005c: MARK TWAIN'S (BURLESQUE) AUTO-BIOGRAPHY AND FIRST ROMANCE Sheldon & Co., New York (1871). [0] Cloth. Second issue has ads for Ball, Black & Co. on copyright page $350.

005d: MARK TWAIN'S (BURLESQUE) AUTO-BIOGRAPHY AND FIRST ROMANCE Sheldon & Co., New York (1871). [0] Wraps. Second issue has ads for Ball, Black & Co. on copyright page $300.

005e: MARK TWAIN'S (BURLESQUE)... AUTO-BIOGRAPHY... ON CHILDREN John Camden Hotten, London, no-date [1871]. [0] Cloth. $350.

005f: MARK TWAIN'S (BURLESQUE)... AUTO-BIOGRAPHY... ON CHILDREN John Camden Hotten, London, no date [1871]. [0] Pictorial wraps $300.

005g: MARK TWAIN'S (BURLESQUE) AUTO-BIOGRAPHY AND FIRST ROMANCE George Routledge & Sons, London, no date [1871]. [] Wraps. First authorized English edition following Hotten's unauthorized edition published 2 weeks earlier $250.

005h: MARK TWAIN'S BURLESQUE AUTO-BIOGRAPHY Peter Pauper Press, Larchmont, 1930. [2] 525 cc $75.

006a: MARK TWAIN'S MEMORANDA. FROM THE GALAXY Canadian News, Toronto, 1871. [0] Offered by various distributors whose imprint appears in place of publisher: A.S. Irving, Wm. Warwich, C.A. Backas, all of Toronto. Publication was unauthorized. Issued in cloth. $2,500.

006b: MARK TWAIN'S MEMORANDA. FROM THE GALAXY Canadian News, Toronto, 1871. [0] Simultaneous issue in wraps $2,000.

007a: EYE OPENERS... John Camden Hotten, London, no date. [0] Cloth. First printing: p.(176) "..Special List for 1871..." $1,000.

007b: EYE OPENERS... John Camden Hotten, London, no date. [0] Wraps. First printing: p.(176) "..Special List for 1871..." No priority between cloth and wraps $1,000.

007c: EYE OPENERS... John Camden Hotten, London, no date. [0] Cloth. Second printing: p.(176) "..Special List for 1872..." $350.

007d: EYE OPENERS... John Camden Hotten, London, no date. [0] Wraps. Second printing: p.(176) "..Special List for 1872..." No priority between cloth and wraps $350.

008a: SCREAMERS... John Camden Hotten, London, no date. [0] Cloth. First issue: text ends on p.172 due to inclusion of story entitled "Vengeance." Ads dated 1871 $1,000.

008b: SCREAMERS... John Camden Hotten, London, no date. [0] Wraps. Same issue point as above. No priority between wraps and cloth $1,000.

008c: SCREAMERS... John Camden Hotten, London, no date. [0] Cloth. Second issue: text ends at p.166; ads dated 1872 $350.

008d: SCREAMERS... John Camden Hotten, London, no date. [0] Wraps. Second issue points same as above. No priority between cloth and wraps $350.

009a: "ROUGHING IT"... COPYRIGHT EDITION George Routledge, London (1872) [0] Pictorial yellow boards. First half of *Roughing It* $1,000.

009b: THE INNOCENTS AT HOME... COPYRIGHT EDITION George Routledge, London (1872). [0] First state of binding pictorial salmon or pictorial yellows boards. Five titles listed on back cover. The first English edition of final portion of *Roughing It and Mark Twain's Burlesque...* Also noted in yellow pictorial wraps (ref.d) $1,000.

009c: THE INNOCENTS AT HOME ... COPYRIGHT EDITION George Routledge, London (1872). [0] Presumed second state of binding pictorial yellow boards. Seven numbered titles and two unnumbered titles are listed on back cover (ref.b identified another state with 9 titles not in BAL which we assume would be an intermediate state). Eleven titles listed per ref.a $600.

009d: THE INNOCENTS AT HOME ... COPYRIGHT EDITION George Routledge, London (1872). [0] Presumed third state of binding pictorial yellow boards. Eleven titles listed on back cover $400.

009e: ROUGHING IT American Publishing Company, Hartford, Connecticut; F.G. Gilman, Chicago; W.E. Bliss, Toledo; Nettleton, Cincinnati; D. Ashmead, Philadelphia; Geo. A. Smith, Boston, 1872. [0] 1,637 cc (MacDonnell Rare Books 5/97) Publisher's prospectus in black cloth consisting of prelims, selections from text, representative illustrations, publisher's ads, spaces for purchasers and two binding samples (ref.d). Also noted in brown cloth (Heritage Book Shop 8/97) $4,000.

009f: ROUGHING IT American Publishing Company, Hartford, Connecticut; F.G. Gilman, Chicago; W.E. Bliss, Toledo; Nettleton, Cincinnati; D. Ashmead, Philadelphia; Geo. A. Smith, Boston; A. Roman, San Francisco, 1872. [0] Issued with variant imprints of agents other than those listed above. Published in black cloth, cloth with gilt edges, sheep, half morocco, half calf. Probable earliest state reads: "Premises-said he | was occupying his |" on p.242:20-21. Seen with and without ads on p.(592), priority unknown. Leather bound copies would be worth more than the cloth bound prices shown $2,000.

009g: ROUGHING IT Publishers and places as above, 1872. [0] Probable second state with letters and/or words lacking on p.242:20-21 $1,000.

009h: THE INNOCENTS AT HOME... Robertson, Melbourne, 1873. [] Printed in Melbourne, copyrighted in Australia $500.

009i: ROUGHING IT Rose Publishing, Toronto, no date. [] The imprint "Rose Publishing " was used from 1883-1894 (Hugh Anson-Cartwright 4/97) $300.

009j: ROUGHING IT IN CALIFORNIA Allen Press, Kentfield, 1953. [2] 200 cc. (Ref.c) $500.

009k: ROUGHING IT Limited Editions Club, New York, 1972. [2] 1,500 sgd cc. In slipcase. Illustrated and signed by Noel Sickles $75/125

010a: A CURIOUS DREAM *and other Sketches* ... George Routledge, London (1872). [0] Yellow pictorial boards. Earliest printing: endpapers blank; leaf L4 blank; "Bradbury, Evans" imprint on pp.(2) and/or p.150 $1,000.

011a: MARK TWAIN'S SKETCHES ... George Routledge, London, 1872. [0] "Copyright Edition." Pictorial boards. Reprint save for author's prefatory note $750.

012a: THE CHOICE HUMOROUS WORKS OF MARK TWAIN John Camden Hotten, London, no date. [0] Published 1873 $500.

012b: THE CHOICE HUMOROUS WORKS OF MARK TWAIN Chatto & Windus, London, 1874. [0] Reprint of above $300.

013a: MARK TWAIN'S LETTER TO THE NEW YORK TRIBUNE No publisher, place or date. [0] Wraps. Issued as an advertisement for the Cunnard Line in Boston in 1873. Printed in blue and red. 4 pages size 7 3/4" x 5 1/4". Probably occurs with imprints of other agencies $750.

014a: THE GILDED AGE *A Tale of Today* American Publishing Company, Hartford, 1873. [] Salesman's Dummy consisting of title page, several chapters of the text, numerous illustrations, folding map, and a final section of blank ruled pages, as well as a prospectus announcing the book's publication. Two binding samples bound in, being the backstrips of cloth and the publisher's sheep. Brown cloth stamped in gilt on the front cover (James Cummins 2/97) $2,500.

014b: THE GILDED AGE ... American Publishing Company, Hartford / F.G. Gilman, Chicago, 1873. [0] Innumerable variants of this book exist, as well as cloth and leather bindings. Leather bound copies are worth more than cloth prices shown and there were 500 copies with all edges gilt (Kevin MacDonnell) which would be worth more.

Point 1: "Everybody's Friend" described as a "truex inde" in ads at end of book, later corrected to "true index"

Point 2: Artist "White" present on title-page, deleted in later state

Point 3: Earliest printing (printings?) of p.(vii) under chapter 5 has "Eschol Sellers" (in reprints it is "Beriah Sellers")

Point 4: p. xvi the final illustration is numbered "211". Later "212

Point 5: p.246:5 (from the bottom) "Hallelujah". Later "Halleluhah,"

Point 6: p.280:18 "Dr. Jackson." Later "Dr. Jackson"

Point 7: p.351: last "would kill me if she could, thought the Colonel; but he". Line absent in later states

Point 8: p.353:1-2 "let him keep it. She looked down into his face with a pitia- / ble tenderness, and said in a weak voice,". Later state above lines absent

Point 9: p.403 no illustration. Later state illustration present

All points:	$3,000.
Lacking points 7 & 8:	$2,500.
Other 1873:	$1,500.
1874:	$600.

014c: THE GILDED AGE ... Three Vols. George Routledge, London / New York, 1874. [0] Includes Author's preface to London edition $2,000.

014d: THE GILDED AGE George Routledge, London, no date [1874]. [0] Cloth. First one-volume English edition (BAL 3606) although ref.c shows an 1883 edition in red cloth as possibly the first one volume edition? $750.

014e: THE GILDED AGE George Routledge, London, no date. [0] Pictorial boards. Issued simultaneously $750.

015a: MARK TWAIN'S SKETCHES Authorized Edition. American News Co., New York (1874). [0] Wraps. Presumed earlier state: front of wraps imprinted, otherwise blank $1,000.

015b: MARK TWAIN'S SKETCHES Authorized Edition. American News Co., New York (1874). [0] Wraps. Presumed later state: back of wraps has ad for Aetna Life Insurance Co. $600.

016a: MARK TWAIN'S SPEECH ON ACCIDENT INSURANCE No publisher, place or date. [0] Wraps printed in blue. Issued as an ad by the Hartford Insurance Co., Hartford, CT, 1874. Four pages 5 3/16" x 3 1/8" $600.

017a: MARK TWAIN'S SKETCHES, NEW AND OLD ... The American Publishing Company, Hartford / Chicago, 1875. [0] Publisher's prospectus with 3 binding samples. Dark blue cloth stamped in gilt and black (ref.d) $2,500.

017b: MARK TWAIN'S SKETCHES, NEW AND OLD ... The American Publishing Company, Hartford / Chicago, 1875. [0] Various bindings. The earliest state: p.119 has footnote; footnote repeated on p.120; p.299 has 11 line skit headed "From Hospital Days". Leather bindings would be worth more than cloth prices shown $1,000.

017c: MARK TWAIN'S SKETCHES, NEW AND OLD ... The American Publishing Company, Hartford / Chicago, 1875. [0] Later state: p.119 footnote present; p.120 footnote not present; p.299 "From Hospital Days" not present $500.

018a: INFORMATION WANTED ... George Routledge & Sons, London, no date [1876]. [0] First state lacks "Honored As a Curiosity" on pp. 128-130 $750.

018b: INFORMATION WANTED ... George Routledge & Sons, London, no date [1876]. [0] Second state includes "Honored As a Curiosity" on pp. 128-130 $500.

018c: INFORMATION WANTED ... George Routledge & Sons, London, no date [circa 1876]. [0] Wraps. Unrecorded in BAL. Octavo; pp. (1)-140 (-144, ads). Advertisements continue on back wrapper (Heritage Book Shop 8/97) $500.

019a: THE ADVENTURES OF TOM SAWYER Chatto & Windus, London, 1876. [0] $15,000.

019b: THE ADVENTURES OF TOM SAWYER Belford Brothers, Toronto, 1876. [0] Assumed to be set from English edition and also preceded U.S. edition $4,000.

019c: THE ADVENTURES OF TOM SAWYER American Publishing Company, Hartford, 1876. [] Prospectus in blue cloth stamped in gold and black (Dorothy Goldberg Collection 8/95) $17,500.

019d: THE ADVENTURES OF TOM SAWYER The American Publishing Co., Hartford, Chicago, Cincinnati; A. Roman & Co., San Francisco, 1876. [0] 5,000 cc (MacDonnell Rare Books 12/96). First printing is on wove paper; half-title and frontispiece on different leaves. Front matter paged (I)-xvi, fly-title, p.(I). Pp.(II-III blank. Frontispiece, p.(iv). Collation: (I)-xvi, (17)-(275); blank, p.(276); 4 pp. ads. (Verso of half-title and preface blank)

Half-morocco (200 cc):	$20,000.
Calf (1,500 cc):	$17,500.
Blue cloth, edges gilt (748 cc):	$15,000.
Blue cloth, edges plain (7,431 cc):	$12,500.

019e: THE ADVENTURES OF TOM SAWYER The American Publishing Company, Hartford, Chicago, Cincinnati; A. Roman & Co., San Francisco, 1876. [0]5,000 cc (MacDonnell Rare Books 12/96). Second printing, issue A: printed on laid paper. Fly-title, p.(II). Pagination: (I-XII), (17)-(275); blank, p.(276); plus ads, pp.(277-280). Mispagination: p.(IX) mispaged XII; p.(X) mispaged XIII; p.(XII) mispaged XVI. Illustration of Tom on verso of half-title and contents on verso of preface. Leather bound copies on this and later issues would be worth more than cloth prices shown. Published the same day as the first printing. $3,500.

019f: THE ADVENTURES OF TOM SAWYER The American Publishing Company, Hartford, Chicago, Cincinnati; A. Roman & Co., San Francisco, 1876. [0] Second printing, issue B: same as second printing, issue A but on wove paper $2,500.

019g: THE ADVENTURES OF TOM SAWYER The American Publishing Company, Hartford, Chicago, Cincinnati; A. Roman & Co., San Francisco, 1876. [0] Second printing, issue C: same as issue A and B but made up of both wove and laid papers within the same copy $2,000.

019h: THE ADVENTURES OF TOM SAWYER The American Publishing Company, Hartford, Chicago, Cincinnati; A. Roman & Co., San Francisco, 1876. [0] Third printing. Printed on laid paper. Pp. (I-II) used as pastedown. Fly-title, p.(v). Frontispiece, p.(VI). Pagination: (I)-XVI, (17)-(275); blank, p.(276); ads, pp.(277-280). Note: in the front matter folio XVI is the only one present $1,000.

019i: THE ADVENTURES OF TOM SAWYER Rose-Belford, Toronto, 1879. [] Sewn self-wraps.

Issued as "Number 1 in the Rose Library." (MacDonnell Rare Books 10/97) $650.

019j: THE ADVENTURES OF TOM SAWYER Random House, New York, 1930. [2] 2,000 sgd no. cc. Signed by Donald McKay. Leather spine. Issued in slipcase $200/250

019k: THE ADVENTURES OF TOM SAWYER Limited Editions Club, Cambridge, 1939. [2] 1,500 sgd no. cc. Issued in slipcase. Illustrated and signed by Thomas Hart Benton $600/750

019l: THE ADVENTURES OF TOM SAWYER World Publishing, Cleveland / New York (1946). [0] Illustrated by Louis Slobodkin. First thus $15/75

019m: THE ADVENTURES OF TOM SAWYER Georgetown University Library / University Publishing, Washington, D.C., 1982. [2] 1,000 cc. Two volumes. Issued in slipcase. A facsimile of the author's holograph manuscript with an introduction by Paul Baender $150/200

020a: OLD TIMES ON THE MISSISSIPPI Belford Bros., Toronto, 1876. [0] Wraps. Title set in Old English, upper and lower case, in a single line. No publisher's notice on title-page. Inner wrap blank (priority between 021a and b unknown) $750.

020b: OLD TIMES ON THE MISSISSIPPI Belford Bros., Toronto, 1876. [0] Wraps. As above but inner wrap has published ads. Also seen in salmon cloth (priority between 021a and b unknown) $750.

020c: OLD TIMES ON THE MISSISSIPPI Belford Bros., Toronto, 1876. [0] Reprint A (no priority): title-page set in Roman and Arabic; title in three lines; imprint dated 1876; page opposite title-page blank. Green cloth stamped in black. P.(160) "...The New Poems..." Also noted a copy similar to reprint A except it is in cream colored wraps. Inside the front wrapper is "New Publications;" the advertisements at end correspond; the inside lower wrapper has "The Wreck of the Chancellor by Jules Verne" advertisement; on the lower wrapper is, "How to Live Long" advertisement (Sotheby's sale of October 29, 1996) $500.

020d: OLD TIMES ON THE MISSISSIPPI Belford Bros., Toronto, 1876. [0] Reprint B (no priority): title-page set in Roman only; title in 3 lines; Publisher's device not present; imprint dated "MDCCCLXXVI;" opposite title-page is ad for *Tom Sawyer*. Green or purple cloth; p.(160): "New and Popular Books..." $500.

020e: OLD TIMES ON THE MISSISSIPPI Belford Bros., Toronto, 1876. [0] Reprint C (no priority): same as reprint B except p.(160): "Norman McLeod's Works...". Variant with p.(160) blank (Waiting For Godot Books 2/95) $400.

020f: OLD TIMES ON THE MISSISSIPPI Belford Bros., Toronto, 1876. [0] Reprint D (no priority): same as reprint B except p.(160) "Common Sense in the Household..." $400.

Note: We had a variant with ads on pages (158, 159), while none of ref.a reprints had ads on page (158).

020g: THE MISSISSIPPI PILOT Ward, Lock & Tyler, London, no date [1877]. [] Wraps $500.

020h: THE MISSISSIPPI PILOT Grand Coliseum Warehouse Co., Glasgow, Scotland, no date [1877]. [0] Title page only lists this title but contents page also includes Bret Harte's *Two Men of Sand Bar* and *Poem* $400.

021a: A TRUE STORY, AND THE RECENT CARNIVAL OF CRIME James R. Osgood & Co.; Late Ticknor & Fields; and Fields, Osgood & Co. Boston, 1877. [0] First state of binding with "JRO

& Co" monogram on front cover. Green or terra-cotta cloth $2,000.

021b: A TRUE STORY, AND THE RECENT CARNIVAL OF CRIME James R. Osgood & Co.; Late Ticknor & Fields; and Fields, Osgood & Co., Boston, 1877. [0] Second state of binding with "HO" (i.e. Houghton, Osgood) on front cover $1,500.

022a: AN IDLE EXCURSION (title page). Rose-Belford Publishing Co., Toronto, 1878. [0] Brown cloth. Also green cloth per Ref.c. No priority known between wraps and cloth binding. 114 pages. Cover title *Rambling Notes of An Idle Excursion* which causes confusion with e & f below $750.

022b: AN IDLE EXCURSION Rose-Belford Publishing Co., Toronto, 1878. [0] Wraps $750.

022c: AN IDLE EXCURSION J. Ross Robertson, Toronto, 1878. [0] Wraps. (Gray wraps per Ref.c.) 36 pages. Title story only. May have preceded above entries per note to BAL 3377 $500.

022d: AN IDLE EXCURSION ... Chatto & Windus, London, 1878. [0] Pictorial boards $500.

022e: RAMBLING NOTES OF AN IDLE EXCURSION Rose-Belford, Toronto, 1878. [0] First printing with device of the Canadian Paper Company on verso of title page (cloth or wraps) $450.

022f: RAMBLING NOTES OF AN IDLE EXCURSION Rose-Belford, Toronto, 1878. [0] Second printing without device (cloth or wraps) $250.

023a: PUNCH, BROTHERS, PUNCH! ... Slote, Woodman & Co., New York (1878). [0] Cloth. First issue: on title-page author's name printed in Roman; p.91:4 from bottom reads "health offi....could..." No priority between cloth and wraps. Undecorated cream-coated endpapers. Blue or green cloth (ref.a), brown cloth (Waiting For Godot 1987) $750.

023b: PUNCH, BROTHERS, PUNCH! ... Slote, Woodman & Co., New York (1878). [0] Wraps. First issue: points as above. Red-coated paperwraps, spine lettered down "Mark Twain's Sketches" $750.

023c: PUNCH, BROTHERS, PUNCH! ... Slote, Woodman & Co., New York (1878). [0] Cloth. Second issue: on title-page author's name is in facsimile autograph; p.91:4 from bottom reads "health officer's funeral could..."; endpapers decorated in blue with a scattering of caricatures $400.

023d: PUNCH, BROTHERS, PUNCH! ... Slote, Woodman & Co., New York (1878). [0] Wraps. Second issue: on title-page author's name is in facsimile autograph; p.91:4 from bottom reads "health officer's funeral could..."; spine lettered down "Mark Twain's Punch" $350.

023e: PUNCH, BROTHERS, PUNCH! ... E. & S. Livingston, Edinburgh, no date [1878]. [0] Pictorial boards. Also noted in stiff green wraps (Charles Agvent 9/94) $350.

024a: MARK TWAIN'S NIGHTMARE ... Ward, Lock & Co. (London, 1878). [0] Wraps. Contains no first edition material and works by other authors. First state imprinted "Ward, Lock & Co. Warwick House, Dorset Buildings, Salisbury Square, E.C." Contains material by other authors $600.

024b: MARK TWAIN'S NIGHTMARE ... Ward, Lock & Co., London (1878). [0] Second state ? imprinted: "Ward, Lock & Co., London: Warwick House, Salisbury Square, E.C. New York: 10, Bond Street" $500.

024c: MARK TWAIN'S NIGHTMARE ... Ward, Lock & Co., London (1878). [0] Wraps. Third state ? imprinted: "Ward, Lock & Co. London: Warwick House, Salisbury Square, E.C. New York: Bond Street" $500.

024d: MARK TWAIN'S NIGHTMARE ... Ward, Lock & Co., London / New York / Melbourne (1878). Wraps. A state not mentioned in BAL (ref.c) $500.

025a: SKETCHES Belfords, Clarke & Co., Toronto, 1879. [0] Includes two first book appearances earliest printing(s?). The verso of title pages has "C.B. Robinson: and "Brown Bros." which are not on later printings $600.

025b: SKETCHES Belford & Co. (Toronto), 1880. [0] Verso of title page blank. "Now first published in complete form" $350.

026a: MARK TWAIN ON BABIES George B. Hatfield (London), no date. [0] Single leaf folded to four pages. Date unknown. 1879? $750.

A BOY'S ADVENTURES see 1928 entry.

027a: A TRAMP ABROAD American Publishing Co., Hartford, 1879. [] Publisher's prospectus. Brown cloth stamped in blind and gilt. Comprising binding samples, preliminaries, frontispiece and illustrated text excerpts, followed by publisher's announcement and 20-page order register (Christie's East 5/96) $2,500.

027b: A TRAMP ABROAD American Publishing Co., Hartford; Chatto & Windus, London, 1880. [0] First state: frontispiece captioned, "Moses". Priority of other points in BAL not established. Leather bindings would be worth more than the cloth prices shown. Also noted a variant in brown cloth (not the usual black) with first state frontispiece. Covers stamped as in usual binding, but the gilt ornaments and rules at the top and bottom of spine are a unrecorded variant pattern (triple rule, with dot at center, flanked by wave-like knobs, instead of the usual filigree ornament). The word "Illustrated" on spine is set in upper and lower capitals; the endpapers are a distinct yellow rather than the usual pale peach (Macdonnell Rare Books 4/96) $1,750.

027c: A TRAMP ABROAD American Publishing Co., Hartford; Chatto & Windus, London, 1880. [0] Experimental binding of midnight blue C cloth. Second state of portrait frontispiece. This binding is so dark as to appear almost black (the usual binding color). (Macdonnell Rare Books 10/96) $1500

027d: A TRAMP ABROAD American Publishing Co., Hartford; Chatto & Windus, London, 1880. [0] Second state: frontispiece captioned, "Titian's Moses" $1,000.

027e: A TRAMP ABROAD ... Chatto & Windus, London, 1880. [0] 2 vols. Ads dated "February, 1880" (ref.d) $2,000.

027f: A TRAMP ABROAD ... Chatto & Windus, London, 1880. [0] One volume edition. Ads dated August 1880 per Ref.c. Also noted with ads dated October 1880 (Ergo Books 11/95) $350.

027g: A TRAMP ABROAD Limited Editions Club (New York, 1966). [2] 1,500 sgd cc. Issued in slipcase. Illustrated and signed by David Knight with 12 illustrations by Twain made "without help." First book appearances? $75/125

028a: (1601) CONVERSATION, AS IT WAS BY THE SOCIAL FIRESIDE, IN THE TIME OF THE TUDORS No place or date. [0] Wraps. 8 9/16" x 7" printed on wove paper, self-wraps. Possibly printed for Alexander Gunn, Cleveland, Ohio, 1880 $NVA

028b: (1601) CONVERSATION, AS IT WAS BY THE SOCIAL FIRESIDE, IN THE TIME OF THE TUDORS No place or date. [0] Wraps. 8 7/16" x 7 1/16". Printed on laid paper, self-wraps. Possibly printed for Alexander Gunn, Cleveland, Ohio, 1880 $NVA

028c: DATE 1601 CONVERSATION, AS IT WAS... ("Academie Press", West Point, New York, 1882.) [0] First authorized edition $15,000.

The following are some of the editions of "1601" we've found. They are listed chronologically with the undated ones at the end:

028d: A CONVERSAZIONE IN THE YEAR MDCI... (Printed by order of the King, Bangkok, 1894.) [2] 20 no. cc (I-XX). Red crushed morocco, marbled endpaper, top edge gilt (ref.d) $750.

028e: A CONVERSAZIONE IN THE YEAR MDCI... (Printed by order of the King, Bangkok, 1894.) [2] 75 no. cc. Japan vellum (ref.d) $600.

028f: 1601 ... No publisher, place or date [circa 1903]. [0] 4to. 10 5/8" x 5 1/4". Cream-colored wraps, 32 pages, stapled. Newspaper article dated 1903 (Waiting For Godot 2/91) $300.

028g: CONVERSATION AS IT WAS BY THE SOCIAL FIRESIDE IN THE TIME OF THE TUDORS No publisher or place [New York?] (November 20, 1904). [2] 55 no. cc (McDonnell Rare Books 8/95) $600.

028h: CONVERSATION AS IT WAS BY THE SOCIA... (Guido Bruno), 1913. [2] 75 no. cc. Issued in decorated wraps. Printed on Japan vellum $500.

0028i: FIRESIDE CONVERSATION IN THE TIME OF QUEEN ELIZABETH OR "1601" Privately Printed, no place, 1919. [] Blue cloth with printed publisher's label on front cover (Waiting For Godot Books 2/95) $125.

028j: FIRESIDE CONVERSATION IN THE TIME OF QUEEN ELIZABETH, OR "1601" Privately Printed, no place, 1920. [] Blue morocco binding with paper label on front cover (Dorothy Goldberg

Collection 8/95). [Note: unusual to put paper label on leather, may be same as above] $175.

028k: THIS EDITION OF MARK TWAIN'S DATE 1601 CONVERSATION... (Privately printed, New York), 1920. [2] 110 cc. Tan stapled wraps (Heritage 3/89) $250.

028l: 1601 Puritan Press, Boston, 1923. [2] 25 cc. Black cloth and burlap (Bookmine 11/92) $150.

028m: 1601 ... Privately printed, 1924. [] 35 cc. Wraps (Book Treasury 1/90) $125.

028n: "1601" ... (Grabhorn Press), San Francisco, 1925. [2] 100 cc. Full calf or morocco $350.

028o: FIRESIDE CONVERSATION IN 1601 ... Privately published, no place, 1925. [2] 500 cc. Wraps. "No. One of the Airdale Series" (ref.d) $100.

028p: FIRESIDE CONVERSATION IN 1601 Privately published, no place, 1925. [2] 500 cc . Issued in gray boards. 18 pp. (Bookshop 7/93) $75.

028q: 1601 ... No publisher or place, 1926. [2] 525 no. cc. Stapled wraps. Semi-Centennial Edition (ref.d) $75.

028r: "1601" ... Privately published, New York, 1927. [2] 125 cc (ref.c). Orange cloth backed, black and gold decorated boards in glassine dustwrapper $100.

028s: 1601 ... (Privately printed, London, 1927.) [2] 101 no. cc. Wraps. 7" x 5" $150.

028t: FIRESIDE CONVERSATION IN THE TIME OF QUEEN ELIZABETH OR "1601" Privately printed, no place, 1928. [2] 1,000 no. cc. Wraps (ref.d) $75.

028u: MARK TWAIN'S DATE 1601... Privately printed, no place, 1929. [2] 110 no. cc. Wraps (ref.d) $150.

028v: 1601 ... Printed at Ye Blew Grasse Press Louisville 1929 [2] 1,000 no. cc. (First work of the Blue Grass Press.) Printed blue boards (ref.d) $100.

028w: 1601, OR A FIRESIDE COMPANION (Privately printed by Laughton Kennedy and Harold Seeger, San Francisco), 1929. [2] 40 cc. Color frontis and one color plate by W. R. Cameron (Boston Book Annex #29). Brown morocco spine over green cloth. In slipcase (Kenneth Karmiole 3/90). Also in red morocco and green cloth with penciled note "Windsor Press" (ref.d). Also noted in gray boards and white calf spine. "Of the 40 copies, 10 were for Seeger, 10 for Kennedy, 10 for Cameron, and 10 for the binder. They often appear in different bindings because many of the copies remained in sheets until there was a request to bind them." This information was "generously provided by Albert Sperisen of San Francisco (The Brick Row Book Shop 11/95) $200.

028x: FIRESIDE CONVERSATION IN 1601 ... No publisher or place, 1932. [2] 1,000 cc. Wraps (ref.c) $75.

028y: MARK TWAIN'S 1601 ... Waverley Lewis Root Paris (1932) [2] 500 no. cc. Printed on Verge de Rives paper (ref.d) $75.

028z: 1601 ... Golden Hind Press (New York), 1933. [0] Preface by Samuel Roth (ref.d) $25/75

028aa: 1601 ... Privately printed, no place?, 1934. [] 250 cc. Cloth without dustwrapper (Polyanthos Park 10/90) $75.

028bb: A CONVERSATION AT YE SOCIAL FIRESIDE... (Glen Donald Editions), Los Angeles,

1934. Red calf with gilt dentelles (Kenneth Karmiole 2/93) $75.

028cc 1601 ... Black Cat Press, Chicago, 1936. [] 300 cc. In red leatherette $75.

028dd: MARK TWAIN'S 1601 ... Lyle Stuart, New York (1938). [] Red cloth. Issued in slipcase. Introduction, footnote and bibliography by Franklin J. Meine (Antic Hay 11/88) $75.

028ee: FIRESIDE CONVERSATION IN THE TIME OF QUEEN ELIZABETH ... Privately printed, no place, 1938. [0] Shimmery light blue cloth. With glassine dustwrapper. In slipcase (ref.d) $75.

028ff: MARK TWAIN'S (1601) CONVERSATION ... Mark Twain Society of Chicago, Chicago, 1939. [2] 550 no. cc. Red cloth. Issued in slipcase. Includes bibliography of 44 editions of *1601* by Franklin J. Meine $100.

028gg: MARK TWAIN'S (1601) CONVERSATION ... Mark Twain Society of Chicago, Chicago, 1939. [2] 1,000 cc (unnumbered). Issued in slipcase. Reprinted by Lyle Stuart in mid 1960's $50.

028hh: MDCI. A FIRESIDE CHATTE ... Ye Three Asterisks at Ye Signe of Ye Gaye Goose, no place, 1941. [2] 300 cc. Printed boards (ref.d) $75.

028ii: MARK TWAIN'S "1601" ... Privately printed (Mexico City, 1943). [2] 1,000 no. cc. Wraps (ref.d). "Price Five Dollars" on title page $75.

028jj: MDCI. A FIRESIDE ... Ye Three Asterisks at Ye Signe of Ye Gaye Goose, no place, 1948. [2] 300 cc. Printed boards (ref.d) $75.

028kk: 1601 Earth Publishing Co., no place (1955). [] Wraps (ref.d) $50.

028ll: 1601 ... Tasmania Press Claremont, Calif October, 1957 [] One leaf, illustrated, folded to make 4 pages (ref.d)_ $35.

028mm: 1601 Black Cat Press, Chicago, 1962. [] Miniature book $75.

028nn: 1601 Brentano's, Paris, 1962. [] Blue-green cloth (J & J House 4/89) $50.

028oo: FIRESIDE CONVERSATIONS... 1601 Presse of The Indian Kidde, Nappanee, 1974. [] About 40 cc (Bookseller #21 -1986) $125.

028pp: "1601" ... (Land's End Press), London (1969). [0] "Printed for Subscribers Only ..." Cloth (ref.d) $15/40

028qq: "1601" ... (Land's End Press), London (1969). [0] "Printed for Subscribers Only ..." Pictorial boards (ref.d) $25/50

028rr: "1601" ... Merlin Verlag, Hamburg (1974). [2] 300 no. cc signed by the illustrator H.G. Rauch. Decorated cloth, folio (ref.d) $150.

028ss: 1601 No publisher, Northampton, Massachusetts, 1978. [2] 200 sgd no. cc. Lazarus Edition (sheets from a privately printed 1920 edition) with Barry Moser frontispiece signed by artist (ref.d) $250.

028tt: IN Ye CLOSET OF Ye VIRGIN QUEENE A.D. 1601 No publisher, place or date [1920's?]. [] Proof. Unbound vellum sheets in three signatures (or gatherings), printed on rectos only, 23 pp., with hand-colored (crudely colored) initials on some pages of text (Waiting For Godot Books 2/95) $150.

028uu: CONVERSATION AS IT WAS BY THE SOCIAL FIRE-SIDE IN THE TIME OF THE TUDORS Ye Puritan Presse At Ye Sign of Ye Jolly Virgin, no place or date [circa 1920's]. [] Tan printed wraps, ribbon sewn. Introduction reprints a letter by John Hay. (See BAL 7810 for similar item published in 1925.) (Waiting For Godot Books 2/95) $75.

028vv: '1601' A FIRESIDE CONVERSATION Printed for Subscribers at Devil's Hole, no place or date [circa 1930?]. [2] 125 no. cc. Purple cloth. Also prints the text of a 1906 letter of Mark Twain to Mr. Orr (Waiting For Godot Books 2/95) $125.

028ww: "1601" FIRESIDE CONVERSATION IN THE TIME OF QUEEN ELIZABETH (Stone Printing, Roanoke), no date [circa 1930's]. [2] numbered copies of unknown limitation. Red marbled boards with cloth spine; (22) pp. (Chapel Hill Rare Books 6/95) $50.

028xx: CONVERSATION AS IT WAS BY THE SOCIAL FIRE-SIDE ... Ye Puritan Presse At Ye Sign of Ye Jolly Virgin, no place or date. [2] 300 no. cc. Printed card wraps with satin tie (ref.d) $75.

028yy: CONVERSATION AS IT WAS BY THE SOCIAL FIRE-SIDE ... Ye Puritan Presse At Ye Sign of Ye Jolly Virgin, no place or date. [2] 500 no. cc. Wraps (ref.d) $75.

028zz: MARK TWAIN'S 1601 ... Privately published, no place or date. [2] 110 cc (ref.b) $100.

028aaa: MARK TWAIN'S (1601) (Lyle Stuart), New York, no date [circa 1961]. [0] Reprint of 1939 edition. Red cloth, with printed slipcase and yellow paper band stating a special pre-publication price of $4.95 (ref.b) $30/60

029a: A CURIOUS EXPERIENCE W.G. Gibson, Toronto, no date. [0] Wraps. Published 1881. Cream-yellow wraps. (Another edition printed with two columns on each page noted by BAL but the title page and cover missing) $450.

030a: THE PRINCE AND THE PAUPER ... Chatto & Windus, London, 1881. [0] Red cloth. Publishers catalog dated Nov. 1881 inserted at back $750.

030b: THE PRINCE AND THE PAUPER ... Dawson Bros., Montreal, 1881. [0] 275 cc. In gray-blue wraps ref.a & c). Presumed to have been issued same time as English edition. (Catalogued for $8,000; auctioned for $200 in 1996?) $1,250.

030c: THE PRINCE AND THE PAUPER ... Dawson Bros., Montreal, 1881. [0] Blue cloth (also tan cloth per Ref.c) $750.

030d: THE PRINCE AND THE PAUPER ... Dawson Bros., Montreal, 1881. [0] Title-page is a cancel with "Author's Canadian Edition..." added. Tan cloth stamped in gold and black (ref.c) $600.

030e: THE PRINCE AND THE PAUPER ... James R. Osgood & Co., Boston, 1882. [0] 6-8 cc. Printed on China paper. Bound in white linen, stamped in gold, inner hinges of blue linen. (The dedication copy to Clara brought $35,000 at auction in 1994) $25,000.

030f: THE PRINCE AND THE PAUPER ... James R. Osgood & Co., Boston, 1882. [0] First state is as follows: at front the true binder's endpapers of white, or toned white, paper; at back leaf (26)8 used as pastedown, and leaf (26)7 present as a blank. Uppermost rosette on spine 1/8" below fillet. Franklin Press imprint on copyright page. Leather binding and cloth with all edges gilt would be worth more than prices shown $1,500.

030g: THE PRINCE AND THE PAUPER ... James R. Osgood & Co., Boston, 1882. [0] Second state: true binder's endpapers at both front and back; leaves (26)7-8 present as blanks; rosette on spine 1/16" below fillet. Franklin Press imprint on copyright page $750.

030h: THE PRINCE AND THE PAUPER... Rose-Belford, Toronto, 1882. [] Pirated edition (Country Lane Books 11/92) $350.

030i: THE PRINCE AND THE PAUPER ... Limited Editions Club (New York), 1964. [2] 1,500 sgd cc. In slipcase. Illustrated and signed by Clarke Hutton $75/100

031a: THE STOLEN WHITE ELEPHANT Chatto & Windus, London, 1882. [0] Presumed first state: list of books on verso of half-title does not list *The White Elephant*; title-page has imprint on verso; foot of p.285 has one line imprint. Publisher's catalog dated May 1882 $450.

031b: THE STOLEN WHITE ELEPHANT Chatto & Windus, London, 1882. [0] Presumed second state: list of books on verso of half-title mentions *The White Elephant*; no imprint on verso of title-page; no imprint at foot of p.285 $350.

031c: THE STOLEN WHITE ELEPHANT James R. Osgood & Co., Boston, 1882. [0] Tan cloth (or cream cloth - MacDonnell Rare Books 12/90) $750.

031d: THE STOLEN WHITE ELEPHANT ... Haldeman-Julius Co., Girard, Kansas, no date [1925]. [0] Wraps. "Little Blue Book No. 931" $50.

032a: LIFE ON THE MISSISSIPPI Chatto & Windus, London, 1883. [0] Red cloth. Advertisements dated March 1883 $1,000.

032b: LIFE ON THE MISSISSIPPI James R. Osgood & Co., Boston, 1883. [] Publisher's prospectus with contents, list of illustrations, 39 leaves of text/illustrations, 3 pages publisher's announcements, 9 leaves of order pages, back pastedown has two leather spine examples and front pastedown has two cloth spine examples $2,500.

032c: LIFE ON THE MISSISSIPPI James R. Osgood & Co., Boston, 1883. [0] 40,000 cc. Bound on date of publication. First state: present on p.441 is a tail-piece depicting an urn, flames, and head of Twain; p.443 the caption reads "The St. Louis Hotel." Leather binding would be worth more than cloth prices shown. First state sheets also noted in the Webster 1888 edition as Twain acquired the sheets after Osgood went bankrupt (Amaranth Books 3/92) $2,000.

032d: LIFE ON THE MISSISSIPPI James R. Osgood & Co., Boston, 1883. [0] Second state: p.441 tail-piece not present; p.443: the caption reads "The St. Charles Hotel" $1,000.

Note: Intermediate states have been noted. Also see 102a

032e: LIFE ON THE MISSISSIPPI Limited Editions Club, New York, 1944. [0] 1,200 no. cc. Illustrated and signed by Thomas Hart Benton. Issued with tissue dustwrapper. In folding box $600/750

032f: LIFE ON THE MISSISSIPPI Heritage Press, New York (1944). [] Contains some previously unpublished passages restored to the text for the first time (Macdonnell Rare Books 11/95). Issued without dustwrapper. In slipcase $25/50

033a: THE ADVENTURES OF HUCKLEBERRY FINN ... Chatto & Windus, London, 1884. [0] Red cloth. Publisher's catalog dated October 1884 inserted at back. $2,000.

033b: ADVENTURES OF HUCKLEBERRY FINN Dawson Bros., Montreal, 1885. [] Issued December 10, 1884. Copyrighted in name of Chatto, but per ref.c, obviously printed from American plates. Red or green cloth (ref.c). The copy at McGill University in Canada is in purplish cloth with spine reading "ADVENTURES OF HUCKLEBERRY FINN"; covers have three rectangular compartments in blind; no lettering on front cover; Dawson's imprint on spine. The copy at the University of Toronto, Fisher Library is identical except it is in green cloth. These copies have the signature mark "11" not seen on any New York 1885 edition. (Steven Temple 6/96) $4,500.

033c: ADVENTURES OF HUCKLEBERRY FINN Dawson Bros., Montreal, 1885. [] Possibly 200 cc. Possible remainder binding of maroon cloth; front cover plain except for blind stamping of borders; spine ruled in gilt and lettered in gilt: "HUCKLE-BERRY | FINN | [rule] | MARK TWAIN"; without publisher's imprint on spine (Steven Temple 6/96) $6,000.

033d: ADVENTURES OF HUCKLEBERRY FINN ... Charles L. Webster & Co., New York, 1885. [0] Publisher's prospectus. Earliest copies reportedly only advertised the book in green cloth (not blue and green) and had the copyright notice dated 1885 (ref.a). Also noted a copy with copyright date of 1884 (Dorothy Goldberg Collection 8/95) $12,500

033e: ADVENTURES OF HUCKLEBERRY FINN ... Charles L. Webster & Co., New York, 1885. [0] Publisher's prospectus in green cloth with spine imprint on back cover and two samples of leather spines on front pastedown, sample text and illustrations and subscriber forms at end. Offers the book in blue or green cloth and sheep or one-half morocco binding $12,500.

033f: THE ADVENTURES OF HUCKLEBERRY FINN ... Charles L. Webster & Co., New York, 1885. [0]30,000 cc (MacDonnell Rare Books 12/96). Issued in blue, and green cloth. Numerous variants exist. It has been suggested that the earliest bound copies were in leather, perhaps because of point 5 below:

Point 1. BAL's earliest state: title page with copyright notice on verso (1884) tipped-in. Later state: leaf bound-in. Some of the prospectuses had copyright as 1885, but no bound copy of the book has been seen with this copyright date. Ref.b notes that neither Merle Johnson nor Adam have a preference, perhaps because one leather bound copy (which are thought to be early) has a bound in title page.

Point 2. Earliest state: p.(13): "Him and another man" listed incorrectly at p.88. Later state: p.(13): "Him and another man" listed correctly at p.87.

Point 3. Earliest state: p.57:11 up: "...with the was..." Later state: "...with the saw..."

Point 4. Earliest state: p.155 Johnson has final 5 in page number same font in various "off-balance" position. Later state: p.155, final 5 absent. BAL lists these two states in reverse order of Johnson but indicates that he is uncertain, both agree on the later state: p.155, final 5 present, wrong font (larger).

Point 5. Earliest state: p.283, seen only in prospectuses and leather bound copies; fly outline of trousers a pronounced curve; leaf bound in. Later state: p.283: engraving redone so fly is a straight line, leaf tipped-in. Final state: p.283: engraving redone, leaf bound-in, although there are those who argue there is no evidence to support a preference between the later two states (see ref.b pages 102-105). In addition, there is a defaced plate known as the "priapic" plate, which shows the gentleman with an erection, but no bound copy of any edition, including the prospectuses has ever been found with this plate. The latter plate was issued in a single sheet 6 9/16" x 8 1/4". Limited to 100 copies (ref.d).

Point 6. Earliest state: Portrait frontispiece; cloth under bust visible; "Heliotype" imprint. Later state: cloth not visible; "Heliotype" imprint. Final state: cloth not visible; "Photogravure" imprint. Note: "Heliotype..." usually about 1/4" below line, while Kevin MacDonnell (11/91) cataloged a copy with the words 3/4" below.

Point 7. Possible point noted by McBride in ref.b as attributed to J ohn S. Van Kohn (Seven Gables Bookshop). Earliest state: p. 143: "l" missing in "Col." that is part of the illustration at top line of text; "b" in "body", line 7, broken. Later state: p.143: period and bottom of "l" in "Col." missing; "body" perfect. Final state: p.143: "l" in "Col." replaced; "body" perfect.

Note: a signature mark "11" on p.161 of the Montreal edition has never been seen in a U.S. edition of 1885; and leaf 23(8), the final leaf, is blank leaf in leather bound copies and later issues. In all cloth bound early issues, the leaf has been excised or pasted under the terminal endpaper.

So, there we have it. General agreement on Points 1, 2, 3, and 6; uncertainty on Points 4 and 5 and Point 7 was noted only as a possible point, having been seen in a leather bound copy and corrected in obvious later states. It would appear that if you have a cloth bound copy with first state points of 1, 2, 3 and 6 and 4 and 5 in one of the first two states, no one can say it is not the earliest state. Given this, the following is a wild guess as to value of nice "first" state copies:

Quoted from Biblioctopus List 38, 10/95 describing a fine copy of Huckleberry Finn. "This copy has most of the printing points associated with the earliest copies in cloth...but using these printing points to establish priority should be accompanied by a snake rattle, as all the text corrections were made before page 283 was canceled in November 1884, and all copies with earlier or later printing points were equally available and randomly issued, four months later, on publication day in March 1885. Consider for yourself, that many copies are known, including (for example) Manney's copy in cloth, with all the later printing points and page 283 as a cancel (B. A. L. state 3). This page was only canceled in copies that were already printed <u>and</u> already bound before December 1884. Thus all the text corrections precede this date, which was three months before publication. Some cloth copies (probably all), without page 283 as a cancel, were also printed before December, 1884 and these are recorded with earlier and later text. All combinations were likely bound by February and all varieties in cloth were equally available and issued randomly when Huck was published in March. Clearly, there is no priority of issue for cloth copies as an 1885 Huck, with any combination of points, could have been purchased on the day of publication.." (Editor's comment- right, but there are states.)

Leather bound with earliest state of Point 5: $12,500.
Leather bound with later state of Point 5: $10,000.
Blue cloth: $10,000.
Green cloth: $7,500.
(copies with gilt edges would be slightly higher)

033g: THE ADVENTURES OF HUCKLEBERRY FINN ... Limited Editions Club, New York, 1933. [2] 1,500 no. cc. Includes original illustrations by E.W. Kemble. Introduction by Booth Tarkington. Issued in slipcase $125/175

033h: THE ADVENTURES OF HUCKLEBERRY FINN ... Limited Editions Club, New York, 1942. [2] 1,500 sgd no. cc. Illustrated and signed by Thomas Hart Benton. Issued in slipcase $600/750

033i: ADVENTURES OF HUCKLEBERRY FINN Pennyroyal Press, West Hatfield, 1985. [2] 350 no. cc. Illustrated and signed by Barry Moser. Issued in slipcase (George Houle Cat. 32) $1,500.

033j: ADVENTURES OF HUCKLEBERRY FINN Detroit, 1983 [] 1,015 cc. Facsimile of manuscript. Issued without dustwrapper. In slipcase $175/200

033k: THE ADVENTURES OF HUCKLEBERRY FINN Random House, New York (1996). [3] Also states "First Edition." "The only complete edition." Published @ $25.00 $6/30

034a: CHOICE BITS FROM MARK TWAIN Diprose & Bateman, London, no date [1885]. [0] Issued in pictorial boards $450.

035a: THE MARK TWAIN BIRTHDAY BOOK Ward, Lock & Co., London, no date [circa 1885]. [0] $450.

036a: ENGLISH AS SHE IS TAUGHT T. Fisher Unwin, London, 1887. [0] Book by Caroline Lerow with 30 page commentary by Twain. (Also see 1900 entry) $400.

037a: COPY OF A LETTER WRITTEN IN ANSWER TO INQUIRIES MADE BY A PERSONAL FRIEND ... No publisher, place or date. [0] Single leaf printed in Hartford, Connecticut, 1887? Issued as testimonial for the Loisette School of Memory $250.

038a: MARK TWAIN'S LIBRARY OF HUMOR Chas. L. Webster & Co., New York, 1888. [0] First issue with index of titles in order of appearance. Anonymously edited by William Dean Howells $250.

038b: MARK TWAIN'S LIBRARY OF HUMOR Chas. L. Webster & Co., New York, 1888. [0] Second issue with index of titles in alphabetical order $200.

038c: MARK TWAIN'S LIBRARY OF HUMOR Chatto & Windus, London, 1888. [0] (Maurice F. Neville Cat. 15) $250.

038d: MARK TWAIN'S LIBRARY OF HUMOR Dawson Brothers, Montreal, 1888. [] (Ref.c) $200.

039a: A YANKEE AT THE COURT OF KING ARTHUR Chatto & Windus, London, 1889. [0] Advertisements dated June 1889 earliest noted. We have put this edition first based on Twain's intentions. In a letter (sold at Park-Bernet in 1956), Twain had instructed Fred Hall to publish the books as follows: Great Britain Dec. 6th, Canada Dec. 8th and U.S. Dec. 10th; and the actual publication dates appear to follow this per BAL 3429, although the books may have actually been available at different times (the Library of Congress deposit copy was received Dec. 5th) $750.

039b: A CONNECTICUT YANKEE IN KING ARTHUR'S COURT G.M. Rose, Toronto (1889). [0] Printed from Hartford edition (below) with "s" like ornament between "The" and "King" on p.59 (not noted in later state) $500.

039c: A CONNECTICUT YANKEE IN KING ARTHUR'S COURT Chas. L. Webster & Co., New York, 1889. [] Publisher's prospectus with half title, frontis illustration, title page, contents page, page stating illustrations not complete, preface, 63 pages of text, publisher's statement regarding illustrations, 15 pages of illustrations, publisher's sample ads and 32 page subscription form section. Two samples of leather on inside front cover, while inside rear cover contains front cover sample (Eldon Steeves #1) $3,500.

039d: A CONNECTICUT YANKEE IN KING ARTHUR'S COURT Chas. L. Webster & Co., New York, 1889. [0] Earliest state: p.(59) has a small "s" like ornament between "The" and "King" in the caption $1,250.

039e: A CONNECTICUT YANKEE IN KING ARTHUR'S COURT Chas. L. Webster & Co., New York, 1889. [0] Later state/printing: p.(59) no "s" like ornament in caption "The King" $750.

039f: A CONNECTICUT YANKEE IN KING ARTHUR'S COURT Limited Editions Club, New York, 1949. [2] 1,500 no. cc. Signed by illustrator Honore Guilbeau. Issued in slipcase $60/100

040a: FACTS FOR MARK TWAIN'S MEMORY BUILDER Chas. L. Webster & Co., New York,

1891. [0] Wraps. Designed to accompany "Mark Twain's Memory Builder," a board game (includes board and small box with *Facts...* booklet and pins) $750.

041a: THE AMERICAN CLAIMANT Chas. L. Webster & Co., New York, 1892. [0] Gray-green or olive-green cloth (auction records in 1985 show a 1889 edition, but assume a typo) $200.

041b: THE AMERICAN CLAIMANT Chatto & Windus, London, 1892. [0] Advertisements dated "October, 1892" which is about when it was published, although ref.d notes copies with ads dated "May 1892" are known $175.

042a: MERRY TALES Chas. L. Webster & Co., New York, 1892. [0] Presumed earliest state: white endpapers printed in faded olive-green with an all-over pattern of berries and thorns; also printed in faded olive-green with an over-all pattern of parsley-like leaves; no inserted portrait frontispiece $300.

042b: MERRY TALES Chas. L. Webster & Co., New York, 1892. [0] Presumed later state: same as above but contains inserted portrait frontispiece of Twain $200.

042c: MERRY TALES Chas. L. Webster & Co., New York, 1892. [0] Presumed final state: has inserted frontispiece; plain white endpapers $100.

043a: THE £1,000,000 BANK-NOTE ... Chas. L. Webster & Co., New York, 1893. [0] Publisher's prospectus with frontis and title page only, text pages blank but overall thicker than published book (ref.d) $1,500.

043b: THE £1,000,000 BANK-NOTE ... Chas. L. Webster & Co., New York, 1893. [0] $350.

043c: THE £1,000,000 BANK-NOTE ... Chatto & Windus, London, 1893. [0] Advertisements dated

April 1893. Also noted with ads dated March 1893 (Hermitage Bookshop 5/91) $250.

043d: THE £1,000,000 BANK-NOTE ... Harper & Bros., New York/London (1917). [0] First separate edition with publisher's code "E-R" on copyright page, indicating May 1917 $200.

044a: LIBER SCRIPTORUM The Authors Club, New York, 1893. [2] 251 cc (signed by the contributors). Full leather. Contains poetry and prose works by 109 authors. Twain's contribution is *The Californian's Tale* $3,000.

045a: PUDD'NHEAD WILSON'S CALENDAR FOR 1894 (Century Co., Dawson's Landing, Missouri [actually New York], 1893.) [0] Wraps. Issued in deep buff or orange wrappers and there are 3 known variants. No priority for any variant or wrapper color. Miniature (3" x 2 1/2"), 16 pages. Issued to promote the Century Magazine serialization $2,000.

046a: TOM SAWYER ABROAD... Chas. L. Webster & Co., New York, 1894. [0] Bound in white pictorial cloth. BAL describes the cloth color as "tan", an understandable mistake as most copies are found with the binding badly aged. (MacDonnell Rare Books 11/94) $1,000.

046b: TOM SAWYER ABROAD... Chatto & Windus, London, 1894. [0] Advertisements dated February 1894. Red cloth (reissued in blue cloth) $350.

047a: PUDD'NHEAD WILSON A TALE Chatto & Windus, London, 1894. [0] Advertisements dated September 1894. Red cloth, although also noted in dark blue cloth with same dated ads (Sumner & Stillman 4/92). Later issues noted with ads dated December 1894 (Bell, Book and Radmall 10/97); February 1897 (Julian Nangle 10/97); and in navy blue cloth stamped in gilt. with 32-page catalogue dated May, 1903 (Heritage Book Shop 8/97). $500.

047b: *The Tragedy of* PUDD'NHEAD WILSON *and the Comedy* THOSE EXTRAORDINARY TWINS American Publishing Co., Hartford, Conn., 1894. [] Publisher's prospectus. Brown cloth stamped in gilt and brown. Contains some sample text, illustrations, order sheets and sample back-strips (Heritage Book Shop 8/97) $2,500.

047c: *The Tragedy of* PUDD'NHEAD WILSON *and the Comedy* THOSE EXTRAORDINARY TWINS American Publishing Co., Hartford, Conn., 1894. [0] Earliest state: sheets bulk about 1 1/8"; the title leaf is clearly joined to the next leaf. Includes *Those Extraordinary Twins*, not in English edition. Leather bound copies would be worth more than cloth price shown $1,000.

047d: *The Tragedy of* PUDD'NHEAD WILSON *and the Comedy* THOSE EXTRAORDINARY TWINS American Publishing Co., Hartford, Conn., 1894. [0] Second state: sheets bulk 1 1/4"; title leaf not conjugate with next leaf and is an insert printed on paper which varies slightly from what is used in body of book $600.

047e: PUDD'NHEAD WILSON Limited Editions Club, Avon, Connecticut, 1974. [2] 2,000 sgd cc. Illustrated and signed by John Groth. Also includes *Pudd'nhead Wilson's Calendar*, small, in wraps and also illustrated by Groth. Issued in slipcase $75/125

048a: AMERICAN DROLLERIES Grand Coliseum Warehouse Co., Glasgow, no date [circa 1895?]. [] Reprints from plates of *Jumping Frog* and *Screamers* $350.

048b: AMERICAN DROLLERIES Ward, Lock & Bowden, London / New York / Melbourne, no date [circa 1895] [0] (Ref.c.) Not noted in BAL, so priority uncertain $350.

049a: PERSONAL RECOLLECTIONS OF JOAN OF ARC... Harper & Bros., New York, 1896. [0]

Earliest state: p.(463): "Some books for the Library The Abbey Shakespeare..." The fourth entry is for *Memoirs of Barras* described as in 4 volumes with vols. I-II offered @ $3.75 each; vols. III-IV as "just ready". Twain's name on binding but not title page. 5,000 copies in total (049a and 049b). (MacDonnell Rare Books 11/94) $500.

049b: PERSONAL RECOLLECTIONS OF JOAN OF ARC... Harper & Bros., New York, 1896. [0] Later state: p.(463): "Some books for the Library George Washington..." On p.(464) the *Memoirs of Barras* is described as in 4 vols. @ $15 $350.

049c: PERSONAL RECOLLECTIONS OF JOAN OF ARC... Chatto & Windus, London, 1896. [0] Advertisements dated March 1896 $350.

049d: SAINT JOAN OF ARC... Harper & Bros., New York / London (1919). [1] "Published, May 1919." "D-T" First state: marginal decoration on p.18 in correct position; endpapers printed in green. Illustrated by Howard Pyle $250.

049e: SAINT JOAN OF ARC... Harper & Bros., New York / London (1919). [1] "Published, May 1919." "D-T" Second state: marginal decoration on p.18 is inverted; endpapers unprinted. Noted in proof or variant dustwrapper without prices for the various binding styles of the books listed on the rear panel. Spaces were left by the typesetter. Another state of the dustwrapper has prices listed (Mac-Donnell Rare Books 10/96) $150.

050a: TOM SAWYER ABROAD TOM SAWYER DETECTIVE ... Harper & Bros., New York, 1896. [0] 1,000 cc (Kevin MacDonnell 11/91) $2,000.

051a: TOM SAWYER, DETECTIVE AS TOLD BY HUCK FINN ... Chatto & Windus, London, 1897. [0] Publisher's catalog dated September 1896 inserted at back. Contains first collected appearances of 6 stories (Fine Books 1/92). Also noted with ads dated November 1896 (Country Lane #35) $400.

052a: HOW TO TELL A STORY ... Harper & Bros., New York, 1897. [0] 2,000 cc (MacDonnell Rare Books 12/88.) (Note: Vol. 22 of *Writings*... with this title, contains first appearances not in this edition. See BAL 3458. Also see 1921 entry). One copy recorded in dustwrapper (MacDonnell Rare Books 11/94) $350.

053a: IN MEMORIAM / OLIVIA SUSAN CLEMENS ... No publisher, Lake Lucerne, 1897. [0] Single sheet folded to four pages. At end: "Lake Lucerne: August 18, 1897" $450.

054a: FOLLOWING THE EQUATOR ... American Publishing Company, Hartford, 1897. [] Publisher's prospectus. Reproduction of spine on back cover, 55 leaves of sample text and illustrations, 16 leaves of blank subscription sheets (Heritage Cat. #162 2/88). (There was also a trial binding in two volumes, perhaps unique, at auction in June 1992. It sold for $8,800.) $2,500.

054b: FOLLOWING THE EQUATOR ... American Publishing Company, Hartford, 1897. [0] Title-page also occurs with the following imprint: "Hartford New York / American Publishing Co. Doubleday & McClure Co. / MDCCCXCVII" - no priority over single imprint. Leather bound copies would be worth more than the cloth prices shown $400.

054c: MORE TRAMPS ABROAD ... Chatto & Windus, London, 1897. [0] First English edition of *Following The Equator*. Advertisements dated September 1897 $350.

054d: FOLLOWING THE EQUATOR ... American Publishing Company, Hartford, 1898. [2] 250 sgd no. cc. Also issued with the joint imprint of the American Publishing Co. and Doubleday and

McClure. Ref.c suggests that no more than 60 copies of this were bound. A facsimile of Twain's letter from Vienna dated October 25, 1897 is bound in at front. $5,000.

054e: FOLLOWING THE EQUATOR ... James M. Macgregor, Vancouver, 1899. [] First Canadian edition. Blue cloth decorated in gilt with pictorial paper label on front panel. The U.S. binding with American Publishing Company imprint at base of spine (Michael J. Thompson 9/97) $150.

055a: THE WRITINGS OF MARK TWAIN Autograph Edition. American Pub-lishing Company, Hartford (1899-1907). [2] 512 sgd no. sets. 25 volumes. Signed certificate of issue in vol. I. Ref.c indicates 1,000 copies $7,500.

055b: THE WRITINGS OF MARK TWAIN Chatto & Windus, London, 1899. [2] 620 sgd no. cc. 25 volumes. Volumes 24 and 25 unnumbered as they were published separately by Harpers (Maurice Neville Cat. 12) $6,000.

055c: THE WRITINGS OF MARK TWAIN Riverside Edition. American Publishing Company, Hartford, 1901. [2] 625 sets. 25 volumes. White buckram. In blue cloth dustwrappers $2,500/3,000

055d: (THE WRITINGS OF MARK TWAIN. Hillcrest Edition) Harper & Bros. New York / London, 1906-1907. [0] 25 volumes. Buckram with leather spine labels $1,750.

055e: THE WRITINGS OF MARK TWAIN Definitive Edition. Gabriel Wells, New York, 1922-1925. [2] 1,024 sgd sets. 37 volumes. Author's signature in volume 1. Signed leaves prepared in 1906 $4,000.

055f: THE WRITINGS OF MARK TWAIN Memorial Edition. Harper, New York, 1929. [2] 90 sgd no. sets (signed by the publishers). 37 volumes with leaf of manuscript (half morocco with gilt by Strikeman. Sold at auction in 1986) $15,000.

055g: THE WRITINGS OF MARK TWAIN Stormfield Edition. Harper, New York, 1929. []1,024 sets. 37 volumes. Blue cloth. Issued in dust-wrappers $1,500/2,000

NOTE: there have been numerous sets of Twain's Writings published over the years. The above listings are but a sample of some of the values. Many are not noted in BAL, Johnson, or McBride. We found some listed only in the auction records of *American Book Prices Current*.

056a: THE PAINS OF LOWLY LIFE (Anti-Vivisection Society, London, 1900.) [1] Wraps. "Published for the first time, March 1900." Publisher's address corrected in some copies with pasted-in slip $750.

057a: THE MAN THAT CORRUPTED HADLEY-BURG *and Other Stories* Harper & Bros., New York / London, 1900. [0] Earliest state: sheets bulk about 1 1/16"; the plate opposite p.2 has, in addition to the caption, the line: "[Page 2". One known copy in dustwrapper.(MacDonnell Rare Books 11/94) $500.

057b: THE MAN THAT CORRUPTED HADLEY-BURG *and Other Stories* Harper & Bros., New York / London, 1900. [0] Later state: sheets bulk about 1 3/16"; plate opposite p.2 has caption only $300.

057c: THE MAN THAT CORRUPTED HADLEY-BURG *and Other Stories* Harper & Bros., New York / London, 1900. [0] Final state: sheets bulk about 1 1/4"; the plate opposite p.2 has caption only $200.

057d: THE MAN THAT CORRUPTED HADLEY-BURG *and Other Stories* Chatto & Windus, London, 1900. [0] Advertisements dated June, 1900. Two stories not in U.S. edition $300.

058a: A SALUTATION SPEECH FROM THE NINETEENTH CENTURY TO TWENTIETH ... No publisher or place, 1900. [0] Card prepared for the Red Cross Society (reprinted by Roxburghe Club, San Francisco, 1929) $250.

059a: ENGLISH AS SHE IS TAUGHT Mutual Book Co., Boston (1900). [0] Wraps or cloth. Earliest state: p.16:5 "The fivc" for "The five". First separate edition, originally published as a commentary to Caroline LeRow's book, see 1887 entry $350.

059b: ENGLISH AS SHE IS TAUGHT Mutual Book Co., Boston (1900). [0] Later state: p.16:5 "The five" $175.

059c: ENGLISH AS SHE IS TAUGHT Century, New York, 1901. [0] Revised version. “Copyright 1887 By | The Century Co. | Copyright 1882 By O. M. Dunham” $100.

Note: reissued in wraps imprinted A. M. Davis Co., Boston 1887 (circa 1917 to 1920?)

060a: EDMUND BURKE ON CROKER & TAMMANY (Economist Press, New York, 1901.) [0] Wraps $1,250.

061a: TO THE PERSON SITTING IN DARKNESS... (Anti-Imperialist League, New York, 1901.) [0] Wraps $750.

061b: TO THE PERSON SITTING IN DARKNESS... (Privately printed, no place, 1926. [2] 250 no. cc. Wraps $150.

062a: A DOUBLE BARRELLED DETECTIVE STORY Harper & Bros., New York / London, 1902. [0] Red or maroon cloth. Issued in dustwrapper. Variant binding: red cloth, stamped in gold on front, publisher's name not on spine. "Tabard Inn Library" book plate on front pastedown. Noted in buff dustwrapper with author and title printed in black (Patricia Juvelis 10/95). Three known copies in dustwrapper (MacDonnell Rare Books 11/94). While BAL mentions the Tabard Inn binding in maroon cloth, Mac Donnell Rare Books, 5/97, mentions the "usual blue Tabard Inn binding." $300.

062b: A DOUBLE BARRELLED DETECTIVE STORY Chatto & Windus, London, 1902. [0] Advertisements dated "March, 1902" (ref.d) $200.

063a: DIRECTIONS... TELEPHONE ADDRESS: 150 KINGS BRIDGE No publisher, New York, no date. [0] Card, 2 11/16" x 3 3/4". Prepared by Twain for the convenience of his guests, giving directions to his home in Riverdale, NY. 1902? $125.

064a: EXTRACT FROM LETTER OF "MARK TWAIN" TO FREDERICK W. PEABODY No publisher, place or date. [0] Single leaf 5 7/8" x 4 5/8". Printed in Boston, 1902? Announces Peabody's forthcoming book on Christian Science. (Reprinted and inserted in copies of later editions of Peabody's book but this issue didn't carry notice on forth-coming book) $200.

065a: "A DOGS TALE" REPRINTED BY PERMISSION FROM HARPER'S MAGAZINE... (National Anti-Vivisection Society, London, 1903 [actually 1904]). [0] Wraps. First separate edition. Note by Johnson stated about 50 copies sent to England (Howard S. Mott 12/92) $400.

065b: A DOG'S TALE Harper & Bros., New York / London, 1904. [0] "Pub-lished September, 1904" $250.

066a: MY DEBUT AS A LITERARY PERSON *with Other Essays and Stories* American Publishing Company, Hartford, 1903. [] Volume XXIII of *Mark Twain's WORKS*, The Hillcrest Edition. Blue-green cloth, paper spine label; top edges gilt. Contains first printings of four pieces. A rather odd situation where a volume in a collected edition is actually a first edition. It was dropped from the collected edition when Harper took over publication a few years later (MacDonnell Rare Books 10/96) $250.

067a: PUDD'NHEAD WILSON'S CALENDAR FOR 1904 No publisher or place, 1904. [] Deep buff stapled printed wraps, 2½ x 3 3/8 inches (Waiting For Godot Books 2/95) $1,250.

068a: EXTRACTS FROM ADAM'S DIARY... Harper & Bros., New York / London, 1904. [1] "Published April, 1904" $250.

068b: EXTRACTS FROM ADAM'S DIARY... London / New York, 1904. [] (Kevin MacDonnell Rare Books 11/89) $250.

069a: TO WHOM THIS SHALL COME... No publisher, Florence, Italy, 1904. [0] Printed on folded sheet of mourning stationery. A 9-line acknowledgment of messages of condolence on Mrs. Clemen's death $200.

070a: AN UNEXPECTED ACQUAINTANCE Harper & Bros., New York / London, 1904. [0] Wraps. $750.

070b: AN UNEXPECTED ACQUAINTANCE Harper & Bros., New York / London (1904). [] Stapled wraps. Reissue. (Macdonnell Rare Books 10/96) $450.

071a: KING LEOPOLD'S SOLILOQUY... P.R. Warren Co., Boston, 1905. [0] Wraps. First published edition, first issue: (i-ii), (1)-(50); frontispiece and 5 plates inserted; other illustrations in text; 7 3/8" x 4 3/4"; white paperwraps, outside printed in green and yellow, inside blank; footnote on last line of p.8 "Jordan and other prominent citizens in a petition.."; frontispiece caption set in 2 lines including a reference to p.25; caption on plate opposite p.8 set in 1 line including reference to p.8.

The whole set 2 3/16" wide; caption on plate opposite p.28 set in 2 lines including a reference to p.27; the caption under the illustration on p.32 set in 2 lines. The first word of text immediately below the illustration is the word "out" $750.

071b: KING LEOPOLD'S SOLILOQUY... P.R. Warren Co., Boston, 1905. [0] Wraps. First published edition, second issue: points as above except white paperwraps; outside printed in dark green and yellow; inside blank. Also: white paperwraps. Outside printed in black and yellow. Inside blank; footnote on last line of p.8 "Citizens in a petition..." Frontispiece caption set in 1 line including a reference to p.25; caption on plate opposite p.8 set in 1 line including reference to p.8. The whole set 2 11/16" wide $500.

071c: KING LEOPOLD'S SOLILOQUY... P.R. Warren Co., Boston, 1905. [0] Wraps. First published edition, third issue: points as in 67a except frontispiece and 5 plates inserted. Other illustrations in text. 7 7/16" x 4 3/4"; footnote on last line of p.8 "Citizens in petitions..." Frontispiece caption set in one line including a reference to p.25; caption on plate opposite p.8 set in one line including a reference to p.8. The whole set 2 11/16" wide $400.

071d: KING LEOPOLD'S SOLILOQUY... P.R. Warren Co., Boston, 1905. [0] Wraps. First published edition, fourth issue: (1)-(52). Frontispiece and 5 plates inserted. Other illustrations in text. 7 1/4" x 4 5/8"; white paperwraps. Outside printed in black and yellow. Inside blank; footnote on last line of p.10 "Citizens in petitions..." Frontispiece caption set in one line including a reference to p.27; caption on plate opposite p.10 set in one line including a reference to p.10. The whole set 2 3/4" wide; caption on plate opposite p.28 set in 2 lines including a reference to p.29; the caption under the illustration on p.34 is set in one line. The last word of text immediately under the illustration is the word "pattern" $300.

Note: the second edition so states.

071e: KING LEOPOLD'S SOLILOQUY... T. Fisher Unwin, London, 1907. [] $500.

072a: EDITORIAL WILD OATS Harper & Bros., New York / London, 1905. [1] "Published September, 1905." (Note: dustwrapper with no titles listed on back published later) $150.

073a: MARK TWAIN ON VIVISECTION... New England Anti-Vivisection Society, Boston, no date [circa 1905]. [0] Single leaf of cream-yellow wove paper folded to 4 pages $450.

073b: MARK TWAIN ON VIVISECTION... New York Anti-Vivisection Society, New York, no date [circa 1905]. [0] Single leaf of white laid paper folded to 4 pages. Also contains G.G. Vest's *Eulogy on the Dog* $300.

074a: MARK TWAIN'S LIBRARY OF HUMOR MEN AND THINGS... Harper & Bros., New York / London, 1906. [1] "Published February, 1906" $350.

075a: MARK TWAIN'S LIBRARY OF HUMOR WOMEN AND THINGS... Harper & Bros., New York / London, 1906. [1] "Published April, 1906" $250.

076a: MARK TWAIN'S LIBRARY OF HUMOR THE PRIMROSE WAY... Harper & Bros., New York / London, 1906. [1] "Published April, 1906" $250.

076b: MARK TWAIN'S LIBRARY OF HUMOR A LITTLE NONSENSE Harper, New York, 1906. [1] "Published .. July, 1906" $200.

077a: EVE'S DIARY TRANSLATED FROM THE ORIGINAL MS Harper & Bros., London / New York, 1906. [1] "Published June, 1906." All copies apparently have the imprint "London and New York" $250.

078a: WHAT IS MAN? De Vinne Press, New York, 1906. [2] 250 cc (a & b). Anonymous. First issue: leaf (18)2 is not a cancel; p.131 ends ..."thinks about/". Issued with tissue dustwrapper. In slipcase $1,500.

078b: WHAT IS MAN? De Vinne Press, New York, 1906. [2] 250 cc (a & b). Anonymous. Second issue: leaf (18)2 is a cancel; p.131 ends "thinks about / it." $1,250.

078c: WHAT IS MAN? Watts & Co., London, 1910. [0] First disclosure of authorship $300.

078d: WHAT IS MAN? Harper & Bros., New York / London (1917). [0] Red cloth. "E-R" on copyright page $300.

078e: WHAT IS MAN? Harper & Bros., New York / London (1917). [0] Limp red leather $250.

078f: WHAT IS MAN? Chatto & Windus, London, 1919. [0] $250.

079a: THE $30,000 BEQUEST *and Other Stories* Harper & Bros. NY/L 1906 [0] First state: no ads on copyright page $300.

079b: THE $30,000 BEQUEST *and Other Stories* Harper & Bros., New York / London, 1906. [0] Second state: boxed ads on copyright page $200.

080a: MARK TWAIN ON SIMPLIFIED SPELLING... (The Simplified Spelling Board, New York, 1906.) [0] "The Simplified Spelling Board Circular No. 9, Nov. 10, 1906." Single leaf folded to 4 pages. Presumed first issue: unbroken type p.1:3 "reached except thru you..." $400.

080b: MARK TWAIN ON SIMPLIFIED SPELLING... (The Simplified Spelling Board, New York, 1906.) [0] Presumed second issue: broken type p.1:3 "reached except thru you..." $300.

081a: A BIRTHPLACE WORTH SAVING The Lincoln Farm Association, no place or date [1906]. [0] Single sheet. 16 7/8" x 5 1/2" $200.

082a: CHRISTIAN SCIENCE WITH NOTES... Harper & Bros., New York / London, 1907. [0] Book has appeared in various states (see ref.b). Advertisements on back ending with *Jumping Frog*. Second dustwrapper adds *Christian Science* to list on back.

Point 1: Earlier state: copyright page boxed ads list 17 titles. Later state: copyright page boxed ads list 18 titles.

Point 2: Earlier state: p.(iii): type, including heading is 8 lines long. Later state: p.(iii): type is 6 lines long.

Point 3: Earlier state: frontispiece dated (1906). Later state: frontispiece dated (1907).

Point 4: Earlier state: p.3:9 "farmhouse." Later state: p.3:9 "fa mhouse." Also noted, a copy with "farmhouse."

Point 5: Earlier state: p.5:14 "w" in "why" standard. Later state: p.5:14 "w" in "why" heavy.

Earlier state: $250.
Later/mixed state: $150.

082b: CHRISTIAN SCIENCE WITH NOTES... Harper & Bros., London / New York, 1907. [0] Same as 088a, London listed first on title page (Wm. & Victoria Dailey 3/90) $200.

083a: MARK TWAIN ON CHRISTIAN SCIENCE No publisher, place or date [circa 1907?]. [0] White stapled wraps printed in black on front cover *Mark Twain |on | Christian Science.* The header preceding the printed text on page one states "Christian Science and the Book of Mrs. Eddy by Mark Twain." The first separate edition. *Cosmopolitan* issued an article in October 1899 entitled *Christian Science and the Book of Mrs. Eddy* by Mark Twain. This was collected in *Christian Science* published by Harper & Brothers in 1907. (Waiting For Godot 2/95) $1,750.

084a: A HORSE'S TAIL Harper & Bros., New York / London, 1907. [0] Issued in dustwrapper $200.

085a: MARK TWAIN ON THREE WEEKS No publisher, place or date. [0] Wraps. Privately printed for Mrs. Elinor Glyn for private distribution, probably London 1908. Printed in orchid, on pale orchid, vellum-like paper, tied with orchid cord. Mrs. Glyn's report of an interview with Twain (nine pages) and Twain's letter after reading her report (two pages) $600.

086a: TO MY GUESTS GREETING AND SALUTATION AND PROSPERITY!... No publisher, Redding, Connecticut, 1908. [0] Single leaf. 10 1/4" x 8". An appeal for contributions for the Mark Twain Public Library $300.

087a: IS SHAKESPEARE DEAD?... Harper & Bros., New York / London, 1909. [1] Earliest state: with frontis portraits of Shakespeare and Bacon. "Published April, 1909," without inserted advertisement leaves either between (1)2 and (1)3 or, between (10)6 and (10)7 $250.

087b: IS SHAKESPEARE DEAD?... Harper & Bros., New York / London, 1909. [1] "Published April, 1909." Later state: inserted between leaves (1)2-3 is a one page advertisement referring to Greenwood's *The Shakespeare Problem Restated* $175.

087c: IS SHAKESPEARE DEAD?... Harper & Bros., New York / London, 1909. [1] "Published April, 1909." Later state (no priority between b & c): inserted between (10)6-7 is 2-page advertisement for Greenwood's *The Shakespeare Problem Restated* and *In re Shakespeare Problem* $175.

088a: EXTRACT FROM CAPTAIN STORMFIELD'S VISIT TO HEAVEN Harper & Bros., New York, 1909. [0] Publisher's sample copy in red pictorial cloth, lettered in white. Title page is printed without a copyright notice on verso, and the text consists of two gatherings bound in duplicated sequence to simulate the bulk of the actual published book. Noted with the word, "SAMPLE" stamped on sheet edges and front cover (MacDonnell Rare Books 12/96) $1,500.

088b: EXTRACT FROM CAPTAIN STORMFIELD'S VISIT TO HEAVEN Harper & Bros., New York / London, 1909. [0] Printed on different paper with three different widths, no priority $175.

089a: TRAVELS AT HOME... Harper & Bros., New York / London, 1910. [1]"Published April 1910." Selected by Percival Chubb $250.

090a: TRAVELS IN HISTORY... Harper & Bros., New York / London, 1910. [] $250.

091a: TO THE EDITOR: WE HAVE PREPARED FOR YOUR USE... Harper & Bros. (New York), no date [circa 1910]. [0] Single sheet 20 7/16" x 15 9/16". Text set in 6 columns. Promotional material $300.

092a: MARK TWAIN'S SPEECHES WITH INTRODUCTION BY WILLIAM DEAN HOWELLS Harper & Bros., New York / London, 1910. [1] "Published June, 1910." (Waiting For Godot Books 2/95 offered a copy in dustwrapper) $250.

092b: MARK TWAIN'S SPEECHES WITH INTRODUCTION BY WILLIAM DEAN HOWELLS

Harper, New York (1923). [1] Also has "D-X." Expanded to include later speeches $75/350

093a: QUEEN VICTORIA'S JUBILEE... No publisher, place or date. [2] 195 no. cc. Privately printed for private distribution only. Probably printed in New York in 1910. Printed white boards, cloth shelf back $750.

094a: [MARK TWAIN'S LONDON LECTURE NOTES] [title assigned] No publisher or place, 1910. [0] 10-12 cc. Single leaf 9"x6" printed with a series of mnemonic caricatures by Clemens used as lecture aid. 10 to 12 copies printed for copyright purposes $NVA

095a: MARK TWAIN'S LETTER TO THE CALIFORNIA PIONEERS Dewitt & Snelling, Oakland, California, 1911. [2] Wraps. Presumed first state with copyright notice on p.(4) and copies unnumbered. Total edition 750 cc (a & b). We had a copy with copyright on page 4 and numbered "643" $200.

095b: MARK TWAIN'S LETTER TO THE CALIFORNIA PIONEERS Dewitt & Snelling, Oakland, California, 1911. [2] Wraps. Presumed second state without copyright notice on p.(4) and numbered. Seems to be scarcer, based on the fact that 11 copies of the "first" have been catalogued in the last 10 years but none of this state $150.

096a: MARK TWAIN AND FAIRHAVEN The Millicent Library, Fairhaven, Massachusetts (1913). [0] Wraps. Tan linen-weave paper wraps $250.

096b: MARK TWAIN AND FAIRHAVEN The Millicent Library Fairhaven, Mass. (1976) Wraps. Revised edition, introduction by Earl Dias $60.

097a: THE SUPPRESSED CHAPTER OF "LIFE ON THE MISSISSIPPI" No publisher, New York, no date [1913]. [2] 250 no. cc. Single leaf folded to

4 pages. Also an unnumbered copy (Waiting For Godot Books 2/96) $600.

098a: DEATH-DISK Edgar S. Werner, New York, no date [circa 1913]. [0] Wraps $200.

099a: THE MYSTERIOUS STRANGER... Harper & Bros., New York / London (1916). [1] "Published October, 1916" and "K-Q" on copyright page. Illustrated by N.C. Wyeth. $250.

100a: HOW TO REACH THE AGE OF SEVENTY... (Edwin B. Hill, Mesa, Arizona, 1916.) [2] 350 cc. Wraps. Reprint of part of Twain's speech on his 70th birthday $300.

101a: SAMUEL LANGHORNE CLEMENS No publisher, place or date. [0] 5-7 cc. Wraps. Said to be printed at the Davis Press, Worcester, Mass. 1916. Printed on paper watermarked "Clemens" $1,250.

101b: SAMUEL LANGHORNE CLEMENS No publisher, place or date. [0] 30-75 cc. Wraps. Said to be printed at the Davis Press, Worcester, Massachusetts, 1916. 30-75 copies on paper watermarked "Mark Twain" $1,000.

102a: WHO WAS SARAH FINDLAY? Clement Shorter, London, 1917. [2] 25 sgd no. cc. Wraps. With a suggested solution by J.M. Barrie. Signed by Shorter $1,000.

103a: MARK TWAIN'S LETTERS... Harper & Bros., New York / London (1917). [2] 350 sets. Two volumes. Limitation certificate in first volume. Uncut edges. Paper labels. Issued in dustwrappers. In slipcase $350/1,000

103b: MARK TWAIN'S LETTERS... Harper & Bros., New York / London (1917). [1] "Published November, 1917" and "L-R" on copyright page. Two volumes. Library edition. Red cloth stamped in gold on spine $200.

103c: MARK TWAIN'S LETTERS... Harper & Bros., New York / London (1917). [1] "Published November, 1917" and "L-R" on copyright page. Two volumes. Trade edition. Paper watermarked "Olde Style" $150/500

WHAT IS MAN? see 1906 entry

104a: MARK TWAIN'S CALENDAR [for 1918] (Sulley & Kleinteich, New York, no date [1917]. [0] Large 8vo marbled paper decorated in gold, 56 pages printed on rectos only, each page printed in green and black. Furnished with cord for hanging. Issued in publisher's lidded box (Waiting For Godot 2/95) $300/500

105a: IN DEFENSE OF HARRIET SHELLEY ... Harper & Bros., New York / London (1918). [0] Ref.a does not indicate "First Edition" is stated. Code letters "B-S" on copyright page. Issued in limp leather series. There was a later printing with the code letters "D-T" on the copyright page $250.

106a: MY WATCH, AN INSTRUCTIVE LITTLE TALE Waltham Watch Co., Waltham, Massachusetts, no date [circa 1918). [0] Stapled wraps. First separate edition $300.

107a: AN ADDITION TO THE PRIVATE HISTORY OF THE "JUMPING FROG" STORY... (Privately printed), New York, 1918. [2] 10 cc $NVA

108a: THE CURIOUS REPUBLIC OF GONDOUR *and Other Whimsical Sketches* ... Boni & Liveright, New York, 1919. [0] Seems to show up in dustwrapper more than any other Twain title before 1930 $200/600

SAINT JOAN OF ARC... see PERSONAL... 1896 entry

109a: MOMENTS WITH MARK TWAIN Harper & Bros., New York / London, 1920. [1] "Published

March, 1920" and code letters "B-U" on copyright page. Issued in imitation leather, assume no dustwrapper (ref.d) $250.

109b: MOMENTS WITH MARK TWAIN Harper & Bros., New York / London, 1920. [1] "Published March, 1920" and code letters "B-U" on copyright page $125/500

110a: MARK TWAIN ABLE YACHTSMAN... No publisher, place or date. [2] 12 no. cc. Bound in cream paper boards with blue line shelfback. Total edition (a & b) 109 copies. Privately printed in New York in 1920. (Merle Johnson's copy to NY Public Library, number 51, we had one numbered 49), therefore (obviously), the boards were not the first 12 copies $2,000.

110b: MARK TWAIN ABLE YACHTSMAN... No publisher, place or date. [2] 97 no. cc. Wraps $1,500.

111a: THE SANDWICH ISLANDS No publisher, New York, 1920. [] Proof in stapled, unprinted white wraps. Pages printed on rectos only (Waiting For Godot Books 2/95) $3,000.

111b: THE SANDWICH ISLANDS No publisher, New York, 1920. [2] 30 cc. Issued in 3/4 morocco $3,000.

112a: (THE MAMMOTH COD) No publisher, New York, no date [circa 1920]. [2] 20 no. cc. 4 pages in white rough-tooth paper. 1-4 blank, 2-4 unsigned sketches by Merle Johnson. P.3 Twain's verse $1,000.

112b: (THE MAMMOTH COD) No publisher, place or date. [2] A single leaf (unillustrated) printed, 6" x 3 1/2", white paper. Printed in New York circa 1920? Merle Johnson first saw this in 1930. Ref.d had a copy with a note on back indicating it had been "given me by Bliss, son of American Publishing Co. Hartford, Connecticut 11/17/1915" $750.

112c: (THE MAMMOTH COD) (Hammer & Chisel Club, New York, 1937.) [2] 19 cc. Stated Second Edition. On pale bluff paper $450.

112d: THE MAMMOTH COD AN ADDRESS TO THE STOMACH CLUB Maledicta (Milwaukee), 1976. [2] Unspecified number of copies (copy cited by ref.b is no. 1,019). Green cloth. Introduction by G. Legman $15/75

113a: (A PROSE POEM FROM HAWAII) (Mercantile Press, Honolulu), no date [circa 1920]. [0] Single sheet folded to 4 pages. Title at head of p.2 $300.

114a: EIGHT HUMOROUS SKETCHES... Haldeman-Julius Co., Girard, Kansas (1921). [0] Stapled light blue printed wraps. 64 pp. Issued as "Ten Cent Pocket Series No. 231" $50.

114b: EIGHT HUMOROUS SKETCHES Haldeman-Julius Co., Girard, Kansas (1921). [] Stapled light blue printed wraps. 57 pages followed by ads. "Peoples Pocket Series" issue (Waiting For Godot 2/95) $35.

114c: HUMOROUS SKETCHES Haldeman-Julius Co., Girard, Kansas (1921). [] Stapled yellowish-tan printed wraps. Issued as "Little Blue Book No. 231." 59 pages. Same contents as *Eight Humorous Sketches* ? (Waiting For Godot 2/95) $35.

115a: HOW TO TELL A STORY (P.F. Collier & Son, New York, 1921.) [0] Wraps. First printing: no boxed ad on p.(ii); inner front wrapper printed in deep purple with Twain portrait; inner back wrapper has illustration from *The Celebrated Jumping Frog*. (also see 1897 entry) $300.

115b: HOW TO TELL A STORY (P.F. Collier & Son, New York, 1921 [circa 1925]). [0] Wraps. Second printing: boxed ad on p.(ii); inner back wrapper printed in green with picture of "Author's National Edition" $150.

115c: HOW TO TELL A STORY (P.F. Collier & Son, New York, 1921 [circa 1925]) [0] Wraps. Third printing: on front cover is author's facsimile autograph $100.

116a: "COMING OUT" A LETTER TO A ROSE-BUD... No publisher (New York, 1921). [2] 200 cc. Rose paper boards, imitation vellum shelfback $400.

117a: THE MYSTERIOUS STRANGER *and Other Stories* Harper & Bros., New York / London, 1922. [1] "Also has code letters "D-W" on copyright page. First book appearance for 4 of the stories. Three spine stampings. No priority. Bindings described by BAL have dots on either side of the publisher's imprint. Also noted a variant without the dots (MacDonnell Rare Books 5/97) $200/750

118a: MARK TWAIN'S JUMPING FROG *and Other Humorous Tales* Haldeman-Julius Co., Girard, Kansas, no date [circa 1922]. [] Stapled light blue printed wraps. Issued as "Little Blue Book No. 291." (Waiting For Godot Books 2/95) $35.

119a: MARK TWAIN'S SPEECHES... Harper & Bros., New York / London (1923). [1] "Large Paper" edition, leaf size 8 1/8" x 5 7/16". Profile of Mark Twain blind stamped on front cover $200/1,000

119b: MARK TWAIN'S SPEECHES... Harper & Bros., New York / London (1923). [1] Trade edition. Red cloth, circular devise in gold on front cover. "D-X" on copyright page $125/500

120a: EUROPE AND ELSEWHERE Harper & Bros., New York / London (1923). [1] Code letters "E-X" on copyright page $125/500

121a: ... AMUSING ANSWERS TO CORRES-PONDENTS, *and Other Pieces* Haldeman-Julius Co., Girard, Kansas, no date [1924]. [0] Wraps. Little Blue Book No. 662 $40.

122a: ... HUMOROUS FABLES... Haldeman-Julius Co., Girard, Kansas, no date [1924]. [0] Wraps. Little Blue Book No. 668 $40.

123a: ... JOURNALISM IN TENNESSEE ... Haldeman-Julius Co., Girard, Kansas, no date. [0] Wraps. Little Blue Book No. 663 $40.

124a: MARK TWAIN'S AUTOBIOGRAPHY... Harper & Bros., New York / London, 1924. [1] Two volumes. Advance copies with pages uncut. (See ref.c & d). Laid in blue cloth bindings; all edges uncut, 9 11/16 x 6 3/16" (Howard S. Mott 3/94) $1500.

124b: MARK TWAIN'S AUTOBIOGRAPHY... Harper & Bros., New York / London, 1924. [1] Two volumes. Presumed earliest state with 2 pages of ads in back of vol. 2. "H-Y" on copyright page. In dustwrapper and box $150/500

124c: MARK TWAIN'S AUTOBIOGRAPHY... Harper & Bros., New York / London, 1924. [1] Two volumes. "H-Y" on copyright page. Presumed later state without ads at back of vol. 2 $100/400

124d: THE AUTOBIOGRAPHY OF MARK TWAIN Harper & Bros., New York (1959). [] Contains some new material per ref.c. $20/100

124e: THE AUTOBIOGRAPHY OF MARK TWAIN Chatto & Windus, London, 1960. [] Contains about 40,000 words of text never before published (Ulysses 9/95) $20/100

125a: ...A CURIOUS EXPERIENCE *and Other Amusing Pieces*... Haldeman-Julius Girard, Kansas, no date [1925]. [0] Wraps. Little Blue Book No. 932 $40.

126a: S.L.C. TO C.T. No publisher, place or date [1925], [2] Wraps. 100 cc $600.

127a: THE STOLEN WHITE ELEPHANT *And Other Stories* Haldeman-Julius Co., Girard, Kansas (1925). [] Stapled light blue printed wraps. Issued as "Little Blue Book No. 931" (Waiting For Godot Books 2/95) $40.

128a: SKETCHES OF THE SIXTIES... John Howell, San Francisco, 1926. [2] 250 no. cc. Printed on Strathmore Japan paper. Written with Bret Harte $150/450

128b: SKETCHES OF THE SIXTIES... John Howell, San Francisco, 1926. [2] 2,000 cc. Tan boards, brown-orange cloth shelfback $75/300

128c: SKETCHES OF THE SIXTIES... John Howell, San Francisco, 1927. [] Enlarged edition $30/150

129a: MARK TWAIN VS. THE STREET RAILWAY CO. Privately Printed, no place, 1926. [1] Wraps. "Printed November, 1926." Includes facsimiles of Twain's letters, essay by John S. Mayfield $100.

130a: MARK TWAIN IN NEVADA Nevada ... University Women, no place, 1927. [] Wraps. First separate publication of section from *Roughing It*. 26 pages in white wraps and printed dustwrappers $50/150

131a: MORE MAXIMS OF MARK No publisher or place, 1927. [2] 50 no. cc. Privately printed in New York. Paper boards, cloth shelf-back (ref.b) $750.

132a: THE QUAKER CITY HOLY LAND... (Privately Printed), no place, 1927. [2] 200 cc. Wraps. Published by M. Harzof, New York, who claims to have destroyed all but about 50 copies. However, as nine or ten copies have been catalogued in the last ten years, there would appear to be some doubt that only 50 exist $500.

132b: THE QUAKER CITY HOLY LAND Buttonmaker Press, Omaha, 1986. [2] 150 sgd no. cc (signed by illustrator John de Pol?) (Wm. Graf 6/94) $100.

133a: THE ADVENTURES OF THOMAS JEFFERSON SNODGRASS... Pascal Covici, Chicago, 1928. [2] 375 no. cc. Brown paper boards, tan buckram spine $100/400

134a: ...A BOY'S ADVENTURE... No publisher, place or date. [0] Single leaf folded to four pages. Privately printed by Merle Johnson, NY 1928. Originally in *Bazaar Budget*, 1880 $300.

135a: THE SUPPRESSED CHAPTER OF FOLLOWING THE EQUATOR No publisher, place or date. [2] 30 no. cc of which all but 5, including galleys, were destroyed (Nick Karanovich). Not bound, not published. Privately printed for Merle Johnson, New York, 1928. (2 copies per ref.a) $3,500.

136a: A LETTER FROM MARK TWAIN TO HIS PUBLISHER, CHATTO & WINDUS... The Penguin Press, San Francisco, 1929. [2] 50 cc. Wraps $600.

137a: A GREETING FROM THE NINETEENTH TO THE TWENTIETH CENTURY... James Tuft for the Roxburghe Club, San Francisco, 1929. [0] Wraps (ref.d) $175.

138a: INNOCENCE AT HOME No publisher, place or date [1929]. [0] Single leaf printed in black on pale green block, 9" x 6" $250.

139a: THREE ACES JIM TODD'S EPISODE (Privately printed, Westport, Conn. [*i.e.* N.Y.]), 1929 [circa 1930]. [2] "50 copies." Wraps. Certificate of issue is false in terms of who, where and when this was published $300.

140a: A CHAMPAGNE COCKTAIL... (Privately printed), no place (1930). [2] "...Limited Edition...Xmas 1930" Wraps. (Comment above also applies to this book) $250.

141a: THE PRIVATE LIFE OF ADAM AND EVE Harper & Bros., New York / London (1931). [1] Code letters "E-F" on copyright page. First one volume edition with frontis of ALS not previously published $75/300

142a: MARK TWAIN'S EARLY WRITINGS IN HANNIBAL MISSOURI PAPERS Willard S. Morse, Santa Monica, 1931. [0] (Ref.b) $50/200

143a: THE STORY OF ARCHIMEDES Single Tax Publishing Co., New York (1931). [] 12 pages in white printed, stapled wraps. Reprinted from the Sydney (Australia) *Standard* (Waiting For Godot 4/89) $600.

144a: BE GOOD, BE GOOD (Privately printed, New York, 1931.) [0] 10-12 cc. Single sheet folded to 4 pages, printed in blue on vellum. Privately printed by Merle Johnson as a Christmas token. $1,000.

144b: BE GOOD, BE GOOD (Privately printed, New York, 1931.) [0] Single sheet French folded to 4 pages. Printed throughout in green $350.

145a: MARK TWAIN THE LETTER WRITER Meador Publishing Co., Boston, 1932. [0] $50/200

146a: THERE'LL BE A HOT TIME IN THE OLD TOWN TO-NIGHT Jacob Blanck, New York, 1932. [2] 299 cc. Christmas card greeting. Twain's statement, previously unpublished (Kevin MacDonnell Rare Books 11/89) $100.

147a: CONCERNING THE JEWS Harper & Bros., New York / London, 1934. [0] Wraps. Code letters "G-I" on copyright page $250.

148a: THE FAMILY MARK TWAIN Harper & Bros., New York / London (1935). [0] $50/200

149a: THE COMPLETE SHORT STORIES AND HUMOROUS SKETCHES OF MARK TWAIN Centennial Edition 1835-1935. Wise & Co., New York, 1935. [] Assume not issued in dustwrapper (Waiting For Godot 6/89) $125.

150a: SLOVENLY PETER... Limited Editions Club, New York, 1935. [2] 1,500 sgd no. cc. Illustrated and signed by Fritz Kredel. Pictorial cloth with tissue dustwrapper, folding box and slipcase $250/300

151b: SLOVENLY PETER... Harper & Bros., New York / London, 1935. [1] Code letters "K-K" on copyright page. Illustrated by Fritz Kredel. (Pepper & Stern cataloged this as preceding the Limited Editions Club edition by 2 1/2 months, while ref.a shows the LEC deposit copy in August and the Harper in November?) $100/250

152a: MARK TWAIN'S WIT AND WISDOM Stokes, New York, 1935. [] Edited by Cyril Clemens, preface by Stephen Leacock (ref.b) $30/150

153a: MARK TWAIN'S NOTEBOOK... Harper & Bros., New York / London, 1935. [1] "I-K" on copyright page. Prepared by Albert Bigelow Paine. Ref.a notes that Harper stopped the press in the middle of the run and changed to "Second Edition" but left the "I-K" on page $50/200

153b: MARK TWAIN'S NOTEBOOK... Harper & Bros., New York / London, 1935. [] "Second Edition" but with "I-K" on copyright page $25/125

154a: MARK TWAIN'S GOOD-BYE Davis, Hannibal (1935). [] Wraps. Sheet music, words by Twain, music by Paul Rottman $100.

155a: MARK TWAIN'S MARGINS ON THACKERY'S SWIFT Gotham House, New York, 1935. [2] 1,000 no. cc. Twain's annotations $100.

156a: AURELIA'S UNFORTNATE YOUNG MAN Eucalyptus Press, no place, 1936. [] Paper over flexible boards $175.

157a: LETTERS FROM THE SANDWICH ISLANDS... Grabhorn Press, San Francisco, 1937. [2] 550 cc. Issued in plain green dustwrapper (ref.b) $250/350

157b: LETTERS FROM THE SANDWICH ISLANDS... Stanford University Press, California (1938). [0] $30/150

158a: EXTRACTS FROM PUDD'NHEAD WILSON'S CALENDAR Golden Hind Press, Madison, New Jersey, 1937. [2] 110 no. cc. Wraps (Antic Hay 11/88) $150.

159a: ...HOW TO CURE A COLD (The Cloister Press), San Francisco, 1937. [2] About 200 cc $250.

160a: THE WASHOE GIANT... George Fields, San Francisco, 1938. [0] $35/175

161a: THE COYOTE The Rounce & Coffin Club, no place, 1938. [2] 25 cc. Wraps $350.

162a: MARK TWAIN'S LETTER TO WILLIAM BOWEN Book Club of California, San Francisco, 1938. [2] 400 cc. Plain tan dustwrapper $125/150

162b: MARK TWAIN'S LETTER TO WILLIAM BOWEN University of Texas, Austin, 1941. [] Wraps $75.

163a: LETTERS FROM HONOLULU... Thomas Nickerson, Honolulu, 1939. [2] 1,000 cc. In glassine dustwrapper? “Cellophane wrap” i.e. cellophane dustwrapper (Peripatetic Bibliophile 5/95) $175.

164a: MARK TWAIN'S TRAVELS WITH MR. BROWN Knopf, New York, 1940. [2] 1,795 no. cc. Issued in dustwrapper $75/200

165a: MARK TWAIN IN ERUPTION Harper & Bros., New York / London (1940). [1] 500 cc. On thin paper in flexible binding. Issued simultaneously with 158b, no priority. Issued without dustwrapper (Kevin MacDonnell Rare Books 11/91) $150.

165b: MARK TWAIN IN ERUPTION Harper & Bros., New York / London (1940). [1] 7,000 cc. Issued in dustwrapper. "K-P" on copyright page $100/150

166a: TOM SAWYER A DRAMA No publisher (Washington, D.C., 1940). [2] 25 cc. Large paper edition. 9 1/4" x 6 1/4". First printing of Twain's synopsis of *The Adventures of Tom Sawyer* $1,000.

166b: TOM SAWYER A DRAMA No publisher (Washington, D.C., 1940). [2] 100 cc. Small paper edition. Single sheet French folded to 4 pages. 7 7/8" x 5 3/8" $350.

167a: REPUBLICAN LETTERS... International Mark Twain Society, Webster Groves, Missouri, 1941. [0] Edited by Cyril Clemens. Red cloth. Assume issued without dustwrapper $200.

168a: AN UNPUBLISHED MARK TWAIN LETTER (American Literature), no place or date. [0] Single leaf folded to 4 pages. Reprinted from *American Literature*, Vol. 13, No. 4, January 1942 $250.

169a: MARK TWAIN'S LETTERS IN THE MUSCATINE JOURNAL... Mark Twain Association of America, Chicago, 1942. [2] 300 no. cc. Wraps $200.

170a: WASHINGTON IN 1868... International Mark Twain Society / T. Werner Laurie, Webster Groves, Missouri / London, 1943. [0] Red cloth. Assume without dustwrapper $200.

171a: A MURDER, A MYSTERY, AND A MARRIAGE... (Manuscript House, New York), 1945. [2] 16 cc. Wraps $750.

172a: SELECTED SHORT STORIES OF MARK TWAIN Armed Services Editions, New York, no date [circa 1945]. [] Wraps (James Dourgarian Books 2/89) $100.

173a: MARK TWAIN, BUSINESS MAN... Little, Brown & Co., Boston, 1946. [1] $50/150

174a: THE PORTABLE MARK TWAIN Viking Press, New York, 1946. [1] Edited by Bernard DeVoto $25/100

175a: THREE SKETCHES BY MARK TWAIN Overbrook Press, Stamford, Connecticut, 1946. [2] 100 cc. (Bromer Booksellers 10/92) $100.

175b: THREE SKETCHES BY MARK TWAIN Overbrook Press, Stamford, Connecticut, 1946. [] Wraps. (Macdonnell Rare Books 7/94) $50.

176a: ...LETTERS OF QUINTUS CURTIUS SNODGRASS... University Press, Southern Methodist University, Dallas, 1946. [0] $25/100

177a: MARK TWAIN AND HAWAII The Lakeside Press, Chicago, 1947. [2] 1,000 sgd no. cc. Issued in glassine dustwrapper. By Walter Francis Frear and signed by him. Includes much previously unpublished Twain material $200.

178a: MARK TWAIN IN THREE MOODS Friends of the Huntington Library, San Marino, 1948. [2] 1,200 no. cc $60.

179a: MARK TWAIN AT YOUR FINGERTIPS Beechurst Press, New York (1948). [] Edited by Caroline Thomas Harnsberger $35/150

180a: MARK TWAIN Printed for C. Charles Burlingame, Hartford, 1948. [] Illustrated by Kathryn Howard. Pictorial boards in glassine dustwrapper. Twain aphorisms as a Christmas greeting (ref.d) $40.

181a: MARK TWAIN TO MRS. FAIRBANKS... Huntington Library, San Marino, 1949. [1] $15/75

182a: THE LOVE LETTERS OF MARK TWAIN Harper & Bros., New York, 1949. [] Advance sample copy in stapled printed wraps. 20 pages. Prints a synopsis of the book as well as sample pages of text, including the text of some Mark Twain letters (Waiting For Godot Books 3/95) $100.

182b: THE LOVE LETTERS OF MARK TWAIN... Harper & Bros., New York, 1949. [2] 155 sgd no. cc. Twain signature has been in possession of publisher for 50 years. In dustwrapper and box $2,000/2,500

182c: THE LOVE LETTERS OF MARK TWAIN Harper & Bros., New York, 1949. [1] $30/150

183a: THE STORY OF A BAD LITTLE BOY THAT BORE A CHARMED LIFE (Allen Press, Hillsborough, 1949.) [] 75 cc (*American Book Prices Current* 1989). Also listed as *The Christmas Fireside,* assume same book $750.

184a: MARK TWAIN'S STRANGE DREAM Volcano House, Hawaii National Park (Hawaii), no date [circa 1950's?]. [] Stapled pictorial wraps. First separate edition (Waiting For Godot Books 2/95) $75.

185a: SOME THOUGHTS ON THE SCIENCE OF ONANISM... No publisher or place, 1952. [2] 100 cc. Single sheet French folded to 4 pages $300.

185b: SOME THOUGHTS ON THE SCIENCE OF ONANISM... (Privately printed), no place, 1964. [2] 1,000 cc. Wraps; 17.1 x 10.7 mm; rear outer wrapper has no printing (ref.b) $60.

185c: SOME THOUGHTS ON THE SCIENCE OF ONANISM... (Privately printed) no place, 1964. [2] 1,000 cc. Wraps; 17 x 11.4 mm; rear outer wrapper states: "FACSIMILE EDITION" $40.

186a: REPORT FROM PARADISE... Harper & Bros., New York, 1952. [1] Code letters "F-B" on copyright page $30/150

187a: MARK TWAIN'S FIRST STORY... Prairie Press (Iowa City, 1952). [0] Unprinted wraps in printed dustwrapper (Waiting For Godot Books 2/95) $60.

188a: MARK TWAIN TO UNCLE REMUS... The Library of Emory University, Atlanta, 1953. [0] Wraps $75.

189a: MARK TWAIN FOR YOUNG PEOPLE Whittier Books, New York, 1953. [] Compiled by Cyril Clemens, introduction by James Hilton. Assume no dustwrapper (ref.b) $60.

190a: MARK TWAIN'S LETTERS FROM HAWAII Appleton-Century, New York, 1956. [5] (Ref.b) $20/100

191a: AN OPEN LETTER TO COMMODORE VANDERBILT No publisher, Boston (1956). [2] 123 cc. Wraps. "One of very few with the blank handmade envelope." Inscribed by publisher, Frank C. Wilson (In Our Time 3/92) $300.

192a: MARK TWAIN OF THE ENTERPRISE... University of California Press, Berkeley, 1957. [] (Ref.b) $20/100

193a: MARK TWAIN: SAN FRANCISCO ... CORRESPONDENT Book Club of California, San Francisco, 1957. [2] 400 cc. Cloth backed boards, tissue dustwrapper (ref.b) $350.

194a: THE COMPLETE SHORT STORIES OF MARK TWAIN Hanover House, Garden City, 1957. [] (Ref.b.) Also Doubleday, Garden City (1957) (ref.d) $25/75

195a: MARK TWAIN'S JEST BOOK Mark Twain Journal, Kirkwood, Missouri, 1957. [] (Ref.b.) Pictorial wraps. Edited by Cyril Clemens, foreword by Carl Sandburg $100.

195b: MARK TWAIN'S JEST BOOK Mark Twain Journal, Kirkwood, Missouri, 1963. [] Second edition. Pictorial wraps (ref.b) $50.

195c: MARK TWAIN'S JEST BOOK Mark Twain Journal, Kirkwood, Missouri, 1965. [] Third edition with new material. Pictorial wraps (ref.b) $40.

196a: TRAVELLING WITH THE INNOCENTS ABROAD University of Oklahoma Press, Norman (1958). [] (Ref.b) $25/100

197a: CONCERNING CATS... Book Club of California, San Francisco, 1959. [2] 450 cc. Unprinted white dustwrapper (ref.b) $275/300

198a: THE ART, HUMOR & HUMANITY OF MARK TWAIN University of Oklahoma Press, Norman, 1959. [] (Ref.b) $25/100

199a: MARK TWAIN-HOWELLS LETTERS... Belknap Press of Harvard University, Cambridge, Massachusetts, 1960. [] Two volumes (ref.b) $40/100

199b: SELECTED MARK TWAIN-HOWELLS LETTERS... Belknap Press of Harvard University, Cambridge, Massachusetts, 1967. [] First one volume edition (ref.b) $10/50

200a: OUR MARK TWAIN. SOME WRITINGS ... Image of America, New York (1960). Assume issued without dustwrapper (Waiting For Godot) $40.

201a: MARK TWAIN AND THE GOVERNMENT Caxton Printers, Caldwell, Idaho, 1960. [] Selected and arranged by Svend Petersen $25/75

202a: MY DEAR BROTHER... The Berkeley Albion (Berkeley), 1961. [] Wraps. Letter to his brother Orion in either teal or buff wraps $60.

203a: MARK TWAIN WIT AND WISECRACKS Peter Pauper Press, Mt.Vernon, New York (1961). [] (Ref.b) $10/40

204a: MARK TWAIN'S LETTERS TO MARY Columbia University Press, New York, 1961. [0] Edited by Lewis Leary. (Ref.b) $25/75

205a: MARK TWAIN: LIFE AS I FIND IT Hanover House, Garden City (1961). [] (Ref.b) $10/50

206a: "AH SIN" A DRAMATIC WORK Book Club of California, San Francisco, 1961. [2] 450 cc. Issued in unprinted green dustwrapper. (Ref.b) $250/300

207a: MARK TWAIN ON THE ART OF WRITING Salisbury Club, Buffalo, 1961. [] $40.

208a: THE COMPLETE HUMOROUS SKETCHES AND TALES OF MARK TWAIN Hanover House, Garden City (1961). [] (Ref.b.) Also noted with publisher listed as Doubleday (Dorothy Goldberg Collection 8/95) $15/60

209a: MARK TWAIN ON THE DAMNED HUMAN RACE Hill & Wang, New York (1962). [] Cloth in dustwrapper (The Bookshop 8/92). Ref.b lists only wraps $15/50

209b: MARK TWAIN ON THE DAMNED HUMAN RACE Hill & Wang, New York (1962). [] Wraps. (Ref.b) $40.

210a: MARK TWAIN'S BEST: EIGHT SHORT STORIES... Scholastic Book Services, New York (1962). [] Wraps. (Ref.b) $35.

211a: MARK TWAIN, LETTERS FROM THE EARTH Harper & Row, New York (1962). [] Galley proofs. Spiral bound in house logo wraps (William Reese Co. 11/90) $300.

211b: MARK TWAIN, LETTERS FROM THE EARTH Harper & Row, New York (1962). [1] Also code letters "H-M" $25/100

212a: SELECTED SHORTER WRITINGS... Houghton Mifflin, Boston (1962). [] Wraps. (Ref.b) $35.

213a: MARK TWAIN'S SAN FRANCISCO McGraw-Hill, New York / Toronto / London (1963). [] (Ref.b) $25/75

214a: THE COMPLETE ESSAYS OF MARK TWAIN Doubleday & Co., Garden City, 1963. [] (Ref.b) $25/75

215a: AS MARK TWAIN SAYS (Printed for friends of May McNeer and Lynd Ward, no place (1963). [0] Wraps. 16 pages stapled $75.

216a: THE FORGOTTEN WRITINGS... Citadel Press, New York (1963). [] Wraps. (Ref.b) $40.

216b: THE FORGOTTEN WRITINGS... Philosophical Library, New York (1963). [] Blue cloth. Twain's writings for the *Buffalo Press*. Edited by Henry Duskis (The 19th Century Shop 2/90) $15/75

217a: SIMON WHEELER, DETECTIVE New York Public Library, New York, 1963. [2] 1,500 cc (ref.b, 1,000 cc ref.d). Green cloth, tissue dust-wrapper $75.

218a: JIM BAKER'S BLUEJAY YARN Orion Press, New York (1963). [] First edition thus, extracted from *A Tramp Abroad* (Macdonnell Rare Books 11/95) $10/50

219a: NOTICE. TO THE NEXT BURGLAR Mark Twain Memorial, Hartford, no date [1960's?]. [0] Broadside, single sheet printed in red, blue, yellow and black, measuring about 9½ x 12". First? Separate appearance. (Waiting For Godot Books 2/95) $50.

220a: THE COMPLETE NOVELS... Doubleday & Co., Garden City, 1964. [1] Two volumes. (Ref.b) $50/100

221a: MARK TWAIN: A CURE FOR THE BLUES Charles Tuttle Co., Rutland, Vermont (1964). [] (Ref.b) $25/75

222a: THE ADVENTURES OF COLONEL SELLERS... Doubleday & Co., Garden City, 1965. [1] $25/75

222b: THE ADVENTURES OF COLONEL SELLERS Chatto & Windus, London, 1966. [0] $25/75

223a: SUZY AND MARK TWAINS' FAMILY DIALOGUES Harper, New York (1965). [] (Ref.b) $15/75

224a: MARK TWAIN'S LETTERS FROM HAWAII Appleton-Century, New York (1966). [1] (Ref.c) $25/100

224b: MARK TWAIN'S LETTERS FROM HAWAII Chatto & Windus, London, 1967. [] (Dinkytown 10/91) $20/75

225a: A CURTAIN LECTURE CONCERNING SKATING Donald M. Kunde, Denver, 1967. [2] 50 sgd no. cc. Signed by Kunde. Special presentation copy. Issued without dustwrapper? $150.

225b: A CURTAIN LECTURE CONCERNING SKATING Donald M. Kunde, Denver, 1967. [2] 265 no. cc. Issued without dustwrapper $75.

225c: A CURTAIN LECTURE CONCERNING SKATING AND MRS. MARK TWAIN'S SHOE Baldwin, Denver, 1986. [] Second edition with new material. Wraps? (Astoria Books 12/89) $40.

226a: MARK TWAIN'S WHICH WAS THE DREAM? + University of California Press, Berkeley, California, 1967. [0] $25/75

227a: MARK TWAIN'S SATIRES & BURLESQUES University of California Press, Berkeley / Los Angeles, 1967. [0] $25/75

228a: A TREASURY OF MARK TWAIN... Hallmark Editions, Kansas City (1967). [] Issued without dustwrapper? $30.

229a: MARK TWAIN'S LETTERS TO HIS PUBLISHERS, 1867-1894 University of California Press, Berkeley, 1967. [] (Macdonnell Rare Books 11/95) $25/75

230a: THE WAR PRAYER St. Crispin / Harper & Row (New York, 1968). [0] First separate edition. Illustrated by John Groth $25/100

231a: MARK TWAIN'S CORRESPONDENCE WITH HENRY HUTTLESTON ROGERS 1893-1909 University of California Press, Berkeley / Los Angeles, 1969. [] $25/75

232a: CLEMENS OF THE CALL: MARK TWAIN IN SAN FRANCISCO University of California Press, Berkeley, 1969. [] Edited by E.M. Branch (William Reese Co. 9/89) $25/75

233a: MARK TWAIN'S HANNIBAL, HUCK & TOM University of California Press, Berkeley / Los Angeles, 1969. [] (Ref.b) $25/75

234a: MARK TWAIN'S THE MYSTERIOUS STRANGER MANUSCRIPTS University of California, Berkeley / Los Angeles, 1969. [] $25/75

235a: MARK TWAIN'S LETTERS TO THE ROGERS FAMILY Reynolds-De Walt (New Bedford, Mass.), 1970. [] Tissue dustwrapper (ref.b) $75.

236a: MAN IS THE ONLY ANIMAL THAT BLUSHES... Random House (New York, 1970). [] (Ref.b) $25/75

237a: AN INGLORIOUS PEACE IS BETTER THAN A DISHONORABLE WAR! Wheeler Action Committee, Berkeley (1970). [] Orange pictorial wraps. A collection of Twain's anti-war statements (Macdonnell Rare Books 8/95) $75.

238a: MARK TWAIN ON MAN AND BEAST Lawrence & Co., New York / Westport, Connecticut, 1972. [] Wraps (ref.b) $40.

239a: THE GREAT LANDSLIDE CASE University of California Press, no place, 1972. [] Wraps (ref.c) $60.

240a: MARK TWAIN'S FABLES OF MAN University of California Press, Berkeley / Los Angeles, 1972. [] $25/75

241a: A MARK TWAIN TURNOVER: ADVICE FOR GOOD LITTLE GIRLS with MARK TWAIN AND THE DEVIL Robt. E. Massmann, New Britain, Connecticut, 1972. [2] 250 cc. 1 1/2" square miniature book in slipcase $175.

242a: THE MOST PRODIGIOUS ASSET OF A COUNTRY Folger Library, Washington, D.C., 1972. [0] Wraps. Reproduces a previously unpublished five page hand corrected section of Twain's *Autobiography*. Issued in folded wraps. A keepsake for an exhibition (Pepper & Stern 1987) $75.

243a: EVERYONE'S MARK TWAIN A. S. Barnes / Thomas Yoseloff, South Brunswick, New Jersey / New York / London (1972). [] Issued without dustwrapper (ref.b) $50.

244a: A PEN WARMED-UP IN HELL Harper & Row, New York / Evanston / San Francisco / London (1972). [] (Ref.b) $12/60

245a: MARK TWAIN AND THE THREE R'S... Bobbs-Merrill, Indiana and New York (1973). [] Wraps. (Sylvester & Orphanos) $35.

246a: MARK TWAIN TO GENERAL GRANT (Kent State University, Ohio, 1973.) [2] 200 cc. Wraps. Facsimile of a letter. Single page folded to 4 pages (Waiting For Godot 2/91) $75.

247a: WHAT IS MAN? AND OTHER PHILOSOPHICAL WRITINGS University of California Press, Berkeley, 1973. [] (Macdonnell Rare Books 11/95) $12/60

248a: MARK TWAIN'S NOTEBOOKS & JOURNALS VOLUME I (1855-1873) University of California Press, Berkeley / Los Angeles, 1975. [] $12/60

249a: MARK TWAIN'S NOTEBOOKS & JOURNALS VOLUME II (1877-1883) University of California Press, Berkeley / Los Angeles, 1975. [] $12/60

250a: MARK TWAIN'S NOTEBOOKS & JOURNALS VOLUME III (1883-1891) University of California Press, Berkeley / Los Angeles, 1979. [] $12/60

251a: MARK TWAIN SPEAKING University of Iowa Press (Iowa City, 1976). [] (Ref.b) $12/60

252a: THE HIGHER ANIMALS... A MARK TWAIN BESTIARY Thomas Y. Crowell, New York (1976). [] (Ref.b) $10/50

253a: TALE OF THE CALIPH STORK Windhover Press, Iowa City, 1976. [] Proof in cloth marked "pp" (printer's proof). Twain was translator (James S. Jaffe 7/96) $450.

253b: TALE OF THE CALIPH STORK Windhover Press, Iowa City, 1976. [] Cloth. Issued without dustwrapper? Translated by Twain $35/75

254a: THE UNABRIDGED MARK TWAIN Running Press, Philadelphia (1976). [] Opening remarks by Kurt Vonnegut, Jr. (Ref.b) $25/75

254b: THE UNABRIDGED MARK TWAIN Running Press, Philadelphia (1979). [] Volume II $10/50

255a: THE COMIC MARK TWAIN READER Doubleday & Co., Garden City, 1977. [] (Ref.b) $10/50

256a: MARK TWAIN SPEAKS FOR HIMSELF Perdue University Press, West Lafayette, 1978. [] (Ref.b) $10/50

257a: THE ILLUSTRATED MARK TWAIN New Orchard Editions, Poole [Dorset], no date [but after 1978]. [] (Dorothy Goldberg Collection 8/95) $25/75

258a: EARLY TALES AND SKETCHES VOLUME I (1851-1864) University of California Press, Berkeley / Los Angeles / London, 1979. [] (See Volume II below) $10/50

259a: JIM WOLF AND THE CATS Hillside Press, Buffalo, 1979. [2] 225 cc. Miniature book in slipcase (ref.b), but we've had three copies and none had a slipcase $60/75

260a: THE LATE BENJAMIN FRANKLIN (Privately printed, San Francisco, 1980.) [2] 125 cc. Wraps. Printed by Lawton Kennedy (Geo. Houle 1985) $100.

261a: MARK TWAIN: SOCIAL CRITIC FOR THE 80's AT Press, San Francisco, 1980. [] $10/50

262a: THE DEVIL'S RACE TRACK : MARK TWAIN'S GREAT DARK WRITING University of California, Berkeley (1980). [] $10/50

262b: THE DEVIL'S RACE TRACK : MARK TWAIN'S GREAT DARK WRITING University of California, Berkeley (1980). [] Wraps $30.

263a: A MARK TWAIN SAMPLER (Lime Rock Press, Salisbury, Connecticut, 1980.) [2] 1,001 cc. Wraps. Illustrated and signed by Catryna Ten Eyck. A miniature book (3x2 1/2") $50.

264a: ADAM'S DIARY (Lime Rock Press, Salisbury, Connecticut, 1980.) [2] 25 cc. Published @$195. $250.

265a: EARLY TALES AND SKETCHES VOLUME II (1864-1865) University of California Press, Berkeley / Los Angeles / London, 1981. [] $10/50

266a: THE NEW WAR-SCARE Neville Publishing, Santa Barbara, 1981. [2] 15 lettered copies with original clipped signature, in full leather $1,750.

266b: THE NEW WAR-SCARE Neville Publishing, Santa Barbara, 1981. [2] 100 no. cc $125.

267a: MARK TWAIN ON THE DAMNED HUMAN RACE Hill/Wang, New York (1981). [] Wraps $30.

268a: WAPPING ALICE Bancroft Library, Berkeley, 1981. [] Wraps $50.

269a: POOR LITTLE STEPHEN GIRARD Schocken Books, New York, 1981. [] (Dorothy Goldberg Collection 8/95) $15/50

270a: A LETTER FROM MARK TWAIN CONCERNING THE PAIGE COMPOSITOR Vance Gerry, Glendale, 1982. [2] 200 cc. Wraps (Pepper & Stern Cat 22) $50.

271a: THE SELECTED LETTERS OF MARK TWAIN Harper, New York (1982). [3] Also states "First Edition." Edited and introduction by Charles Neider. Maroon cloth $10/50

272a: HOW I EDITED AN AGRICULTURAL PAPER Scot Free Press, Overland Park, Kansas, 1982.

[2] 270 sgd no. cc (signed by the artist, Duane C. Scott). Brown cloth with black leather spine (Dorothy Goldberg Collection 8/95) $100.

273a: MARK TWAIN'S RUBAIYAT Jenkins / Karpeles, Austin / Santa Barbara (1983). [2] 20 cc. Issued in green quarter morocco (Kevin MacDonnell Rare Books 1987) $200.

273b: MARK TWAIN'S RUBAIYAT Jenkins / Karpeles, Austin / Santa Barbara (1983). [2] 50 editorial out-of-series copies $150.

273c: MARK TWAIN'S RUBAIYAT Jenkins / Karpeles, Austin / Santa Barbara (1983). [2] 600 no. cc of which about 50 lost in fire $125.

274a: SELECTED WRITINGS OF AN AMERICAN SKEPTIC Prometheus Books, New York (1983). [] $10/50

275a: MARK TWAIN'S WEST Lakeside Press, Chicago, 1983. [] Brown cloth. Selection of autobiographical writings. Issued without dustwrapper in Lakeside's Christmas series (The 19th Century Shop 2/90) $50.

276a: SAMUEL LANGHORNE CLEMENS, PRINTER... (Privately Printed, Lafayette, California, 1984.) [] Wraps. In envelope $50.

277a: THE HIDDEN MARK TWAIN... Greenwich House, New York, 1984. [] (Dorothy Goldberg Collection 8/95) $15/50

278a: MARK TWAIN COMPLIMENTS THE PRESIDENT'S WIFE Anne & David Bromer (Boston), 1984. [2] 50 no. cc. Miniature book (Bert Babcock Cat. 47) $200.

278b: MARK TWAIN COMPLIMENTS THE PRESIDENT'S WIFE Anne & David Bromer (Boston), 1984. [2] 200 no. cc. Bound in cloth. Miniature book $100.

279a: PLYMOUTH ROCK AND THE PILGRIMS AND OTHER SALUTARY PLATFORM OPINIONS Harper, New York (1984). [3] Also states "First Edition." Selected and edited by Charles Neider $10/50

280a: THE GRANGERFORD-SHEPHERDSON FEUD Friends of the Bancroft Library, 1985. [] Wraps. Issued as Keepsake No. 33. Not For Sale $60.

281a: CONCERNING THE JEWS Ronning Press, Philadelphia (1985). [] Pictorial wraps (ref.d) $40.

282a: MARK TWAIN AT HIS BEST ... Doubleday, Garden City, 1986. [] Selected, edited and introduction by Charles Neider (ref.d) $8/40

283a: TWO STORIES Hillside Press, Buffalo, 1986. [2] 300 no. cc. First separate printing. Miniature book (Waiting For Godot 6/89) $75.

284a: UNION CATALOG OF CLEMENS LETTERS University of California, Berkeley (1986). [] Issued without dustwrapper. A Union list of every known Twain letter (over 9,000) listed by recipient, date, place first line of text and source or location. A pocket at rear contains microfiche with place list, date list, source list, etc. (Macdonnell Rare Books Cat. 11 11/94) $75.

285a: MARK TWAIN'S RAFT PASSAGE Sunflower Press, Mill Valley, California, 1986. [2] 75 sgd no. cc (signed by the designer/ printer, Carol Cunningham). From *Life on the Mississippi*. Full leather (Dorothy Goldberg Collection 8/95) $175.

286a: THE OUTRAGEOUS MARK TWAIN Doubleday, Garden City, 1987. [] Selected, edited and introduction by Charles Neider (ref.d) $8/40

287a: A CAT TALE Ashton Scholastic, Sydney, 1987. [] Wraps $35.

288a: THE WIT AND WISDOM OF MARK TWAIN Harper, New York (1987). [] Edited by Alex Ayres (ref.d) $8/40

289a: LEGEND OF SAGENFELD P.I.C., New York, 1987. [] $15/50

289b: LEGEND OF SAGENFELD P.I.C. (Sydney, 1987). [1] Issued in dustwrapper (Dorothy Goldberg Collection 8/95) $15/50

290a: MARK TWAIN'S LETTERS *Volume 1: 1853-1866* University of California Press, 1988. [] $8/40

291a: THE OLD-TIME PRINTER Xavier Press, Baltimore, 1988. [2] 175 sgd no. cc (signed by the printer, Francis X. Harrigan). Brown cloth. With two type-slugs in pockets inside back cover (Dorothy Goldberg Collection 8/95) $200.

292a: MARK TWAIN'S NICODEMUS DODGE Ash Ranch Press, San Diego, 1989. [2] 26 ltr cc signed by Don Hildreth, the illustrator. Deluxe editions with blue bonded leather spine in slipcase. Story from *A Tramp Abroad* (Wilder Books 11/91) $300.

293a: MARK TWAIN'S AQUARIUM *The Samuel Clemens Angelfish Correspondence 1905-1910* University of Georgia, Athens (1991). [3] Edited by John Cooley $7/35

294a: COLLECTED TALES, SKETCHES, SPEECHES & ESSAYS Library of America, New York, 1992. [] 2 volumes. Advance reading copy. Volume one: bound signatures laid into card covers. Volume two: unbound signatures laid into card covers $75.

295a: COLLECTED TALES, SKETCHES, SPEECHES & ESSAYS 1852-1890 Library of America, New York, 1992. [] 2 volumes $35/75

296a: MARK TWAIN'S WEAPONS OF SATIRE *Anti-Imperialist Writings on the Philippine-American War* Syracuse University Press, Syracuse, 1992. [] (Published July 1992 @ $32.50) $10/40

297a: MARK TWAIN'S LETTERS *Volume 4: 1870-1871*. University of California Press, Berkeley, 1995. [] (Macdonnell Rare Books 4/86) $10/50

298a: THE BIBLE ACCORDING TO MARK TWAIN University of Georgia Press, Athens, Georgia / London, 1995. [] (Dorothy Goldberg Collection 8/95) $10/35

299a: LEGEND OF THE CASTLES (John and Jo Fleming, New York, 1995.) [] Blue wraps. Privately printed. Christmas greeting consisting of a chapter from *A Tramp Abroad* (MacDonnell Rare Books 5/97) $35.

300a: MARK TWAIN'S LETTERS *Volume 5: 1872-1873* University of California Press, Berkeley, 1997. [] Published @ $60.00

301a: THE OXFORD MARK TWAIN Oxford University Press, New York, 1997? [2] 240 sets (each volume signed by the author of the introduction and the author of the afterword, with the exception of James Wilson and Pascal Covici, Jr. Who died before the set could be completed). 29 volumes. Deluxe Signed Edition. Issued in dustwrappers. Issued @ $1,000.

301b: THE OXFORD MARK TWAIN Oxford University Press, New York, 1997? [] Deluxe Edition. 29 volumes. Printed on acid-free paper, smythe sewn binding, library grade cloth covers, colored endpapers. Issued in dustwrappers. Issued @ $495

301c: THE OXFORD MARK TWAIN Oxford University Press, New York, 1997? [] Standard Edition. 29 volumes. Issued in dustwrappers. Issued @ $395

JOHN UPDIKE

Updike was born in 1932 in Shillington, Pennsylvania. He graduated from Harvard in 1954 and was a staff reporter on *The New Yorker* from 1955 to 1957. He won the National Book Award in 1964 and Pulitzer Prizes in 1982 and 1991. One of our best and certainly one of our most prolific authors.

Unless noted all entries were based on reference "a" up to 1980 and reference "b" until early 1986 which only left 125 further entries to bring it up to 1998.

REFERENCES:

(a) Roberts, Ray A. JOHN UPDIKE: A Bibliographic Checklist in *American Book Collector*, January/February. 1980.

(b) FIRST PRINTINGS OF AMERICAN AUTHORS. Volume 5. Detroit: Gale Research (1987).

(c) Inventory or dealer catalogs.

001a: THE CARPENTERED HEN *and Other Tame Creatures* Harper, New York (1958). [1] 2,000 cc (Fine Books Co. #31). First issue dustwrapper mentions "2 children" $150/750

001b: THE CARPENTERED HEN *and Other Tame Creatures* Harper, New York (1958). [1] 2,000 cc. Second issue with "4 children" $150/350

001c: HOPING FOR A HOOPOE Gollancz, London, 1959. [0] New title and additional "Author's Note" $25/125

001d: THE CARPENTERED HEN *and Other Tame Creatures* Knopf, New York, 1982. [] Uncorrected proof in green wraps (Waiting For Godot 2/95) $100.

001e: THE CARPENTERED HEN *and Other Tame Creatures* Knopf, New York, 1982. [1] "First Knopf edition." Revised and new foreword (ref.b) $8/40

002a: THE POORHOUSE FAIR Knopf, New York, 1959. [1] 5,000 cc. (Note: the second printing dustwrapper has a biographical note as second paragraph on back flap which is not on first printing dustwrapper) $100/500

002b: THE POORHOUSE FAIR Gollancz, London, 1959. [0] $75/350

002c: THE POORHOUSE FAIR and RABBIT, RUN Modern Library, New York (1965). [1] New foreword dated October 1964 $25/75

002d: THE POORHOUSE FAIR Knopf, New York, 1977. [0] "New Edition published Feb. 1977." Contains a 14 page "Introduction to the 1977 Edition" $10/50

003a: THE SAME DOOR Knopf, New York, 1959. [1] First dustwrapper has "Also by John Updike *The Poorhouse Fair* (later has "The novels and Stories of John Updike" listing through *The Centaur*) $75/450

003b: THE SAME DOOR Deutsch (London, 1962). [1] $60/300

004a: RABBIT, RUN Knopf, New York, 1960. [1] 10,000 cc. Top edge stained. Also noted without top edge stained, assume remainder? The first edition dustwrapper has 16-line blurb (unsigned, but by Updike) on front flap. Later printing dustwrappers have blurb by Richard Gilman $150/750

004b: RABBIT, RUN Deutsch (London, 1961). [1] $50/250

004c: RABBIT, RUN Penguin (Harmondsworth, 1964). [0] "This revised edition published ... 1964." Wraps $50.

004d: See also 002c

004e: RABBIT, RUN Franklin Library, Franklin Center, 1977. [2] 12,619 copies. Limited signed edition. Issued in full leather. Contains a "Special Message..." $125.

005a: THE FIRST AND SOUTH CONGREGATIONAL CHURCH OF IPSWICH, MASSACHUSETTS (Ipswich, 1961.) [0] Folded leaf (ref.b) $600.

006a: PIGEON FEATHERS *and Other Stories* Knopf, New York, 1962. [1] $50/250

006b: PIGEON FEATHERS *and Other Stories* Deutsch (London, 1962). [1] $30/150

006c: PIGEON FEATHERS *and Other Stories* Franklin Library, Franklin Center, 1981. [2] "Limited Edition." Issued in full leather $75.

007a: THE MAGIC FLUTE Knopf, New York (1962). [0] Illustrations by Warren Chappell. Pictorial mustard cloth. Issued in dustwrapper $500/1,000

007b: THE MAGIC FLUTE Knopf, New York (1962). [] Pictorial cloth. Issued without dustwrapper $500.

007c: THE MAGIC FLUTE Deutsch & Ward (London, 1964). [1] $150/450

008a: THE CENTAUR Knopf, New York, 1963. [] Uncorrected galley proofs. Issued in spiral bound plain wraps (William Reese Co. 5/89) $2,000.

008b: THE CENTAUR Knopf, New York, 1963. [1] National Book Award for 1964 $50/250

008c: THE CENTAUR Deutsch (London, 1963). [1] $30/150

009a: TELEPHONE POLES *and Other Poems* Knopf, New York, 1963. [] Uncorrected galley proofs. Issued in spiral bound plain wraps with typed label (William Reese 5/89) $1,500.

009b: TELEPHONE POLES *and Other Poems* Knopf, New York, 1963. [1] $25/125

009c: TELEPHONE POLES *and Other Poems* Deutsch (London, 1964). [1] $15/75

010a: OLINGER STORIES Vintage Books, New York (1964). [1] Wraps $100.

011a: THE RING Knopf, New York (1964). [0] $300/600

011b: THE RING Knopf, New York (1964). [0] Pictorial cloth. Issued without dustwrapper $350.

011c: THE RING Knopf, New York (1964). [0] "Gibraltar Library binding" is different from 011b (Waiting For Godot 4/90). Issued without dustwrapper $150.

012a: ASSORTED PROSE Knopf, New York, 1965. [] Uncorrected galley proofs. Issued in spiral bound printed wraps (William Reese Co. 5/89) $1,500.

012b: ASSORTED PROSE Knopf, New York, 1965. [1] With tipped-in page signed by Updike $175/250

012c: ASSORTED PROSE Knopf, New York, 1965. [1] 10,000 cc (both a & b) $25/125

012d: ASSORTED PROSE Deutsch (London, 1965). [1] First issue dustwrapper priced 25 shillings (Alphabet Books 11/91) $25/100

013a: OF THE FARM Knopf, New York, 1965. [] Uncorrected galley proofs in spiral bound printed wraps which was reportedly extensively revised for published version (William Reese Co. 5/89) $1,750.

013b: OF THE FARM Knopf, New York, 1965. [1] 15,000 cc $25/125

013c: OF THE FARM Deutsch (London, 1966). [1] $15/75

014a: A CHILD'S CALENDAR Knopf, New York (1965). [0] $150/300

014b: A CHILD'S CALENDAR Knopf, New York (1965). [0] "Gibraltar Library Binding." Issued without dustwrapper in two variants but not clear what the difference was (Waiting For Godot 4/90) $125.

015a: DOG'S DEATH Adams House (Cambridge), 1965. [2] 100 sgd no. cc. Broadside $1,500.

016a: VERSE ... Crest Books, Greenwich (1965). [1] Wraps $60.

017a: THE MUSIC SCHOOL Knopf, New York, 1966. [] Uncorrected galley proof. Issued in spiral bound printed wraps (William Reese Co. 5/89) $1,500.

017b: THE MUSIC SCHOOL Knopf, New York, 1966. [1] 10,000 cc (a, b & c). P.46:15 starts "The state..." $200/300

017c: THE MUSIC SCHOOL Knopf, New York, 1966. [1] P.46:15 starts "The King..." on tipped-in leaf $75/150

017d: THE MUSIC SCHOOL Knopf, New York, 1966. [1] P.46:15 starts "The King..." on integral leaf $15/75

017e: THE MUSIC SCHOOL Deutsch (London, 1967). [1] $15/75

018a: COUPLES Knopf, New York, 1968. [1] 25,000 cc $25/125

018b: COUPLES Deutsch (London, 1968). [1] $15/75

019a: BATH AFTER SAILING Country Squire's Books, Stevenson, Connecticut (1968). [2] 125 sgd no. cc. Issued in stiff wraps $900.

020a: THE ANGELS King & Queen Press, Pensacola, 1968. [2] 150 cc. Sewn in wraps. Issued in mailing envelope $800.

021a: THREE TEXTS FOR EARLY IPSWICH *A Pageant* 17th Century Day Committee, Ipswich, Massachusetts, 1968. [2] 50 sgd no. cc $750.

021b: THREE TEXTS FOR EARLY IPSWICH *A Pageant* 17th Century Day Committee, Ipswich, Massachusetts, 1968. [2] 950 cc $100.

021c: THREE TEXTS FOR EARLY IPSWICH *A Pageant* 17th Century Day Committee, Ipswich, Massachusetts, 1968. [2] 26 sgd ltr cc. Issued in cloth with glassine dustwrapper. (Bound and distributed in 1978.) Also four "Author's Presentation copies" $1,000.

022a: ON MEETING AUTHORS Wickford Press, Newburyport, 1968. [2] 250 no. cc. Wraps $750.

023a: DECEMBER (Edward Naumberg, Jr., New York, 1968.) [0] 100 cc. Uncolored Christmas card. Issued in plain envelope $600.

023b: DECEMBER (Edward Naumberg, Jr., New York, 1968.) [0] Colored red or green Christmas card. Issued in plain envelope $400.

024a: MIDPOINT *and Other Poems* Knopf, New York, 1969. [2] 350 sgd no. cc. Issued in dustwrapper (differs from trade edition). In slipcase $175/250

024b: MIDPOINT *and Other Poems* Knopf, New York, 1969. [1] Preceded 024a by a few weeks (Alphabet Books 11/91) $15/75

024c: MIDPOINT *and Other Poems* Deutsch (London, 1969). [1] $10/50

025a: BOTTOM'S DREAM. *Adapted from William Shakespeare's A Midsummer Night's Dream* Knopf, New York (1969). [0] Blue pictorial cloth. Issued in dustwrapper $150/300

025b: BOTTOM'S DREAM... Knopf, New York (1969). [0] Pictorial cloth. Issued without dustwrapper $150.

026a: PENS AND NEEDLES Gambit, Boston, 1969. [2] 300 sgd no. cc. Literary caricatures by David Levine. Selected and introduction by Updike. Signed by both $250/350

026b: PENS AND NEEDLES Gambit, Boston, 1969. [] Trade edition $25/75

027a: THE DANCE OF THE SOLIDS (Scientific America, New York, 1969.) [0] 6,200 cc. Wraps. Was to be used as a Season's Greeting (along with W.H. Auden's *A New Year Greeting.* Both in cardboard sleeve which has "Seasons Greetings from *Scientific American*" or "From----" $1,000.

028a: BECH: A BOOK Knopf, New York, 1970. [] Long folded original galley proofs (William Reese Co. 5/89) $1,250.

028b: BECH: A BOOK Knopf, New York, 1970. [2] 500 sgd no. cc. Issued in dustwrapper (differs from trade edition). In slipcase $75/125

028c: BECH: A BOOK Knopf, New York, 1970. [1] $10/50

028d: BECH: A BOOK Deutsch (London, 1970). [] $10/50

029a: DIE NEVEN HEILIGEN... Fabrik Biberach an der Riss (1970). [0] Wraps. Single leaf folded for use as holiday greeting (ref.b) $250.

030a: RABBIT REDUX Knopf, New York, 1971. [] Uncorrected proof. Issued in cream colored wraps (Waverley Books 5/88) $1,000.

030b: RABBIT REDUX Knopf, New York, 1971. [2] 350 sgd no cc. Issued in acetate dustwrapper. In slipcase $275/350

030c: RABBIT REDUX Knopf, New York, 1971. [1] $12/60

030d: RABBIT REDUX Deutsch (London, 1972). [1] $10/50

030e: RABBIT REDUX Franklin Library, Franklin Center, 1979. [2] Signed limited edition. Issued in full leather. (Also another issued in 1981?) $100.

031a: A CONVERSATION WITH JOHN UPDIKE (Union College, Schenec-tady, 1971) [0] Wraps. Edited by Frank Gado $75.

032a: THE INDIAN Blue Cloud Abbey, Marvin, South Dakoda (book cover), no date [1971]. [0] Wraps (ref.b and c) $100.

033a: STOLEN APPLES Doubleday & Co., Garden City, New York 1971. [] Book by Yevtushenko; English adaptation by Updike (Bev Chaney, Jr. 1/95) $15/75

034a: SEVENTY POEMS Penguin (Harmondsworth, 1972). [1] Wraps. "Published in Penguin Books 1972" $60.

035a: MUSEUMS AND WOMEN *and Other Stories* Knopf, New York, 1972. [2] 350 sgd no. cc. Issued in dustwrapper (differs from trade edition). In slipcase $175/250

035b: MUSEUMS AND WOMEN *and Other Stories* Knopf, New York, 1972. [1] $10/50

035c: MUSEUMS AND WOMEN *and Other Stories* Deutsch (London, 1973) [] $10/50

036a: WARM WINE AN IDYLL Albondocani Press, New York, 1973. [2] 26 sgd ltr cc. Wraps $600.

036b: WARM WINE AN IDYLL Albondocani Press, New York, 1973. [2] 250 sgd no. cc. Wraps $175.

037a: PHI BETA KAPPA POEM Harvard, Cambridge, 1973. [0] Seven mimeographed sheets. Stapled $175.

038a: A GOOD PLACE... Aloe (New York), 1973. [2] 26 sgd ltr cc. Wraps $600.

038b: A GOOD PLACE... Aloe (New York), 1973. [2] 100 sgd no. cc. Wraps $450.

039a: SIX POEMS Aloe (New York), 1973. [2] 26 sgd ltr cc. Wraps $600.

039b: SIX POEMS Aloe (New York), 1973. [2] 100 sgd no. cc. Wraps $450.

040a: BUCHANAN DYING Knopf, New York, 1974. [1] $15/75

040b: BUCHANAN DYING Deutsch (London, 1974). [1] $10/50

040c: BUCHANAN DYING San Diego State University (San Diego), 1977. [0] 8 1/2" x 11" sheets in printed brown covers with program bound in back. Last page of play notes "...printed by ... in Limited Edition for ..." Play produced in March 1977. Both ref. a & b state "1976," but copy in inventory states "1977" which would seem to be correct as it was produced then. Acting edition adapted by Robert McCoy and ref.a states approximately 36 copies were for sale $500.

041a: QUERY (Albondocani Press and Ampersand Books, New York, 1974.) [0] 75 cc. First issue with illustration upside-down was reportedly suppressed (Phoenix Bookshop 8/88) $300.

041b: QUERY (Albondocani Press and Ampersand Books, New York, 1974.) [0] Wraps. Holiday greeting with publishers' names on 160 copies and without names and title in lower left hand corner on 260 copies $100.

042a: CUNTS Hallman, New York (1974). [2] 26 sgd ltr cc. Boards $750.

042b: CUNTS Hallman, New York (1974). [2] 250 sgd no. cc. Boards. There were also 15 extra copies reserved for the editor and signed by Updike (George Robert Minkoff 1/90) $350.

042c: "CUNTS" in *The New York Quarterly* Summer, 1973. [2] 26 sgd ltr cc with limitation notice and signature on page 65 $125.

042d: "CUNTS" in *The New York Quarterly* Summer, 1973. [2] 457 sgd no. cc with limitation notice and signature on page 65 $75.

043a: A MONTH OF SUNDAYS Knopf, New York, 1975. [] Uncorrected proof in narrow blue wraps (Waiting For Godot 4/90) $400.

043b: A MONTH OF SUNDAYS Knopf, New York, 1975. [2] 450 sgd no. cc. Issued in dustwrapper (differs from trade edition). In slipcase $150/200

043c: A MONTH OF SUNDAYS Knopf, New York, 1975. [1] $8/40

043d: A MONTH OF SUNDAYS Deutsch (London, 1975). [1] $8/40

044a: SUNDAY IN BOSTON (Rook Press, Derry, Pennsylvania, 1975.) [2] 100 sgd no. cc. Illustrated by Wm. Lint. Broadside (signed by both) $200.

044b: SUNDAY IN BOSTON (Rook Press, Derry, Pennsylvania, 1975.) [2] 100 no. cc (101-200). Not signed or illustrated $75.

044c: SUNDAY IN BOSTON (Rook Press, Derry, Pennsylvania, 1975.) [2] 100 sgd no. cc (201-300). Signed by Updike, not illustrated $100.

045a: FLIRT (International Poetry Forum, Pittsburgh, 1975.) [0] about 500 cc. Broadside issued on white, blue, salmon and purple paper (no priority) $250.

046a: PICKED-UP PIECES Knopf, New York, 1975. [] Uncorrected proof in narrow blue wraps (Waiting For Godot 6/89) $450.

046b: PICKED-UP PIECES Knopf, New York, 1975. [2] 250 sgd no. cc. Issued in dustwrapper (differs from trade dustwrapper). In slipcase $275/350

046c: PICKED-UP PIECES Knopf, New York, 1975. [1] $12/60

046d: PICKED-UP PIECES Deutsch (London, 1976). [1] $10/50

047a: SCENIC (Roxburghe Club, San Francisco, 1976.) [] 150 cc. Broadside $300.

048a: COUPLES *A Short Story* Halty Ferguson, Cambridge, 1976. [2] 26 sgd ltr cc. Wraps $500.

048b: COUPLES *A Short Story* Halty Ferguson, Cambridge, 1976. [2] 250 sgd no. cc. Wraps $175.

049a: MARRY ME *A Romance* Franklin Library, Franklin Center, 1976. [2] 12,646 cc. "Limited Edition." With two-page introductory note by

Updike. Illustrated by Barbara Fox. (Black Sun #71 offered a cloth bound copy imprinted with "Record and Reference Copy" on spine and front). Issued in full leather $75.

049b: MARRY ME *A Romance* Knopf, New York, 1976. [2] 300 sgd no. cc. Issued in dustwrapper (differs from trade dustwrapper). In slipcase $125/200

049c: MARRY ME *A Romance* Knopf, New York, 1976. [1] Dustwrapper has code "394-40856-X" on back panel (BOMC dustwrapper does not have numbers) $10/50

049d: MARRY ME *A Romance* Deutsch (London, 1977). [1] $8/40

050a: RAINING AT MAGENS BAY John Updike Newsletter (Northridge, 1977). [2] 26 ltr cc. Broadside $250.

050b: RAINING AT MAGENS BAY John Updike Newsletter (Northridge, 1977). [2] 200 no. cc. Broadside $100.

051a: TOSSING AND TURNING *Poems* Knopf, New York, 1977. [] Uncorrected proof in tan wraps (Old New York Book Shop 5/98) $125.

051b: TOSSING AND TURNING *Poems* Knopf, New York, 1977. [1] $20/100

051c: TOSSING AND TURNING *Poems* Deutsch (London, 1977). [1] $12/60

052a: HUB FANS BID KID ADIEU Lord John Press, Northridge, 1977. [2] 26 sgd ltr cc. Issued without dustwrapper $600.

052b: HUB FANS BID KID ADIEU Lord John Press, Northridge, 1977. [2] 350 sgd no. cc. Preface is new. Issued without dustwrapper $200.

053a: FROM THE JOURNAL OF A LEPER Lord John Press, Northridge, 1978. [2] 26 sgd ltr cc. Black cloth spine. Issued without dustwrapper (also 9 over-run copies with individual names) $500.

053b: FROM THE JOURNAL OF A LEPER Lord John Press, Northridge, 1978. [2] 300 sgd no. cc. Issued without dustwrapper. (Red cloth spine) $150.

054a: THE COUP Knopf, New York, 1978. [2] 350 sgd no. cc. Issued in dustwrapper (which differs from trade dustwrapper). In slipcase $175/250

054b: THE COUP Knopf, New York, 1978. [1] Trade issue. With tipped in page signed by the author (Between The Covers 8/94) $50/100

054c: THE COUP Knopf, New York, 1978. [1] First issue with top edge yellow $12/60

054d: THE COUP Knopf, New York, 1978. [1] Second issue with top edge black. (Also noted with top edge unstained and lacking last two lines of text on last page. "This book was composed ... Vermont" which Waiting For Godot catalogued at $650.) $10/50

054e: THE COUP Deutsch (London, 1979). [1] $10/50

055a: THE LOVELORN ASTRONOMER G.K. Hall (Boston, 1978). [0] Wraps. 400 cc. Copyright notice handwritten. Issued as a Holiday Greeting $500.

055b: THE LOVELORN ASTRONOMER G.K. Hall (Boston, 1978). [0] Wraps. 1,400 cc. Copyright notice printed $150.

056a: THE DICK CAVETT SHOW A CONVERSATION... (Waggoner, Washington, D.C., 1979.) [] Unbound Xeroxed sheets (ref.b) $75.

057a: SIXTEEN SONNETS Halty Ferguson, Cambridge, 1979. [2] 26 sgd ltr cc. Issued in cloth without dustwrapper $600.

057b: SIXTEEN SONNETS Halty Ferguson, Cambridge, 1979. [2] 250 sgd no. cc. Wraps $100.

058a: TOO FAR TO GO *The Maples Stories* Fawcett, New York (1979). [3] Wraps. No. 2-4002-9 $75.

058b: YOUR LOVER JUST CALLED... Penguin (Harmondsworth, 1980). [] Wraps. New title (ref.b) $60.

059a: THREE ILLUMINATIONS... Targ Editions, New York, 1979. [2] 350 sgd no. cc. Issued with plain white tissue dustwrapper $150.

060a: AN ODDLY LOVELY DAY ALONE Waves Press, Richmond, 1979. [] Proof. A single sheet rubber stamped "Proof Copy" above the colophon (Waiting For Godot Books 2/96) $60.

060b: AN ODDLY LOVELY DAY ALONE Waves Press, Richmond, 1979. [2] 26 sgd ltr cc. Broadside $300.

060c: AN ODDLY LOVELY DAY ALONE Waves Press, Richmond, 1979. [2] 250 sgd no. cc. Broadside $100.

061a: THE VISIONS OF MACKENZIE KING (John Updike Newsletter, Northridge, 1979.) [2] 150 cc. Broadside $125.

062a: PROBLEMS *and Other Stories* Knopf, New York, 1979. [2] 350 sgd no. cc. Issued in dustwrapper (differs from trade dustwrapper). In slipcase $150/200

062b: PROBLEMS *and Other Stories* Knopf, New York, 1979. [1] $10/50

062c: PROBLEMS *and Other Stories* Deutsch (London, 1980). [1] (Ref.b) $10/50

063a: PIGEON FEATHERS (Perfection Form Co. Logan, Iowa 1979) [] Wraps. Cover title. First separate edition $35.

064a: EARTHWORM (Ontario Review, Princeton, 1979.) [] 100 cc (a & b). Postcard with earliest issue: "God Bless" stanza 3:1 $100.

064b: EARTHWORM (Ontario Review, Princeton, 1979.) [] Stanza 3:1 changed to "God blesses" $50.

065a: TALK FROM THE FIFTIES Lord John Press, Northridge, 1979. [2] 75 sgd no. cc. Issued without dustwrapper $225.

065b: TALK FROM THE FIFTIES Lord John Press, Northridge, 1979. [2] 300 sgd no. cc. Issued without dustwrapper (ref.b) $125.

066a: THE CHASTE PLANET Metacom Press, Worcester, 1980. [2] 26 sgd ltr cc. Issued in cloth without dustwrapper (ref.b) $500.

066b: THE CHASTE PLANET Metacom Press, Worcester, 1980. [2] 300 sgd no. cc. Wraps $125.

067a: IOWA Press-22, Portland (1980). [2] 26 sgd ltr cc. Broadside (ref.b) $200.

067b: IOWA Press-22, Portland (1980). [2] 200 sgd no. cc. Broadside (ref.b) $100.

068a: EGO AND ART IN WALT WHITMAN Targ Editions, New York, 1980. [2] 350 sgd no. cc. Issued in plain tan dustwrapper (ref.b & c) $125.

069a: FIVE POEMS Bits Chapbook (Cleveland, 1980). [2] 50 sgd no. cc (1-50). Issued on handmade paper $450.

069b: FIVE POEMS Bits Chapbook (Cleveland, 1980). [2] 135 sgd no. cc (51-185). Issued in paper wallet (Bert Babcock #56) $125.

070a: PEOPLE ONE KNOWS *Interviews with Insufficiently Famous Americans* Lord John Press,

Northridge, 1980. [2] 100 sgd no. cc. Issued without dustwrapper. In slipcase (ref.b & c) $150/200

070b: PEOPLE ONE KNOWS *Interviews with Insufficiently Famous Americans* Lord John Press, Northridge, 1980. [2] 350 sgd no. cc. Issued without dustwrapper. In slipcase (ref.b & c) $75/100

071a: A SENSE OF SHELTER (Perfection Form Co., Logan, 1980.) [] Cover title $40.

072a: HAWTHRONE'S CREED Targ Editions, New York (1981). [2] 250 sgd no. cc (ref.b). Issued in unprinted pale gray/green dustwrapper $125/150

073a: INVASION OF THE BOOK ENVELOPES Wm. Ewert (Concord, 1981). [] 4 cc. Uncorrected proof (Ken Lopez) $750.

073b: INVASION OF THE BOOK ENVELOPES Wm. Ewert (Concord, 1981). [2] 10 sgd cc. Leather spine. Separate colophon and half-title not in 73c (description provided by publisher) $750.

073c: INVASION OF THE BOOK ENVELOPES Wm. Ewert (Concord, 1981). [2] 125 cc in wraps. Issued in envelope $125.

074a: RABBIT IS RICH Knopf, New York, 1981. [] Uncorrected proof. In salmon colored wraps (Waiting For Godot 10/90). Pulitzer winner $250.

074b: RABBIT IS RICH Knopf, New York, 1981. [] With signed tipped in page (Joseph the Provider #33). Pulitzer winner $100/150

074c: RABBIT IS RICH Knopf, New York, 1981. [2] 350 sgd no. cc. Issued in dustwrapper (differs from trade edition). In slipcase (ref.c). Pulitzer winner $225/300

074d: RABBIT IS RICH Knopf, New York, 1981. [1] Pulitzer winner $10/50

074e: RABBIT IS RICH Deutsch (London, 1982). [1] (Ref.b.) Pulitzer winner $10/50

074f: RABBIT IS RICH Franklin Library, Franklin Center, 1984. [2] "Limited Edition." Issued in full leather (ref.c). Pulitzer winner $75.

075a: THE BELOVED Lord John Press, Northridge, 1982. [2] 100 sgd no. cc $175.

075b: THE BELOVED Lord John Press, Northridge, 1982. [2] 300 sgd no. cc $125.

076a: STYLES OF BLOOM No publisher [Palaemon Press Limited], no place [Winston-Salem], 1982. [] Proof. Broadside poem, single printed sheet. Rubber stamped at top margin "Publisher's Copy" (Waiting For Godot Books 2/96) $250.

076b: STYLES OF BLOOM Palaemon (Winston-Salem, 1982). [2] 26 sgd no. cc. Broadside No. 35 $200.

076c: STYLES OF BLOOM Palaemon (Winston-Salem, 1982). [2] 55 sgd no. cc. Issued in Palaemon Broadside Folio $125.

077a: SMALL-CITY PEOPLE Lord John Press, Northridge, 1982. [2] 26 sgd ltr cc. Broadside 15" X 22" (Detering Book Gallery 12/94) $175.

077b: SMALL-CITY PEOPLE Lord John Press, Northridge, 1982. [2] 100 sgd no. cc. Broadside $125.

078a: SPRING TRIO Palaemon Press Limited, no place [Winston-Salem] (1982). [] Uncorrected galley proof. Unbound large octavo sheets printed on rectos only; 8 pp. Printed on thin stock paper (Waiting For Godot Books 2/96) $300.

078b: SPRING TRIO Palaemon Press Limited, no place [Winston-Salem] (1982). [] Uncorrected Proof. Large octavo sheets printed on rectos only; 8 pages stapled Rubber stamped on the front cover "Publisher's Copy". Printed on white stock paper (Waiting For Godot Books 2/96) $300.

078c: SPRING TRIO Palaemon (Winston-Salem, 1982). [2] 10 sgd no. cc (Roman numerals) $600.

078d: SPRING TRIO Palaemon (Winston-Salem, 1982). [2] 26 sgd ltr cc $450.

078e: SPRING TRIO Palaemon (Winston-Salem, 1982). [2] 100 sgd no. cc. (Also 8 out-of-series copies) $150.

079a: BECH IS BACK Knopf, New York, 1982. [] Uncorrected proof in yellow wraps (Waiting For Godot 4/89) $175.

079b: BECH IS BACK Knopf, New York, 1982. [2] 500 sgd no. cc. Issued in dustwrapper (differs from trade edition). In slipcase $75/125

079c: BECH IS BACK Knopf, New York, 1982. [1] First state dustwrapper with "FPT, 10/82" on front flap and "394-52806-9" on rear panel (Rob Warren 2/96) $8/40

079d: BECH IS BACK Deutsch (London, 1983). [1] $8/40

080a: HUGGING THE SHORE *Essays and Criticism* Knopf, New York, 1983. [] Uncorrected proof. In blue printed wraps $250.

080b: HUGGING THE SHORE *Essays and Criticism* Knopf, New York, 1983. [1] $15/75

080c: HUGGING THE SHORE *Essays and Criticism* Deutsch (London, 1984). [1] U.S. sheets (ref.b) $10/50

081a: TWO SONNETS. *Whose Titles Came to Me Simultaneously* Palaemon Press, Winston-Salem, 1983. [2] 75 sgd no. (?) cc. Broadside. Included in Northern Lights portfolio with other authors' broadsides and available only in the portfolio according to the publisher. Ref.b indicated 26 sgd ltr cc. Also 15 ltr cc for contributors with 2 extra broadsides for that contributor, others unsigned (Geo. Robert Minkoff 8/90). Perhaps only 75 copies in total? $750.

082a: CONFESSIONS OF A WILD BORE Tamazunchale Press, Newton, 1984. [2] 250 no. cc. Miniature leather book. Issued without dustwrapper $75.

083a: JESTER'S DOZEN Lord John Press, Northridge, 1984. [2] 50 sgd no. cc $250.

083b: JESTER'S DOZEN Lord John Press, Northridge, 1984. [2] 150 sgd no. cc. Issued without dustwrapper $125.

084a: EMERSONIANISM Bits Press, Cleveland (1984). [2] 203 sgd cc. Revised from *The New Yorker* appearance. (Published March 1985 @ $75) $150.

085a: THE WITCHES OF EASTWICK Knopf, New York, 1984. [] Uncorrected proof. First state in brick red printed wraps with passages not in later proof or published version (Waiting For Godot #7) $350.

085b: THE WITCHES OF EASTWICK Knopf, New York, 1984. [] Uncorrected proof. Second state in Salmon-colored wraps (mauve wraps [Ken Lopez 7/95]) $175.

085c: THE WITCHES OF EASTWICK Franklin Library, Franklin Center, 1984. [2] "Signed Limited" edition. Issued in full leather. Includes "Special message" from author $100.

085d: THE WITCHES OF EASTWICK Knopf, New York, 1984. [2] 350 sgd no. cc. Issued without dustwrapper. In slipcase $125/175

085e: THE WITCHES OF EASTWICK Knopf, New York, 1984. [1] 110,000 cc (PW) $8/40

085f: THE WITCHES OF EASTWICK Deutsch (London, 1984). [] Uncorrected proof. In blue wraps (Bev Chaney 6/91) $175.

085g: THE WITCHES OF EASTWICK Deutsch (London, 1984). [1] $8/40

085h: THE WITCHES OF EASTWICK Andre Deutsch / Rigby Publishers, London / Stonyfell, South Australia, 1984. [] (Larsen Books 10/96) $8/40

086a: A & P and SHOULD WIZARD HIT MOMMY? Tales For Travellers, San Francisco (1985). [0] Single sheet map folded to 24 pages. First separate edition $40.

087a: FACING NATURE Knopf, New York, 1985. [] Uncorrected proof. In blue wraps (Bev Chaney List C) $175.

087b: FACING NATURE *Poems* Knopf, New York, 1985. [1] $12/60

087c: FACING NATURE *Poems* Deutsch, London, 1985. [] Uncorrected proof. In blue wraps (Joseph A. Dermont 2/96) $100.

087d: FACING NATURE *Poems* Deutsch (London, 1986). [] $10/50

088a: IMPRESSIONS Sylvester & Orphanos, Los Angeles, 1985. [2] 4 sgd no. cc with recipient's name $NVA

088b: IMPRESSIONS Sylvester & Orphanos, Los Angeles, 1985. [2] 26 sgd ltr cc. Not For Sale $450.

088c: IMPRESSIONS Sylvester & Orphanos, Los Angeles, 1985. [2] 300 sgd no. cc (in-print). Also noted, an unknown number of copies with letterpress designation "Presentation Copy" in addition to the 330 copies accounted for in the colophon (William Reese Company 2/96) $250.

089a: SEVEN GOTHIC TALES A NEW INTRODUCTION BY JOHN UPDIKE Book-of-the-Month Club (New York, 1986). [0] Wraps. Pamphlet containing Updike's introduction $40.

090a: ROGER'S VERSION Knopf, New York, 1986. [] Uncorrected proof. In ochre wraps (Waverley 10/89), yellow (Joseph Dermont 3/90) and yellow-gold (Waiting For Godot 2/91), orange (Lame Duck Books 3/93). [Another eye of the beholder award] $150.

090b: ROGER'S VERSION Franklin Library, Franklin Center, 1986. [2] “Limited” signed edition. Issued in full leather $100.

090c: ROGER'S VERSION Knopf, New York, 1986. [2] 350 sgd no. cc. Issued in acetate dustwrapper. In slipcase $125/175

090d: ROGER'S VERSION Knopf, New York, 1986. [1] (Published September 10, 1986 @ $17.95) $8/40

090e: ROGER'S VERSION Deutsch (London, 1986). [1] $8/40

091a: A & P : LUST IN THE AISLES Redpath, Minneapolis, Minnesota (1986). [0] 5,000 cc. Wraps. (Front flap blank, later printing [Bert Babcock #56]) $30.

092a: A SOFT SPRING NIGHT IN SHILLINGTON Lord John Press, Northridge, 1986. [2] 50 sgd no. cc. Issued with leather spine. In slipcase. $150

092b: A SOFT SPRING NIGHT IN SHILLINGTON Lord John Press, Northridge, 1986. [2] 250 sgd no. cc. Issued without dustwrapper $50.

093a: GETTING OLDER Eurographica, Helsinki (1986). [2] 350 sgd no. cc. Stiff wraps. Issued in dustwrapper. Three stories $200.

094a: A PEAR LIKE A POTATO Lord John Press, Northridge (1986). [2] 26 sgd ltr cc. Broadside $250.

094b: A PEAR LIKE A POTATO Lord John Press, Northridge (1986). [2] 100 sgd no. cc $125.

095a: TRUST ME Knopf, New York, 1987. [1] Uncorrected proof. In cream colored wraps $150.

095b: TRUST ME Knopf, New York, 1987. [2] 350 sgd no. cc. Issued in slipcase $125/175

095c: TRUST ME Knopf, New York, 1987. [1] 50,000 cc (PW). (Published May 1987 @ $17.95) $8/40

095d: TRUST ME Andre Deutsch (London, 1987). [] Uncorrected proof. In blue wraps (Waiting For Godot 10/89) $100.

095e: TRUST ME Andre Deutsch, (London, 1987). [] $8/40

096a: THE AFTERLIFE Sixth Chamber Press, London, 1987. [2] 26 sgd no. cc. Issued in quarter leather. In slipcase (Published May 1987 @ £200) $500/600

096b: THE AFTERLIFE Sixth Chamber Press, London, 1987. [2] 175 sgd no. cc. Issued in full cloth (Published May 1987 @ £60) $175.

See also 128

097a: THE ART OF ADDING AND THE ART OF TAKING AWAY Harvard Library, Cambridge,

1987. [] Wraps. Reproductions of Updike's manuscripts and drawings with his introduction $45.

098a: MORE STATELY MANSIONS Nouveau Press, Jackson, 1987. [2] 40 sgd no. cc (Roman numerals). Not For Sale. (Published May 1987) $350.

098b: MORE STATELY MANSIONS Nouveau Press, Jackson, 1987. [2] 300 sgd no. cc. Issued without dustwrapper $125.

099a: HOWELLS AS ANTI-NOVELIST Wm. Dean Howells Memorial Committee, Kittery Point, Maine, 1987. [2] 150 cc. Issued in stiff printed wraps (Wm. Reese Co. 2/91) $100.

100a: S Knopf, New York, 1988. [1] Uncorrected proof. In red wraps $100.

100b: S Knopf, New York, 1988. [2] 350 sgd no. cc. Issued in acetate dustwrapper. In slipcase $125/175

100c: S Knopf, New York, 1988. [1] 100,000 cc (PW). (Published March 1988 @ $17.95) $7/35

100d: S Andre Deutsch (London, 1988). [2] 12 sgd no. (Roman) cc. Bound in full green calf. Assume in marbled paper slipcase $600/650

100e: S Andre Deutsch (London, 1988). [2] 10 sgd ltr cc. Issued in quarter leather. In marbled paper slipcase. (Not for sale) $600/650

100f: S Andre Deutsch (London, 1988). [2] 75 sgd no. cc. Issued in quarter leather. In marbled paper slipcase $250/300

100g: S Andre Deutsch (London, 1988). [] Trade edition $8/40

101a: ON THE MOVE Bits Press, Cleveland (1988). [2] 120 sgd cc. Wraps $125.

102a: APPOINTMENT IN SAMARA *A New Introduction* Book-of-the-Month Club, no place or date [1988] [] Wraps. Separate leaflet issued when BOMC reissued book $30.

103a: TWO SONNETS Northouse & Northouse (Texas, 1988). [2] 26 sgd ltr cc. Broadside 17x 13" $250.

103b: TWO SONNETS Northouse & Northouse (Texas, 1988). [2] 100 no. cc Signed? $125.

104a: SELF CONSCIOUSNESS : MEMOIRS (Knopf, New York, 1988.) [] Uncorrected proof. In buff/cream colored wraps. Beige wraps (Bev Chaney Jr. 1/95) $100.

104b: SELF CONSCIOUSNESS : MEMOIRS (Knopf, New York, 1988.) [] Promotional broadside with photograph of Updike (Henry Turlington 7/89) $60.

104c: SELF CONSCIOUSNESS: MEMOIRS Easton Press, Connecticut (1989). [2] Signed limited edition. "This Leather-bound First Edition personally signed by John Updike." Full blue leather. Issued without dustwrapper. (Waiting For Godot Books 2/97) $125.

104d: SELF CONSCIOUSNESS : MEMOIRS Knopf, New York, 1989. [2] 350 sgd no. cc. Issued in acetate dustwrapper. In slipcase $125/175

104e: SELF CONSCIOUSNESS : MEMOIRS Knopf, New York, 1989. [1] 50,000 cc (PW). Trade edition $6/30

104f: SELF CONSCIOUSNESS : MEMOIRS Andre Deutsch, London (1989). [] Uncorrected proof. In blue wraps $75.

104g: SELF CONSCIOUSNESS : MEMOIRS Andre Deutsch, London (1989). [] Trade edition $8/40

105a: GETTING THE WORDS OUT Lord John Press, Northridge, 1988. [2] 50 sgd no. cc. Issued in quarter leather $150.

105b: GETTING THE WORDS OUT Lord John Press, Northridge, 1988. [2] 250 sgd no. cc. Issued without dustwrapper. In slipcase $50.

106a: JUST LOOKING : ESSAYS ON ART Knopf, New York, 1989. [] Uncorrected proof. In white wraps $100.

106b: JUST LOOKING : ESSAYS ON ART Knopf, New York, 1989. [] 8 page publicity color brochure (Bev Chaney 9/89) $50.

106c: JUST LOOKING : ESSAYS ON ART Knopf, New York, 1989. [2] 350 sgd no. cc. Issued in acetate dustwrapper. In slipcase $150/200

106d: JUST LOOKING : ESSAYS ON ART Knopf, New York, 1989. [1] (Published October 1989 @ $35) $8/40

106e: JUST LOOKING: ESSAYS ON ART Deutsch, London, 1989. [] $10/50

107a: IN MEMORIAM : FELIS FELIX Sixth Chamber Press, Leamington Spa, 1989. [2] 12 sgd Roman numbered cc sgd by the author and illustrator. Bound in quarter leather (David Rees 11/94) $750.

107b: IN MEMORIAM : FELIS FELIX Sixth Chamber Press, Leamington Spa, 1989. [2] 26 sgd ltr cc. Signed by Updike and R.R. Kitaj (illustrator). Issued in slipcase $600/650

107c: IN MEMORIAM : FELIS FELIX Sixth Chamber Press, Leamington Spa, 1989. [2] 200 no. cc (not signed). Issued in acetate dustwrapper $125.

108a: THE COMPLETE BOOK OF COVERS FROM THE NEW YORKER 1925-1989 Knopf, New York, 1989. [1] Introduction by Updike. (Published November 1989 @ $75) $25/75

109a: GOING ABROAD Eurographica, Helsinki (1988). [2] 350 sgd no. cc. Issued in stiff wraps (Herb Yellin 3/90) $200.

110a: BROTHER GRASSHOPPER Metacom Press, Worcester, Massachusetts 1990. [2] 26 sgd ltr cc $500.

110b: BROTHER GRASSHOPPER Metacom Press, Worcester, Massachusetts, 1990. [2] 150 sgd no. cc $150.

111a: MITES & OTHER POEMS IN MINIATURE Lord John Press, Northridge, 1990. [2] 26 sgd ltr cc. Issued in slipcase $300.

111b: MITES & OTHER POEMS IN MINIATURE Lord John Press, Northridge, 1990. [2] 200 sgd no. cc. Issued without slipcase $60.

112a: RABBIT AT REST Knopf, New York, 1990. [1] Uncorrected proof in yellow wraps. Only 200 copies per publisher. Pulitzer winner $200.

112b: RABBIT AT REST Knopf, New York, 1990. [1] Signed uncorrected proof. In white wraps printed in green. In publisher's green slipcase. About 1,000 copies per publisher. Pulitzer winner $175/200

112c: RABBIT AT REST Franklin Library, Franklin Center, 1990. [] Signed "limited" "first edition." With special message not in trade edition. Pulitzer winner $125.

112d: RABBIT AT REST Knopf, New York, 1990. [2] 350 sgd no. cc. Issued in slipcase. Pulitzer winner $200/250

112e: RABBIT AT REST Knopf, New York, 1990. [1] 100,000 cc. Pulitzer win-ner. (Published October 1990 @ $21.95) $8/40

112f: RABBIT AT REST Andre Deutsch, London, 1990. [] Pulitzer winner $8/40

113a: "FULL FORTY YEARS ..." (Privately Printed, Pennsylvania, 1990.) [0] 8" x 10" untitled broadside written for his high school reunion. Reportedly 100 copies, of which 55 were given away at the event (Bert Babcock 2/91) $100.

114a: THANATOPSES Bits Press, Cleveland, 1991. [] 237 cc. Wraps $75.

115a: RECENT POEMS 1986-1990 Eurographica, Helsinki (1991). [2] 350 sgd no. cc. Issued in stiff wraps. In dustwrapper (Jett W. Whitehead 2/96) $175.

116a: THE FIRST PICTURE BOOK Whitney Museum, New York, 1991. [2] 25 deluxe copies. Bound in full leather with additional photogravures, 24 offset lithographs by Mary Steichen Calderone and Edward Steichen. Afterword by Updike $1,250.

117a: ODD JOBS : ESSAYS AND CRITICISM Knopf, New York, 1991. [] Uncorrected proof. In yellow wraps (Bert Babcock 2/92) $100.

117b: ODD JOBS : ESSAYS AND CRITICISM Knopf, New York, 1991. [1] (Published November 7, 1991 @ $30) $10/40

118a: MEMORIES OF THE FORD ADMINIS-TRATION Knopf, New York, 1992. [] Uncorrected proof. In printed light gray wraps (Bev Chaney, Jr. 1/95) $100.

118b: MEMORIES OF THE FORD ADMINIS-TRATION Knopf, New York, 1992. [1] $6/30

118c: MEMORIES OF THE FORD ADMINISTRATION Hamish Hamilton, London, 1993. [] Uncorrected proof in pictorial wraps and proof dustwrapper (David Rees 11/95) $50/100

118d: MEMORIES OF THE FORD ADMINISTRATION Hamish Hamilton, London, 1993. [] $7/35

119a: COLLECTED POEMS 1953-1993 Knopf, New York, 1993. [] Uncor-rected proof. In printed dark gray wraps (Bev Chaney, Jr. 1/95) $100.

119b: COLLECTED POEMS 1953-1993 Knopf, New York, 1993. [1] (Bev Chaney, Jr. 1/95) (Published 4/93 @ $27.50) $7/35

119c: COLLECTED POEMS 1953-1993 Hamish Hamilton, London, 1993. [] (Nicholas and Helen Burrows 2/96) $8/40

119d: COLLECTED POEMS 1953-1993 Knopf, New York, 1995. [] Wraps. (Published 7/95 @ $15.00) $15.

120a: CONCERTS AT CASTLE HILL Lord John Press, Northridge, 1993. [2] 50 sgd no. deluxe copies. Quarter leather. Issued without dustwrapper. In slipcase $200.

120b: CONCERTS AT CASTLE HILL Lord John Press, Northridge, 1993. [2] 250 sgd no. cc. In two piece binding, as issued. Issued without dustwrapper (Bev Chaney Jr. 1/95) $75.

121a: BABY'S FIRST STEP James Cahill Publishing, Huntington Beach (1993). [2] Signed "Artists Copy" in green cloth (Book Time 12/94) $75.

121b: BABY'S FIRST STEP James Cahill Publishing, Huntington Beach (1993). [2] 26 sgd ltr cc. Issued without dustwrapper. In slipcase $200/250

121c: BABY'S FIRST STEP James Cahill Publishing, Huntington Beach (1993). [2] 100 sgd no. cc Issued without dustwrapper. In slipcase $100.

122a: THE TWELVE TERRORS OF CHRISTMAS Gotham Book Mart, New York (1993). [2] 26 sgd ltr cc. Illustrated and signed by Edward Gorey as well as Updike. (James S. Jaffe 5/95) $450.

122b: THE TWELVE TERRORS OF CHRISTMAS Gotham Book Mart, New York (1993). [2] 100 sgd no. cc. Hardbound. Issued without dustwrapper Illustrated and signed by Gorey as well as Updike. $250.

122c: THE TWELVE TERRORS OF CHRISTMAS Gotham Book Mart, New York (1993). [2] 400 sgd no. cc. In pictorial wraps. Illustrated and signed by Gorey as well as Updike $150.

122d: THE TWELVE TERRORS OF CHRISTMAS Gotham Book Mart, New York (1994). [] Stapled wraps. Trade edition issued one year after the limited edition (Detering Book Gallery 12/95) $35.

123a: JULY Knopf, New York, 1993. [] Broadside poem. Signed (James S. Jaffe 9/93) $150.

124a: "MY FIRST THOUGHT ABOUT ART..." Alquando Press (Toronto), September 1993. [2] 50 cc. Broadside (Alphabet Books 10/94) $75.

125a: CONSENT Lord John Press, Northridge, 1993. [2] 250 sgd no. cc $75.

126a: LOVE FACTORIES Eurographica, Helsinki, 1993. [2] 350 sgd no. cc. Issued in card wraps with dustwrapper. Contains three stories: *The Football Factory, Part of the Process* and *The Lens Factory* and 6-page foreword by Updike (Ulysses 9/95) $150.

127a: BRAZIL Knopf, New York, 1994. [] Uncorrected proof. White oversize photocopied sheets, tape bound (Waverley Books 1/97) $100.

127b: BRAZIL Knopf, New York, 1994. [] Uncorrected proof. In printed beige wraps (Bev Chaney, Jr. 1/95). Also noted as cream colored $125.

127c: BRAZIL Franklin Library, Franklin Center, 1993. [2] Signed limited edition. In full leather (Vagabond Books 12/94) $75.

127d: BRAZIL Knopf, New York, 1994. [] Advance reading copy. In pictorial wraps (Gordon Beckhorn 1/95) $100.

127e: BRAZIL Knopf, New York, 1994. [1] 75,000 cc. (Published 2/23/94 @ $23.00) $6/30

127f: BRAZIL Hamish Hamilton, London, 1994. [] (Nicholas and Helen Burrows 2/96) $8/40

128a: THE AFTERLIFE *and Other Stories* Knopf, New York, 1994. [] Uncorrected Proof in light gray printed wraps (Chloe's Books 1/95) $100.

128b: THE AFTERLIFE *and Other Stories* Knopf, New York, 1994. [1] (Bev Chaney Jr. 1/95) $6/30

128c: THE AFTERLIFE *and Other Stories* Hamish Hamilton, London (1994). [] (James S. Jaffe 5/95) $8/40

129a: CONVERSATIONS WITH JOHN UPDIKE University Press of Mississippi, Jackson (1994). [] Edited by James Plath. (Published @ $37.00.) (Bev Chaney Jr. 1/95) $20/40

129b: CONVERSATIONS WITH JOHN UPDIKE University Press of Mississippi, Jackson (1994). [] Wraps. (Published @ $14.95) $15.

130a: POEM BEGUN ON THURSDAY, OCTOBER 14, 1993 AT O'HARE AIRPORT TERMI-

NAL 3, AROUND SIX O'CLOCK [pamphlet issue] Literary Renaissance, Louisville, 1994. [2] 26 sgd ltr cc Green, hand- decorated wraps. Printed at the Warwick Press. Contains a printed dedication not present in the broadside issue (Waiting For Godot Books 2/97) $250.

130b: POEM BEGUN ON THURSDAY, OCTOBER 14, 1993 AT O'HARE AIRPORT TERMINAL 3, AROUND SIX O'CLOCK [pamphlet issue] Literary Renaissance, Louisville, 1994. [2] 1 00 sgd no. cc. In gray wraps. Printed at the Warwick Press. Contains a printed dedication not present in the broadside issue $75.

130c: POEM BEGUN ON THURSDAY, OCTOBER 14, 1993 AT O'HARE AIRPORT TERMINAL 3, AROUND SIX O'CLOCK [broadside issue] Literary Renaissance, Louisville, 1994. [2] 26 sgd ltr cc. Broadside. Approximately 15 x 32 inches. Lacks printed dedication present in wraps issue. Printed at the Warwick Press (Waiting For Godot Books 2/97) $125.

130d: POEM BEGUN ON THURSDAY, OCTOBER 14, 1993 AT O'HARE AIRPORT TERMINAL 3, AROUND SIX O'CLOCK [broadside issue] Literary Renaissance, Louisville, 1994. [2] 100 sgd cc. Broadside. Approximately 15 x 32 inches. Lacks printed dedication present in wraps issue. Printed at the Warwick Press (Waiting For Godot Books 2/97) $50.

131a: A HELPFUL ALPHABET OF FRIENDLY OBJECTS Alfred A. Knopf, New York, 1995. [] Folded and gathered sheets laid into dustwrapper (Bookfinders 9/96) $25.

131b: A HELPFUL ALPHABET OF FRIENDLY OBJECTS Alfred A. Knopf, New York (1995). [] (Bev Chaney, Jr. 10/95) $5/25

132a: RABBIT ANGSTROM A TETRALOGY *Rabbit Run, Rabbit Redux, Rabbit is Rich* and *Rabbit at Rest* Everyman's Library / Knopf, New York (1995). [] The four Rabbit novels collected with new introduction by Updike (Bev Chaney, Jr. 10/95) $8/40

133a: IN THE CEMETERY HIGH ABOVE SHILLINGTON William B. Ewert, Concord, 1995. [2] 15 sgd no. cc (signed by Updike and Barry Moser). Deluxe issue bound in quarter leather with paper covered boards. Issued with a paper portfolio that contains a suite of three individually-signed relief engravings by Barry Moser. Issued in cloth slipcase-box. Published @ $750. (Waiting For Godot 2/97) $750.

133b: IN THE CEMETERY HIGH ABOVE SHILLINGTON William B. Ewert, Concord, 1995. [2] 50 sgd no. cc. In cloth of which 35 were for sale. Signed by Updike and Barry Moser, the illustrator. Published @ $285.00 (Bev Chaney, Jr. 2/96) $350.

133c: IN THE CEMETERY HIGH ABOVE SHILLINGTON William B. Ewert, Concord, 1995. [2] 100 sgd no. cc in wraps of which 70 were for sale. Signed by Updike and Barry Moser, the illustrator. Published @ $165.00 $200.

134a: FRIENDS FROM PHILADELPHIA Penguin Books, London, 1995. [] Pictorial wraps. First thus (Nouveau 10/95). Also noted cataloged as 1994? $20.

135a: IN THE BEAUTY OF THE LILIES Alfred A. Knopf, New York, 1996. [] Uncorrected proof. In light blue printed wraps. (Waverley Books 3/96) $100.

135b: IN THE BEAUTY OF THE LILIES Franklin Library, Franklin Center, 1996. [2] 3,000-3,500 cc (estimate of Ken Lopez 8/96). Signed limited edition. Issued in full leather. With special by the author for this edition $125.

135c: IN THE BEAUTY OF THE LILIES Alfred A. Knopf, New York, 1996. [1] 75,000 cc (Ken Lopez 8/96). "First Trade Edition" (Bev Chaney, Jr. 2/96) $5/25

135d: IN THE BEAUTY OF THE LILIES Hamish Hamilton, London (1996). [] $6/30

136a: GOLF DREAMS *Writings on Golf* Alfred A. Knopf, New York, 1996. [1] Uncorrected proof. In blue printed wraps (Waverley Books 8/96) $100.

136b: GOLF DREAMS *Writings on Golf* Alfred A. Knopf, New York, 1996. [1] $6/30

136c: GOLF DREAMS *Writings on Golf* Alfred A. Knopf, New York, 1996. [1] Reportedly 500 sgd cc. Large print edition. Noted with the publisher's "Signed by the Author" label on front panel (Bev Chaney, Jr. 12/96). Published simultaneously $125.

136d: GOLF DREAMS *Writings on Golf* Alfred A. Knopf, New York, 1996. [1] Large print edition. Published simultaneously $5/25

137a: DOWN TIME William B. Ewert, Concord, New Hampshire, 1997. [2] 30 sgd cc (of a total edition of 90 copies of which 25 copies were for sale). Broadside. Deluxe copies, 13 x 11½ inches. Printed on Twinrocker Tale handmade paper. Illustrated by Barry Moser. Printed by Firefly Press. Issued @ $185. $200.

137b: DOWN TIME William B. Ewert, Concord, New Hampshire, 1997. [2] 60 sgd cc (of a total edition of 90 copies of which 45 copies were for sale). Broadside. 13 x 11½ inches. Printed on Rives heavyweight paper. Illustrated by Barry Moser. Printed by Firefly Press. Issued @$115. $135.

138a: TOWARD THE END OF TIME Alfred A. Knopf, New York, 1997. [] Uncorrected proof. In blue wraps (Annex Books 5/98) $75.

138b: TOWARD THE END OF TIME Alfred A. Knopf, New York, 1997. [] Published @ $25.

138c: TOWARD THE END OF TIME Hamish Hamilton, London, 1997 [] $7/35

139a: JANUARY William Ewert, Concord, NH, 1997. [2] 40 sgd cc. Wraps. Issued @ $185 (Bev Chaney, Jr. 5/98) $250.

KURT VONNEGUT, JR.

Vonnegut was born in 1922 in Indianapolis, educated at Cornell and the University of Chicago. He served during World War II, and was awarded a Purple Heart. Vonnegut was a police reporter in Chicago after the war and also worked in public relations for the General Electric Company before turning to free lance writing in 1950.

Vonnegut was initially labeled a science fiction writer but he did not like the label. He preferred to think of himself as a 20th century Mark Twain. Critics consider his work, except for the earliest, predominately satire.

REFERENCES:

(a) Pieratt, Asa B., Jr. and Jerome Klinkowitz. KURT VONNEGUT, JR. *A Descriptive Bibliography...* No place: Archon Books, 1974.

(b) Currey, L.W. SCIENCE FICTION AND FANTASY AUTHORS... Boston: G.K. Hall & Co. (1979).

(c) Bruccoli, Matthew J. (editor). FIRST PRINTINGS OF AMERICAN AUTHORS. Volume 1. Detroit: Gale Research (1977).

(d) Inventory or dealer catalogs.

001a: PLAYER PIANO Charles Scribner's Sons, New York, 1952. [5] 25 to 30 cc. Wraps. Advance copies for review using dustwrapper as self wraps with flaps pasted on front pastedown and endpaper $1,500.

001b: PLAYER PIANO Charles Scribner's Sons, New York, 1952. [5] 7,600 cc. Has "A" and Scribner's seal. Doubleday Book Club edition has an "A" also, but no seal $300/1,500

001c: PLAYER PIANO Macmillan, London, 1953. [] Approximately 2,000 cc. 3,000 copies were printed but approximately 1,000 were pulped $150/750

001d: PLAYER PIANO Macmillan, London, 1953. [] Colonial Issue in red cloth with "Macmillan's Overseas Library" stamped on the rear flap of the dustwrapper. (Ferret Fantasy 11/94) $150/750

001e: UTOPIA 14 Bantam Books, New York (1954). [1] Wraps. "1st printing... October 1954." New Title. "Bantam Giant A 1262" $60.

002a: THE SIRENS OF TITAN Dell (New York, 1959). [1] 177,500 cc. Wraps. "First printing October, 1959" $150.

002b: THE SIRENS OF TITAN Houghton Mifflin Co., Boston, 1961. [1] 2,500 cc Fewer than 750 cc (Vagabond Books). First issue dustwrapper with "Previously published as an | original paperback book by | Dell Publishing Co., Inc." at top edge of front flap (L. W. Currey 4/97) $300/1,750

002c: THE SIRENS OF TITAN Houghton Mifflin Co., Boston, 1961. [1] Second issue dustwrapper lacks statement about previous publication $300/1,500

002d: THE SIRENS OF TITAN Gollancz, London, 1962. [0] Red cloth with spine stamped in gold $60/300

002e: THE SIRENS OF TITAN Easton Press, Norwalk, Connecticut, 1990. [] Signed copies (quantity not stated). "Special Collector's Edition" Full leather; issued without dustwrapper (Bert Babcock 4/97) $100.

003a: CANARY IN A CAT HOUSE Gold Medal / Fawcett, Greenwich, Connecticut (1961). [1] 175,000 cc. Wraps. "First printing September 1961." Gold Medal Book S 1153. Also distributed in England. All but one story later collected in *Welcome To The Monkey House* (ref.b) $200.

004a: MOTHER NIGHT Gold Medal / Fawcett, Greenwich, Connecticut (1962). [1] 175,000 cc. Wraps. Also distributed in England $200.

004b: MOTHER NIGHT Harper & Row, New York (1966). [] Uncorrected proof. In spiral bound printed blue wraps (William Reese Co. 7/89) $1,500.

004c: MOTHER NIGHT Harper & Row, New York (1966). [] Uncorrected proof. In perfect bound yellow wraps $750.

004d: MOTHER NIGHT Harper & Row, New York (1966). [1] 5,500 cc. Adds introduction by author $60/300

004e: MOTHER NIGHT Jonathan Cape, London (1968). [1] $40/200

005a: CAT'S CRADLE Holt, Rinehart & Winston, New York/Chicago/San Francisco (1963). [1] 6,000 cc $150/750

005b: CAT'S CRADLE Victor Gollancz, London, 1963. [0] $75/350

006a: GOD BLESS YOU, MR. ROSEWATER.... Holt Rinehart & Winston, New York/Chicago/San Francisco (1965). [1] Uncorrected proof. In beige wraps with plastic spiral binding (Robert Wendler 12/94) $1250.

006b: GOD BLESS YOU, MR. ROSEWATER... Holt, Rinehart & Winston, New York/Chicago/San Francisco (1965). [1] 6,000 cc $100/500

006c: GOD BLESS YOU, MR. ROSEWATER... Jonathan Cape, London (1965). [1] Maroon paper over boards, spine printed in gold. Later printings are black paper over boards $50/250

007a: HAVE YOU EVER BEEN TO BARNSTABLE (Venture Magazine), no place, 1966. [] 2 leaves folded to make 8 pages. An offprint (Fine Books #30) $250.

008a: WELCOME TO THE MONKEY HOUSE... Delacorte (New York, 1968). [] Uncorrected proof. In spiral bound salmon colored wraps (Joseph Dermont 6/92) $1,250.

008b: WELCOME TO THE MONKEY HOUSE... Delacorte (New York, 1968). [1] 5,000 cc $150/600

008c: WELCOME TO THE MONKEY HOUSE... Jonathan Cape, London (1969). [] Uncorrected proof. In bright pink publisher's wraps $500.

008d: WELCOME TO THE MONKEY HOUSE... Jonathan Cape, London (1969). [1] $50/250

008e: WELCOME TO THE MONKEY HOUSE Dramatic Publishing Company, Chicago (1970). [0] Wraps. Dramatization by Christopher Sergel $50.

009a: SLAUGHTERHOUSE-FIVE... Delacorte Press, New York (1969). [] Uncorrected proof. In green spiral bound wraps, printed in black, 6" X 11". According to the printer there were 39 copies bound as such in November, 1968 for review. (Robert Wendler 12/94) $3,500.

009b: SLAUGHTERHOUSE-FIVE... Delacorte, no place (1969). [1] 10,000 cc. First issue dustwrapper with "0369" on rear flap (Stephen Lupack 10/95) $150/750

009c: SLAUGHTERHOUSE FIVE Jonathan Cape, London, 1970. [] Uncorrected proof. In trial dustwrapper. This trial proof dustwrapper, rejected by the publisher, has an image of a dismembered hand with an eye placed in its center, and close by a man with gun in holster holding a sword. (Andrew Sclanders 11/94) $250/750

009d: SLAUGHTERHOUSE FIVE... Jonathan Cape, London (1970). [1] $60/300

009e: SLAUGHTERHOUSE FIVE... Franklin Library, Franklin Center, 1978. [2] "Signed Limited Edition" with special message not in trade edition. Issued in full leather $150.

009f: SLAUGHTERHOUSE FIVE Delacorte Press, New York (1994). [] Twenty-fifth Anniversary edition (Captain's Bookshelf 10/94) $7/35

010a: TORTURE AND BLUBBER Peoples Union, no place or date [circa 1971]. [] Broadside. First separate appearances of this piece from the *New York Times* (another author on back) (Waiting For Godot 10/86) $150.

011a: HAPPY BIRTHDAY, WANDA JUNE Delacorte, New York, 1971. [1] 3,000 cc. Black cloth and orange endpapers. Dustwrapper priced at top of front flap. We have seen several copies of a book club edition in black paper-covered boards with white endpapers. These copies state "First Printing" and look like they may be the same sheets as the true first. The first is much scarcer than a quantity of 3,000 would indicate. So, we think Delacorte may have only bound part of the edition and sent some of the sheets off to the book club. Noted with both "0971" and "3456" on "Book Club" dustwrappers $300/1,500

011b: HAPPY BIRTHDAY, WANDA JUNE Delta, New York, 1971. [1] Wraps. "First Delta Printing..." Assume published simultaneously $100.

011c: HAPPY BIRTHDAY, WANDA JUNE Wanda June/Filmakers, Hollywood, 1971. [] Wraps. Original screenplay (Pepper & Stern #22) $250.

011d: HAPPY BIRTHDAY, WANDA JUNE Jonathan Cape, London (1973). [1] (Published June 14, 1973 @ £1.95) $75/350

011e: HAPPY BIRTHDAY, WANDA JUNE French, New York (1974). [0] Wraps. Drops author's note $40.

012a: BETWEEN TIME AND TIMBUKTU Delacorte (New York, 1972). [1] 2,500 cc (publisher supplied) $150/600

012b: BETWEEN TIME AND TIMBUKTU Panther (St. Albans, 1975). [1] Wraps. No U.K. hardcover edition $150.

013a: BREAKFAST OF CHAMPIONS (Delacorte, New York, 1973.) [1] 100,000 cc $15/75

013b: BREAKFAST OF CHAMPIONS Jonathan Cape, London (1973). [1] $15/75

014a: [UNPUBLISHED INTERVIEW] No publisher, place or date (circa 1973). [0] Galley sheets of an unpublished interview with Vonnegut by Loree Rackstraw and Jerome Klikkowitz. Seven galleys, each 4 x 24 inches, folded in half. A lengthly interview with Vonnegut which was never published. One copy noted signed by Vonnegut in 1976 (Ken Lopez 5/98 catalogued a signed copy at $1,750) $NVA

015a: ONE GREAT NOVELIST OF THE 70'S WRITES ABOUT ANOTHER... Ballantine (New York, 1974). [] Vonnegut on Joseph Heller's *Something Happened. New York Times Book Review*. 8 pages in blue wraps with white and black letters. Generated in connection with the release of the paperback edition of Heller's book (Between the Covers) $125.

016a: WAMPETERS FOMA & GRANFALLOONS Delacorte (New York, 1974). [] Uncorrected page proof. In pale blue wraps (Joseph A. Dermont) $250.

016b: WAMPETERS FOMA & GRANFALLOONS Delacorte (New York, 1974). [1] (Ref.c) 20,000 cc $20/100

016c: WAMPETERS FOMA & GRANFALLOONS Jonathan Cape, London (1975). [1] (Ref.c) $15/75

017a: SLAPSTICK... (Delacorte), New York (1976). [] Uncorrected proof. In gray wraps $150.

017b: SLAPSTICK... (Delacorte), New York (1976). [1] 85,000 cc. Actually issued a month before 016c & d (ref.b) $10/50

017c: SLAPSTICK... (Delacorte), New York (1976). [2] 250 sgd no. cc. Issued without dustwrapper. In slipcase (ref.b) $200/250

017d: SLAPSTICK... Franklin Library, Franklin Center, 1976. [2] "Limited Edition" with special message by the author. Full leather binding (ref.b) $100.

017e: SLAPSTICK... Jonathan Cape, London (1976). [] Uncorrected proof. In yellow wraps. This production appears to have been photocopied from a U.S. edition (including cover). In proof dustwrapper with " Proof only provisional publication date November 4, 1976" on back flap $75/200

017f: SLAPSTICK... Jonathan Cape, London (1976). [1] (Ref.d) $10/50

018a: JAILBIRD Franklin Library, Franklin Center, 1979. [2] "Limited Edition" with special message by the author (Vagabond Books 4/95) $100.

018b: JAILBIRD Delacorte, New York (1979). [] Uncorrected proof. In yellow (mustard) wraps $125.

018c: JAILBIRD (Delacorte, New York, 1979.) [2] 500 sgd no. cc. Issued without dustwrapper. In slipcase (ref.d) $100/150

018d: JAILBIRD Delacorte, New York (1979). [1] (Ref.d) 90,700 cc $7/35

018e: JAILBIRD Jonathan Cape, London (1979). [0] Uncorrected proof. In red wraps $100.

018f: JAILBIRD Jonathan Cape, London (1979). [1] (Ref.d) $10/50

019a: SUN MOON STAR Harper & Row (New York, 1980). [1] $15/75

019b: SUN MOON STAR Hutchinson, London (1980). [1] $12/60

020a: HOW TO WRITE WITH STYLE International Paper Co. (Elmsford, New York, 1980). [0] Wraps. Single sheet, folded once. Illustrated with photos. Offprint of Company's magazine ad $50.

021a: PALM SUNDAY Delacorte, New York (1981). [] Uncorrected proof. In yellow wraps $125.

021b: PALM SUNDAY Delacorte, New York (1981). [2] 500 sgd no. cc. Issued without dustwrapper. In slipcase $100/150

021c: PALM SUNDAY Delacorte, New York (1981). [1] 69,500 cc $7/35

021d: PALM SUNDAY Jonathan Cape, London (1981). [] Uncorrected proof. In green wraps (Bev Chaney) $100.

021e: PALM SUNDAY Jonathan Cape, London (1981). [1] $10/50

022a: DEADEYE DICK Delacorte (New York, 1982). [] Uncorrected proof. In red wraps $125.

022b: DEADEYE DICK Delacorte (New York, 1982). [2] 350 sgd no. cc. Issued without dustwrapper. In slipcase $150/200

022c: DEADEYE DICK Delacorte (New York, 1982). [1] 100,000 cc $8/40

022d: DEADEYE DICK Jonathan Cape, London (1983). [ ] $8/40

023a: BOB AND RAY / A RETROSPECTIVE Museum of Broadcasting, New York (1982). [] An appreciation by Vonnegut. Folio sheet folded to make 6 pages/panels $75.

024a: FATES WORSE THAN DEATH [cover title]. (Bertrand Russell Peace..., Nottingham, no date [1982]. [0] Wraps. Spokesman Pamphlet No. 80. Text of Vonnegut speech $60.

(Also see 1991 entry)

025a: NOTHING IS LOST SAVE HONOR Nouveau Press, Jackson, Miss., 1984. [2] 40 sgd no. cc. Printed on handmade Japanese Etching. Half-bound in Nigerian Oasis goatskin and cloth $450.

025b: NOTHING IS LOST SAVE HONOR Nouveau Press, Jackson, Miss., 1984. [2] 300 sgd no. cc. Boards. Issued without dustwrapper $150.

026a: GALAPAGOS Delacorte, New York, 1985. [1] Uncorrected proof. In pale blue printed wraps $100.

026b: GALAPAGOS Franklin Library, Franklin Center, 1985. [2] "Limited Signed Edition." Issued in full leather. Adds an original 2-page introduction. Reported to precede Delacorte edition $100.

026c: GALAPAGOS Delacorte, New York, 1985. [2] 500 sgd no. cc. Issued without dustwrapper. In slipcase $125/175

026d: GALAPAGOS Delacorte, New York, 1985. [1] (Published October 4, 1985 @ $16.95) $6/30

026e: GALAPAGOS Johnathan (sic) Cape, London (1985). [ ] Uncorrected proof. In red wraps (Joseph A. Dermont 7/93) $125.

026f: GALAPAGOS Jonathan Cape, London (1985). [] Advance uncorrected proof. In publisher's brown printed wraps (Dalian 9/92) $75.

026g: GALAPAGOS Jonathan Cape, London (1985). [1] $8/40

027a: BLUEBEARD Delacorte (New York, 1987). [] Uncorrected proof. In red wraps $100.

027b: BLUEBEARD Franklin Library, Franklin Center, 1987. [2] Signed limited edition. Issued in full leather $100.

027c: BLUEBEARD Delacorte (New York, 1987). [2] 500 sgd no. cc. Issued without dustwrapper. In slipcase $75/125

027d: BLUEBEARD Delacorte (New York, 1987). [1] $8/40

027e: BLUEBEARD Jonathan Cape, London, 1988. [] $8/40

028a: VARGA, THE ESQUIRE YEARS *A Catalogue Raisonee* Alfred Van Der Marck Editions, 1987. [2] Signed limited edition (PW). Announced for $350. Never seen. Foreword by Vonnegut $NVA

028b: VARGA, THE ESQUIRE YEARS *A Catalogue Raisonne* Alfred Van Der Marck Editions, 1987. [] 35,000 cc (PW). Foreword by Vonnegut $25/75

029a: WHO AM I THIS TIME? Redpath Press, Minneapolis, 1987. [0] Wraps. Issued in plain envelope. The book and an envelope for mailing are in a plastic bag with an information sheet (Chloe's Books 12/94) $40.

030a: PRECAUTIONARY LETTER TO THE NEXT GENERATION Volkswagon (1988). [0] Off-print of an ad in *Time* magazine (Ken Lopez 4/91) $75.

031a: CONVERSATION WITH KURT VONNEGUT University of Mississippi, Jacksonville (1988). [] $25/50

031b: CONVERSATION WITH KURT VONNEGUT University of Mississippi, Jacksonville (1988). [] Wraps $30.

032a: "TO WHOM IT MAY CONCERN" (Poetry Center of the 92nd Street Y, New York, 1990.) [0] Wraps (Waiting For Godot 10/90) $60.

033a: HOCUS POCUS OR, WHAT'S THE HURRY, SON Putnam, New York (1990). [] Uncorrected proof. In gold wraps (Waiting For Godot 2/91) $75.

033b: HOCUS POCUS OR, WHAT'S THE HURRY, SON Franklin Library, Franklin Center, 1990. [2] Signed limited edition. Issued in full leather. Frontis illustration by Edith Vonnegut. Squibb and special message to readers by the author $100.

033c: HOCUS POCUS OR, WHAT'S THE HURRY, SON Putnam, New York (1990). [2] 250 sgd no. cc. Issued without dustwrapper. In slipcase $200/250

033d: HOCUS POCUS OR, WHAT'S THE HURRY, SON Putnam, New York (1990). [] (Published June 1990 @ $19.95) $10/40

033e: HOCUS POCUS OR, WHAT'S THE HURRY, SON Jonathan Cape, London, 1990. [] Uncorrected proof. In pictorial wraps $75.

033f: HOCUS POCUS OR, WHAT'S THE HURRY, SON Jonathan Cape, London, 1990. [ ] $10/50

034a: FATES WORSE THAN DEATH Putnam, New York (1991). [] Uncorrected proof. In red wraps $75.

(Also see 1982 entry)

034b: FATES WORSE THAN DEATH Easton Press, Norwalk, 1991. [2] Signed and limited edition. In full leather $100.

034c: FATES WORSE THAN DEATH Putnam, New York (1991). [2] 200 sgd no. cc. Issued without dustwrapper. In slipcase $200/250

034d: FATES WORSE THAN DEATH Putnam, New York (1991). [3] Signed on tipped-in page (Bert Babcock 2/92) $75/100

034e: FATES WORSE THAN DEATH Putnam, New York (1991). [3] (Published August 1991 @ $22.95) $10/50

034f: FATES WORSE THAN DEATH Jonathan Cape, London, 1991. [] Uncorrected proof. In pictorial wraps $75.

034g: FATES WORSE THAN DEATH Jonathan Cape, London, 1991. [ ] $10/40

035a: TIMEQUAKE Putnam, New York (1997). [] Uncorrected proof. In printed white wraps (Bev Chaney, Jr. 5/98) $50.

035b: TIMEQUAKE Putnam, New York (1997). [2] 225 sgd no. cc. Issued without dustwrapper. In cloth covered slipcase $150/200

035c: TIMEQUAKE Putnam, New York (1997). [3] (Published @ $23.95) $6/30

035d: TIMEQUAKE Jonathan Cape, London, 1997. [] Uncorrected proof. In glossy wraps (Red Snapper Books 5/98) $40.

035e: TIMEQUAKE Jonathan Cape, London (1997). [3] “Published by Jonathan Cape 1997” $10/50

035f: TIMEQUAKE Easton Press, Norwalk, 1977. [2] Signed limited edtion in full leather $75.

In addition to his writing, Vonnegut is also an artist. His works include the following. Prices shown are current as of 1998, and can be ordered from the Quill & Brush: e-mail *firsts@qb.com,* or from the address shown for the APGs.

"EGYPTIAN ARCHITECT" Limited Edition. Signed silkscreen print. (Petro III Graphics, Lexington, Kentucky), 1993. One of 50 signed, numbered copies of this print which is featured in Vonnegut's Discover Card ad appearing on TV. Hand printed White Lenox paper (20 x 26 inches) in four colors: yellow, medium blue, olive green, and black $800.

"SELF-PORTRAIT #1" Limited Edition. Signed silkscreen Print. (Petro III Graphics, Lexington, Kentucky), 1993. First edition. One of 235 signed, numbered copies of Vonnegut's profile self-portrait. Hand printed on Rives paper (22 x 30 inches) in four colors: dark gray, blue-gray, cobalt blue and red $600.

"SELF-PORTRAIT #2" Limited Edition. Signed silkscreen print. (Petro III Graphics, Lexington, Kentucky), 1993. One of 100 signed, numbered copies of Vonnegut's profile self-portrait. Hand printed on White Lenox paper (22 x 30 inches) in three colors: dark gray, light gray, and fire red $450.

"SELF-PORTRAIT #3" Limited Edition. Signed silkscreen print. (Petro III Graphics, Lexington, Kentucky), 1993. One of 100 signed, numbered copies of Vonnegut's profile self-portrait. Hand printed on White Lenox paper (12.5 x 18 inches) in three colors: dark gray and red $300.

"SELF-PORTRAIT #3" Poster for Midway College. Limited Edition. Signed silkscreen print. (Petro III Graphics, Lexington, Kentucky), 1993. One of 200 unnumbered impressions. Hand printed on White Lenox paper (26 x 40 inches) in five colors: dark red, fire red, cobalt blue, dark gray and light gray $150.

"SPHINCTER, AUGUST 10, 1993" White Edition. Limited Edition. Signed Silkscreen Print. (Petro III Graphics, Lexington, Kentucky), 1993. One of 12 signed numbered copies of Vonnegut's signature asterisk which made its first appearance in *Breakfast of Champions*. Hand printed on White Rives paper (22 x 30 inches) in one color: graphite $450.

"SPHINCTER, AUGUST 10, 1993" Gray Edition. Limited Edition. Signed silkscreen print. (Petro III Graphics, Lexington, Kentucky), 1993. One of 12 signed numbered copies. Hand printed on Gray Folio paper (22 x 30 inches) in one color: graphite $450.

"SPHINCTER, AUGUST 10, 1993" Black Edition. Limited Edition. Signed silkscreen print. (Petro III Graphics, Lexington, Kentucky), 1993. One of 12 signed numbered copies. Hand printed on Black Arches paper (22 x 30 inches) in one color: white $450.

"SPHINCTER, AUGUST 10, 1993" Gray Edition. Limited Edition. Signed silkscreen print. (Petro III Graphics, Lexington, Kentucky), 1993. One of 12 signed numbered copies. Hand printed on Gray Folio paper (22 x 30 inches) in one color: graphite $450.

"SPHINCTER, AUGUST 10, 1993" White Edition. Limited Edition. Signed silkscreen print. (Petro III

Graphics, Lexington, Kentucky), 1993. One of 12 signed numbered copies of Vonnegut's signature asterisk which made its first appearance in *Breakfast of Champions.* Hand printed on White Rives paper (22 x 30 inches) in one color: graphite $450.

"THREE MADONNAS" Limited Edition. Signed silkscreen print. (Petro III Graphics, Lexington, Kentucky), 1993. One of 50 signed, numbered copies of this print which is featured in Vonnegut's Discover Card ad appearing on TV. Hand printed Rives White paper (25¾ x 22 inches) in six colors: red, yellow, medium gray, light blue, brown and black $800.

"VASECTOMY" Limited Edition. Signed silkscreen print. (Petro III Graphics, Lexington, Kentucky), 1993. One of 50 signed numbered copies. Hand printed on Gray Folio paper (22 x 27 inches) in eight colors: yellow, red, medium gray, light blue, green, white, purple and black $750.

"WASP WAIST" A portfolio containing six individually signed, silkscreened prints. (Petro III Graphics, Lexington, Kentucky), 1993-94. One of only 10 portfolios containing six silkscreened prints of Vonnegut's nude with a "W. A. S. P."-ish waist, outlined in dark gray on Gray Folio paper (22 x 30 inches) and pulled in six varying colors: tan, yellow, fire red, cobalt blue, burgundy red, and cerulean blue. Also includes one cover sheet with an introduction by Vonnegut pulled in black on Gray Folio paper, and one pulled in black on Black Arches paper. All the sheets in the portfolio are signed and numbered in pencil. $6,500.

"CHEOPS" Limited Edition. signed silkscreen print. (Petro III Graphics, Lexington, Kentucky), 1994. One of 40 signed numbered copies. Hand printed on White Lenox paper (20 x 26 inches) in three colors: red, yellow, and black. $850.

"GOOD NEWS" Limited Edition. Signed silkscreen print. (Petro III Graphics, Lexington, Kentucky), 1994. One of 40 signed and numbered copies. Hand printed on White Lenox paper (25 x 28.5 inches) in five colors: red, medium purple, green, blue, and black. $750.

"GOOD NEWS" Deluxe Edition. Limited Edition. Signed silkscreen print. (Petro III Graphics, Lexington, Kentucky), 1994. One of 16 signed and numbered copies. Hand printed on Gray Folio (22 x 30 inches) in six colors: red, medium purple, green, blue, white, and black. $800.

"NOSTALGIA" Limited Edition. Signed silkscreen print. (Petro III Graphics, Lexington, Kentucky), 1994. One of 40 signed and numbered copies. Hand printed on White Lenox paper (25 x 33 inches) in five colors: yellow, purple, blue gray, light maroon, and black. $900.

"NOSTALGIA" Deluxe Edition. Limited Edition. Signed silkscreen print. (Petro III Graphics, Lexington, Kentucky), 1994. One of 12 signed and numbered copies. Hand printed on Gray Folio (22 x 30 inches) in six colors: yellow, purple, blue gray,, light maroon, white, and black. $1,000.

"ONE-EYED JACK" Cerulean Edition. Limited Edition. Signed silkscreen print. (Petro III Graphics, Lexington, Kentucky), 1994. One of 14 signed and numbered copies. Hand printed on White Rives paper (22 x 30 inches) in four colors: cerulean blue, yellow, dark yellow, and cobalt blue. $900.

"ONE-EYED JACK" Dark Gray Edition. Limited Edition. Signed silkscreen print. (Petro III Graphics, Lexington, Kentucky), 1994. One of 24 signed and numbered copies. Hand printed on White Rives paper (22 x 30 inches) in four colors: dark gray, yellow, dark yellow, and cobalt blue. $800.

"ONE-EYED JACK" Red Edition. Limited Edition. Signed silkscreen print. (Petro III Graphics, Lexington, Kentucky), 1994. One of 10 signed and numbered copies. Hand printed on White Rives paper (22 x 30 inches) in four colors: red, yellow, dark yellow, and cobalt blue. $1,000.

"TRIO" Limited Edition. Signed silkscreen print. (Petro III Graphics, Lexington, Kentucky), 1994. One of 40 signed and numbered copies. Hand printed on White Lenox paper (20 x 26 inches) in five colors: red, blue, medium gray, yellow, and black. $750.

"ABSOLUT VONNEGUT" Limited Edition. Signed silkscreen monotype print. (Petro III Graphics, Lexington, Kentucky), 1995. One of 30 signed and numbered copies, each numbered 1/1. Hand printed on White paper (22 x 30 inches) in nineteen colors. $1,500.

"HELEN" Limited Edition. Signed silkscreen print. (Petro III Graphics, Lexington, Kentucky), 1995. One of 99 signed and numbered copies of this print which is featured in Vonnegut's Discover Card ad appearing currently on TV. Hand printed on White Lenox paper (13 x 22 inches) in five colors: umber, light umber, sienna, light, and graphite. $550.

"WASP WAIST" An aluminum cut-out sculpture. (Petro III Graphics, Lexington, Kentucky), 1995. One of 9 copies signed and numbered at the foundry. Each sculpture was cut from quarter-inch aluminum with a half-inch thick base. The height is approximately 24 inches, with a 6-inch base. The image of Vonnegut's nude with a "W. A. S. P."-ish waist is in relief and painted in black. $1,800.

"ANNE" Limited Edition. Signed silkscreen print. (Petro III Graphics, Lexington, Kentucky), 1996. One of 30 signed and numbered copies. Hand printed on White Coventry paper (22 x 30 inches) in six colors: blue, green, yellow, red, tan and black. $750.

"ASTRONOMY" Limited Edition. Signed silkscreen print. (Petro III Graphics, Lexington, Kentucky), 1996. One of 30 signed and numbered copies. Hand printed on White Stonghenge paper (10 5/8 x 5½ inches) in six colors: purple, yellow, light blue, fire red, green, and orange. $450.

"BIRTHDAY" Limited Edition. Signed silkscreen print. (Petro III Graphics, Lexington, Kentucky), 1996. One of 30 signed and numbered copies. Hand printed on White Coventry paper (15 x 22 inches) in five colors: red, sienna, green, yellow, and black. $500.

"IDENTICAL TWIN" Limited Edition. Signed silkscreen print. (Petro III Graphics, Lexington, Kentucky), 1996. One of 30 signed and numbered copies. Hand printed on White Coventry paper (15 x 22 inches) in five colors: light green, light blue, light purple, yellow, and cerulean blue. $750.

"JOE PETRO, III" Limited Edition. Signed silkscreen print. (Petro III Graphics, Lexington, Kentucky), 1996. One of 30 signed and numbered copies. Hand printed on Warm White Stonghenge paper (22 x 30 inches) in five colors: red, orange, yellow, light blue, , and black. $800.

"NOV. 11, 1918" Limited Edition. Signed silkscreen print. (Petro III Graphics, Lexington, Kentucky), 1996. One of 30 signed and numbered copies. Hand printed on White Coventry paper (22 x 30 inches) in six colors: orange, red, dark blue, medium blue, green, and medium gray. $750.

"PROZAC" Limited Edition. Signed silkscreen print. (Petro III Graphics, Lexington, Kentucky), 1996. One of 30 signed and numbered copies. Hand printed on White Coventry paper (15 x 22 inches) in three colors: yellow, light blue, and black. $550.

"SMERDYAKOV" Limited Edition. Signed silkscreen print. (Petro III Graphics, Lexington, Kentucky), 1996. One of 99 signed and numbered copies. Hand printed on White Lenox paper (8½ x 11¾ inches) in two colors: yellow and black. $300.

"STILL LIFE" [20-color.] Limited Edition. Signed silkscreen print. (Petro III Graphics, Lexington, Kentucky), 1996. One of 30 signed and numbered copies. Hand printed on White Coventry paper (30 x 44 inches) in twenty colors: blues, browns, yellows, grays, greens, and reds. $1,500.

"STILL LIFE" [3-color.] Limited Edition. Signed silkscreen print. (Petro III Graphics, Lexington, Kentucky), 1996. One of 30 signed and numbered copies. Hand printed on White Coventry paper (22 x 30 inches) in three colors: yellow, pea green, and black. $750.

"STILL LIFE" Exhibition poster for Barnes & Noble Café Gallery. Limited Edition. Signed silkscreen poster. (Petro III Graphics, Lexington, Kentucky), 1996. One of 12 signed and numbered copies of the poster created for Vonnegut's September 1996 opening at the 1/1A Gallery, Denver, Colorado.. Hand printed on White Coventry paper (38 x 50 inches) in 22 colors: blues, browns, yellows, greens, grays, and reds. $600.

"STILL LIFE" Exhibition poster for 1/1A Gallery. Limited Edition. Signed silkscreen poster. (Petro III Graphics, Lexington, Kentucky), 1996. One of 20 signed and numbered copies of the poster created for Vonnegut's September 1996 opening at the 1/1A Gallery, Denver, Colorado. Hand printed on White Coventry paper (38 x 50 inches) in six colors. $300.

"STRINGS" Limited Edition. Signed silkscreen print. (Petro III Graphics, Lexington, Kentucky), 1996. One of 30 signed and numbered copies. Hand printed on White Coventry paper (15 x 22 inches) in four colors: yellow, medium blue, tan, and black. $650.

"TRALFMADOR #1" Limited Edition. Signed silkscreen print. (Petro III Graphics, Lexington,

Kentucky), 1996. One of 30 signed and numbered copies. Hand printed on White Coventry paper (22 x 30 inches) in six colors: light blue, green, medium brown, dark red, medium red, and black. $1,100.

"TRALFMADOR #2" Limited Edition. Signed silkscreen print. (Petro III Graphics, Lexington, Kentucky), 1996. One of 30 signed and numbered copies. Hand printed on White Coventry paper (22 x 30 inches) in eight colors: green, purple, red, yellow, brown, light blue, cobalt blue, and black. $1,100.

"TRIED TO DO MY FRIEND YEVGENY-MISSED BY A MILE" (Parchment Gallery Graphics / University of Charleston, Charleston, West Virginia, 1996). One of less than 10 cc signed by Vonnegut and the Russian poet Yevtushenko. 11 x 8.5 inches. Off-white paper printed on one side in black. Yevtushenko has signed in Russian. The University of Charleston's March 1996 show "From Russia with Love" featured art by Yevtushenko and Vonnegut, with a lecture and dramatic readings in person by Yevtushenko, and Vonnegut discussing his art by telephone. Because of the friendship of the two author/artists, a limited edition of drawings by each of the other was planned. Unfortunately, both drawings were not completed in time. The coordinator of the event, who possesses the original drawing, asked Vonnegut for his permission to print 20 copies. Of these he gave 10 to Yev, and he kept 10 which Yev signed for him and we bought. We sold one of the 10 immediately, then recently sent them to a friend of Vonnegut's who kept one (presumably signed) and gave two to Vonnegut (presumably unsigned). So, it may be a stretch but we're assuming there are on 7 copies of this unpublished item signed by Vonnegut $250.

"GUILDED CAGE" Limited Edition. Signed silk-screen print. (Petro III Graphics, Lexington, Kentucky), 1997. One of 26 signed and numbered copies. Hand printed on White Lenox paper (7 x 11 inches) in one color: gold. $175.

"GUILDED CAGE" Black Edition. Limited Edition. Signed silkscreen print. (Petro III Graphics, Lexington, Kentucky), 1997. One of 4 signed and numbered copies. Hand printed on Black Arches paper (22 x 30 inches) in one color: gold. $450.

"GUILDED CAGE" Deluxe Edition. Limited Edition. Signed silkscreen print. (Petro III Graphics, Lexington, Kentucky), 1997. One of 10 signed and numbered copies with a self-portrait remarque in pencil by Vonnegut. Hand printed on White Stonehenge paper (14 x 10¼ inches) in one color: gold. $300.

"GUILDED CAGE" Gray Edition. Limited Edition. Signed silkscreen print. (Petro III Graphics, Lexington, Kentucky), 1997. One of 4 signed and numbered copies with a self-portrait remarque in pencil by Vonnegut. Hand printed on White Stonehenge paper (22 x 30 inches) in one color: gold. $450.

"TROUT IN COHOES" Limited Edition., Signed silkscreen print. (Petro III Graphics, Lexington, Kentucky), 1997. One of 77 numbered copies signed by Vonnegut and "Kilgore Trout." Hand printed on White Rives paper (22 x 30 inches) in three colors: medium green, medium blue, and graphite. This image of Kilgore Trout was featured in Vonnegut's book TIMEQUAKE. $1,000.

"TROUT IN COHOES" Deluxe Edition. Limited Edition. Signed silkscreen print. (Petro III Graphics, Lexington, Kentucky), 1997. One of 18 signed and numbered copies with "Kilgore Trout in Cohoes, New York, 1975" and self-portrait remarque in pencil by Vonnegut. Hand printed on warm white Stonehenge paper (20½ x 28¾ inches) in eight colors: medium green, light green, medium blue, light blue, light gray, white gray, gold, and graphite. This image of Kilgore Trout was featured in Vonnegut's TIMEQUAKE. $1,400.

EUDORA WELTY

Eudora Welty was born in Jackson, Mississippi in 1909. She was educated at Mississippi State College For Women, University of Wisconsin and Columbia University School of Advertising in New York. Miss Welty has been writing full-time for over 50 years. During that career she has received about all the fellowships and prizes a writer can garner, including a Pulitzer Prize for *The Optimist's Daughter* in 1973. When she was 86 years old Miss Welty was awarded France's highest award for outstanding service, the French Legion of Honor.

REFERENCES:

(a) Bruccoli Clark. FIRST PRINTINGS OF AMERICAN AUTHORS. Detroit: Gale Research (1977). (Used for U.S. editions through 1975 unless otherwise stated.)

(b) Polk, Noel (compiler). "Eudora Welty: A Bibliographical Checklist." *American Book Collector.* Volume 2, Number 1. January/February 1981. (Used for British editions through 1980 and U.S. editions 1975 - 1980 unless otherwise stated.)

(c) Turlington, H.E. *Southern Women Writers 1922-1984*. Catalog 27. (Issued in March 1986.)

(d) Inventory, dealer catalogs, *Publishers Weekly*, etc.

001a: EUDORA WELTY *A Note on the Author and Her Work* Written by Katherine Anne Porter... (Doubleday Doran, Garden City, 1941.) [0] Pictorial wraps. A pre-publicity pamphlet for *A Curtain of Green* containing Welty's short story *The Key* $2,500.

002a: A CURTAIN OF GREEN Doubleday Doran, Garden City, 1941. [1] 2,476 cc (Alice Robbins 11/95) $300/1,500

002b: A CURTAIN OF GREEN John Lane Bodley Head, London (1943). [1] $100/500

003a: THE ROBBER BRIDEGROOM Doubleday Doran, Garden City, 1942. [1] $200/1,000

003b: THE ROBBER BRIDEGROOM John Lane Bodley Head, London (1944). [1] Illustrated by James Holland. First illustrated edition $150/500

003c: THE ROBBER BRIDEGROOM Pennyroyal Press, West Hatfield, Massachusetts, 1987. [2] 150 no. cc. Signed by Welty and Barry Moser (the illustrator). In full red leather. Issued without slipcase $750.

003d: THE ROBBER BRIDEGROOM Harcourt Brace, San Diego (1987). [] Illustrated by Barry Moser $12/60

004a: THE WIDE NET *and Other Stories* Harcourt Brace, New York (1943). [1] First issue with top edge stained green (source?) $200/1,000

004b: THE WIDE NET *and Other Stories* John Lane Bodley Head, London (1945). [1] On reverse of Welty dustwrapper is jacket for F.E. Mills Young's *Unlucky Farm* $75/450

005a: DELTA WEDDING Harcourt Brace, New York (1946). [1] $75/350

005b: DELTA WEDDING Bodley Head, London (1947). [1] $50/250

006a: MUSIC FROM SPAIN The Levee Press, Greenville, Mississippi, 1948. [2] 750 sgd no. cc. Issued in glassine dustwrapper. Also noted a copy signed, but not numbered. Possibly, a review copy. (MacDonnell Rare Books 2/97) $750.

007a: THE GOLDEN APPLES Harcourt Brace, New York (1949). [1] $60/300

007b: THE GOLDEN APPLES Bodley Head, London (1950). [1] First issue in brown cloth lacks front endpapers (Peter Jolliffe 7/90) $50/200

008a: SHORT STORIES Harcourt Brace, New York (1949). [2] 1,500 cc. Issued in glassine dustwrapper $200.

009a: THE PONDER HEART Harcourt Brace, New York (1954). [1] $40/200

009b: THE PONDER HEART Hamish Hamilton, London (1954). Advance copy. Brown wraps. Issued in dustwrapper (Nicholas Pounder 12/91) $250.

009c: THE PONDER HEART Hamish Hamilton, London (1954). [1] $25/125

009d: THE PONDER HEART *A Play* Random House, New York (1956). [1] Adapted by Joseph Feilds and Jerome Chodorov. (Published May 18, 1956 @ $2.95) $15/75

010a: SELECTED STORIES OF EUDORA WELTY Modern Library, New York (1954). [1] Introduction by Katherine Anne Porter $15/75

011a: THE BRIDE OF THE INNISFALLEN *and Other Stories* Harcourt Brace, New York (1955). [1] Copyright notice of first issue contains only one date: "copyright ... 1955, by Eudora Welty." Issued in blue and green mottled boards with green cloth spine and silver stamping (ref.b) $300/500

011b: THE BRIDE OF THE INNISFALLEN *and Other Stories* Harcourt Brace, New York (1955).

[1] Second issue copyright contains 5 dates: "copyright...1949, 1951, 1952, 1954, 1955..." Copyright page tipped in. Issued in blue and green mottled boards with green cloth spine and silver stamping (ref.b) $100/250

011c: THE BRIDE OF THE INNISFALLEN *and Other Stories* Harcourt Brace, New York (1955). [1] Third issue and second binding: copyright notice with 5 dates as in 011b but issued in light grayish-brown cloth with blue and gold stamping (ref.b) $30/150

011d: THE BRIDE OF THE INNISFALLEN *and Other Stories* Hamish Hamilton, London (1955). [1] $40/200

012a: PLACE IN FICTION (South Atlantic Quarterly, no place or date [circa 1956]) [0] Printed wraps. Approximately 50 cc. An off-print from the *South Atlantic Quarterly* (Ref.c) $800.

012b: PLACE IN FICTION House of Books, New York, 1957. [2] 26 sgd ltr cc. Issued in glassine dustwrapper $1,000.

012c: PLACE IN FICTION House of Books, New York, 1957. [2] 300 sgd no. cc. Issued in glassine dustwrapper. Part of edition was destroyed (estimated at 50 to 75 copies [MacDonnell Rare Books 7/94]) $600.

013a: OCTOBER 7-25, 1958 EXHIBITION OF RECENT SCULPTURE JOHN ROOD The Contemporaries, New York (1958). [0] Stiff white wraps. Welty wrote text for this art exhibition catalogue. (Pictorial wraps per William Reese Co. 1/87) $600.

014a: HENRY GREEN *A Novelist* ... (The Texas Quarterly, Austin, 1961.) [0] 50 cc. Wraps. 12 page offprint of article which appeared in *The Texas Quarterly* Special Issue, Britain 2 Autumn 1961. (While ref.c indicates there were only 25 copies, the Captain's Bookshelf 3/95 states 50 copies) $600.

015a: THREE PAPERS ON FICTION Smith College, Northampton, Massachusetts, 1962. [0] Wraps. 1,300 cc (Serendipity Cat. 43) $200.

016a: THE SHOE BIRD Harcourt Brace, New York (1964). [1] $50/250

017a: THIRTEEN STORIES Harcourt Brace, New York (1965). [1] Wraps. Selected and introduction by Ruth M. Van de Kieft $75.

018a: A SWEET DEVOURING Albondocani Press, New York, 1969. [2] 26 sgd ltr cc. Wraps $600.

018b: A SWEET DEVOURING Albondocani Press, New York, 1969. [2] 150 sgd no. cc. Wraps $350.

019a: LOSING BATTLES Random House, New York (1970). [2] 300 sgd no. cc. Issued in acetate dustwrapper. In slipcase $350/400

019b: LOSING BATTLES Random House, New York (1970). [1] $15/75

019c: LOSING BATTLES Virago (London, 1982). [] Uncorrected proof. In green and white stiff wraps. Issued in dustwrapper (Fugitive Phoenix 5/90) $150.

019d: LOSING BATTLES Virago (London, 1982). [1] "Published by ... 1982" $15/75

020a: A FLOCK OF GUINEA HENS ... (Albondocani Press, New York, 1970.) [0] 100 cc. Wraps. Has greeting and "Albondocani Press / Ampersand Books" on first page (Ref.b). 110 copies (Beasley Books 7/92) $250.

020b: A FLOCK OF GUINEA HENS ... (Albondocani Press, New York, 1970.) [0] 210 cc. Wraps. Greeting only on first page. Printed for use as Christmas card (ref.b) $175.

021a: ONE TIME, ONE PLACE ... Random House, New York (1971). [2] 300 sgd no. cc. Issued in acetate dustwrapper. In brown slipcase. (MacDonnell Rare Books states this was issued in an edition of 350 copies but publisher's records indicates only 337 copies were bound) $350/400

021b: ONE TIME, ONE PLACE ... Random House, New York (1971). [1] $30/150

021c: ONE TIME, ONE PLACE ... University Press of Mississippi, Jackson, Mississippi (1996). [2] 125 no. cc. Issued in slipcase (Bev Chaney, Jr. 2/96) $150.

021d: ONE TIME, ONE PLACE ... University Press of Mississippi, Jackson, Mississippi (1996). [ ] (Bev Chaney, Jr. 2/96) $6/30

022a: THE OPTIMIST'S DAUGHTER Random House, New York (1972). [2] Approximately 225 sgd no. cc. Approximately 75 copies destroyed of projected edition of 300 because of defective bindings (ref.b). Issued without dustwrapper. In slipcase $350/400

022b: THE OPTIMIST'S DAUGHTER Random House, New York (1972). [1] Pulitzer Prize for 1973 $20/100

022c: THE OPTIMIST'S DAUGHTER Andre Deutsch (London, 1973). [1] $15/75

022d: THE OPTIMIST'S DAUGHTER Franklin Library, Franklin Center, 1978. [2] "Limited Edition." Issued in brown leather $50.

022e: THE OPTIMIST'S DAUGHTER Franklin Library, Franklin Center, 1980. [2] Signed "Limited Edition." Contains 7-page special message from Welty to subscribers. Issued in maroon leather $100.

023a: SOME NOTES ON TIME IN FICTION Mississippi Quarterly, Jackson, Mississippi, 1973. [0] Wraps. Offprint from *Mississippi Quarterly* Vol. XXVI, No. 4 (ref.c) $450.

024a: A PAGEANT OF BIRDS Albondocani Press, New York, 1974. [2] 26 sgd ltr cc. Wraps. In dustwrapper $400/500

024b: A PAGEANT OF BIRDS Albondocani Press, New York, 1974. [2] 300 sgd no. cc. Wraps. In dustwrapper $200/300

025a: IS PHOENIX JACKSON'S GRANDSON REALLY DEAD ... (Critical Enquiry, Chicago, 1974.) [0] Wraps. An off-print. Estimated at 25 to 50 copies (Glenn Horowitz #7) $450.

026a: FAIRY TALE OF THE NATCHEZ TRACE The Mississippi Historical Society, Jackson, Mississippi, 1975. [0] 1,000 cc. Issued without dustwrapper. In publisher's envelope (Joseph the Provider Cat. 24) $100.

027a: IMAGES OF THE SOUTH Center For Southern Folklore, Memphis, 1977. [1] Wraps. Visits with Eudora Welty and Walker Evans $75.

028a: ACROBATS IN A PARK Delta, no place, 1977. [] Wraps. Off-print from *Delta Magazine* (ref.c) $350.

028b: ACROBATS IN A PARK Lord John Press, Northridge, California, 1980. [2] 100 sgd no. cc. Issued without dustwrapper. In green cloth with brown stamping $350.

028c: ACROBATS IN A PARK Lord John Press, Northridge, California, 1980. [2] 300 sgd no. cc. Issued without dustwrapper. In green, gold and rust marbled boards, green cloth spine with gold stamping $225.

029a: THE EYE OF THE STORY Random House, New York (1978). [] Uncorrected proof. Issued in red wraps. Contains four essays (almost 50 pages) not included in final book (Bookfinders 9/92) $1,000.

029b: THE EYE OF THE STORY ... Random House, New York (1978). [2] 300 sgd no. cc. Issued without dustwrapper. In light gray slipcase $300/350

029c: THE EYE OF THE STORY ... Random House, New York (1978). [1] $15/75

029d: THE EYE OF THE STORY ... Virago (London), 1987. [] (Ken Lopez 9/91) $12/60

030a: IDA M'TOY University of Illinois Press, Urbana / Chicago / London (1979). [2] 350 sgd no. cc. Issued without dustwrapper. In green or red cloth (no priority). Also in black (Bert Babcock). 160 in red cloth; 190 in green cloth (Joseph the Provider Books) $250.

031a: WOMEN! MAKE A TURBAN IN OWN HOME! Palaemon Press (Winston-Salem, North Carolina, 1979). [2] 35 sgd no. cc. Numbered I-XXXV $500.

031b: WOMEN! MAKE A TURBAN IN OWN HOME! Palaemon Press (Winston-Salem, North Carolina, 1979). [2] 200 sgd no. cc. Issued without dustwrapper $200.

032a: CRITICAL ESSAYS University Press of Mississippi, Jackson, 1979. [] Edited by Peggy Whitman Prenshaw (Bev Chaney) $25/75

033a: MOON LAKE ... Franklin Library, Franklin Center, 1980. [2] "Limited Edition." Issued in dark green leather. Same stories as in *Thirteen Stories* (017a) $150.

034a: TWENTY PHOTOGRAPHS Palaemon Press (Winston-Salem, North Carolina, 1980). [2] 20 sgd no. (Roman) copies. Photographs mounted on heavy rag board. In clamshell folio box. Errata slip laid in. Five of these copies were for the author's use $3,000.

034b: TWENTY PHOTOGRAPHS Palaemon Press (Winston-Salem, North Carolina, 1980). [2] 75 sgd no. cc. Issued in clam-shell box. Errata slip laid in $2,250.

035a: THE COLLECTED STORIES Harcourt Brace Jovanovich, New York (1980). [] Uncorrected proof. In blue wraps (Lame Duck Books 4/94) $750.

035b: THE COLLECTED STORIES ... Franklin Library, Franklin Center, 1980. [2] "Limited Edition." In red leather. Includes one page special message $100.

035c: THE COLLECTED STORIES ... Harcourt Brace Jovanovich, New York / London (1980). [2] 500 sgd no. cc. Issued without dustwrapper. In maroon slipcase with white label $250/300

035d: THE COLLECTED STORIES ... Harcourt Brace Jovanovich, New York / London (1980). [0] States "A limited first edition has been privately printed BCDE" on copyright page $15/75

035e: THE COLLECTED STORIES ... Marion Boyars, London, 1981. [] Also wraps? $15/75

036a: BYE-BYE BREVOORT New Stage Theatre, Jackson, Mississippi (1980). [2] 26 sgd ltr cc. Issued without dustwrapper. In boards with leather spine $500.

036b: BYE-BYE BREVOORT New Stage Theatre, Jackson, Mississippi (1980). [2] 50 sgd no. (Roman) copies. Issued without dustwrapper $400.

036c: BYE-BYE BREVOORT New Stage Theatre, Jackson, Mississippi (1980). [2] 400 sgd cc. Unnumbered. Issued without dustwrapper $150.

037a: WHITE FRUITCAKE (Albondocani Press, New York, 1980.) [0] 175 cc. Wraps. "Albondocani Press / Ampersand Books" and greeting printed on first page. Issued with mailing envelope $125.

037b: WHITE FRUITCAKE (Albondocani Press, New York, 1989.) [0] 275 cc. Wraps. Greeting only printed on first page. Printed for use as Christmas card. Issued with mailing envelope $75.

038a: RETREAT Palaemon Press (Winston-Salem, North Carolina, 1981). [2] 7 sgd no. cc. With signed numbered woodcut by Ann Carter Pollard tipped in before title page. Not For Sale (Joseph Dermont #40) $600.

038b: RETREAT Palaemon Press (Winston-Salem, North Carolina, 1981). [2] 50 sgd no. cc. Each containing an original aquatint by Ann C. Pollard (Joseph Dermont #40) $500.

038c: RETREAT Palaemon Press (Winston-Salem, North Carolina, 1981). [2] 40 sgd no. cc. Numbered I-XL. Issued for the private use of the author and publisher (Joseph Dermont #40) $350.

038d: RETREAT Palaemon Press (Winston-Salem, North Carolina, 1981). [2] 150 sgd no. cc. Bound with cloth spine and light blue decorated paper-covered boards $250.

039a: ONE WRITER'S BEGINNINGS Harvard University Press, Cambridge, 1984. [] Uncorrected proof. In printed green wraps (Bev Chaney 9/91). "It is estimated that only 50 (copies) were produced" (Tristero 12/94) $450.

039b: ONE WRITER'S BEGINNINGS Harvard University Press, Cambridge / London, 1984, [2] 350 sgd no. cc. Issued without dustwrapper. In cloth slipcase $350/400

039c: ONE WRITER'S BEGINNINGS Harvard University Press, Cambridge, 1984. [3] $15/75

039d: ONE WRITER'S BEGINNINGS Faber, London (1985). [] Wraps. (No hardback in England (Maurice Neville 7/88) $60.

040a: FOUR PHOTOGRAPHS (Lord John Press, Northridge, California, 1984.) [2] 150 sgd no. cc. Broadside $250.

041a: THE MacNEIL / LEHRER NEW HOUR. Transcript #2230. Journal Graphics, New York (1984). [0] Stapled self wraps. The transcript of a broadcast interview (on PBS) with Welty entitled "Eudora Welty at 75." Published in an edition of 300 copies (Jos. The Provider 3/89). Although in talking to *Journal Graphics* we got the impression that the copies were run off as ordered and there would be no way to differentiate later runs. This may possibly still be ordered from *Journal Graphics* $25.

042a: CONVERSATIONS WITH EUDORA WELTY University Press of Mississippi, Jackson (1984). [] Edited by Peggy Whitman Prenshaw $25/50

042b: CONVERSATIONS WITH EUDORA WELTY University Press of Mississippi, Jackson (1984). [] Wraps $30.

043a: IN BLACK AND WHITE Lord John Press, Northridge, 1985. [2] 100 sgd no. cc. Special binding, marbled boards with leather spine. In slipcase. Introduction by Anne Tyler. Signed by both $350/400

043b: IN BLACK AND WHITE Lord John Press, Northridge, 1985. [2] 300 sgd no. cc. Cloth spine. Issued without dustwrapper or slipcase $225.

044a: THE LITTLE STORE Tamazunchale Press, Newton, Iowa, 1985. [2] 250 no. cc. Full leather. Miniature book (not signed) $100.

045a: THE FAULKNER INVESTIGATION Cordelia Editions, Santa Barbara, 1985. [2] 500 cc. Wraps. Written with Ross Macdonald $60.

046a: MORGANA University Press of Mississippi, Jackson (1988). [2] 26 sgd ltr cc. Two stories from *The Golden Apples*. Illustrated by Mildred Nungester Wolf (signed by both). Issued without dustwrapper. In slipcase $450/500

046b: MORGANA University Press of Mississippi, Jackson (1988). [2] 250 sgd no. cc. Issued without dustwrapper. In slipcase $250/300

046c: MORGANA University Press of Mississippi, Jackson (1988). [] 3,000 cc $12/60

047a: THE COMPLETE WORKS OF EUDORA WELTY Rinsen, Kyoto, 1988. [] 9 vols. Edited by Isuzu Tanabe. In English (Anacapa Books 3/94) $750.

048a: PHOTOGRAPHS University Press of Mississippi, Jackson (1989). [2] 52 sgd ltr cc. Foreword by Reynolds Price. Issued in full leather. With separate photo. In cloth covered box (Magnum Opus 9/91) $850/1,000

048b: PHOTOGRAPHS University Press of Mississippi, Jackson (1989). [2] 375 sgd no. cc. Issued without dustwrapper. In slipcase $250/300

048c: PHOTOGRAPHS University Press of Mississippi, Jackson (1989). [3] 6,500 cc (Nouveau Books 2/90) $50/100

049a: THE WELTY COLLECTION University of Mississippi, Jackson (1989). [] A catalog of the Welty collection at the Mississippi Department of Archives & History. Includes manuscript pages and a selection of photographs. (Published @ $27.50) $15/35

050a: THE HEART OF THE STORY University Press of Mississippi, Jackson (1991). [ ] (Bev Chaney, Jr. 1/95) $10/40

051a: A WRITER'S EYE *Collected Book Reviews* University Press of Mississippi, Jackson (1994). [ ] Edited by Pearl Amelia McHenry. (Published 4/94 @ $27.50) $10/35

052a: MORE CONVERSATIONS WITH EUDORA WELTY University Press of Mississippi, Jackson, 1996. [ ] (Published April 1996 @ $39.50) $20/50

052b: MORE CONVERSATIONS WITH EUDORA WELTY University Press of Mississippi, Jackson, 1996. [ ] (Published April 1996 @ $16.95) $20.

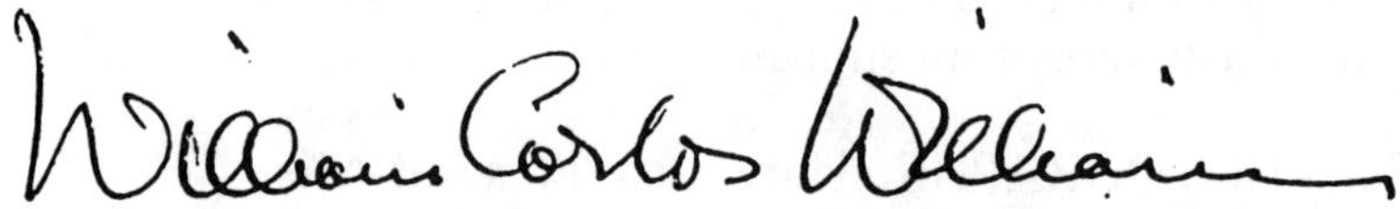

WILLIAM CARLOS WILLIAMS
1883-1963

Williams was born Rutherford, N.J. He received his M.D. from the University of Pennsylvania and did graduate work at the University of Leipzig. But aside from college he didn't travel much - "What the hell is there to see, anyway, compared with what's on the inside?" (ref.d)

He grew up in Rutherford, married a local girl, practiced medicine, wrote (in the house he bought in 1913), and died there in 1963.

He is known for his vivid, realistic and precise recording of the easily overlooked details of experience.

"There are a few things in life that one comes to want to do as one grows older, apart from turning over a little cash. I wanted to write... I've been writing, trying to get a few things said, ever since I started to study medicine. One feeds the other... Both seem necessary to me. One gets you out among the neighbors, the other permits me to express what I've been turning over in my mind as I go along." (ref.d)

REFERENCES:

(a) Wallace, Emily Mitchell. A BIBLIOGRAPHY OF WILLIAM CARLOS WILLIAMS. Middletown, Connecticut: Wesleyan University Press (1968).

(b) Bruccoli, Matthew J., et al. FIRST PRINTINGS OF AMERICAN AUTHORS. Volume 3. Detroit: Gale Research (1978).

(c) Information provided by New Directions.

(d) Kunitz & Haycraft. TWENTIETH CENTURY AUTHORS. New York: H.W. Wilson Co. 1942.

Ref.a, an excellent bibliography, was used for all entries through item 059, unless otherwise noted.

001a: POEMS (Reid Howell, Rutherford, New Jersey) 1909. [0] 100 cc. Wraps. Never published. Two copies known to have survived. Brown paper covers. First state contained numerous misprints and errors, line 5 of the first poem "Innocence" reads "of youth himself,all rose-y-clad" $35,000.

001b: POEMS (Reid Howell, Rutherford, New Jersey) 1909 [0] 100 cc. Wraps. Second state with numerous text corrections including line 5 of the poem "Innocence" which reads "of youth himself all rose-yclad." Fewer than 15 of this second state known $25,000.

002a: THE TEMPERS Elkin Mathews, London, 1913. [0] Probably 1,000 cc. Issued in glassine dustwrapper $1,000.

003a: AL QUE QUIERE! The Four Seas Company, Boston, 1917. [0] 1,000 cc. Yellow-orange paper boards printed in black. $750.

003b: AL QUE QUIERE! The Four Seas Company, Boston, 1917. [0] Variant with tan paper boards. Author's name misspelled "Willams" on spine. Priority assumed $650.

004a: KORA IN HELL *Improvisations* The Four Seas Company, Boston, 1920. [0] 1,000 cc. Orange dustwrapper printed in black. (Some copies had glassine dustwrappers) $250/750

004b: KORA IN HELL *Improvisations* City Lights Books, San Francisco (1957). [0] 1,500 cc. Wraps.

The Pocket Poets Series No. Seven. With a new prologue by Williams $60.

005a: SOUR GRAPES The Four Seas Company, Boston, 1921. [0] 1,000 cc. Author's name on spine label only $250/850

006a: THE GREAT AMERICAN NOVEL Three Mountains Press, Paris, 1923. [2] 300 no. cc. Some copies have a rectangular slip covering name of the press (on the title page) upon which is printed "Contact Editions 29 Quai d'Anjou, Paris" -priority unknown (ref.b). Dustwrapper not mentioned $650.

007a: SPRING AND ALL (Contact Publishing Co., Paris, 1923.) [0] 300 cc. Wraps. Issued in glassine dustwrapper $750.

007b: SPRING AND ALL Frontier Press (West Newburyport, Massachusetts), 1970. [0] Galley proofs. 27 narrow leaves (Wm. Reese Co. #40) $250.

007c: SPRING AND ALL Frontier Press (West Newburyport, Massachusetts), 1970. [0] Wraps (ref.b) $45.

008a: (First printed leaf) MANIKIN NUMBER TWO (Second printed leaf) GO GO No publisher, New York (1923). [0] 150 cc. *Manikin Number Two* by Monroe Wheeler, *Go Go* by Williams. Gray card-board covers printed in blue, tied with blue string in stabbed holes at fold $1,000.

009a: IN THE AMERICAN GRAIN Albert & Charles Boni, New York, 1925. [0] Original price $3.00, but raised to $3.50 right after publication (ref.a) $250/750

009b: IN THE AMERICAN GRAIN New Directions, Norfolk (1939). [0] 1,120 cc. Yellow cloth boards, lettered in red. Yellow dustwrapper printed in green and red $50/150

009c: IN THE AMERICAN GRAIN New Directions (New York, 1966). [] 5,043 cc. Wraps. "Third Printing" stated. First revised edition $30.

009d: IN THE AMERICAN GRAIN New Directions (New York, 1967). [] 1,000 cc. Clothbound issue of 009c $15/75

009e: IN THE AMERICAN GRAIN MacGibbon & Kee (London, 1967). [1] 2,000 cc. "First published in Great Britain...1966" Actually published in March 1967 $12/60

010a: A VOYAGE TO PAGANY Macaulay Company, New York, 1928. [0] $100/400

010b: A VOYAGE TO PAGANY New Directions (New York, 1970). [] With an introduction by Harry Levin $10/50

011a: LAST NIGHTS OF PARIS Macaulay Company, New York, 1929. [0] William's translation of the work by Philippe Soupault $100/400

011b: LAST NIGHTS OF PARIS Full Court Press, New York (1982). [2] 100 sgd no. cc. Enlarged edition. New introduction by Soupault and signed by him (Joseph The Provider #31) $100.

012a: A NOVELETTE AND OTHER PROSE (1921-1931) TO Publishers (Toulon, France, 1932). [0] Approximately 500 cc. Wraps $650.

013a: THE KNIFE OF THE TIMES *and Other Stories* The Dragon Press, Ithaca, N.Y. (1932). [2] 500 cc. Some copies have tipped-in slip near foot of title page reading "The Dragon Press, Publishers, Duffield & Green, distributors" - priority unknown. Glassine dustwrapper covered by gray paper dustwrapper printed in blue $350/750

014a: THE COD HEAD Harvest Press, San Francisco (1932). [2] 125 cc. Wraps. (Geo. Robert

Minkoff - List 86-F catalogued a variant without place and date on front cover and "Friends of Milton Arbenethy" in place of standard colophon. Baltimore Book Auctions lists apparent unrecorded trial copy with second "e" in surname in wrong type and 100 copies for limitation.) Also title, colophon ("100 copies") and two pages of text, without wraps (William Reese Co. 5/91) $600.

015a: COLLECTED POEMS 1921-1931 The Objectivist Press, New York, 1934. [0] 500 cc $150/600

016a: AN EARLY MARTYR *and Other Poems* The Alcestis Press, New York, 1935. [2] 20 sgd cc. Numbered I-XX. Stiff yellow wraps, glassine dustwrapper and yellow slipcase $3,000/3,500

016b: AN EARLY MARTYR *and Other Poems* The Alcestis Press, New York, 1935. [2] 135 sgd cc. Numbered 1-135. Yellow wraps, glassine dustwrapper and green slipcase. (Also 10 copies out-of-series for review) $2,000/2,500

017a: ADAM & EVE & THE CITY The Alcestis Press, Peru, VT., 1936. [2] 20 sgd cc. Numbered I-XX. Olive-green wraps. In green slipcase $4,000/5,000

017b: ADAM & EVE & THE CITY The Alcestis Press, Peru, VT., 1936. [2] 135 sgd cc. Numbered 1-135. Olive-green wraps. In green slip-case. (Also 12 copies marked out-of-series, 2 for copyright) $3,500/4,000

018a: WHITE MULE New Directions, Norfolk, Conn., 1937. [0] 1,100 cc. White cloth boards printed in black or gray cloth, printed in crimson on spine - priority unknown. (The second printing of 300 copies is probably indistinguishable from the first printing.) At least 445 sets of sheets not sold as they were used for 026a below $100/500

018b: WHITE MULE MacGibbon & Kee (London, 1965). [1] 2,000 cc $15/75

019a: WILLIAM ZORACH TWO DRAWINGS WILLIAM CARLOS WILLIAMS TWO POEMS Stovepipe Press, no place, 1937. [2] 500 cc (430 for sale). Wraps $200.

020a: LIFE ALONG THE PASSAIC RIVER New Directions, Norfolk, Conn., 1938. [0] 1,006 cc $150/600

021a: THE COMPLETE COLLECTED POEMS 1906-1938 New Directions, Norfolk, Conn. (1938). [2] 50 sgd no. cc. Dark blue cloth stamped in gold on spine. In pale blue slipcase. (Actually 52 copies were printed) $2,000/2,500

021b: THE COMPLETE COLLECTED POEMS 1906-1938 New Directions, Norfolk, Conn. (1938). [0] 816 cc. Bound in dark green cloth. There were 506 copies bound in October 1938 and 310 copies in February 1939, both in dark green $150/600

021c: THE COMPLETE COLLECTED POEMS 1906-1938 New Directions, Norfolk, Conn. (1938). [0] 650 cc. Bound in dark blue cloth in 1940 and later (same sheets as 021a & b). There were 400 copies bound in January 1940 and 250 "may" have been bound in April 1945 $100/400

022a: CHARLES SHEELER PAINTINGS DRAWINGS PHOTOGRAPHS MOMA, New York, 1939. [2] 5,500 cc. Wraps. Introduction by William Carlos Williams $125.

023a: IN THE MONEY / WHITE MULE Part II. New Directions, Norfolk, Conn. (1940) [0] Approximately 1,500 cc (of which we assume 445 copies were used for 026a below) $75/350

023b: IN THE MONEY MacGibbon & Kee (London, 1966). [1] 2,000 cc $15/75

024a: THE BROKEN SPAN New Directions, Norfolk, Conn. (1941). [0] 300 cc. First binding: gray paper boards printed in black and fuchsia.

Front flap of dustwrapper has comments about book, rear flap lists 12 Poet of the Month pamphlets $75/350

024b: THE BROKEN SPAN New Directions, Norfolk, Conn. (1941). [0] 1,500 cc. Second binding: blank stiff white paper covers. Dustwrapper as in 024a $40/200

024c: THE BROKEN SPAN New Directions, Norfolk, Conn. (1941). [0] Approximately 200 cc. Yellow paper wraps not attached at spine $200.

025a: THE WEDGE The Cummington Press (Cummington, Mass.), 1944. [2] 380 cc. Glassine dustwrapper $600.

026a: FIRST ACT (IN THE MONEY / WHITE MULE) New Directions, Norfolk, Conn., 1937 / 1940 (1945). [0] 445 copies of sheets of the second printing of 018a and 023a bound together, original title pages used and no additional title page added. Dustwrapper title and spine imprint is *"First Act"* $100/500

027a: THREE POEMS (General Mag & Historical Chronicle), Philadelphia (1945). [] Wraps. An offprint (Glenn Horowitz #9) $400.

028a: PATERSON (BOOK ONE) New Directions (Norfolk, Conn., 1946). [2] 1,063 cc (952 bound for publication date, 111 copies bound April 1948). "... one thousand copies have been printed..." $100/400

029a: PATERSON (BOOK TWO) New Directions (Norfolk, Conn., 1948). [2] 1,009 cc (1,002 bound 4/1/48, 7 cc bound 4/13/48). "... one thousand copies have been printed ..." $60/300

030a: THE CLOUDS ... Wells College Press / The Cummington Press, no place, (1948). [2] 60 sgd cc. Numbered I-LX on English handmade paper bound in slate cloth boards. In slipcase $2,000/2,500

030b: THE CLOUDS ... Wells College Press / The Cummington Press, no place, (1948). [2] 250 no. cc. Numbered 61-310 on rag paper in similar binding (to 030a) but issued without slipcase $450.

031a: A DREAM OF LOVE... (New Directions, Norfolk, Conn., 1948.) [0] 1,700 cc. Wraps. Heavy, brown paper covers printed in black $250.

032a: SELECTED POEMS (New Directions, Norfolk, Conn., 1949.) [0] 3,591 cc. Tan end papers (second issue has white end papers). Introduction by Randall Jarrell. First issue dustwrapper without NBA notice and priced $1.50 $35/175

Note: A later (1968) printing of the New Direction Paperbook No. 131 of this title was enlarged by the addition of 25 poems)

033a: THE PINK CHURCH Golden Goose Press, Columbus, Ohio, 1949. [2] 25 sgd no. cc. Numbered 1-25. Wraps $1,750.

033b: THE PINK CHURCH Golden Goose Press, Columbus, Ohio, 1949. [2] 375 no. cc. Numbered 26-400. Wraps $350.

034a: PATERSON (BOOK THREE) New Directions (Norfolk, Conn., 1949). [2] 999 cc. "... one thousand copies have been printed ..." $50/250

PATERSON (COLLECTED EDITIONS)

035a: PATERSON (COLLECTED BOOKS 1 & 2) New Directions, Norfolk, Conn. (1949). [ ] 1,577 cc. Front flap of dustwrapper has "Paterson Books 1 & 2"; and "NC26" [New Classics Series 26] on spine $30/150

035b: PATERSON (COLLECTED BOOKS 1 & 2) Peter Owen Limited, London (1953). [ ] 500 cc. American sheets (Ian McKelvie 10/94) $30/150

035c: PATERSON (COLLECTED BOOKS 1, 2, & 3) New Directions, Norfolk, Conn. (1950). [ ] 1,507 cc. Front flap of dustwrapper has "Paterson Books 1, 2 & 3"; and "NC26" [New Classics Series 26] on spine $30/150

035d: PATERSON (COLLECTED BOOKS 1, 2, 3, & 4) New Directions, Norfolk, Conn. (1951). [ ] 2,000 cc. Front flap of dustwrapper has "Paterson Books 1, 2, 3 & 4"; and "NC26" [New Classics Series 26] on spine $25/125

035e: PATERSON (COLLECTED BOOKS 1-5, including notes for a projected Book 6) New Directions (New York, 1963). [1] Wraps. 8,598 cc. "ND Paperbook 152." Includes first five books and notes for the sixth $40.

035f: PATERSON BOOKS I-IV MacGibbon & Kee, London, 1964. [1] 1,500 cc $25/100

035g: PATERSON *Revised Edition* New Directions, New York, 1992. [] Edited by Christopher MacGowan. (Published November 1992 @ $35) $25/50

036a: PICASSO THE FIGURE Louis Carre Gallery, New York (1950). [0] Folio exhibition folder containing an essay by Williams $200.

037a: THE COLLECTED LATER POEMS New Directions (Norfolk, Conn., 1950). [2] 100 sgd no. cc. "The Rose" section loosely inserted. Issued without dustwrapper. In slipcase $1,500/1,750

037b: THE COLLECTED LATER POEMS New Directions (Norfolk, Conn., 1950). [0] 1,993 cc. "The Rose" section loosely inserted. (8 leaves, stapled at fold, numbered 233-245). Total quantity (a, b & c) originally printed was 4,700 which apparently did not include the Horace Mann editions $35/175

037c: THE COLLECTED LATER POEMS New Directions (Norfolk, Conn., 1950). [0] Approximately 2,441 cc. Later binding of 036b with pages 233-245 correctly bound in $25/125

037d: THE COLLECTED LATER POEMS New Directions (Norfolk, Conn., 1950 [actually 1956]). [2] 52 copies of which 50 are signed numbered copies in red. Facing title page "Horace Mann School Editions." Gray slipcase. "The Rose" section bound in. Printed from first edition plates in 1956 $1,000/1,250

037e: THE COLLECTED LATER POEMS New Directions (Norfolk, Conn., 1950 [actually 1956].) [0] 522 cc. Plain brown dustwrapper with circular cut-out to reveal H. Mann School seal. "The Rose" section loosely inserted. Printed from first edition plates in 1956 $25/125

037f: THE COLLECTED LATER POEMS New Directions (Norfolk, Conn., 1963). [] 2,904 cc. "Revised Edition" stated. First thus $10/50

037g: THE COLLECTED LATER POEMS MacGibbon & Kee, London, 1965. [] 1,500 cc. (Revised edition) $12/60

038a: MAKE LIGHT OF IT COLLECTED STORIES Random House, New York (1950). [1] 5,000 cc. Includes one story which had not appeared in print before ("Lena") $20/100

039a: A BEGINNING ON THE SHORT STORY The Alicat Book-Shop Press, Yonkers, NY, 1950. [2] 1,000 cc. Wraps. White or tan heavy paper covers, no priority. "This copy one of 750 offered for sale" $100.

040a: PATERSON (BOOK FOUR) New Directions (Norfolk, Conn., 1951). [2] 995 cc. "... one thousand copies have been printed ..." $40/200

041a: AUTOBIOGRAPHY Random House, New York (1951). [1] 5,000 cc $25/100

041b: THE AUTOBIOGRAPHY OF WILLIAM CARLOS WILLIAMS MacGibbon & Kee, London, 1968. [] (Dalian Books 4/90.) Assume this is the same book $15/75

042a: THE COLLECTED EARLIER POEMS New Directions (Norfolk, Conn., 1951). [0] 5,000 cc $25/125

042b: THE COLLECTED EARLIER POEMS MacGibbon & Kee (London, 1967). [1] 1,500 cc. Verso of title page states "Second printing / manufactured in the United States." Back dustwrapper flap "Printed in Great Britain" $12/60

043a: EMANUEL RAMANO Passedoit Gallery, New York (1951). [0] 500 cc. Wraps. Four page exhibition catalog with text by Williams $200.

044a: THE BUILD-UP Random House, New York (1952). [1] 6,000 cc printed but sticker pasted on title page of 684 copies in 1965 when New Directions acquired plates $25/100

044b: THE BUILD-UP MacGibbon & Kee (London, 1969). [] (Ref.b) $10/50

045a: THE DESERT MUSIC *and Other Poems* Random House, New York (1954). [2] 111 cc of which 100 were signed and numbered. Glassine dustwrapper. In slipcase $850/1,000

045b: THE DESERT MUSIC *and Other Poems* Random House, New York (1954). [0] 2,532 cc $30/150

046a: THE DOG AND THE FEVER *A Perambulatory Novella* The Shoe String Press, Hamden, Connecticut (1954). [0] 1,000 cc. Translation of work of Francisco de Queredo (aka Pedro Espinosa) by Williams and Raquel Helene Williams $12/60

047a: SELECTED ESSAYS Random House, New York (1954). [] Uncorrected galley proofs. Punch-bound in blue wraps (Joseph The provider 12/88) $400.

047b: SELECTED ESSAYS Random House, New York (1954). [1] 3,350 cc. "New Directions" sticker pasted on title page of 992 copies in June 1965 when New Directions acquired Random House plates $25/100

047c: SELECTED ESSAYS New Directions, New York, 1969. [1] Wraps. "New Directions Paperbook 273." Published March 26, 1969 @ $2.45 (ref.c) $25.

048a: JOURNEY TO LOVE Random House, New York (1955). [0] 3,000 cc $25/125

049a: THE SELECTED LETTERS McDowell, Obolensky, New York (1957). [2] 75 sgd no. cc. Issued without dustwrapper. In slipcase $600/750

049b: THE SELECTED LETTERS McDowell, Obolensky, New York (1957). [0] 2,000 cc $25/125

050a: THE GIFT (New Directions, New York, 1957.) [0] 2,500 cc. Wraps. Christmas greeting (also issued as Christmas card by Hallmark in 1962) $75.

051a: SAPPHO (Poems in Folio, San Francisco, 1957.) [2] 150 sgd no. cc. Translation by Williams. Issued as broadside $350.

051b: SAPPHO (Poems in Folio, San Francisco, 1957.) [0] 1,000 cc. Translation by Williams. Issued as broadside $75.

052a: I WANTED TO WRITE A POEM Beacon Press, Beacon Hill, Boston (1958). [] Spiral bound galley proof. In gray wraps with label (Glenn Horowitz #11) $400.

052b: I WANTED TO WRITE A POEM Beacon Press, Beacon Hill, Boston (1958). [0] 3,543 cc. Reported and edited by Edith Heal $25/100

052c: I WANTED TO WRITE A POEM Cape, London, 1967. [] (Ref.b) Wraps. In dustwrapper (David Mayou #23) $25/75

052d: I WANTED TO WRITE A POEM New Directions, New York, 1978. [1] 3,000 cc. New Directions Paperbook 469 (ref.c). (Published October 19, 1978 @ $3.45) $30.

053a: A NOTE ON THE TURN OF THE VIEW TOWARD POETIC TECHNIQUE Hanover Forum, Hanover, Indiana (1958). [0] 8 pages. In stapled wraps $150.

054a: PATERSON (BOOK FIVE) New Directions (Norfolk, Conn., 1958). [0] 3,000 cc $30/150

055a: W.C.W. - F.H.W. APRIL 18, 1959 (Press of Igals, Roodenko, 1959.) [2] 100 cc. Printed for New Directions (consists of William's "To Be Recited to Flossie on Her Birthday") $150.

056a: YES, MRS. WILLIAMS *A Personal Record of My Mother* McDowell, Obolensky, New York (1959). [0] $15/75

056b: YES, MRS. WILLIAMS *A Personal Record of My Mother* New Directions, New York, 1982. [1] New Directions Paperbook 534 (ref.c). (Published June 30, 1982 @ $5.95) $20.

057a: THE FARMERS' DAUGHTERS New Directions (Norfolk, Conn., 1961). [1] 1,500 cc $30/150

057b: THE FARMERS' DAUGHTERS New Directions (Norfolk, Conn., 1961). 10,000 cc. Wraps. On spine "ND Paperbook 106." Published simultaneously $35.

058a: MANY LOVES *and Other Plays* New Directions (Norfolk, Conn., 1961). [0] 1,983 cc $25/125

058b: MANY LOVES *and Other Plays* New Directions (Norfolk, Conn., 1965). [0] 2,443 cc. Wraps. On back cover "A New Directions Paperbook NDP 191." Not bound and published until 1965 $30.

059a: PICTURES FROM BRUEGHEL *and Other Poems* New Directions Paperbook (Norfolk, Conn., 1962). [1] 7,500 cc. "ND Paperbook 118" Pulitzer Prize in Poetry for 1963 $100.

059b: PICTURES FROM BRUEGHEL *and Other Poems* MacGibbon & Kee, London, 1963. [1] 1,500 copies printed, 950 copies bound. First cloth bound edition $40/200

060a: COLLECTED PLAYS Oxford, London, 1963. [] Introduction by John Heath-Stubbs. First appearance of two plays (Boston Book Annex #21) $25/75

061a: THE WILLIAM CARLOS WILLIAMS READER New Directions (New York, 1966). [0] 3,000 cc. Yellow cloth stamped in blind and gold (ref.a). Also yellow cloth stamped in black and blind (William Reese Co. 2/91) $25/75

061b: THE WILLIAM CARLOS WILLIAMS READER MacGibbon & Kee (London,1966). [1] 2,000 cc. Actually published 3/20/67 $20/60

THE AUTOBIOGRAPHY OF WILLIAM CARLOS WILLIAMS see 1951

062a: IMAGINATIONS New Directions (New York, 1970). [0] 3,557 cc. (Published August 24, 1970 @ $10.) ref.c $12/60

062b: IMAGINATIONS MacGibbon & Kee (London, 1970). [] (Ref.b) $12/60

063a: FIVE EXPERIMENTAL PROSE PIECES Macgibbon and Kee, London (1970). [ ] (Bev Chaney, Jr. 10/95) $12/60

064a: THE EMBODIMENT OF KNOWLEDGE New Directions (New York, 1974). [0] 2,064 cc. Edited by Ron Loewinsohn (ref.c). (Published November 27, 1974 @ $18.75) $12/60

065a: (POEM, 1911) I WILL SING A JOYOUS SONG Lockwood Memorial Library Buffalo 1974 [2] 25 no. cc. Broadside (ref.b) $125.

065b: (POEM, 1911) I WILL SING A JOYOUS SONG Lockwood Memorial Library, Buffalo, 1974. [1] 2,000 cc. Broadside (apparently not for sale) ref.b $40.

066a: SELECTED POEMS Penguin, London, 1976. [] Wraps. Edited and introduction Charles Tomlinson (Ian McKelvie 7/89) $35.

066b: SELECTED POEMS New Directions, New York, 1985. [] Revised and updated (Howard Woolmer 8/93) $10/40

066c: SELECTED POEMS New Directions, New York, 1985. [] Wraps `$15.

067a: INTERVIEWS WITH WILLIAM CARLOS WILLIAMS "SPEAKING STRAIGHT AHEAD" New Directions (New York, 1976). [0] Edited by Linda Welshimer Wagner (ref.c). (Published November 9, 1976 @ $8.50) $10/40

067b: INTERVIEWS WITH WILLIAM CARLOS WILLIAMS "SPEAKING STRAIGHT AHEAD" New Directions (New York, 1976). [0] Wraps. "ND Paper-book 421." Simultaneously published with cloth edition (ref.c) $20.

068a: A RECOGNIZABLE IMAGE: WILLIAM CARLOS WILLIAMS ON ART & ARTISTS New

Directions, New York, 1978. [1] 2,555 cc. (Published October 29, 1978 @ $16.00) ref.c $20/50

069a: WILLIAM CARLOS WILLIAMS AND THE AMERICAN SCENE 1920-1940 Whitney Museum (New York), 1978. [] Wraps. 11 pages. First separate edition of this selection. Selected by Dickran Tashjian (Waiting For Godot) $40.

070a: SELECTED POEMS Snake River Press (Sussex, 1981). [2] 25 no. cc. Folio. Half burgundy morocco over Roma paper boards (Geo. Houle Cat. 27) $400.

071a: AT THE BALLGAME Red Ex Press, Ferndale (1981). [2] 13 sgd cc (signed by the photographer, Carl Schurer). White cloth with baseball ticket tipped on. A poem by Williams and 18 original black & white photographs by Carl Schurer. In acetate dustwrapper (James S. Jaffe 7/96) $850.

072a: A VOICE IN THE GARDEN *Six Poems* (Emil Adler), no place, 1982. [0] Sheet music by Emil Adler. 29 pages. The poems by Williams are written in. Reproduced copy in stapled sheets. Assume never published (Howard Woolmer 11/93) $150.

073a: FLOWERS OF AUGUST Windhover Press, Iowa City, 1983. [2] 260 cc. (Actually published in 1984.) Issued without dustwrapper (William Reese Co. Cat. 30) $125.

074a: WILLIAM CARLOS WILLIAMS / JOHN SANFORD *A Correspondence* Oyster Press, Santa Barbara, 1984. [2] 75 no. cc signed by John Sanford. Issued in dustwrapper $75/125

074b: WILLIAM CARLOS WILLIAMS / JOHN SANFORD *A Correspondence* Oyster Press, Santa Barbara, 1984. [2] 425 cc. Issued in dustwrapper $25/50

074c: WILLIAM CARLOS WILLIAMS / JOHN SANFORD *A Correspondence* Oyster Press, Santa Barbara, 1984. [2] 2,000 cc. Wraps $30.

075a: SELECTED POEMS Franklin Library, Franklin Center, 1984. [2] "Limited Edition." In full red leather $75.

076a: THE DOCTOR STORIES New Directions, New York, 1984. [1] (Published October 12, 1984 @ $13.50) ref.c $15/50

076b: THE DOCTOR STORIES New Directions, New York, 1984. [1] New Directions Paperbook 585 (ref.c) $20.

076c: THE DOCTOR STORIES Faber & Faber, London (1987). [] wraps (Howard Woolmer 8/93) $25.

077a: SOMETHING TO SAY New Directions, New York, 1985. [] (Published October 10, 1985 @ $23.95) ref.c $10/40

078a: DEAR EZ: LETTERS FROM WILLIAM CARLOS WILLIAMS Friends of the Lilly Library, Bloomington, 1985. [2] 203 no. cc (Beasley Books #23) $100/150

079a: JANUARY MORNING (New York, 1986.) [] Triple fold pamphlet issued as greeting (Phoenix Book Shop 10/88) $35.

080a: COLLECTED POEMS OF WILLIAM CARLOS WILLIAMS Volume I. 1909-1936. New Directions, New York (1986). [] Edited by A. Walton Litz and Christopher MacGowen $15/50

081a: COLLECTED POEMS OF WILLIAM CARLOS WILLIAMS Volume II. 1939-1962. New Directions, New York (1988). [] $15/50

082a: THE NORMAL AND ADVENTITIOUS DANGER PERIODS FOR PULMONARY DIS-

EASE IN CHILDREN Dim Gray Bar, New York, 1988. [2] 100 cc. Wraps. Williams' medical article originally published in the *Archives Pediatrics* in 1913. Signed by the publisher, Barry Magid, M.D. (William Reese Co. 7/90) $75.

083a: WILLIAM CARLOS WILLIAMS AND JAMES LAUGHLIN *Selected Letters* Norton, New York (1989). [] Edited by Hugh Witemeyer (Chloe's Books 9/89) $15/40

084a: THE AMERICAN IDIOM *A Correspondence.* Bright Tyger Press, San Francisco, 1990. [] Williams and Harold Norse. Hardbound without dustwrapper $45.

085a: THE LETTERS OF WILLIAM CARLOS WILLIAMS AND CHARLES TOMLINSON Dim Gray Bar Press, New York, 1992. [2] 26 sgd ltr cc. Signed and preface by Tomlinson. Edited by Barry Magid and Hugh Witemeyer. Introduction by Hugh Kenner. Goatskin and handmade paperboards $300.

085b: THE LETTERS OF WILLIAM CARLOS WILLIAMS AND CHARLES TOMLINSON Dim Gray Bar Press, New York, 1992. [2] 124 sgd no. cc. Signed by Tomlinson. Cloth and boards $150.

086a: TWO LETTERS TO RENE TAUPIN Dim Gay Bar Press, New York, 1993. [2] 50 sgd no. cc (signed by Barry Magid, owner of one of the letters). Printed for friends of Dim Gay Bar Press. None offered for sale (Gordon Beckhorn 1/95) $125.

087a: THIS IS JUST TO SAY Poems on the Underground, London, no date. [] Oblong Broadside. Approximately 24 x 11 inches (J. Howard Woolmer 3/95) $45.

088a: SELECTED CORRESPONDENCE OF EZRA POUND AND WILLIAM CARLOS WILLIAMS 1907-1963 New Directions, New York (1996). [] Bev Chaney, Jr. 2/96) $10/40

089a: THE COLLECTED STORIES New Directions, New York, 1996. [] Wraps. Published @ $14.9 $15.

FIRST EDITION IDENTIFICATION
BY PUBLISHER

In the case of titles published before 1900, the key to first edition identification is often the date on the title page. The vast majority of first editions published before 1900 had the year of publication on the title page (this is true for fiction and nonfiction titles). The presence of a date on the title page alone may identify books published prior to the mid-1800s as first editions. A matching date on the copyright page (or the back of the title page) often identifies a book published in the mid- to late 1800s as a first edition. After 1900, a number of publishers did not or currently do not put the date on the title page of their first editions.

In the early 1900s, many publishers began to identify the first edition on the copyright page. A variety of statements have been and continue to be used to denote a first edition such as "First Edition," "First Printing," "First Impression," "First published (Year, or Month and Year)," or simply "Published (Year, or Month and Year)." A few publishers have placed or place their logo, colophon, or a code (generally "1" or "A") on the copyright page of the first edition. Publishers who did not or do not use a first edition statement, in most cases, note subsequent printings on the copyright page. For these publishers, the absence of a later printing statement is the key to identifying the first edition.

Over the last few decades, the majority of publishers have used a number row on the copyright page to identify a book's printing and occasionally the date of publication. Sometimes the number row is accompanied by a first edition statement (often it is not). It is important to note that regardless of the order of the numbers in the row the lowest number indicates the printing. The presence of the number "1" (with few exceptions) indicates a first printing. Some examples follow:

"1 2 3 4 5 6 7 8 9 10"
"10 9 8 7 6 5 4 3 2 1" *and*
"1 3 5 7 9 10 8 6 4 2"
all indicate a first edition

"76 77 78 79 80 10 9 8 7 6 5 4 3 2"
indicates a second printing published in 1976

"3 4 5 6 7 8 9 10 90 89 88 87 86"
indicates a third printing published in 1986

"1 3 5 7 9 11 13 15 17 19 H/C 20 18 16 14 12 10 8 6 4 2"
indicates a first printing, manufactured by "H" in a cloth binding (used by Scribner's)

Unfortunately, publishers sometimes fail to omit a first edition statement from subsequent printings:

First Edition
3 4 5 6 7 8 9 10

and

First Printing
10 9 8 7 6 5 4 3 90 89 88 87 86 85 84

are both third printings.

The list below provides at-a-glance information for first edition identification by publisher. For more detailed information on identifying first editions by a wide range of publishers we recommend the 1995 edition of Edward N. Zempel and Linda A. Verkler's First Editions: A Guide to Identification (The Spoon River Press, 2319-C West Rohmann Avenue, Peoria, IL 61604). This superb reference provides publishers' verbatim statements, collected over nearly 70 years, on their practices for identifying first editions and later printings. In addition, we highly recommend the occasional series " A Collector's Guide to Publishers" featured in the monthly magazine for book collectors, *Firsts.* This interesting and informative series provides a history, some notable writers and books published, standard practices for first edition identification (and, in some cases, notable exceptions), for the publishers profiled—over 30 major publishers to date. We used our experience over the last 30 years, our stock, and both of the above mentioned references to compile the list below. A final, important note: It is always prudent to consult a bibliography for conclusive first edition identification (see *Selected Bibliography of Works Consulted* at the back of this book for a comprehensive list of bibliographies).

D. Appleton & Co. *Used a numerical identification, in parenthesis or brackets, at the foot of the last page:* " (1)" = *first printing,* " (2)" = *second printing, etc. (May have occasionally used a "first edition" statement instead of the numerical identification.)*

D. Appleton-Century Co. *Prior to the 1980s, used a numerical identification, in parenthesis or brackets, at the foot of the last page:* "(1)" = *first printing,* "(2)" = *second printing, etc.*

(May have occasionally used a "first edition" statement instead of the numerical identification.) Since the 1980s, have used a number row to indicate year of publication and printing.

Arkham House / Arkham House Publishers, Inc. *With the exception of collected works of H.P. Lovecraft, did not reprint titles and, as late as the 1980s, always included a colophon at the back of each book (reprints would be noted there). According to the publisher, began using a first edition statement and noting later printings on the copyright page sometime in the late 1970s to early 1980s.*

Atlantic Monthly Press *Prior to 1925, did not use a first edition statement (or put the publication date on the title page of first editions as was the case for many publishers in the late-1800s to early 1900s) and did not consistently list later printings on the copyright page. See Little, Brown for books published after 1925 (Little, Brown began publishing the Atlantic Monthly Books in 1925 and using their methods for first edition identification).*

Atheneum *States first edition on copyright page. Began using a number row in the mid-1980s.*

Avalon Books *Does not normally reprint books, but according to the publisher, later printings would be noted.*

Ballantine Books *In general, hardcover editions stated "First edition (Month, Year)" or "First printing (Month, Year)"; paperback originals carried no statement on the copyright page for first printings, later printings were noted.*

Robert A. Ballou *No consistent practice.*

A.S. Barnes *According to the publisher, have noted later printings on the copyright page since at least 1976. Prior to this, designation of later printings was erratic. (Does not use a first edition statement.)*

Ernest Benn *States "First published in (Year)" on the copyright page of first editions; or sometimes omits the "first published" statement and puts the year of publication on the title page with their imprint to designate a first edition. In either case, subsequent printings are noted.*

William Blackwood *No statement on first editions, but subsequent printings noted. (According to the publisher, in the early 1900s may have designated some first editions "second edition" as a marketing tool.)*

Blakison *Reprint publisher.*

Bobbs-Merrill *Prior to the 1920s, sometimes used a bow-and-arrow design on the copyright page of their first editions; after 1920, generally stated "First edition" or "First printing" (but not consistent in either practice).*

Bodley Head *States "First published 19.." or "First published in Great Britain 19.."; subsequent printings would presumably be noted.*

Boni & Liveright *May have occasionally stated first edition but, in general, the absence of a later printing statement indicates a first edition.*

Albert & Charles Boni *No statement on first editions, but subsequent printings noted.*

Book Supply Co. *Uses a first edition statement; subsequent printings presumably noted.*

Brentano's *Prior to 1928, no statement on first editions; subsequent printings noted. In 1928, began stating "First printed 19.." on copyright page of first editions and continued noting subsequent printings.*

Edgar Rice Burroughs, Inc. *Published only the books of Edgar Rice Burroughs. No statement on books published prior to 1933; began using a first edition statement sometime in 1933 (Although both were published in 1933, there is no statement on the first edition of Apache Devil but Tarzan and the City of Gold states first edition on the copyright page).*

A.L. Burt *Primarily a reprint publisher, but published the first U.S. edition of P.G. Wodehouse's Man With Two Left Feet (states first edition on the copyright page). For those authors whose first editions have become very high priced, A.L. Burt reprints in dust jackets closely matching the first edition's are sometimes desirable.*

Calder & Boyars *States "First published (Year)" or "First published in Great Britain (Year)"; subsequent printings would presumably be noted.*

Jonathan Cape & Harrison Smith *States "First published (Year)" or "First published in America (Year)"; subsequent printings would presumably be noted.*

Jonathan Cape *States "First published (Year)" or "First published in Great Britain (Year)" on copyright page of first editions; subsequent printings noted.*

Cassell & Co. *Prior to the early 1920s, put the year of publication on the title page of the first edition and left the copyright page blank; subsequent printings would presumably be noted or carry a later date on the copyright page. In the early 1920s, began stating "First published (Year)" or "First published in Great Britain (Year)" on copyright page of first editions; subsequent printings noted.*

Caxton Printers *No statement on first editions, but subsequent printings noted.*

Century Co. *No consistent practice.*

Chapman & Hall *Either stated "First published (Year)" or made no statement on first editions; subsequent printings noted.*

Chatto & Windus *In general, no statement on first editions, although sometimes states "Published by Chatto & Windus" (without a date); subsequent printings noted. May have added a number row in the early 1990s.*

Clarke, Irwin *No statement on the first edition; subsequent printings presumably noted.*

Collier *In our limited experience with this publisher, no statement on the first edition; subsequent printings presumably noted.*

Collins (U.K.) *No statement on the first edition; presumably subsequent printings would be noted (with either a statement, or a date subsequent to the copyright date).*

Contact Editions *Limited editions included a colophon page. Did not generally use a first edition statement on trade editions, but subsequent printings would presumably be noted.*

Covici McGee *No statement on the first edition, but presumably later printings would be noted.*

Pascal Covici *May have occasionally stated first edition but, in general, the absence of a later printing statement indicates a first edition.*

Covici-Friede *No statement on first editions, but subsequent printings noted.*

Coward-McCann *Not consistent in their practices for identifying first editions but, in general, subsequent printings noted. (Until mid-1930s, usually placed a colophon with a torch design on the copyright page of first editions and removed the torch portion of the colophon on subsequent printings. After 1935, stated "first American edition" on the copyright page of books first published outside the U.S., but made no statement on books first published in the U.S.)*

Coward, McCann and Geoghehan *No statement on first editions, but subsequent printings noted.*

Creative Age *No statement on first editions, but subsequent printings noted.*

Crime Club (U.K.) *See Collins*

Crime Club (U.S.) *See Doubleday, Doran & Co.*

Thomas Y. Crowell *No statement on first editions, but subsequent printings noted. May have used a number row to indicate printings as early as the 1940s.*

Crown Publishers *Prior to the 1970s, no statement on first editions, but subsequent printings noted. Began using a number row and first edition statement in the 1970s.*

John Day Co. / John Day in association with Reynal and Hitchcock [1935-38] / John Day & Co. *First few years (beginning in 1928) may have stated "First Published (Month, Year)" on first editions and noted later printings. In the 1930s, switched to designating only later printings (no statement on first editions). In the 1970s, began using a number row. (In the late 1970s, may have added a first edition statement to the number row.)*

Delacorte Press / Seymour Lawrence *Presently uses a number row; previously stated "first printing" or "first American printing."*

Devin-Adair *Although may have consistently stated "First Edition" in recent years, in general, first editions can be identified by the absence of a later printing statement.*

Dial Press *Although occasionally stated "First Printing" prior to the mid-1960s, did not list subsequent printings. In general, first editions published prior to the mid-1960s can be identified by the presence of the same date on the title page and the copyright page (also true for books published before the mid-1930s with the imprint "Lincoln MacVeagh / The Dial Press"). In the late 1960s, began stating "First Printing (Year)" on first editions and noting subsequent printings. Currently uses a number row.*

Dillingham *In our limited experience with this publisher, no statement on the first edition; subsequent printings would presumably be noted.*

Dodd, Mead *Prior to 1976, no statement on first editions and, often, subsequent printings were not noted. In late 1976, added a number row to most titles (occasionally deleting the row from subsequent printings and replacing it with a later printing statement). Note: According to Firsts Magazine, in the 1970s, first printing dust jackets of some mystery titles were issued without a price on the flap, making them appear to be book club editions.*

George H. Doran *Generally placed a colophon with the initials "GHD" on the copyright page of the first edition (but not consistently until the early 1920s). Occasionally, stated "first printing." Merged with Doubleday in 1927.*

Doubleday & Co. *States "first edition" on copyright page; no statement on later printings.*

Doubleday, Doran & Co. *States "first edition" on copyright page; no statement on later printings.*

Doubleday & McClure Co. *In general, the date on the title page should match last date on the copyright page of a first edition.*

Doubleday, Page & Co. *Before the early 1920s, no statement on the first edition. In early 1920s, began stating "first edition," but may not have used any statement on books first published outside the U.S. (no statement on later printings).*

Duell, Sloan and Pearce *In general, either stated "First Edition" or placed a Roman numeral "I" on the copyright page of first editions. Later printings were usually denoted similarly, i.e., "Second Printing" or "II."*

E.P. Dutton *Prior to 1929, the date on the title page should match the last date on the copyright page of a first edition. In the 1930s, began stating "First edition" or "First printing." In recent years, added a number row (they adjust the numbers for subsequent printings, but often fail to remove the first edition statement).*

Editions Poetry *States "First published...(Year)" on the copyright page of the first edition; subsequent printings would presumably be noted.*

Egoist Press *Limited editions included a colophon page. Did not generally use a first edition statement on trade editions, but subsequent printings would presumably be noted.*

Eyre & Spottiswoode *Either printed the year of publication under their name at the bottom of the title page of first editions, or stated "This book, first published 19.., is printed..." on the copyright page; subsequent printings were noted.*

Faber & Faber, Ltd. *States "First Published (Month, Year)" on copyright page and notes subsequent printings. Prior to 1968, the year of publication was in Roman numerals; beginning in 1968, switched to Arabic numerals. Since World War II, the month has generally been omitted from the first edition statement. Recently added a number row to most publications.*

Faber & Gwyer, Ltd. *Stated "First published by Faber & Gwyer in (Month, Year)" on copyright page of first editions; noted subsequent printings.*

Fantasy Press *States "First Edition" on copyright page; may have occasionally left "First Edition" statement of original publisher on offset reprints with their imprint.*

Farrar, Rinehart *Publisher's logo appears on the copyright page of first editions; no statement on subsequent printings. Very rarely stated "first edition" (in place of the logo).*

Farrar, Straus & Cudahy *States either "First published (Year)" or "First printing" on the copyright page of first editions.*

Farrar, Straus & Giroux *States either "First published (Year)," "First printing (Year)," or "First edition (Year)" on the copyright page of first editions.*

Farrar, Straus *Publisher's stylized initials (FS) appear on the copyright page of first editions; no statement on subsequent printings.*

Farrar, Straus & Young *Used either a first edition statement or a colophon on the copyright page of first editions.*

Fawcett *Uses a number row to designate printings.*

Four Seas *In general, no statement on first editions, but subsequent printings noted.*

Funk & Wagnalls *Used a Roman numeral "1" (I) on the copyright page of first editions. According to the publisher's statements, beginning in 1929, stated "First published (Month, Year)" on first editions and noted subsequent printings (presumably no statement on first editions published prior to 1929). But, the first edition of John Cheever's* The Enormous Radio, *published in 1953, has the Roman numeral "1" and does not have a first edition statement.*

Lee Furman *Made no attempt to identify first editions or subsequent printings.*

Gambit, Inc. *States "First printing" on the copyright page of first editions; subsequent printings are noted.*

Bernard Geis *States "First printing" on the copyright page of first editions; presumably subsequent printings are noted.*

Gnome Press *States "First Edition" on copyright page; may have occasionally left "First Edition" statement of original publisher on offset reprints with their imprint.*

Victor Gollancz, Ltd. *Prior to 1984, no statement on first editions, but subsequent printings noted (i.e., "First published (Year) | Second impression (Year)"). In 1984, began stating "First published in..." on the copyright page of first editions.*

Grosset & Dunlap *Primarily a reprint house, but some notable first editions have been published by Grosset & Dunlap:* King Kong *(photoplay); Nancy Drew and Hardy Boys series; Fran*

Striker's "Lone Ranger" series; and Zane Grey's The Redheaded Outfield and Other Stories. In addition, Grosset & Dunlap's "photoplay" editions (illustrated with stills from motion pictures) are collectable. In our experience, there is no statement of edition or printing on Grossett & Dunlap publications. It is, however, possible to eliminate obvious later printings by checking the list of other books published in the series. A later printing would most likely list titles that were published after the book in hand. [Note: For those authors whose first editions have become very high priced, Grosset & Dunlap reprints in dust jackets closely matching the first edition's are sometimes desirable].

Grove Press *First editions and subsequent printings are always noted on the copyright page; currently uses a number row. Later printing dustwrappers are identifiable by small letter code on the rear panel (e.g., "ii" designates a second printing dustwrapper).*

Robert Hale *Prior to 1958, either no statement on first editions or stated "First published (Year)" but, in both cases, subsequent printings were noted. Beginning in 1958, stated "First published in Great Britain in (Year)" on first editions; continued to identify subsequent printings. According to the publisher, a number row was adopted in 1994 for non-fiction titles only.*

Hamish Hamilton *States "First published (Year)" or "First published in Great Britain in (Year)" on copyright page; notes subsequent printings. Added a number row in 1988.*

Harcourt, Brace & World *Usually states "first edition" or "first American edition" on the copyright page. More recently, placed "First Edition/BCDE" on the copyright page of first editions, omitting "First Edition" and adjusting the letter row on later printings (i.e. a letter row beginning with "B" and without a "First Edition" statement indicates a second printing; a letter row beginning with "C" indicates a third printing, etc.).*

Harcourt, Brace & Co. *In the 1920s, usually placed a "1" on the copyright page of first printings, "2" on second printings, etc. Occasionally, stated "Published (Month) (Year)" on the copyright page of first printings (later printings were noted). In the mid-1930s began stating "First Edition" or "First American Edition." More recently, may have placed "First Edition/BCDE" on the copyright page of first editions, omit-*

ting "First Edition" and adjusting the letter row on later printings (i.e. a letter row beginning with "B" and without a "First Edition" statement indicates a second printing; a letter row beginning with "C" indicates a third printing, etc.).

Harcourt, Brace & Howe *Usually placed the number "1" on the copyright page of first printings, "2" on second printings, etc. May have occasionally stated "Published (Month) (Year)" on the copyright page of first printings and noted later printings.*

Harcourt Brace Jovanovich *States "first edition" or "first American edition" on the copyright page. As recently as 1976, placed "First Edition/BCDE" on the copyright page of first editions, omitting "First Edition" on later printings. Currently places "First Edition/ABCDE" on the copyright page of first editions, omitting "First Edition" on later printings.*

Harper & Brothers *Prior to 1912, the date on the title page should match the last date on the copyright page. Began stating "First Edition" on the copyright page in 1922. A letter code for the month and year of publication was introduced in 1912. In most cases for first editions published between 1912 and 1922, the letter code for the year on the copyright page should match the date on the title page.*

Months *(the letter "J" was not used)*

A = January	D = April	G = July	K = October
B = February	E = May	H = August	L = November
C = March	F = June	I = September	M = December

Years *(the letter "J" was not used)*

M = 1912	W = 1922	G = 1932	R = 1942
N = 1913	X = 1923	H = 1933	S = 1943
O = 1914	Y = 1924	I = 1934	T = 1944
P = 1915	Z = 1925	K = 1935	U = 1945
Q = 1916	A = 1926	L = 1936	V = 1946
R = 1917	B = 1927	M = 1937	W = 1947
S = 1918	C = 1928	N = 1938	X = 1948
T= 1919	D = 1929	O = 1939	Y = 1949
U = 1920	E = 1930	P = 1940	Z = 1950
V = 1921	F = 1931	Q = 1941	A = 1951

Harper & Row *States "First Edition" on the copyright page (also see month and date code above). In the late 1960s, added a number row to the bottom of the last page (directly before the rear free endpaper) but often failed to remove the "First Edition" statement from later printings. By the mid-1970s, the number row was usually placed on the copyright page (still often failed to remove "First Edition" statement from later printings).*

HarperCollins [Harper & Row changed its name to HarperCollins in 1990] *States "First Edition" and uses a number row which indicates the year of publication and printing (may sometimes fail to remove the "First Edition" statement from later printings).*

Hart-Davis, MacGibbon Limited *States "Published...(Year)" on first editions; subsequent printings are noted.*

Rupert Hart-Davis *Although usually stated "First published (Year)" on copyright page of first editions, sometimes placed the publication date on the title page of first editions (with no statement on the copyright page); in both cases, subsequent printings were noted.*

Harvard University Press *Places the year of publication on the title page of first editions, removing it from subsequent printings and adding a notice to the copyright page. In addition, may have used a number row in the 1980s.*

W. Heinemann, Ltd. / William Heinemann, Ltd. / William Heinemann *From 1890 to 1921, placed the year of publication on the title page of first editions, removing it from subsequent printings and adding a notice to the copyright page (very occasionally, books reprinted in the year of initial publication may not have a notice on the copyright page). In the 1920s, began stating "First published (Year)" or "First published in Great Britain (Year)" on copyright page of first editions; continued to note subsequent printings.*

Heritage Press *Publishes reprints or "trade editions" of the Limited Editions Club.*

Hodder & Stoughton Ltd. *Prior to the 1940s, had no consistent practice for identifying first editions or later printings. In the 1940s, may have begun to state "First Printed (Year)" on first editions and to note subsequent printings. By 1976, were consistent in stating "First published in (Year)" on first editions and noting subsequent printings.*

Hogarth Press *No statement on first editions; subsequent printings are identified on the title page and/or copyright page. Currently use a number row.*

Henry Holt *Prior to 1945, first editions can generally be identified by the lack of a later printing statement on the copyright page. Beginning in 1945, usually placed a first edition statement on the copyright page of books produced in the U.S. (no statement on books produced outside the U.S.). After 1985, began using a first edition statement and number row.*

Holt, Rinehart & Winston *Prior to the 1970s, may have used a first edition statement (with the exception of books produced outside the U.S.). Presumably in the 1970s, began using a first edition statement and number row.*

Houghton, Mifflin *Almost invariably places the date, in Arabic numerals, on the title page of first printings, removing it on subsequent printings. Additionally, in the late 1950s, began consistently placing a "first printing" statement on the copyright page. In the early 1970s, replaced the "first printing" statement with a number row which includes a manufacturer code.*

B.W. Huebsch *No statement on first editions; subsequent printings noted.*

Hurst *Reprint publisher*

Hutchinson & Co. *States "First published (Year)" or "First published in Great Britain (Year)" on copyright page of first editions. (May be no statement on books published early in this century).*

Michael Joseph Ltd. *Since at least the mid-1930s, have stated "First published ... (Month, Year)" on copyright page of first editions, and noted subsequent printings. In the late 1980s and early 1990s, a number row was added to the printing statement.*

Alfred A. Knopf *Until 1933-1934, sometimes stated "Published (Month or Year)" on the copyright page of first editions; later printings were noted. Since 1933-1934 have consistently stated "First Edition" (with the possible exception of children's books). Books with "First and second printings before publication" on the copyright page are second printings (e.g., booksellers' demand warranted a second printing prior to the publication date)*

John Lane *Prior to 1925, no statement on first editions, but subsequent printings were noted. Since 1925, have stated "First Published in (Year, or Month and Year)" on first editions and continued to note subsequent printings.*

Limited Editions Club *Does not reprint titles (see Heritage Press for "trade" editions), and always includes a colophon at the back of each book. In general, limited to 1,500 copies; issued in fine bindings and slipcases or boxes. Nearly all the titles are signed by the illustrator, and occasionally by the author or others.*

J.B. Lippincott *Until mid-1920s, the date on the title page should match the date on the copyright page, but, in the case of "fall titles," the date on the title page may pre-date the one on the copyright page by one year. Beginning in roughly 1925, sometimes placed a first edition statement on the copyright page but always indicated later printings (or "impressions"). In the mid-1970s, added a number row to the first edition statement.*

Lippincott and Crowell *States "First Edition" and uses a number row.*

Little, Brown *Prior to the early 1930s, no statement on first editions, but subsequent printings noted. In the 1930s, stated "Published (Month) (Year)" on the copyright page of first editions; later printings were normally indicated. Since 1940, have stated "First Edition" or "First Printing," and added a number row in the late 1970s.*

Horace Liveright, Inc. / Liveright Publishing Corp. *Prior to the 1970s, in general, no statement on first editions, but subsequent printings noted (may have occasionally used a first edition statement). In recent years, may have used a number row in addition to stating "First Edition."*

John Long *No statement on first editions, but subsequent printings noted.*

Longmans, Green Co. (U.K.) *Prior to the late 1920s, no statement on the first edition, but subsequent printings noted. Since the late 1920s, have stated "First Published (Year)" on the copyright page of first editions; subsequent printings are noted.*

Longmans, Green Co. (U.S.) *Prior to the late 1920s, no statement on the first edition; subsequent printings are presumably noted or carry a date on the copyright page later than the date on the title page. Since the late 1920s, have stated "First Edition" on the copyright page and noted subsequent printings.*

The Macaulay Co. *No statement on first editions, subsequent printings generally noted.*

The Macmillan Co. / Macmillan Publishing Co., Inc. (U.K.) *Prior to the mid-1920s, no statement on the first edition, but subsequent printings noted. Since the mid-1920s, have stated "First Published (Year)" on the copyright page of first editions.*

The Macmillan Co. / Macmillan Publishing Co., Inc. (U.S.) *Prior to the late 1800s, the date on the title page should match the last date on the copyright page for first editions (did not always designate later printings, but did change the date on the copyright page). Also, beginning sometime in the late 1800s, usually placed the statement "Set up and electrotyped. Published (Month, Year)" on first editions, and generally indicated subsequent printings. Mid-year 1936, began stating "First printing" on the copyright page; added a number row in the 1970s.*

Macmillan of Canada *Does not designate first editions.*

Robert M. McBride *Stated "First Published (Month, Year)," "Published (Month, Year)" or, more recently, "First Edition" on the copyright page of first editions; subsequent printings were noted.*

McClure, Phillips *Either no statement or "Published (Month, Year [occasionally followed by a letter code)" on the copyright page of the first edition; subsequent printings presumably noted with either a statement or later date.*

A.C. McClurg *Stated "Published in (Year)" on the first edition, but may have failed to change this notice on later printings.*

McDowell, Obolensky *No statement on the first edition or sometimes stated "First printing"; subsequent printings would presumably be noted.*

McGraw-Hill *Until 1956, may not have used a first edition statement. Since 1956, have used a first edition statement, and noted subsequent printings.*

Methuen & Co. *Since 1905, have stated "First published in (Year)" or "First published in Great Britain (Year)" on the copyright page of first editions, and noted subsequent printings. Prior to 1905, no statement on first editions, but subsequent printings noted (sometimes with a "thousands" statement on the title-page such as "43rd Thousand").*

Metropolitan Books *No statement on the first edition; subsequent printings presumably noted.*

Modern Library *Reprint series published by Random House (prior to 1925 published by Boni & Liveright). Early titles in the series, especially in dust jacket, "Modern Library Giants," and titles with new forewords by the author or original publisher are collectable. Since 1925, have stated "First Modern Library Edition" on the copyright page of the first edition (only haphazardly prior to 1925); occasionally left the first edition statement on subsequent printings, but the presence of later-published titles within the book in hand will often identify it as a later edition. Note: Later issue dust jackets are often found on the first editions.*

William Morrow *Prior to 1973, only sometimes placed "First Printing (Month, Year)" on the copyright page but always indicated later printings. Since 1973, have used a number row and sometimes a first edition statement (occasionally fail to remove first edition statement from later printings).*

Museum of Modern Art *No statement on first editions but subsequent printings are noted.*

Mycroft & Moran *see Arkham House*

New American Library *Uses a first edition statement and number row.*

New Directions *Not consistent in using a first edition statement or identifying subsequent printings, and often bound up first editions sheets later, so binding variations are important in first edition identification.*

New English Library *States "First published by New English Library in (Year)" or "First published in Great Britain (Year)" on the copyright page of first editions. In general, the year in the "first published" notice should match the copyright year.*

George Newnes *No statement on first editions.*

W. W. Norton *In past years, usually used a first edition statement, but did not indicate later printings. Currently uses a first edition statement and number row, but occasionally fails to remove the first edition statement from subsequent printings.*

Peter Owen *States "First published by Peter Owen (Year)" on the copyright page of first editions and notes subsequent printings.*

Oxford University Press (New York and U. K.) *Until the late 1980s, no statement on first editions, but subsequent printings noted. Started using a number row in the late 1980s.*

Pantheon Books, Inc. *Until 1964, no statement on first editions, but subsequent printings noted (may have occasionally stated "First Printing"). Since 1964, have stated "First Edition." May have begun using a number row, in addition to the first edition statement, in the late 1980s.*

Payson & Clarke *No statement on first editions, but subsequent printings noted.*

G.P. Putnam's Sons *Prior to 1985, no statement on first editions, but subsequent printings noted. Since 1985, have used a number row.*

Random House *States "First Edition" on the first printing; does not indicate subsequent printings. In recent years, added a number row beginning with "2," i.e., "First Edition/23456789," to first editions, and removed the first edition statement from subsequent printings (e.g., "23456789" without a first edition statement would indicate a second printing).*

Rapp & Whiting *Generally stated "First published (Year)" on the copyright page of the first edition.*

Reynal & Hitchcock *Until 1947, no statement on first editions, but subsequent printings noted. For books published after 1947, see Harcourt, Brace & Co.*

Grant Richards *No statement on the first edition.*

Rinehart & Co. *Placed an "R" in a circle on first editions and removed from subsequent printings (subsequent printings not otherwise noted).*

St. Martin's Press *Until the early 1980s, no first edition statement, but subsequent printings noted. Since the early 1980s, have used a number row and a first edition statement.*

Scribners *Until 1930, the Scribner's seal and the date of publication (month and year) generally appeared on first editions, and subsequent printings were usually noted (although did not strictly adhered to either practice). Since 1930, have used an "A" on the copyright page to denote the first edition, sometimes with the Scribner seal, and sometimes with a code representing the month and year of publication and the book's manufacturer (later printings were either not noted, or indicated with a "B," etc.). In the 1970s, added a number row which includes a letter code for the manufacturer and type of binding (at the center).*

Martin Secker, Ltd. / Secker & Warburg *Prior to the 1940s, no statement on first editions or occasionally stated "First Published in ...(Year)"; subsequent printings noted. In the 1940s, began stating "First published in ... (Year)" on the copyright page of first editions; continued noting subsequent printings.*

Simon & Schuster *Until 1952, no statement on first editions, but subsequent printings noted (possibly with symbols as, reportedly, a few titles in the 1930s carried a series of dots or asterisks on the copyright page to indicate additional printings). In 1952, began using a first edition statement. In the early 1970s, began using a number row (occasionally with a first edition statement).*

William Sloane Associates *States "First Printing" on the copyright page of first editions, and notes subsequent printings.*

Small, Maynard *No statement on the first edition.*

Smith, Elder *No statement on the first edition.*

Harrison Smith & Robert Haas *Not consistent in use of a first edition statement, but subsequent printings noted.*

Stanton & Lee *see Arkham House*

Frederick A. Stokes Co. *No statement on first editions, but subsequent printings noted.*

Sun Dial *Reprint publisher*

Alan Swallow *No statement on the first edition; subsequent printings presumably noted.*

Tower Books *See World Publishing Co.*

Time Inc. / Time-Life Books *Until 1976, used a small hourglass design on the last page to designate the printing (i.e., one hourglass for the first printing, two for the second, etc.); since 1976, have stated the printing on the copyright page.*

Triangle *Reprint publisher.*

Trident Press *In our limited experience with this publisher, no statement on the first edition; subsequent printings presumably noted.*

United Book *In our limited experience with this publisher, no statement on the first edition; subsequent printings presumably noted.*

T. Fisher Unwin *Prior to 1914, no statement on the first edition. Since 1914, states "First published in (Year)" on the copyright page of the first edition.*

Vanguard *No statement on first editions, and sometimes failed to note subsequent printings. In the 1970s, instituted a number row (but may have abandoned it in the mid-1980s).*

Viking Press *Until the late 1930s, no first edition statement, but subsequent printings noted. In 1937, began stating "First Published by Viking in (Year)" or "Published by Viking in (Year)" on first editions, and continued the practice of noting subsequent printings. In the 1980s, added a number row to later printings only.*

Villard Books *See Random House*

Vintage Books *See Random House*

Walker and Co. *States "First Published ... (Year)" on first editions, and uses a number row to indicate subsequent printings.*

Ward, Lock *Prior to the 1930s, generally placed the year of publication on the title page of first editions and removed it from subsequent printings. Beginning in the mid-1930s, generally stated "First published in..." on the copyright page of first editions.*

Weidenfeld & Nicolson *Either states "First published in..." or no statement on first editions, but subsequent printings are generally noted.*

Wesleyan University *States "First Edition" or "First Printing" on first editions, and notes subsequent printings.*

John Wiley & Sons *Prior to 1969, no statement on first editions, but subsequent printings noted. Have used a number row since 1969.*

John C. Winston *Until the 1940s, no statement on either first editions or subsequent printings. Started stating the printing some time in the 1940s.*

World Publishing Co. *States "First Edition" or "First Printing" on the copyright page of the first edition. Note: World's "Tower Books" are reprints, with the exception of two Raymond Chandler first editions: Red Wind and Spanish Blood (both state "First Printing (Month, Year)".*